A Prelude to Calculus

Sheldon Axler

Third Edition

for Michigan State University
Precalculus/MATH 116

WILEY *Custom*
LEARNING SOLUTIONS

Custom Brief Contents

www.wileyplus.com

Wiley is committed to making your entire *WileyPLUS* experience productive & enjoyable by providing the help, resources, and perso support you & your students need, when you need it.
It's all here: www.wileyplus.com −

TECHNICAL SUPPORT:

- A fully searchable knowledge base of FAQs and help documentation, available 24/7
- Live chat with a trained member of our support staff during business hours
- A form to fill out and submit online to ask any question and get a quick response
- **Instructor-only** phone line during business hours: 1.877.586.0192

FACULTY-LED TRAINING THROUGH THE WILEY FACULTY NETWORK:
Register online: www.wherefacultyconnect.com
Connect with your colleagues in a complimentary virtual seminar, with a personal men in your field, or at a live workshop to share best practices for teaching with technolog

1ST DAY OF CLASS...AND BEYOND!

Resources You & Your Students Need to Get Started
& Use *WileyPLUS* from the first day forward.

- 2-Minute Tutorials on how to set up & maintain your *WileyPLUS* course
- User guides, links to technical support & training options
- ***WileyPLUS for Dummies***: Instructors' quick reference guide to using *WileyPLUS*
- Student tutorials & instruction on how to register, buy, and use *WileyPLUS*

YOUR *WileyPLUS* ACCOUNT MANAGER:
Your personal *WileyPLUS* connection for any assistance you need!

QuickStart

SET UP YOUR *WileyPLUS* COURSE IN MINUTES!
Selected *WileyPLUS* courses with QuickStart contain pre-loaded assignments & presentations created by subject matter experts who are also experienced *WileyPLUS* users.

Interested? See and try WileyPLUS *in action!*
Details and Demo: www.wileyplus.com

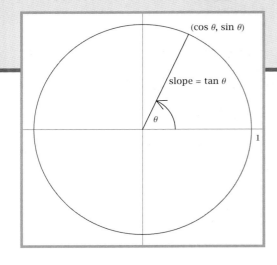

Precalculus
A Prelude to Calculus

with
Student Solutions Manual

Sheldon Axler
San Francisco State University

WILEY   JOHN WILEY & SONS, INC.

PUBLISHER	Laurie Rosatone
ACQUISITIONS EDITOR	Jessica Jacobs
SENIOR EDITORIAL ASSISTANT	Jeff Benson
DEVELOPMENT EDITOR	Anne Scanlan-Rohrer
SENIOR PRODUCTION EDITOR	Ken Santor
PHOTO EDITOR	Elle Wagner
MARKETING MANAGER	Jaclyn Elkins
SENIOR MARKETING ASSISTANT	Chelsee Pengal
DESIGN DIRECTOR	Madelyn Lesure
MEDIA EDITOR	Melissa Edwards

This book was typeset in LaTeX by the author. Printing and binding by RR Donnelley, Jefferson City. Cover printed by Phoenix Color Corporation.

About the Cover   The diagram on the cover contains the crucial definitions of trigonometry.

The 1 shows that the trigonometric functions are defined in the context of the unit circle. The arrow shows that angles are measured counterclockwise from the positive horizontal axis. The point labeled $(\cos\theta, \sin\theta)$ shows that $\cos\theta$ is the first coordinate of the endpoint of the radius corresponding to the angle θ, and $\sin\theta$ is the second coordinate of this endpoint. Because this endpoint is on the unit circle, the identity $\cos^2\theta + \sin^2\theta = 1$ immediately follows. The equation slope $= \tan\theta$ shows that $\tan\theta$ is the slope of the radius corresponding to the angle θ; thus $\tan\theta = \frac{\sin\theta}{\cos\theta}$.

To order books or for customer service please, call 1-800-CALL WILEY (225-5945).

ISBN-13   978-0470-41674-7 (hardcover)
ISBN-13   978-0470-18072-3 (softcover)
ISBN-13   978-0470-41813-0 (binder ready)

Printed in the United States of America
10 9 8 7 6 5 4 3 2 1

About the Author

Sheldon Axler is Dean of the College of Science & Engineering at San Francisco State University, where he joined the faculty as Chair of the Mathematics Department in 1997.

Axler was valedictorian of his high school in Miami, Florida. He received his AB from Princeton University with highest honors, followed by a PhD in Mathematics from the University of California at Berkeley.

As a postdoctoral Moore Instructor at MIT, Axler received a university-wide teaching award. Axler was then an assistant professor, associate professor, and professor at Michigan State University, where he received the first J. Sutherland Frame Teaching Award and the Distinguished Faculty Award.

Axler received the Lester R. Ford Award for expository writing from the Mathematical Association of America in 1996. In addition to publishing numerous research papers, Axler is the author of *Linear Algebra Done Right* (which has been adopted as a textbook at over 225 universities and colleges) and co-author of *Harmonic Function Theory* (a graduate/research-level book).

Axler has served as Editor-in-Chief of the *Mathematical Intelligencer* and as Associate Editor of the *American Mathematical Monthly*. He has been a member of the Council of the American Mathematical Society and a member of the Board of Trustees of the Mathematical Sciences Research Institute. Axler currently serves on the editorial board of Springer's series Undergraduate Texts in Mathematics, Graduate Texts in Mathematics, and Universitext.

Contents

---

*Section can be skipped if focusing only on material needed for first-semester calculus.

---

*Section can be skipped if focusing only on material needed for first-semester calculus.

Preface to the Instructor

Goals and Prerequisites

This book seeks to prepare students to succeed in calculus. Thus this book focuses on topics that students need for calculus, especially first-semester calculus. Many important subjects that should be known by all educated citizens but that are irrelevant to calculus have been excluded.

Precalculus is a one-semester course at most universities. Nevertheless, typical precalculus textbooks contain about a thousand pages (not counting a student solutions manual), far more than can be covered in one semester. By emphasizing topics crucial to success in calculus, this book has a more manageable size even though it includes a student solutions manual. A thinner textbook should indicate to students that they are truly expected to master most of the content of the book.

The prerequisite for this course is the usual course in intermediate algebra. Many students in precalculus classes have had a trigonometry course previously, but this book does not assume that the students remember any trigonometry. In fact the book is fairly self-contained, starting with a review of the real numbers in Chapter 0, whose numbering is intended to indicate that many instructors will prefer to skip this beginning material or cover it quickly.

Chapter 0 could have been titled
A Prelude to A Prelude to Calculus.

Inverse Functions

The unifying concept of inverse functions are introduced early in the book in Section 1.5. This crucial idea has its first major use in this book in the definition of $y^{1/m}$ as the number that when raised to the mth power gives y (in other words, the function $y \mapsto y^{1/m}$ is the inverse of the function $x \mapsto x^m$; see Section 3.1). The second major use of inverse functions occurs in the definition of $\log_b y$ as the number such that b raised to this number gives y (in other words, the function $y \mapsto \log_b y$ is the inverse of the function $x \mapsto b^x$; see Section 3.2).

Thus students should be comfortable with using inverse functions by the time they reach the inverse trigonometric functions (arccosine, arcsine, and arctangent) in Section 5.7. This familiarity with inverse functions should help students deal with inverse operations (such as antidifferentiation) when they reach calculus.

Algebraic Properties of Logarithms

Logarithms play a key role in calculus, but many calculus instructors complain that too many students lack appropriate algebraic manipulation skills with logarithms. In Chapter 3 logarithms are defined as the inverse functions of exponentiation. The base for logarithms here is arbitrary, although most of the examples and motivation in Chapter 3 use logarithms base 2 or logarithms base 10. In Chapter 3, the algebraic properties of logarithms are easily derived from the algebraic properties of exponentiation.

The initial separation of logarithms and e should help students master both concepts.

The crucial concepts of e and natural logarithms are saved for a later chapter. Thus students can concentrate in Chapter 3 on understanding logarithms (arbitrary base) and their properties without at the same time worrying about grasping concepts related to e. Similarly, when natural logarithms arise naturally in Chapter 4, students should be able to concentrate on issues surrounding e without at the same time learning properties of logarithms.

Half-life and Exponential Growth

All precalculus textbooks present radioactive decay as an example of exponential decay. Amazingly, the typical precalculus textbook states that if a radioactive isotope has a half-life of h, then the amount left at time t will equal e^{-kt} times the amount present at time 0, where $k = \frac{\ln 2}{h}$.

A much clearer formulation would state, as this textbook does, that the amount left at time t will equal $2^{-t/h}$ times the amount present at time 0. The unnecessary use of e and $\ln 2$ in this context may suggest to students that e and natural logarithms have only contrived and artificial uses, which is not the message that students should receive from their textbook. Using $2^{-t/h}$ helps students understand the concept of half-life, with a formula connected to the meaning of the concept.

Similarly, many precalculus textbooks consider, for example, a colony of bacteria doubling in size every 3 hours, with the textbook then producing the formula $e^{(t \ln 2)/3}$ for the growth factor after t hours. The simpler and natural formula $2^{t/3}$ seems not to be mentioned in such books. This book presents the more natural approach to such issues of exponential growth and decay.

Area

About half of calculus (namely, integration) deals with area, but most precalculus textbooks barely mention the subject.

Chapter 4 in this book builds the intuitive notion of area starting with squares, and then quickly derives formulas for the area of rectangles, triangles, parallelograms, and trapezoids. A discussion of the effects of stretching either horizontally or vertically easily leads to the familiar formula for the area enclosed by a circle. Chapter 4 uses the same ideas to derive the formula for the area inside an ellipse.

Chapter 4 then turns to the question of estimating the area under parts of the curve $y = \frac{1}{x}$ by using rectangles. This easy nontechnical introduction, with its emphasis on ideas without the clutter of the notation of Riemann sums, will serve students well when they reach integral calculus in a later course.

e, The Exponential Function, and the Natural Logarithm

Most precalculus textbooks either present no motivation for e or motivate e via continuously compounding interest or through the limit of an indeterminate expression of the form 1^∞; these concepts are difficult for students at this level to understand.

Chapter 4 presents a clean and well-motivated approach to e and the natural logarithm. We do this by looking at the area (intuitively defined) under the curve $y = \frac{1}{x}$, above the x-axis, and between the lines $x = 1$ and $x = c$.

A similar approach to e and the natural logarithm is common in calculus courses. However, this approach is not usually adopted in precalculus textbooks. Using obvious properties of area, the simple presentation given here shows how these ideas can come through clearly without the technicalities of calculus or Riemann sums. Indeed, this precalculus approach to the exponential function and the natural logarithm shows that a good understanding of these subjects need not wait until the calculus course. Students who have seen the approach given here should be well prepared to deal with these concepts in their calculus courses.

The approach taken here also has the advantage that it easily leads, as we will see in Chapter 4, to the approximation $\ln(1 + h) \approx h$ for small values of h. Furthermore, the same methods show that if r is any number, then $(1 + \frac{r}{x})^x \approx e^r$ for large values of x. A final bonus of this approach is that the connection between continuously compounding interest and e becomes a nice corollary of natural considerations concerning area.

Trigonometry

Should the trigonometric functions be introduced via the unit circle or via right triangles? Calculus requires the unit-circle approach (because, for example, discussing the Taylor series for $\cos x$ requires us to consider negative values of x and values of x that are more than $\frac{\pi}{2}$ radians). Thus this textbook uses the unit-circle approach, but quickly gives applications to right triangles. The unit-circle approach also allows for a well-motivated introduction to radian measure.

The trigonometry section of this book concentrates almost exclusively on the functions cosine, sine, and tangent and their inverse functions, with only cursory mention of secant, cosecant, and cotangent. These latter three functions, which are simply the multiplicative inverses of the three key trigonometric functions, add little content or understanding.

Exercises and Problems

Students learn mathematics by actively working on a wide range of exercises and problems. Ideally, a student who reads and understands the material in a section of this book should be able to do the exercises and problems in that section without further help. However, some of the exercises require application of the ideas in a context that students may not have seen before, and many students will need help with these exercises. This help is available from the complete worked-out solutions to all the odd-numbered exercises that appear at the end of each section.

Each exercise has a unique correct answer, usually a number or a function; each problem has multiple correct answers, usually explanations or examples.

Because the worked-out solutions were written solely by the author of the textbook, students can expect a consistent approach to the material. Furthermore, students will save money by not having to purchase a separate student solutions manual.

The exercises (but not the problems) occur in pairs, so that an odd-numbered exercise is followed by an even-numbered exercise whose solution uses the same ideas and techniques. A student stumped by an even-numbered exercise should be able to tackle it after reading the worked-out solution to the corresponding odd-numbered exercise. This arrangement allows the text to focus more centrally on explanations of the material and examples of the concepts.

This book contains what is usually a separate book called the student solutions manual.

My experience with teaching precalculus is that most students read the student solutions manual when they are assigned homework, even though they are reluctant to read the main text. The integration of the student solutions manual within this book might encourage students who would otherwise read only the student solutions manual to drift over and also read the main text. To reinforce this tendency, the worked-out solutions to the odd-numbered exercises at the end of each section are typeset with a slightly less appealing style (smaller type, two-column format, and not right justified) than the main text. The reader-friendly appearance of the main text might nudge students to spend some time there.

Exercises and problems in this book vary greatly in difficulty and purpose. Some exercises and problems are designed to hone algebraic manipulation skills; other exercises and problems are designed to push students to genuine understanding beyond rote algorithmic calculation.

Some exercises and problems intentionally reinforce material from earlier in the book. For example, Exercise 27 in Section 5.3 asks students to find the smallest number x such that $\sin(e^x) = 0$; students will need to understand that they want to choose x so that $e^x = \pi$ and thus $x = \ln \pi$. Although such exercises require more thought than most exercises in the book, they allow students to see crucial concepts more than once, sometimes in unexpected contexts.

A Book Designed to be Read

Mathematics faculty frequently complain, with justification, that most students in lower-division mathematics courses do not read the textbook. When doing homework, a typical precalculus student looks only at the relevant section of the textbook or the student solutions manual for an example similar to the homework problem at hand. The student reads enough of that example to imitate the procedure, does the homework problem, and then follows the same process with the next homework problem. Little understanding may take place.

In contrast, this book is designed to be read by students. The writing style and layout are meant to induce students to read and understand the material. Explanations are more plentiful than typically found in precalculus books, with examples of the concepts making the ideas concrete whenever possible.

The Calculator Issue

To aid instructors in presenting the kind of course they want, the symbol ✆ appears with exercises and problems that require students to use a calculator.

The issue of whether and how calculators should be used by students has generated immense controversy.

Some sections of this book have many exercises and problems designed for calculators (for example Section 3.4 on exponential growth and Section 6.2 on the law of sines and the law of cosines), but some sections deal with material not as amenable to calculator use. The emphasis throughout the text has been on giving students both the understanding and the skills they need to succeed in calculus. Thus the book does not aim for an artificially predetermined percentage of exercises and problems in each section requiring calculator use.

Some exercises and problems that require a calculator are intentionally designed to make students realize that by understanding the material, they can overcome the limitations of calculators. As one example among many, Exercise 41 in Section 3.3 asks students to find the number of digits in the decimal expansion of 7^{4000}. Brute force with a calculator will not work with this problem because the number involved has too many digits. However, a few moments' thought should show students that they can solve this problem by using logarithms (and their calculators!).

The calculator icon can be interpreted for some exercises, depending on the instructor's preference, to mean that the solution should be a decimal approximation rather than the exact answer. For example, Exercise 3 in Section 4.5 asks how much would need to be deposited in a bank account paying 4% interest compounded continuously so that at the end of 10 years the account would contain $10,000. The exact answer to this exercise is $10000/e^{0.4}$ dollars, but it may be more satisfying to the student (after obtaining the exact answer) to use a calculator to see that approximately $6,703 needs to be deposited. For such exercises, instructors can decide whether to ask for exact answers or decimal approximations (the worked-out solutions for the odd-numbered exercises will usually contain both).

Regardless of what level of calculator use an instructor expects, students should not turn to a calculator to compute something like $\cos 0$, *because then* cos *has become just a button on the calculator.*

What to Cover

Different instructors will want to cover different sections of this book. I usually cover Chapter 0 (The Real Numbers), even though it should be review, because it deals with familiar topics in a deeper fashion than students may have previously seen. I frequently cover Section 2.5 (Rational Functions) only lightly because graphing rational functions, and in particular finding local minima and maxima, is better done with calculus. Many instructors will prefer to skip Chapter 7 (Sequences, Series, and Limits), leaving that material to a calculus course. A one-semester precalculus course will probably not have time to cover the sections denoted with an asterisk (*); those sections can safely be skipped by courses focusing only on material needed for first-semester calculus.

What's New as Compared to the Preliminary Edition

Numerous improvements have been made throughout the text based upon suggestions from faculty and students who used the Preliminary Edition. For example, the introduction to e now gives instructors a gentler path to help lead students to discover this remarkable number. More exercises and problems have been added to many sections.

Some faculty requested coverage of additional topics because their precalculus courses serve other purposes beyond preparing students for first-semester calculus. Thus three new optional sections have been added, dealing with complex numbers, systems of equations and matrices, and vectors.

A major redesign using full color has led to considerable improvements in the appearance of the book.

Finally, a comprehensive index now allows users to locate topics within the book quickly.

Comments Welcome

I seek your help in making this a better book. Please send me your comments and your suggestions for improvements. Thanks!

Sheldon Axler
San Francisco State University

e-mail: precalculus@axler.net
web page: www.axler.net

Acknowledgments

Most of the results in this book belong to the common heritage of mathematics, created over thousands of years by clever and curious people.

As usual in a textbook, as opposed to a research article, little attempt has been made to provide proper credit to the original creators of the ideas presented in this book. Where possible, I have tried to improve on standard approaches to this material. However, the absence of a reference does not imply originality on my part. I thank the many mathematicians who have created and refined our beautiful subject.

I chose Wiley as the publisher of this book because of the company's commitment to excellence. The people at Wiley have made outstanding contributions to this project, providing wise editorial advice, superb design expertise, high-level production skill, and insightful marketing savvy. I am truly grateful to the following Wiley folks, all of whom helped make this a better and more successful book than it would have been otherwise: Angela Battle, Jeff Benson, Melissa Edwards, Jaclyn Elkins, Jessica Jacobs, Madelyn Lesure, Chelsee Pengal, Laurie Rosatone, Christopher Ruel, Ken Santor, Anne Scanlan-Rohrer, Elle Wagner.

The accuracy checkers (Victoria Green, Celeste Hernandez, Nancy Matthews, Yan Tian, and Charles Waiveris) and copy editors (Katrina Avery and Patricia Brecht) excelled at catching my mathematical and linguistic mistakes.

The instructors and students who used the Preliminary Edition of this book provided wonderfully useful feedback. Numerous reviewers gave me terrific suggestions as the book progressed through various stages of development. I am grateful to all the class testers and reviewers whose names are listed on the following pages.

Like most mathematicians, I owe thanks to Donald Knuth, who invented TeX, and to Leslie Lamport, who invented LaTeX, which I used to typeset this book.

Thanks also to Wolfram Research for producing *Mathematica*, which is the software I used to create the graphics in this book.

My awesome partner Carrie Heeter deserves considerable credit for her astute advice and continual encouragement throughout the long book-writing process.

Many thanks to all of you!

Sheldon

Class Testers and Reviewers

- Alison Ahlgren, University of Illinois, Urbana-Champaign
- Margo Alexander, Georgia State University
- Ulrich Albrecht, Auburn University
- Caroline Autrey, University of West Georgia
- Robin Ayers, Western Kentucky University
- Robert Bass, Gardner Webb University
- Jo Battaglia, Penn State University
- Chris Bendixen, Lake Michigan College
- Kimberly Bennekin, Georgia Perimeter College
- Allan Berele, DePaul University
- Rebecca Berg, Bowie State University
- Andrew Beyer, San Francisco State University
- Michael Boardman, Pacific University
- Bob Bradshaw, Ohlone College
- Ellen Brook, Cuyahoga Community College
- David Buhl, Northern Michigan University
- William L. Burgin, Gaston College
- Brenda Burns-Williams, North Carolina State University
- Nick Bykov, San Joaquin Delta College
- Keith G. Calkins, Andrews University
- Tom Caplinger, University of Memphis
- Jamylle Carter, San Francisco State University
- Yu Chen, Idaho State University
- Charles Conley, University of North Texas
- Robert Crise Jr., Crafton Hills College
- Joanne Darken, Community College of Philadelphia
- Joyati Debnath, Winona State University
- Donna Densmore, Bossier Parish Community College
- Jeff Dodd, Jacksonville State University
- Benay Don, Suffolk County Community College
- Marcia Drost, Texas A & M University
- Douglas Dunbar, Okaloosa-Walton Community College
- Jason Edington, Mendocino College
- Thomas English, Penn State University, Erie
- Kevin Farrell, Lyndon State College
- Karline Feller, Georgia Perimeter College
- Terran Felter, California State University, Bakersfield
- Maggie Flint, Northeast State Community College
- Heng Fu, Thomas Nelson Community College
- Igor Fulman, Arizona State University
- Abel Gage, Skagit Valley College
- Gail Gonyo, Adirondack Community College
- Ivan Gotchev, Central Connecticut State University
- Peg Greene, Florida Community College
- Michael B. Gregory, University of North Dakota
- Julio Guillen, New Jersey City University
- Mako Haruta, University of Hartford
- Judy Hayes, Lake-Sumter Community College
- Richard Hill, Idaho State University
- Alan Hong, Santa Monica College
- Mizue Horiuchi, San Francisco State University
- Miles Hubbard, St. Cloud State University
- Stacey Hubbard, San Francisco State University
- Brian Jue, California State University, Stanislaus
- Dongrim Kim, Arizona State University
- Mohammed Kazemi, University of North Carolina, Charlotte
- Curtis Kifer, San Francisco State University
- Betty Larson, South Dakota State University
- Richard Leedy, Polk Community College
- Mary Legner, Riverside Community College
- Richard Low, San José State University
- Jane Mays, Grand Valley State University
- Eric Miranda, San Francisco State University
- Scot Morrison, Western Nevada College
- Scott Mortensen, Dixie State College
- Susan Nelson, Georgia Perimeter College
- Nicholas Passell, University of Wisconsin, Eau Claire
- Vic Perera, Kent State University, Trumbull

- David Ray, University of Tennessee, Martin
- Alexander Retakh, Stony Brook University
- Erika Rhett, Claflin University
- Randy Ross, Morehead State University
- Carol Rychly, Augusta State University
- David Santos, Community College of Philadelphia
- Virginia Sheridan, California State University, Bakersfield
- Barbara Shipman, University of Texas, Arlington
- Tatiana Shubin, San José State University
- Dave Sobecki, Miami University
- Jacqui Stone, University of Maryland
- Karel Stroethoff, University of Montana, Missoula
- Janet Tarjan, Bakersfield College
- Chia-chi Tung, Minnesota State University
- Hanson Umoh, Delaware State University
- Charles Waiveris, Central Connecticut State University
- Jeff Waller, Grossmont College
- Amy Wangsness, Fitchburg State College
- Rachel Winston, Cerro Coso Community College
- Elizabeth Wisniewski, Marymount College of Fordham University
- Tzu-Yi Alan Yang, Columbus State Community College
- David Zeigler, California State University, Sacramento

Preface to the Student

This book will help prepare you to succeed in calculus. If you master the material in this book, you will have the knowledge, the understanding, and the skills needed to do well in a calculus course.

To learn this material well, you will need to spend serious time reading this book. You cannot expect to absorb mathematics the way you devour a novel. If you read through a section of this book in less than an hour, then you are going too fast. You should pause to ponder and internalize each definition, often by trying to invent some examples in addition to those given in the book. For each result stated in the book, you should seek examples to show why each hypothesis is necessary. When steps in a calculation are left out in the book, you need to supply the missing pieces, which will require some writing on your part. These activities can be difficult when attempted alone; try to work with a group of a few other students.

You will need to spend several hours per section doing the exercises and problems. Make sure that you can do all the exercises and most of the problems, not just the ones assigned for homework. By the way, the difference between an exercise and a problem in this book is that each exercise has a unique correct answer that is a mathematical object such as a number or a function. In contrast, the solutions to problems consist of explanations or examples; thus problems have multiple correct answers.

Complete worked-out solutions to the odd-numbered exercises are given at the end of each section.

Have fun, and best wishes in your studies!

Sheldon Axler
San Francisco State University

web page: www.axler.net

The Parthenon was built in Athens over 2400 years ago. The ancient Greeks developed and used remarkably sophisticated mathematics.

The Real Numbers

Success in this course and in your future mathematics courses will require a good understanding of the basic properties of the real number system. Thus this book begins with a review of the real numbers. This chapter has been labeled "Chapter 0" to emphasize its review nature.

The first section of this chapter starts with the construction of the real line. This section contains as an optional highlight the ancient Greek proof that no rational number has a square equal to 2. This beautiful result appears here not because you will need it for calculus, but because it should be seen by everyone at least once.

Although this chapter will be mostly review, a thorough grounding in the real number system will serve you well throughout this course and then for the rest of your life. You will need good algebraic manipulation skills; thus the second section of this chapter reviews the fundamental algebra of the real numbers. You will also need to feel comfortable working with inequalities and absolute values, which are reviewed in the last section of this chapter.

Even if your instructor decides to skip this chapter, you may want to read through it. Make sure you can do all the exercises.

The Real Line

SECTION OBJECTIVES

By the end of this section you should

- understand the correspondence between the system of real numbers and the real line;
- appreciate the proof that no rational number has a square equal to 2.

The **integers** are the numbers

$$\ldots, -3, -2, -1, 0, 1, 2, 3, \ldots,$$

where the dots indicate that the numbers continue without end in each direction. The sum, difference, and product of any two integers are also integers.

The quotient of two integers is not necessarily an integer. Thus we extend arithmetic to the **rational numbers**, which are numbers of the form

$$\frac{m}{n},$$

The use of a horizontal bar to separate the numerator and denominator of a fraction was introduced by Arabic mathematicians about 900 years ago.

where m and n are integers and $n \neq 0$.

Division is the inverse of multiplication, in the sense that we want the equation

$$\frac{m}{n} \cdot n = m$$

to hold. In the equation above, if we take $n = 0$ and (for example) $m = 1$, we get the nonsensical equation $\frac{1}{0} \cdot 0 = 1$. This equation is nonsensical because multiplying anything by 0 should give 0, not 1. To get around this problem, we leave expressions such as $\frac{1}{0}$ undefined. In other words, division by 0 is prohibited.

The rational numbers form a terrifically useful system. We can add, multiply, subtract, and divide rational numbers (with the exception of division by 0) and stay within the system of rational numbers. Rational numbers suffice for all actual physical measurements, such as length and weight, of any desired accuracy.

However, geometry, algebra, and calculus force us to consider an even richer system of numbers—the real numbers. To see why we need to go beyond the rational numbers, we will investigate the real number line.

Construction of the Real Line

Imagine a horizontal line, extending without end in both directions. Pick an arbitrary point on this line and label it 0. Pick another arbitrary point to the right of 0 and label it 1, as in the figure below.

Two key points on the real line.

Once the points 0 and 1 have been chosen on the line, everything else is determined by thinking of the distance between 0 and 1 as one unit of length. For example, 2 is one unit to the right of 1, and then 3 is one unit to the right of 2, and so on. The negative integers correspond to moving to the left of 0. Thus −1 is one unit to the left of 0, and then −2 is one unit to the left of −1, and so on.

The symbol for zero was invented in India more than 1100 years ago.

Integers on the real line.

If n is a positive integer, then $\frac{1}{n}$ is to the right of 0 by the length obtained by dividing the segment from 0 to 1 into n segments of equal length. Then $\frac{2}{n}$ is to the right of $\frac{1}{n}$ by the same length, and $\frac{3}{n}$ is to the right of $\frac{2}{n}$ by the same length again, and so on. The negative rational numbers are placed on the line in a similar fashion, but to the left of 0.

In this fashion, we associate with every rational number a point on the line. No figure can show the labels of all the rational numbers, because we can include only finitely many labels. The figure below shows the line with labels attached to a few of the points corresponding to rational numbers.

Some rational numbers on the real line.

We will use the intuitive notion that the line has no gaps and that every conceivable distance can be represented by a point on the line. With these concepts in mind, we call the line shown above the **real line**. We think of each point on the real line as corresponding to a **real number**. The undefined intuitive notions (such as "no gaps") will become more precise when you reach more advanced mathematics courses. For now, we let our intuitive notions of the real line serve to define the system of real numbers.

Is Every Real Number Rational?

We have seen that every rational number corresponds to some point on the real line. Does every point on the real line correspond to some rational number? In other words, is every real number rational?

If more and more labels of rational numbers were placed on the figure above, the real line would look increasingly cluttered. Probably the first people to ponder these issues thought that the rational numbers fill up the entire real line. However, the ancient Greeks realized that this is not true. To see how they came to this conclusion, we make a brief detour into geometry.

Recall that for a right triangle, the sum of the squares of the lengths of the two sides that form the right angle equals the square of the length of the hypotenuse. The figure below illustrates this result, which is called the Pythagorean Theorem.

This theorem is named in honor of the Greek mathematician and philosopher Pythagoras who proved it over 2500 years ago. The Babylonians discovered this result a thousand years earlier than that.

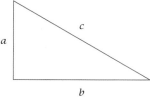

The Pythagorean Theorem for right triangles: $c^2 = a^2 + b^2$.

Now consider the special case where both sides that form the right angle have length 1, as in the figure below. In this case, the Pythagorean Theorem states that the length c of the hypotenuse has a square equal to 2.

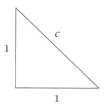

An isosceles right triangle. The Pythagorean Theorem implies that $c^2 = 2$.

Because we have constructed a line segment whose length c satisfies the equation $c^2 = 2$, a point on the real line corresponds to c. In other words, there is a real number whose square equals 2. This raises the question of whether there exists a rational number whose square equals 2.

We could try to find a rational number whose square equals 2 by experimentation. One striking example is

$$\left(\frac{99}{70}\right)^2 = \frac{9801}{4900};$$

here the numerator of the right side misses being twice the denominator by only 1. Although $\left(\frac{99}{70}\right)^2$ is close to 2, it is not exactly equal to 2.

Another example is $\frac{9369319}{6625109}$. The square of this rational number is approximately 1.9999999999992, which is very close to 2 but again is not exactly what we seek.

Because we have found rational numbers whose squares are very close to 2, you might suspect that with further cleverness we could find a rational number whose square equals 2. However, the ancient Greeks proved this is impossible. This course does not focus much on proofs, and probably your calculus course will not be proof oriented either. The Greek proof that there is no rational number whose square equals 2 could be skipped without endangering your future success. However, the Greek proof, as one of the great intellectual achievements of humanity, should be experienced by every educated person. Thus it is presented below for your enrichment.

What follows is a proof by contradiction. We will start by assuming that the desired result is false. Using that assumption, we will arrive at a contradiction. So our assumption that the desired result was false must have been wrong. Thus the desired result is true.

Understanding the logical pattern of thinking that goes into this proof will be a valuable asset if you continue to other parts of mathematics beyond calculus.

No rational number has a square equal to 2.

Proof: Suppose there exist integers m and n such that

$$\left(\frac{m}{n}\right)^2 = 2.$$

By canceling any common factors, we can choose m and n to have no factors in common. In other words, $\frac{m}{n}$ is reduced to lowest terms.

The equation above is equivalent to the equation

$$m^2 = 2n^2.$$

This implies that m^2 is even; hence m is even. Thus $m = 2k$ for some integer k. Substituting $2k$ for m in the equation above gives

$$4k^2 = 2n^2,$$

or equivalently

$$2k^2 = n^2.$$

This implies that n^2 is even; hence n is even.

We have now shown that both m and n are even, contradicting our choice of m and n as having no factors in common. This contradiction means our original assumption that there is a rational number whose square equals 2 must be false.

"When you have excluded the impossible, whatever remains, however improbable, must be the truth."
—Sherlock Holmes

The result above shows that not every point on the real line corresponds to a rational number. In other words, not every real number is rational. Thus the following definition is useful:

Irrational numbers

A real number that is not rational is called an **irrational number**.

We have just seen that $\sqrt{2}$, which is the positive real number whose square equals 2, is an irrational number. The real numbers π and e, which we will encounter in later chapters, are also irrational numbers.

Once we have found one irrational number, finding others is much easier, as shown in the example below.

EXAMPLE 1

Show that $3 + \sqrt{2}$ is an irrational number.

The attitude of the ancient Greeks toward irrational numbers persists in our everyday use of "irrational" to mean "not based on reason".

SOLUTION   Suppose $3 + \sqrt{2}$ is a rational number. Because

$$\sqrt{2} = (3 + \sqrt{2}) - 3,$$

this implies that $\sqrt{2}$ is the difference of two rational numbers, which implies that $\sqrt{2}$ is a rational number, which is not true. Thus our assumption that $3 + \sqrt{2}$ is a rational number must be false. In other words, $3 + \sqrt{2}$ is an irrational number.

The next example provides another illustration of how to use one irrational number to generate another irrational number.

EXAMPLE 2

Show that $8\sqrt{2}$ is an irrational number.

SOLUTION   Suppose $8\sqrt{2}$ is a rational number. Because

$$\sqrt{2} = \frac{8\sqrt{2}}{8},$$

this implies that $\sqrt{2}$ is the quotient of two rational numbers, which implies that $\sqrt{2}$ is a rational number, which is not true. Thus our assumption that $8\sqrt{2}$ is a rational number must be false. In other words, $8\sqrt{2}$ is an irrational number.

PROBLEMS

The problems in this section may be harder than typical problems found in the rest of this book.

1. Show that $\frac{6}{7} + \sqrt{2}$ is an irrational number.

2. Show that $5 - \sqrt{2}$ is an irrational number.

3. Show that $3\sqrt{2}$ is an irrational number.

4. Show that $\frac{3\sqrt{2}}{5}$ is an irrational number.

5. Show that $4 + 9\sqrt{2}$ is an irrational number.

6. Explain why the sum of a rational number and an irrational number is an irrational number.

7. Explain why the product of a nonzero rational number and an irrational number is an irrational number.

8. Suppose t is an irrational number. Explain why $\frac{1}{t}$ is also an irrational number.

9. Give an example of two irrational numbers whose sum is an irrational number.

10. Give an example of two irrational numbers whose sum is a rational number.

11. Give an example of three irrational numbers whose sum is a rational number.

12. Give an example of two irrational numbers whose product is an irrational number.

13. Give an example of two irrational numbers whose product is a rational number.

| *Algebra of the Real Numbers*

SECTION OBJECTIVES

By the end of this section you should

- recall how to manipulate algebraic expressions using the commutative, associative, and distributive properties;
- understand the order of algebraic operations and the role of parentheses;
- recall the crucial algebraic identities involving additive inverses and multiplicative inverses.

The operations of addition, subtraction, multiplication, and division extend from the rational numbers to the real numbers. We can add, subtract, multiply, and divide any two real numbers and stay within the system of real numbers, again with the exception that division by 0 is prohibited.

Exercises woven throughout this book have been designed to sharpen your algebraic manipulation skills as we cover other topics.

In this section we review the basic algebraic properties of the real numbers. Because this material should indeed be review, no effort has been made to show how some of these properties follow from others. Instead, this section focuses on highlighting key properties that should become so familiar to you that you can use them comfortably and without effort.

Commutativity and Associativity

Commutativity is the formal name for the property stating that order does not matter in addition and multiplication:

Commutativity

$$a + b = b + a \quad \text{and} \quad ab = ba$$

Here (and throughout this section) a, b, and other variables denote either arbitrary real numbers or expressions that take on values that are real numbers. For example, the commutativity of addition implies that $x^2 + \frac{x}{5} = \frac{x}{5} + x^2$.

Neither subtraction nor division is commutative because order does matter for those operations. For example, $5 - 3 \neq 3 - 5$, and $\frac{6}{2} \neq \frac{2}{6}$.

Associativity is the formal name for the property stating that grouping does not matter in addition and multiplication:

Associativity

$$(a + b) + c = a + (b + c) \quad \text{and} \quad (ab)c = a(bc)$$

Expressions inside parentheses should be calculated before further computation. For example, $(a + b) + c$ should be calculated by first adding a and b, and then adding that sum to c. The associative property of addition asserts that this number will be the same as $a + (b + c)$, which should be calculated by first adding b and c, and then adding that sum to a.

Because of the associative property of addition, we can dispense with parentheses when adding three or more numbers, writing expressions such as

$$a + b + c + d$$

without worrying about how the terms are grouped. Similarly, because of the associative property of multiplication we do not need parentheses when multiplying together three or more numbers. Thus we can write expressions such as $abcd$ without specifying the order of multiplication or the grouping.

Neither subtraction nor division is associative because the grouping does matter for those operations. For example, $(9 - 6) - 2 = 3 - 2 = 1$, but $9 - (6 - 2) = 9 - 4 = 5$, which shows that subtraction is not associative.

Because subtraction is not associative, we need a way to evaluate expressions that are written without parentheses. The standard practice is to evaluate subtractions from left to right unless parentheses indicate otherwise. For example, $9 - 6 - 2$ should be interpreted to mean $(9 - 6) - 2$, which equals 1.

The Order of Algebraic Operations

Consider the expression

$$2 + 3 \cdot 7.$$

This expression contains no parentheses to guide us to which operation should be performed first. Should we first add 2 and 3, and then multiply the result by 7? If so, we would interpret the expression above as

$$(2 + 3) \cdot 7,$$

which equals 35.

Or to evaluate

$$2 + 3 \cdot 7$$

should we first multiply together 3 and 7, and then add 2 to that result. If so, we would interpret the expression above as

Note that $(2 + 3) \cdot 7$ does not equal $2 + (3 \cdot 7)$. Thus the order of these operations does matter.

$$2 + (3 \cdot 7),$$

which equals 23.

So does $2 + 3 \cdot 7$ equal $(2 + 3) \cdot 7$ or $2 + (3 \cdot 7)$? The answer to this question depends on custom rather than anything inherent in the mathematical situation. Every mathematically literate person would interpret $2 + 3 \cdot 7$ to mean $2 + (3 \cdot 7)$. In other words, people in the modern era have adopted the convention that multiplications should be performed before additions unless parentheses dictate otherwise. You need to become accustomed to this convention, which will be used throughout this course and all your further courses that use mathematics.

Multiplication and division before addition and subtraction

Unless parentheses indicate otherwise, products and quotients are calculated before sums and differences.

Thus, for example, $a + bc$ is interpreted to mean $a + (bc)$, although almost always we dispense with the parentheses and just write $a + bc$.

As another illustration of the principle above, consider the expression

$$4m + 3n + 11(p + q).$$

The correct interpretation of this expression is that 4 should be multiplied by m, 3 should be multiplied by n, 11 should be multiplied by $p + q$, and then the three numbers $4m$, $3n$, and $11(p + q)$ should be added together. In other words, the expression above equals

$$(4m) + (3n) + (11(p + q)).$$

The three newly added sets of parentheses in the expression above are unnecessary, although it is not incorrect to include them. However, the version of the same expression without the unnecessary parentheses is cleaner and easier to read.

When parentheses are enclosed within parentheses, expressions in the innermost parentheses are evaluated first.

The size of parentheses is sometimes used as an optional visual aid to indicate the order of operations. Smaller parentheses should be used for more inner parentheses. Thus expressions enclosed in smaller parentheses should usually be evaluated before expressions enclosed in larger parentheses.

Evaluate inner parentheses first

In an expression with parentheses inside parentheses, evaluate the innermost parentheses first and then work outward.

Evaluate the expression $2(6 + 3(1 + 4))$.

EXAMPLE 1

SOLUTION   Here the innermost parentheses surround $1 + 4$. Thus start by evaluating that expression:

$$2\big(6 + 3\underbrace{(1 + 4)}_{5}\big) = 2(6 + 3 \cdot 5).$$

Now to evaluate the expression $6 + 3 \cdot 5$, first evaluate $3 \cdot 5$, getting 15, then add that to 6, getting 21. Multiplying by 2 completes our evaluation of this expression:

$$2\underbrace{\big(6 + 3\underbrace{(1 + 4)}_{5}\big)}_{21} = 42.$$

The Distributive Property

The distributive property connects addition and multiplication, converting a product with a sum into a sum of two products.

Distributive property

$$a(b + c) = ab + ac$$

Because multiplication is commutative, the distributive property can also be written in the alternative form

$$(a + b)c = ac + bc.$$

The distributive property provides the justification for factoring expressions.

Sometimes you will need to use the distributive property to transform an expression of the form $a(b+c)$ into $ab+ac$, and sometimes you will need to use the distributive property in the opposite direction, transforming an expression of the form $ab+ac$ into $a(b+c)$. Because the distributive property is usually used to simplify an expression, the direction of the transformation depends on the context. The next example shows the use of the distributive property in both directions.

EXAMPLE 2

Simplify the expression $2(3m + x) + 5x$.

SOLUTION   First use the distributive property to transform $2(3m + x)$ into $6m + 2x$:

$$2(3m + x) + 5x = 6m + 2x + 5x.$$

Now use the distributive property again, but in the other direction, to transform $2x + 5x$ to $(2 + 5)x$:

$$6m + 2x + 5x = 6m + (2 + 5)x = 6m + 7x.$$

Putting all this together, we have used the distributive property (twice) to transform

$$2(3m + x) + 5x$$

into the simpler expression

$$6m + 7x.$$

One of the most common algebraic manipulations involves expanding a product of sums, as in the following example.

EXAMPLE 3

Expand $(a + b)(c + d)$.

SOLUTION   Think of $(c + d)$ as a single number and then apply the distributive property to the expression above, getting

$$(a + b)(c + d) = a(c + d) + b(c + d).$$

Now apply the distributive property twice more, getting

$$(a + b)(c + d) = ac + ad + bc + bd.$$

After you use this formula several times, it will become so familiar that you can use it routinely without needing to pause. Note that every term in the first set of parentheses is multiplied by every term in the second set of parentheses.

If you are comfortable with the distributive property, there is no need to memorize the last formula from the example above, because you can always derive it again. Furthermore, by understanding how the identity above was obtained, you should have no trouble finding formulas for more complicated expressions such as $(a + b)(c + d + t)$.

An important special case of the identity above occurs when $c = a$ and $d = b$. In that case we have

$$(a + b)(a + b) = a^2 + ab + ba + b^2,$$

which, with a standard use of commutativity, becomes the identity

$$(a + b)^2 = a^2 + 2ab + b^2.$$

Additive Inverses and Subtraction

The **additive inverse** of a real number a is the number $-a$ such that

$$a + (-a) = 0.$$

The connection between subtraction and additive inverses is captured by the identity

$$a - b = a + (-b).$$

In fact, the equation above can be taken as the definition of subtraction.

You need to be comfortable using the following identities that involve additive inverses and subtraction:

Identities involving additive inverses and subtraction

$$-(-a) = a$$
$$-(a + b) = -a - b$$
$$(-a)(-b) = ab$$
$$(-a)b = a(-b) = -(ab)$$
$$(a - b)c = ac - bc$$
$$a(b - c) = ab - ac$$

Be sure to distribute the minus signs correctly when using the distributive property, as in the example below.

EXAMPLE 4

Expand $(a + b)(a - b)$.

SOLUTION   Start by thinking of $(a + b)$ as a single number and applying the distributive property. Then apply the distributive property twice more, paying careful attention to the minus signs:

$$(a + b)(a - b) = (a + b)a - (a + b)b$$
$$= a^2 + ba - ab - b^2$$
$$= a^2 - b^2$$

You need to become sufficiently comfortable with the following identities so that you can use them with ease.

> **Identities arising from the distributive property**
> $$(a + b)^2 = a^2 + 2ab + b^2$$
> $$(a - b)^2 = a^2 - 2ab + b^2$$
> $$(a + b)(a - b) = a^2 - b^2$$

EXAMPLE 5

Without using a calculator, evaluate 43×37.

SOLUTION $43 \times 37 = (40 + 3)(40 - 3) = 40^2 - 3^2 = 1600 - 9 = 1591$

Multiplicative Inverses and Division

*The multiplicative inverse of b is sometimes called the **reciprocal** of b.*

The **multiplicative inverse** of a real number $b \neq 0$ is the number $\frac{1}{b}$ such that

$$b \cdot \frac{1}{b} = 1.$$

The connection between division and multiplicative inverses is captured by the identity

$$\frac{a}{b} = a \cdot \frac{1}{b}.$$

In fact, the equation above can be taken as the definition of division.

You need to be comfortable using the following identities that involve multiplicative inverses and division:

Identities involving multiplicative inverses and division

$$\frac{a}{b} + \frac{c}{d} = \frac{ad + bc}{bd} \qquad\qquad \frac{\dfrac{a}{b}}{c} = a\frac{c}{b}$$

$$\frac{a}{b} \cdot \frac{c}{d} = \frac{ac}{bd} \qquad\qquad \frac{-a}{b} = \frac{a}{-b} = -\frac{a}{b}$$

$$\frac{ac}{ad} = \frac{c}{d} \qquad\qquad \frac{-a}{-b} = \frac{a}{b}$$

Let's look at these identities a bit more carefully. In all the identities above, we assume that none of the denominators equals 0. The first identity above gives a formula for adding two fractions. The second identity above states that the product of two fractions can be computed by multiplying together the numerators and multiplying together the denominators. Note that the formula for adding fractions is more complicated than the formula for multiplying fractions.

Never, ever, make the mistake of thinking that $\frac{a}{b} + \frac{c}{d}$ equals $\frac{a+c}{b+d}$.

The third identity above, when used to transform $\frac{ac}{ad}$ into $\frac{c}{d}$, is the usual simplification of canceling a common factor from the numerator and denominator. When used in the other direction to transform $\frac{c}{d}$ into $\frac{ac}{ad}$, the third identity above becomes the familiar procedure of multiplying the numerator and denominator by the same factor.

In the fourth identity above, the size of the fraction bars are used to indicate that

$$\frac{a}{\dfrac{b}{c}}$$

should be interpreted to mean $a/(b/c)$. This identity gives the key to unraveling fractions that involve fractions, as shown in the following example.

Simplify the expression

$$\frac{\dfrac{a}{b}}{\dfrac{c}{d}}.$$

EXAMPLE 6

SOLUTION The size of the fraction bars indicates that the expression to be simplified is $(a/b)/(c/d)$. Dividing by $\frac{c}{d}$ is the same as multiplying by $\frac{d}{c}$. Thus we have

$$\frac{\dfrac{a}{b}}{\dfrac{c}{d}} = \frac{a}{b} \cdot \frac{d}{c}$$

$$= \frac{ad}{bc}.$$

When faced with complicated expressions involving fractions that are themselves fractions, remember that division by a fraction is the same as multiplication by the fraction flipped over.

EXERCISES

For Exercises 1–4, determine how many different values can arise by inserting one pair of parentheses into the given expression.

1. $19 - 12 - 8 - 2$
2. $3 - 7 - 9 - 5$
3. $6 + 3 \cdot 4 + 5 \cdot 2$
4. $5 \cdot 3 \cdot 2 + 6 \cdot 4$

For Exercises 5–18, expand the given expression.

5. $(x - y)(z + w - t)$
6. $(x + y - r)(z + w - t)$
7. $(2x + 3)^2$
8. $(3b + 5)^2$
9. $(2c - 7)^2$
10. $(4a - 5)^2$
11. $(x + y + z)^2$
12. $(x - 5y - 3z)^2$
13. $(x + 1)(x - 2)(x + 3)$
14. $(y - 2)(y - 3)(y + 5)$
15. $(a + 2)(a - 2)(a^2 + 4)$
16. $(b - 3)(b + 3)(b^2 + 9)$
17. $xy(x + y)\left(\frac{1}{x} - \frac{1}{y}\right)$
18. $a^2z(z - a)\left(\frac{1}{z} + \frac{1}{a}\right)$

For Exercises 19–40, simplify the given expression as much as possible.

19. $4(2m + 3n) + 7m$
20. $3(2m + 4(n + 5p)) + 6n$
21. $\frac{3}{4} + \frac{6}{7}$
22. $\frac{2}{5} + \frac{7}{8}$
23. $\frac{3}{4} \cdot \frac{14}{39}$
24. $\frac{2}{3} \cdot \frac{15}{22}$
25. $\dfrac{\frac{5}{7}}{\frac{2}{3}}$
26. $\dfrac{\frac{6}{5}}{\frac{7}{4}}$
27. $\frac{m + 1}{2} + \frac{3}{n}$
28. $\frac{m}{3} + \frac{5}{n - 2}$
29. $\frac{2}{3} \cdot \frac{4}{5} + \frac{3}{4} \cdot 2$
30. $\frac{3}{5} \cdot \frac{2}{7} + \frac{5}{4} \cdot 2$
31. $\frac{2}{5} \cdot \frac{m + 3}{7} + \frac{1}{2}$
32. $\frac{3}{4} \cdot \frac{n - 2}{5} + \frac{7}{3}$
33. $\frac{2}{x + 3} + \frac{y - 4}{5}$
34. $\frac{x - 3}{4} - \frac{5}{y + 2}$
35. $\frac{1}{x - y}\left(\frac{x}{y} - \frac{y}{x}\right)$
36. $\frac{1}{y}\left(\frac{1}{x - y} - \frac{1}{x + y}\right)$
37. $\frac{(x + a)^2 - x^2}{a}$
38. $\dfrac{\frac{1}{x + a} - \frac{1}{x}}{a}$
39. $\dfrac{\frac{x - 2}{y}}{\frac{z}{x + 2}}$
40. $\dfrac{\frac{x - 4}{y + 3}}{\frac{y - 3}{x + 4}}$

PROBLEMS

Some problems require considerably more thought than the exercises. Unlike exercises, problems usually have more than one correct answer.

41. Explain how you could show that $51 \times 49 = 2499$ in your head by using the identity $(a + b)(a - b) = a^2 - b^2$.

42. Show that
$$a^3 + b^3 + c^3 - 3abc$$
$$= (a + b + c)(a^2 + b^2 + c^2 - ab - bc - ac).$$

43. Give an example to show that division does not satisfy the associative property.

44. The sales tax in San Francisco is 8.5%. Diners in San Francisco often compute a 17% tip on their before-tax restaurant bill by simply doubling the sales tax. For example, a $64 dollar food and drink bill would come with a sales tax of $5.44; doubling that amount would lead to a 17% tip of $10.88 (which might be rounded up to $11). Explain why this technique is an application of the associativity of multiplication.

45. A quick way to compute a 15% tip on a restaurant bill is first to compute 10% of the bill (by shifting the decimal point) and then add half of that amount for the total tip. For example, 15% of a $43 restaurant bill is $4.30 + $2.15, which equals $6.45. Explain why this technique is an application of the distributive property.

46. The first letters of the phrase "Please excuse my dear Aunt Sally" are used by some people to remember the order of operations: parentheses, exponentiation (which we will discuss in a later chapter), multiplication, division, addition, subtraction. Make up a catchy phrase that serves the same purpose but with exponentiation excluded.

47. (a) Verify that
$$\frac{16}{2} - \frac{25}{5} = \frac{16 - 25}{2 - 5}.$$

(b) From the example above you may be tempted to think that
$$\frac{a}{b} - \frac{c}{d} = \frac{a - c}{b - d}$$
provided none of the denominators equals 0. Give an example to show that this is not true.

WORKED-OUT SOLUTIONS *to Odd-numbered Exercises*

Do not read these worked-out solutions before first struggling to do the exercises yourself. Otherwise you risk the danger of mimicking the techniques shown here without understanding the ideas.

Best way to learn: Carefully read the section of the textbook, then do all the odd-numbered exercises (even if they have not been assigned) and check your answers here. If you get stuck on an exercise, reread the section of the textbook—then try the exercise again. If you are still stuck, then look at the worked-out solution here.

For Exercises 1–4, determine how many different values can arise by inserting one pair of parentheses into the given expression.

1. $19 - 12 - 8 - 2$

    SOLUTION Here are the possibilities:

    $$19(-12 - 8 - 2) = -418$$
    $$19(-12 - 8) - 2 = -382$$
    $$19(-12) - 8 - 2 = -238$$
    $$(19 - 12) - 8 - 2 = -3$$
    $$19 - 12 - (8 - 2) = 1$$
    $$19 - (12 - 8) - 2 = 13$$
    $$19 - (12 - 8 - 2) = 17$$
    $$19 - 12 - 8(-2) = 23$$
    $$19 - 12(-8) - 2 = 113$$
    $$19 - 12(-8 - 2) = 139$$

Other possible ways to insert one pair of parentheses lead to values already included in the list above. For example,
$$(19 - 12 - 8) - 2 = -3.$$

Thus ten values are possible; they are -418, -382, -238, -3, 1, 13, 17, 23, 113, and 139.

3. $6 + 3 \cdot 4 + 5 \cdot 2$

    SOLUTION Here are the possibilities:

    $$(6 + 3 \cdot 4 + 5 \cdot 2) = 28$$
    $$6 + (3 \cdot 4 + 5) \cdot 2 = 40$$
    $$(6 + 3) \cdot 4 + 5 \cdot 2 = 46$$
    $$6 + 3 \cdot (4 + 5 \cdot 2) = 48$$
    $$6 + 3 \cdot (4 + 5) \cdot 2 = 60$$

Other possible ways to insert one pair of parentheses lead to values already included in the list above. For example,
$$(6 + 3 \cdot 4 + 5) \cdot 2 = 46.$$

Thus five values are possible; they are 28, 40, 46, 48, and 60.

For Exercises 5-18, expand the given expression.

5. $(x - y)(z + w - t)$

   SOLUTION

   $(x - y)(z + w - t)$

   $\qquad = x(z + w - t) - y(z + w - t)$

   $\qquad = xz + xw - xt - yz - yw + yt$

7. $(2x + 3)^2$

   SOLUTION

   $\quad (2x + 3)^2 = (2x)^2 + 2 \cdot (2x) \cdot 3 + 3^2$

   $\qquad\qquad = 4x^2 + 12x + 9$

9. $(2c - 7)^2$

   SOLUTION

   $\quad (2c - 7)^2 = (2c)^2 - 2 \cdot (2c) \cdot 7 + 7^2$

   $\qquad\qquad = 4c^2 - 28c + 49$

11. $(x + y + z)^2$

    SOLUTION

    $(x + y + z)^2$

    $\quad = (x + y + z)(x + y + z)$

    $\quad = x(x + y + z) + y(x + y + z) + z(x + y + z)$

    $\quad = x^2 + xy + xz + yx + y^2 + yz$

    $\qquad + zx + zy + z^2$

    $\quad = x^2 + y^2 + z^2 + 2xy + 2xz + 2yz$

13. $(x + 1)(x - 2)(x + 3)$

    SOLUTION

$(x + 1)(x - 2)(x + 3)$

$\qquad = ((x + 1)(x - 2))(x + 3)$

$\qquad = (x^2 - 2x + x - 2)(x + 3)$

$\qquad = (x^2 - x - 2)(x + 3)$

$\qquad = x^3 + 3x^2 - x^2 - 3x - 2x - 6$

$\qquad = x^3 + 2x^2 - 5x - 6$

15. $(a + 2)(a - 2)(a^2 + 4)$

    SOLUTION

    $(a + 2)(a - 2)(a^2 + 4) = ((a + 2)(a - 2))(a^2 + 4)$

    $\qquad\qquad = (a^2 - 4)(a^2 + 4)$

    $\qquad\qquad = a^4 - 16$

17. $xy(x + y)(\frac{1}{x} - \frac{1}{y})$

    SOLUTION

    $xy(x + y)\left(\dfrac{1}{x} - \dfrac{1}{y}\right) = xy(x + y)\left(\dfrac{y}{xy} - \dfrac{x}{xy}\right)$

    $\qquad\qquad = xy(x + y)\left(\dfrac{y - x}{xy}\right)$

    $\qquad\qquad = (x + y)(y - x)$

    $\qquad\qquad = y^2 - x^2$

For Exercises 19-40, simplify the given expression as much as possible.

19. $4(2m + 3n) + 7m$

    SOLUTION

    $\quad 4(2m + 3n) + 7m = 8m + 12n + 7m$

    $\qquad\qquad = 15m + 12n$

21. $\dfrac{3}{4} + \dfrac{6}{7}$

    SOLUTION $\quad \dfrac{3}{4} + \dfrac{6}{7} = \dfrac{3}{4} \cdot \dfrac{7}{7} + \dfrac{6}{7} \cdot \dfrac{4}{4} = \dfrac{21}{28} + \dfrac{24}{28} =$
    $\dfrac{45}{28}$

23. $\dfrac{3}{4} \cdot \dfrac{14}{39}$

SOLUTION $\dfrac{3}{4} \cdot \dfrac{14}{39} = \dfrac{3 \cdot 14}{4 \cdot 39} = \dfrac{7}{2 \cdot 13} = \dfrac{7}{26}$

25. $\dfrac{\frac{5}{7}}{\frac{2}{3}}$

SOLUTION $\dfrac{\frac{5}{7}}{\frac{2}{3}} = \dfrac{5}{7} \cdot \dfrac{3}{2} = \dfrac{5 \cdot 3}{7 \cdot 2} = \dfrac{15}{14}$

27. $\dfrac{m+1}{2} + \dfrac{3}{n}$

SOLUTION

$$\dfrac{m+1}{2} + \dfrac{3}{n} = \dfrac{m+1}{2} \cdot \dfrac{n}{n} + \dfrac{3}{n} \cdot \dfrac{2}{2}$$

$$= \dfrac{(m+1)n + 3 \cdot 2}{2n}$$

$$= \dfrac{mn + n + 6}{2n}$$

29. $\dfrac{2}{3} \cdot \dfrac{4}{5} + \dfrac{3}{4} \cdot 2$

SOLUTION

$$\dfrac{2}{3} \cdot \dfrac{4}{5} + \dfrac{3}{4} \cdot 2 = \dfrac{8}{15} + \dfrac{3}{2}$$

$$= \dfrac{8}{15} \cdot \dfrac{2}{2} + \dfrac{3}{2} \cdot \dfrac{15}{15}$$

$$= \dfrac{16 + 45}{30}$$

$$= \dfrac{61}{30}$$

31. $\dfrac{2}{5} \cdot \dfrac{m+3}{7} + \dfrac{1}{2}$

SOLUTION

$$\dfrac{2}{5} \cdot \dfrac{m+3}{7} + \dfrac{1}{2} = \dfrac{2m+6}{35} + \dfrac{1}{2}$$

$$= \dfrac{2m+6}{35} \cdot \dfrac{2}{2} + \dfrac{1}{2} \cdot \dfrac{35}{35}$$

$$= \dfrac{4m + 12 + 35}{70}$$

$$= \dfrac{4m + 47}{70}$$

33. $\dfrac{2}{x+3} + \dfrac{y-4}{5}$

SOLUTION

$$\dfrac{2}{x+3} + \dfrac{y-4}{5} = \dfrac{2}{x+3} \cdot \dfrac{5}{5} + \dfrac{y-4}{5} \cdot \dfrac{x+3}{x+3}$$

$$= \dfrac{2 \cdot 5 + (y-4)(x+3)}{5(x+3)}$$

$$= \dfrac{10 + yx + 3y - 4x - 12}{5(x+3)}$$

$$= \dfrac{xy - 4x + 3y - 2}{5(x+3)}$$

35. $\dfrac{1}{x-y}\left(\dfrac{x}{y} - \dfrac{y}{x}\right)$

SOLUTION

$$\dfrac{1}{x-y}\left(\dfrac{x}{y} - \dfrac{y}{x}\right) = \dfrac{1}{x-y}\left(\dfrac{x}{y} \cdot \dfrac{x}{x} - \dfrac{y}{x} \cdot \dfrac{y}{y}\right)$$

$$= \dfrac{1}{x-y}\left(\dfrac{x^2 - y^2}{xy}\right)$$

$$= \dfrac{1}{x-y}\left(\dfrac{(x+y)(x-y)}{xy}\right)$$

$$= \dfrac{x+y}{xy}$$

37. $\dfrac{(x+a)^2 - x^2}{a}$

SOLUTION

$$\dfrac{(x+a)^2 - x^2}{a} = \dfrac{x^2 + 2xa + a^2 - x^2}{a}$$

$$= \dfrac{2xa + a^2}{a}$$

$$= 2x + a$$

39. $\dfrac{\frac{x-2}{y}}{\frac{z}{x+2}}$

SOLUTION

$$\dfrac{\frac{x-2}{y}}{\frac{z}{x+2}} = \dfrac{x-2}{y} \cdot \dfrac{x+2}{z}$$

$$= \dfrac{x^2 - 4}{yz}$$

0.3 | *Inequalities*

SECTION OBJECTIVES

By the end of this section you should

- recall the algebraic properties involving positive and negative numbers;
- understand inequalities;
- be able to use interval notation for the four types of intervals;
- be able to use interval notation involving $-\infty$ and ∞;
- be able to work with unions of intervals;
- be able to manipulate and interpret expressions involving absolute value.

From now on, "number" means "real number" unless otherwise stated.

Positive and Negative Numbers

The words "positive" and "negative" have many uses in English in addition to their mathematical meaning. Some of these uses, such as in the phrase "photographic negative", are related to the mathematical meaning.

Positive and negative numbers

- A number is called **positive** if it is right of 0 on the real line.
- A number is called **negative** if it is left of 0 on the real line.

Every number is either right of 0, left of 0, or equals 0. Thus every number is either positive, negative, or 0.

$$-3 \quad -\tfrac{5}{2} \quad -2 \quad -\tfrac{115}{76} \quad -1 \quad -\tfrac{2}{3} \quad -\tfrac{1}{3} \quad 0 \quad \tfrac{1}{3} \quad \tfrac{2}{3} \quad 1 \quad \tfrac{12}{7} \quad 2 \quad \tfrac{257}{101} \quad 3$$

negative numbers　　　*positive numbers*

All of the following properties should already be familiar to you.

Example:

$2 + 3 = 5$

$(-2) + (-3) = -5$

-2 *is negative*

$-(-2)$ *is positive*

$2 \cdot 3 = 6$

$(-2) \cdot (-3) = 6$

$2 \cdot (-3) = -6$

$\tfrac{1}{2}$ *is positive*

$\tfrac{1}{-2}$ *is negative*

Algebraic properties of positive and negative numbers

- The sum of two positive numbers is positive.
- The sum of two negative numbers is negative.
- The additive inverse of a positive number is negative.
- The additive inverse of a negative number is positive.
- The product of two positive numbers is positive.
- The product of two negative numbers is positive.
- The product of a positive number and a negative number is negative.
- The multiplicative inverse of a positive number is positive.
- The multiplicative inverse of a negative number is negative.

Lesser and Greater

We say that a number a is **less than** a number b, written $a < b$, if a is left of b on the real line. Equivalently, $a < b$ if and only if $b - a$ is positive. In particular, b is positive if and only if $0 < b$.

$$a < b.$$

We say that a is **less than or equal to** b, written $a \le b$, if $a < b$ or $a = b$. Thus the statement $x < 4$ is true if x equals 3 but false if x equals 4, whereas the statement $x \le 4$ is true if x equals 3 and also true if x equals 4.

We say that b is **greater than** a, written $b > a$, if b is right of a on the real line. Thus $b > a$ means the same as $a < b$. Similarly, we say that b is **greater than or equal to** a, written $b \ge a$, if $b > a$ or $b = a$. Thus $b \ge a$ means the same as $a \le b$.

We now begin discussion of a series of simple but crucial properties of inequalities. The first property we will discuss is called transitivity.

Transitivity

If $a < b$ and $b < c$, then $a < c$.

For example, from the inequalities $\sqrt{15} < 4$ and $4 < \frac{21}{5}$ we can conclude that $\sqrt{15} < \frac{21}{5}$.

To see why transitivity holds, suppose $a < b$ and $b < c$. Then a is left of b on the real line and b is left of c. This implies that a is left of c, which means that $a < c$; see the figure below.

Transitivity: $a < b$ and $b < c$ implies that $a < c$.

Often multiple inequalities are written together as a single string of inequalities. Thus $a < b < c$ means the same thing as $a < b$ and $b < c$.

Our next result shows that we can add inequalities.

Addition of inequalities

If $a < b$ and $c < d$, then $a + c < b + d$.

For example, from the inequalities $\sqrt{8} < 3$ and $4 < \sqrt{17}$ we can conclude that $\sqrt{8} + 4 < 3 + \sqrt{17}$.

To see why this is true, note that if $a < b$ and $c < d$, then $b - a$ and $d - c$ are positive numbers. Because the sum of two positive numbers is positive, this implies that $(b - a) + (d - c)$ is positive. In other words, $(b + d) - (a + c)$ is positive. This means that $a + c < b + d$, as desired.

The next result states that we can multiply both sides of an inequality by a positive number and preserve the inequality. However, if both sides of an inequality are multiplied by a negative number, then the direction of the inequality must be reversed.

Multiplication of an inequality

For example, from the inequality $\sqrt{7} < \sqrt{8}$ we can conclude that $3\sqrt{7} < 3\sqrt{8}$ and $(-3)\sqrt{7} > (-3)\sqrt{8}$.

Suppose $a < b$.

- If $c > 0$, then $ac < bc$.

- If $c < 0$, then $ac > bc$.

To see why this is true, first suppose $c > 0$. We are assuming that $a < b$, which means that $b - a$ is positive. Because the product of two positive numbers is positive, this implies that $(b - a)c$ is positive. In other words, $bc - ac$ is positive, which means that $ac < bc$, as desired.

Now consider the case where $c < 0$. We are still assuming that $a < b$, which means that $b - a$ is positive. Because the product of a positive number and a negative number is negative, this implies that $(b - a)c$ is negative. In other words, $bc - ac$ is negative, which means that $ac > bc$, as desired.

An important special case of the result above is obtained by setting $c = -1$, which gives the following result:

Additive inverse and inequalities

For example, from the inequality $2 < 3$ we can conclude that $-2 > -3$.

If $a < b$, then $-a > -b$.

In other words, the direction of an inequality must be reversed when taking additive inverses of both sides.

The next result shows that the direction of an inequality must also be reversed when taking multiplicative inverses of both sides, unless one side is negative and the other side is positive.

Multiplicative inverse and inequalities

For example, from the inequality $2 < 3$ we can conclude that $\frac{1}{2} > \frac{1}{3}$.

Suppose $a < b$.

- If a and b are both positive or both negative, then $\frac{1}{a} > \frac{1}{b}$.

- If $a < 0 < b$, then $\frac{1}{a} < \frac{1}{b}$.

To see why this is true, first suppose a and b are both positive or both negative. In either case, ab is positive. Thus $\frac{1}{ab} > 0$. Thus we can multiply both sides of the inequality $a < b$ by $\frac{1}{ab}$, preserving the direction of the inequality. This gives

$$a \cdot \frac{1}{ab} < b \cdot \frac{1}{ab},$$

which is the same as $\frac{1}{b} < \frac{1}{a}$, or equivalently $\frac{1}{a} > \frac{1}{b}$, as desired.

The case where $a < 0 < b$ is even easier. In this case $\frac{1}{a}$ is negative and $\frac{1}{b}$ is positive. Thus $\frac{1}{a} < \frac{1}{b}$, as desired.

Intervals

We begin this subsection with an imprecise definition.

> ### Set
>
> A **set** is a collection of objects.

This definition is imprecise because the words "collection" and "objects" are vague.

The collection of positive numbers is an example of a set, as is the collection of odd negative integers. Most of the sets considered in this book are collections of real numbers, which at least removes some of the vagueness from the word "objects".

If a set contains only finitely many objects, then the objects in the set can be explicitly displayed between the symbols { }. For example, the set consisting of the numbers 4, $-\frac{17}{7}$, and $\sqrt{2}$ can be denoted by

$$\{4, -\tfrac{17}{7}, \sqrt{2}\}.$$

Sets can also be denoted by a property that characterizes objects of the set. For example, the set of real numbers greater than 2 can be denoted by

$$\{x : x > 2\}.$$

Here the notation $\{x : \dots\}$ should be read to mean "the set of real numbers x such that" and then whatever follows. There is no particular x here. The variable is simply a convenient device to describe a property, and the symbol used for the variable does not matter. Thus $\{x : x > 2\}$ and $\{y : y > 2\}$ and $\{t : t > 2\}$ all denote the same set, which can also be described (without mentioning any variables) as the set of real numbers greater than 2.

A special type of set occurs so often in mathematics that it gets its own name, which is given by the following definition.

> ### Interval
>
> An **interval** is a set of real numbers that contains all numbers between any two numbers in the set.

For example, the set of positive numbers is an interval because all numbers between any two positive numbers are positive. As a nonexample, the set of integers is not an interval because 0 and 1 are in this set, but $\frac{1}{2}$, which is between 0 and 1, is not in this set. As another nonexample, the set of rational numbers is not an interval, because 1 and 2 are in this set, but $\sqrt{2}$, which is between 1 and 2, is not in this set.

Intervals are so useful in mathematics that special notation has been designed for them. Suppose a and b are numbers with $a < b$. We define the following four intervals with endpoints a and b:

Intervals

- The **open interval** (a, b) with endpoints a and b is the set of numbers between a and b, not including either endpoint:

$$(a, b) = \{x : a < x < b\}.$$

The definition of $[a, b]$ also makes sense when $a = b$; the interval $[a, a]$ consists of the single number a.

- The **closed interval** $[a, b]$ with endpoints a and b is the set of numbers between a and b, including both endpoints:

$$[a, b] = \{x : a \leq x \leq b\}.$$

- The **half-open interval** $[a, b)$ with endpoints a and b is the set of numbers between a and b, including a but not including b:

$$[a, b) = \{x : a \leq x < b\}.$$

The term "half-closed" would make as much sense as "half-open".

- The **half-open interval** $(a, b]$ with endpoints a and b is the set of numbers between a and b, including b but not including a:

$$(a, b] = \{x : a < x \leq b\}.$$

With this notation, a parenthesis indicates that the corresponding endpoint is not included in the set, and a straight bracket indicates that the corresponding endpoint is included in the set. Thus the interval $(3, 7]$ includes the numbers 4, $\sqrt{17}$, 5.49, and the endpoint 7 (along with many other numbers), but does not include the numbers 2 or 9 or the endpoint 3.

Sometimes we need to use intervals that extend arbitrarily far to the left or to the right on the real number line. Suppose a is a real number. We define the following four intervals with endpoint a:

Intervals

Example: $(0, \infty)$ denotes the set of positive numbers.

- The interval (a, ∞) is the set of numbers greater than a:

$$(a, \infty) = \{x : x > a\}.$$

- The interval $[a, \infty)$ is the set of numbers greater than or equal to a:

$$[a, \infty) = \{x : x \geq a\}.$$

Example: $(-\infty, 0)$ denotes the set of negative numbers.

- The interval $(-\infty, a)$ is the set of numbers less than a:

$$(-\infty, a) = \{x : x < a\}.$$

- The interval $(-\infty, a]$ is the set of numbers less than or equal to a:

$$(-\infty, a] = \{x : x \leq a\}.$$

Here the symbol ∞, called **infinity**, should be thought of simply as a notational convenience. Neither ∞ nor $-\infty$ is a real number; these symbols have no meaning in this context other than as notational shorthand. For example, the interval $(2, \infty)$ is defined to be the set of real numbers greater than 2 (note that ∞ is not mentioned in this definition). The notation $(2, \infty)$ is often used because writing $(2, \infty)$ is easier than writing $\{x : x > 2\}$.

As before, a parenthesis indicates that the corresponding endpoint is not included in the set, and a straight bracket indicates that the corresponding endpoint is included in the set. Thus the interval $(2, \infty)$ does not include the endpoint 2, but the interval $[2, \infty)$ does include the endpoint 2. Both of the intervals $(2, \infty)$ and $[2, \infty)$ include 2.5 and 98765 (along with many other numbers); neither of these intervals includes 1.5 or -857.

There do not exist intervals with a closed bracket adjacent to $-\infty$ or ∞. For example, $[-\infty, 2]$ and $[2, \infty]$ do not make sense because the closed brackets indicate that both endpoints should be included. The symbols $-\infty$ and ∞ can never be included in a set of real numbers because these symbols do not denote real numbers.

Some books use the notation $(-\infty, \infty)$ to denote the set of real numbers.

In later chapters we will occasionally find it useful to work with the union of two intervals. Here is the definition of union:

Union

The **union** of two sets A and B, denoted $A \cup B$, is the set of objects that are contained in at least one of the sets A and B.

Similarly, the union of three or more sets is the collection of objects that are contained in at least one of the sets.

Thus $A \cup B$ consists of the objects (usually numbers) that belong either to A or to B or to both A and B.

Write $(1, 5) \cup (3, 7]$ as an interval.

EXAMPLE 1

SOLUTION
As can be seen from the figure here, every number in the interval $(1, 7]$ is either in $(1, 5)$ or is in $(3, 7]$ or is in both $(1, 5)$ and $(3, 7]$. The figure shows that $(1, 5) \cup (3, 7] = (1, 7]$.

The next example goes in the other direction, starting with a set and then writing it as a union of intervals.

Write the set of nonzero real numbers as the union of two intervals.

EXAMPLE 2

SOLUTION   The set of nonzero real numbers is the union of the set of negative numbers and the set of positive numbers. In other words, the set of nonzero real numbers equals $(-\infty, 0) \cup (0, \infty)$.

Absolute Value

The **absolute value** of a number is its distance from 0; here we are thinking of numbers as points on the real line. For example, the absolute value of $\frac{3}{2}$ equals $\frac{3}{2}$, as can be seen in the figure below. More interestingly, the absolute value of $-\frac{3}{2}$ equals $\frac{3}{2}$.

The absolute value of a number is its distance to 0.

The absolute value of a number b is denoted by $|b|$. Thus $|\frac{3}{2}| = \frac{3}{2}$ and $|-\frac{3}{2}| = \frac{3}{2}$. Here is the formal definition of absolute value:

> ### Absolute value
>
> The **absolute value** of a number b, denoted $|b|$, is defined by
>
> $$|b| = \begin{cases} b & \text{if } b \geq 0 \\ -b & \text{if } b < 0. \end{cases}$$

For example, $-\frac{3}{2} < 0$, and thus by the formula above $|-\frac{3}{2}|$ equals $-(-\frac{3}{2})$, which equals $\frac{3}{2}$.

The concept of absolute value is fairly simple—just strip away the minus sign from any number that happens to have one. However, this rule can be applied only to numbers, not to expressions whose value is unknown. For example, if we encounter the expression $|-(x + y)|$, we cannot simplify this expression to $x + y$ unless we know that $x + y \geq 0$. If $x + y$ happens to be negative, then $|-(x + y)| = -(x + y)$; stripping away the negative sign would be incorrect in this case.

> $|-(x + y)| = |x + y|$ regardless of the value of $x + y$, as you are asked to explain in Problem 56.

Inequalities involving absolute values can be written without using an absolute value, as shown in the following example.

EXAMPLE 3

(a) Write the inequality $|x| < 2$ without using an absolute value.

(b) Write the set $\{x : |x| < 2\}$ as an interval.

SOLUTION

(a) A number has absolute value less than 2 if only and only if its distance from 0 is less than 2, and this happens if and only if the number is between -2 and 2. Hence the inequality $|x| < 2$ could be written as

$$-2 < x < 2.$$

(b) The inequality above implies that the set $\{x : |x| < 2\}$ equals the open interval $(-2, 2)$.

In the next example, we end up with an interval not centered at 0.

EXAMPLE 4

(a) Write the inequality $|x - 5| < 1$ without using an absolute value.

(b) Write the set $\{x : |x - 5| < 1\}$ as an interval.

The set

$$\{x : |x - 5| < 1\}$$

is the set of points on the real line whose distance to 5 is less than 1.

SOLUTION

(a) The absolute value of a number is less than 1 precisely when the number is between -1 and 1. Thus the inequality $|x - 5| < 1$ is equivalent to

$$-1 < x - 5 < 1.$$

Adding 5 to all three parts of the inequality above transforms it to the inequality

$$4 < x < 6.$$

(b) The inequality above implies that the set $\{x : |x - 5| < 1\}$ equals the open interval $(4, 6)$.

In the next example, we deal with a slightly more abstract situation, using symbols rather than specific numbers. You should begin to get comfortable working in such situations. To get a good understanding of an abstract piece of mathematics, start by looking at an example using concrete numbers, as in Example 4, before going on to a more abstract setting, as in Example 5.

EXAMPLE 5

Suppose b is a real number and $h > 0$.

(a) Write the inequality $|x - b| < h$ without using an absolute value.

(b) Write the set $\{x : |x - b| < h\}$ as an interval.

The set

$$\{x : |x - b| < h\}$$

is the set of points on the real line whose distance to b is less than h.

SOLUTION

(a) The absolute value of a number is less than h precisely when the number is between $-h$ and h. Thus the inequality $|x - b| < h$ is equivalent to

$$-h < x - b < h.$$

Adding b to all three parts of the inequality above transforms it to the inequality

$$b - h < x < b + h.$$

(b) The inequality above implies that the set $\{x : |x - b| < h\}$ equals the open interval $(b - h, b + h)$.

$\{x : |x - b| < h\}$ *is the open interval of length* $2h$ *centered at b.*

Equations involving absolute values must often be solved by considering multiple possibilities. Here is a simple example:

| EXAMPLE 6 | Find all numbers t such that
$$|3t - 4| = 10.$$

SOLUTION   The equation $|3t - 4| = 10$ implies that $3t - 4 = 10$ or $3t - 4 = -10$. Solving these equations for t gives $t = \frac{14}{3}$ or $t = -2$. Substituting these values for t back into the original equation shows that both $\frac{14}{3}$ and -2 are indeed solutions.

A more complicated example would ask for all numbers x such that

The worked-out solution to Exercise 5 shows how to deal with this sort of situation.

$$|x - 3| + |x - 4| = 9.$$

To find the solutions to this equation, think of the set of real numbers as the union of the three intervals $(-\infty, 3)$, $[3, 4)$, and $[4, \infty)$ and consider what the equation above becomes for x in each of those three intervals.

EXERCISES

In Exercises 1-6, find all numbers x satisfying the given equation.

1. $|2x - 6| = 11$
2. $|5x + 8| = 19$
3. $\left|\frac{x+1}{x-1}\right| = 2$
4. $\left|\frac{3x+2}{x-4}\right| = 5$
5. $|x - 3| + |x - 4| = 9$
6. $|x + 1| + |x - 2| = 7$

In Exercises 7-16, write each union as a single interval.

7. $[2, 7) \cup [5, 20)$
8. $[-8, -3) \cup [-6, -1)$
9. $[-2, 8] \cup (-1, 4)$
10. $(-9, -2) \cup [-7, -5]$
11. $(3, \infty) \cup [2, 8]$
12. $(-\infty, 4) \cup (-2, 6]$
13. $(-\infty, -3) \cup [-5, \infty)$
14. $(-\infty, -6] \cup (-8, 12)$
15. $(-3, \infty) \cup [-5, \infty)$
16. $(-\infty, -10] \cup (-\infty, -8]$

17. Give four examples of pairs of real numbers a and b such that
$$|a + b| = 2 \quad \text{and} \quad |a| + |b| = 8.$$

18. Give four examples of pairs of real numbers a and b such that
$$|a + b| = 3 \quad \text{and} \quad |a| + |b| = 11.$$

In Exercises 19-30, write each set as an interval or as a union of two intervals.

19. $\{x : |x - 4| < \frac{1}{10}\}$

20. $\{x : |x + 2| < \frac{1}{100}\}$
21. $\{x : |x + 4| < \frac{\varepsilon}{2}\}$; here $\varepsilon > 0$
    *[Mathematicians often use the Greek letter ε, which is called **epsilon**, to denote a small positive number.]*
22. $\{x : |x - 2| < \frac{\varepsilon}{3}\}$; here $\varepsilon > 0$
23. $\{y : |y - a| < \varepsilon\}$; here $\varepsilon > 0$
24. $\{y : |y + b| < \varepsilon\}$; here $\varepsilon > 0$
25. $\{x : |3x - 2| < \frac{1}{4}\}$
26. $\{x : |4x - 3| < \frac{1}{5}\}$
27. $\{x : |x| > 2\}$
28. $\{x : |x| > 9\}$
29. $\{x : |x - 5| \geq 3\}$
30. $\{x : |x + 6| \geq 2\}$

The intersection of two sets of numbers consists of all numbers that are in both sets. If A and B are sets, then their intersection is denoted by A ∩ B. In Exercises 31-40, write each intersection as a single interval.

31. $[2, 7) \cap [5, 20)$
32. $[-8, -3) \cap [-6, -1)$
33. $[-2, 8] \cap (-1, 4)$
34. $(-9, -2) \cap [-7, -5]$
35. $(3, \infty) \cap [2, 8]$
36. $(-\infty, 4) \cap (-2, 6]$
37. $(-\infty, -3) \cap [-5, \infty)$
38. $(-\infty, -6] \cap (-8, 12)$
39. $(-3, \infty) \cap [-5, \infty)$
40. $(-\infty, -10] \cap (-\infty, -8]$

PROBLEMS

41. Suppose a and b are numbers. Explain why either $a < b$, $a = b$, or $a > b$.

42. Show that if $a < b$ and $c \le d$, then $a + c < b + d$.

43. Show that if b is a positive number and $a < b$, then
$$\frac{a}{b} < \frac{a+1}{b+1}.$$

44. In contrast to Problem 47 in Section 0.2, show that there do not exist positive numbers a, b, c, and d such that
$$\frac{a}{b} + \frac{c}{d} = \frac{a+c}{b+d}.$$

45. (a) True or false:

    If $a < b$ and $c < d$, then $c - b < d - a$.

    (b) Explain your answer to part (a). This means that if the answer to part (a) is "true", then you should explain why $c - b < d - a$ whenever $a < b$ and $c < d$; if the answer to part (a) is "false", then you should give an example of numbers a, b, c, and d such that $a < b$ and $c < d$ but $c - b \ge d - a$.

46. (a) True or false:

    If $a < b$ and $c < d$, then $ac < bd$.

    (b) Explain your answer to part (a). This means that if the answer to part (a) is "true", then you should explain why $ac < bd$ whenever $a < b$ and $c < d$; if the answer to part (a) is "false", then you should give an example of numbers a, b, c, and d such that $a < b$ and $c < d$ but $ac \ge bd$.

47. (a) True or false:

    If $0 < a < b$ and $0 < c < d$, then $\dfrac{a}{d} < \dfrac{b}{c}$.

    (b) Explain your answer to part (a). This means that if the answer to part (a) is "true", then you should explain why $\frac{a}{d} < \frac{b}{c}$ whenever $0 < a < b$ and $0 < c < d$; if the answer to part (a) is "false", then you should give an example of numbers a, b, c, and d such that $0 < a < b$ and $0 < c < d$ but
    $$\frac{a}{d} \ge \frac{b}{c}.$$

48. Explain why every open interval containing 0 contains an open interval centered at 0.

49. Give an example of an open interval and a closed interval whose union equals the interval $(2, 5)$.

50. Give an example of an open interval and a closed interval whose intersection equals the interval $(2, 5)$.

51. Give an example of an open interval and a closed interval whose union equals the interval $[-3, 7]$.

52. Give an example of an open interval and a closed interval whose intersection equals the interval $[-3, 7]$.

53. Explain why the equation
$$|8x - 3| = -2$$
has no solutions.

54. Explain why
$$|a^2| = a^2$$
for every real number a.

55. Explain why
$$|ab| = |a||b|$$
for all real numbers a and b.

56. Explain why
$$|-a| = |a|$$
for all real numbers a.

57. Explain why
$$\left|\frac{a}{b}\right| = \frac{|a|}{|b|}$$
for all real numbers a and b (with $b \neq 0$).

58. (a) Show that if $a \ge 0$ and $b \ge 0$, then $|a + b| = |a| + |b|$.

    (b) Show that if $a \ge 0$ and $b < 0$, then $|a + b| \le |a| + |b|$.

    (c) Show that if $a < 0$ and $b \ge 0$, then $|a + b| \le |a| + |b|$.

    (d) Show that if $a < 0$ and $b < 0$, then $|a + b| = |a| + |b|$.

    (e) Explain why the previous four items imply that
    $$|a + b| \le |a| + |b|$$
    for all real numbers a and b.

59. Show that if a and b are real numbers such that
$$|a + b| < |a| + |b|,$$
then $ab < 0$.

60. Show that
$$\big||a| - |b|\big| \leq |a - b|$$
for all real numbers a and b.

WORKED-OUT SOLUTIONS *to Odd-numbered Exercises*

In Exercises 1–6, find all numbers x satisfying the given equation.

1. $|2x - 6| = 11$

SOLUTION The equation $|2x - 6| = 11$ implies that $2x - 6 = 11$ or $2x - 6 = -11$. Solving these equations for x gives $x = \frac{17}{2}$ or $x = -\frac{5}{2}$.

3. $\left|\frac{x+1}{x-1}\right| = 2$

SOLUTION The equation $\left|\frac{x+1}{x-1}\right| = 2$ implies that $\frac{x+1}{x-1} = 2$ or $\frac{x+1}{x-1} = -2$. Solving these equations for x gives $x = 3$ or $x = \frac{1}{3}$.

5. $|x - 3| + |x - 4| = 9$

SOLUTION First, consider numbers x such that $x \geq 4$. In this case, we have $x - 3 \geq 0$ and $x - 4 \geq 0$, which implies that $|x - 3| = x - 3$ and $|x - 4| = x - 4$. Thus the original equation becomes
$$x - 3 + x - 4 = 9,$$
which can be rewritten as $2x - 7 = 9$, which can easily be solved to yield $x = 8$. Substituting 8 for x in the original equation shows that $x = 8$ is indeed a solution (make sure you do this check).

Second, consider numbers x such that $x < 3$. In this case, we have $x - 3 < 0$ and $x - 4 < 0$, which implies that $|x - 3| = 3 - x$ and $|x - 4| = 4 - x$. Thus the original equation becomes
$$3 - x + 4 - x = 9,$$
which can be rewritten as $7 - 2x = 9$, which can easily be solved to yield $x = -1$. Substituting -1 for x in the original equation shows that $x = -1$ is indeed a solution (make sure you do this check).

Third, we need to consider the only remaining possibility, which is that $3 \leq x < 4$. In this case, we have $x - 3 \geq 0$ and $x - 4 < 0$, which implies

that $|x - 3| = x - 3$ and $|x - 4| = 4 - x$. Thus the original equation becomes
$$x - 3 + 4 - x = 9,$$
which can be rewritten as $1 = 9$, which holds for no values of x.

Thus we can conclude that 8 and -1 are the only values of x that satisfy the original equation.

In Exercises 7–16, write each union as a single interval.

7. $[2, 7) \cup [5, 20)$

SOLUTION The first interval is the set $\{x : 2 \leq x < 7\}$, which includes the left endpoint 2 but does not include the right endpoint 7. The second interval is the set $\{x : 5 \leq x < 20\}$, which includes the left endpoint 5 but does not include the right endpoint 20. The set of numbers that are in at least one of these sets equals $\{x : 2 \leq x < 20\}$, as can be seen in the figure below:

Thus $[2, 7) \cup [5, 20) = [2, 20)$.

9. $[-2, 8] \cup (-1, 4)$

SOLUTION The first interval is the set $\{x : -2 \leq x \leq 8\}$, which includes both endpoints. The second interval is the set $\{x : -1 < x < 4\}$, which does not include either endpoint. The set of numbers that are in at least one of these sets equals $\{x : -2 \leq x \leq 8\}$, as can be seen in the following figure:

Thus $[-2, 8] \cup (-1, 4) = [-2, 8]$.

11. $(3, \infty) \cup [2, 8]$

SOLUTION   The first interval is the set $\{x : 3 < x\}$, which does not include the left endpoint and which has no right endpoint. The second interval is the set $\{x : 2 \leq x \leq 8\}$, which includes both endpoints. The set of numbers that are in at least one of these sets equals $\{x : 2 \leq x\}$, as can be seen in the figure below:

Thus $(3, \infty) \cup [2, 8] = [2, \infty)$.

13. $(-\infty, -3) \cup [-5, \infty)$

SOLUTION   The first interval is the set $\{x : x < -3\}$, which has no left endpoint and which does not include the right endpoint. The second interval is the set $\{x : -5 \leq x\}$, which includes the left endpoint and which has no right endpoint. The set of numbers that are in at least one of these sets equals the entire real line, as can be seen in the figure below:

Thus $(-\infty, -3) \cup [-5, \infty) = (-\infty, \infty)$.

15. $(-3, \infty) \cup [-5, \infty)$

SOLUTION   The first interval is the set $\{x : -3 < x\}$, which does not include the left endpoint and which has no right endpoint. The second interval is the set $\{x : -5 \leq x\}$, which includes the left endpoint and which has no right endpoint. The set of numbers that are in

at least one of these sets equals $\{x : -5 \leq x\}$, as can be seen in the figure below:

Thus $(-3, \infty) \cup [-5, \infty) = [-5, \infty)$.

17. Give four examples of pairs of real numbers a and b such that

$$|a + b| = 2 \quad \text{and} \quad |a| + |b| = 8.$$

SOLUTION   First consider the case where $a \geq 0$ and $b \geq 0$. In this case, we have $a + b \geq 0$. Thus the equations above become

$$a + b = 2 \quad \text{and} \quad a + b = 8.$$

There are no solutions to the simultaneous equations above, because $a + b$ cannot simultaneously equal both 2 and 8.

Next consider the case where $a < 0$ and $b < 0$. In this case, we have $a + b < 0$. Thus the equations above become

$$-a - b = 2 \quad \text{and} \quad -a - b = 8.$$

There are no solutions to the simultaneous equations above, because $-a - b$ cannot simultaneously equal both 2 and 8.

Now consider the case where $a \geq 0$, $b < 0$, and $a + b \geq 0$. In this case the equations above become

$$a + b = 2 \quad \text{and} \quad a - b = 8.$$

Solving these equations for a and b, we get $a = 5$ and $b = -3$.

Now consider the case where $a \geq 0$, $b < 0$, and $a + b < 0$. In this case the equations above become

$$-a - b = 2 \quad \text{and} \quad a - b = 8.$$

Solving these equations for a and b, we get $a = 3$ and $b = -5$.

Now consider the case where $a < 0$, $b \geq 0$, and $a + b \geq 0$. In this case the equations above become

$$a + b = 2 \quad \text{and} \quad -a + b = 8.$$

Solving these equations for a and b, we get $a = -3$ and $b = 5$.

Now consider the case where $a < 0$, $b \geq 0$, and $a + b < 0$. In this case the equations above become

$$-a - b = 2 \quad \text{and} \quad -a + b = 8.$$

Solving these equations for a and b, we get $a = -5$ and $b = 3$.

At this point, we have considered all possible cases. Thus the only solutions are $a = 5$, $b = -3$, or $a = 3$, $b = -5$, or $a = -3$, $b = 5$, or $a = -5$, $b = 3$.

In Exercises 19–30, write each set as an interval or as a union of two intervals.

19. $\{x : |x - 4| < \frac{1}{10}\}$

SOLUTION   The inequality $|x - 4| < \frac{1}{10}$ is equivalent to the inequality

$$-\frac{1}{10} < x - 4 < \frac{1}{10}.$$

Add 4 to all parts of this inequality, getting

$$4 - \frac{1}{10} < x < 4 + \frac{1}{10},$$

which is the same as

$$\frac{39}{10} < x < \frac{41}{10}.$$

Thus $\{x : |x - 4| < \frac{1}{10}\} = (\frac{39}{10}, \frac{41}{10})$.

21. $\{x : |x + 4| < \frac{\varepsilon}{2}\}$; here $\varepsilon > 0$

SOLUTION   The inequality $|x + 4| < \frac{\varepsilon}{2}$ is equivalent to the inequality

$$-\frac{\varepsilon}{2} < x + 4 < \frac{\varepsilon}{2}.$$

Add -4 to all parts of this inequality, getting

$$-4 - \frac{\varepsilon}{2} < x < -4 + \frac{\varepsilon}{2}.$$

Thus $\{x : |x + 4| < \frac{\varepsilon}{2}\} = (-4 - \frac{\varepsilon}{2}, -4 + \frac{\varepsilon}{2})$.

23. $\{y : |y - a| < \varepsilon\}$; here $\varepsilon > 0$

SOLUTION   The inequality $|y - a| < \varepsilon$ is equivalent to the inequality

$$-\varepsilon < y - a < \varepsilon.$$

Add a to all parts of this inequality, getting

$$a - \varepsilon < y < a + \varepsilon.$$

Thus $\{y : |y - a| < \varepsilon\} = (a - \varepsilon, a + \varepsilon)$.

25. $\{x : |3x - 2| < \frac{1}{4}\}$

SOLUTION   The inequality $|3x - 2| < \frac{1}{4}$ is equivalent to the inequality

$$-\frac{1}{4} < 3x - 2 < \frac{1}{4}.$$

Add 2 to all parts of this inequality, getting

$$\frac{7}{4} < 3x < \frac{9}{4}.$$

Now divide all parts of this inequality by 3, getting

$$\frac{7}{12} < x < \frac{3}{4}.$$

Thus $\{x : |3x - 2| < \frac{1}{4}\} = (\frac{7}{12}, \frac{3}{4})$.

27. $\{x : |x| > 2\}$

SOLUTION   The inequality $|x| > 2$ means that $x > 2$ or $x < -2$. Thus $\{x : |x| > 2\} = (-\infty, -2) \cup (2, \infty)$.

29. $\{x : |x - 5| \geq 3\}$

SOLUTION   The inequality $|x - 5| \geq 3$ means that $x - 5 \geq 3$ or $x - 5 \leq -3$. Adding 5 to both sides of these equalities shows that $x \geq 8$ or $x \leq 2$. Thus $\{x : |x - 5| \geq 3\} = (-\infty, 2] \cup [8, \infty)$.

The intersection *of two sets of numbers consists of all numbers that are in both sets. If A and B are sets, then their intersection is denoted by A ∩ B. In Exercises 31–40, write each intersection as a single interval.*

31. $[2, 7) \cap [5, 20)$

SOLUTION   The first interval is the set $\{x : 2 \leq x < 7\}$, which includes the left endpoint 2 but does not include the right endpoint 7. The second interval is the set $\{x : 5 \leq x < 20\}$, which includes the left endpoint 5 but does not include the right endpoint 20. The set of numbers that are in both these sets equals $\{x : 5 \leq x < 7\}$, as can be seen in the figure below:

Thus $[2,7) \cap [5,20) = [5,7)$.

33. $[-2,8] \cap (-1,4)$

SOLUTION   The first interval is the set $\{x : -2 \leq x \leq 8\}$, which includes both endpoints. The second interval is the set $\{x : -1 < x < 4\}$, which includes neither endpoint. The set of numbers that are in both these sets equals $\{x : -1 < x < 4\}$, as can be seen in the figure below:

Thus $[-2,8] \cap (-1,4) = (-1,4)$.

35. $(3,\infty) \cap [2,8]$

SOLUTION   The first interval is the set $\{x : 3 < x\}$, which does not include the left endpoint and which has no right endpoint. The second interval is the set $\{x : 2 \leq x \leq 8\}$, which includes both endpoints. The set of numbers that are in both these sets equals $\{x : 3 < x \leq 8\}$, as can be seen in the figure below:

Thus $(3,\infty) \cap [2,8] = (3,8]$.

37. $(-\infty,-3) \cap [-5,\infty)$

SOLUTION   The first interval is the set $\{x : x < -3\}$, which has no left endpoint and which does not include the right endpoint. The second interval is the set $\{x : -5 \leq x\}$, which includes the left endpoint and which has no right endpoint. The set of numbers that are in both these sets equals $\{x : -5 \leq x < -3\}$, as can be seen in the figure below:

Thus $(-\infty,-3) \cap [-5,\infty) = [-5,-3)$.

39. $(-3,\infty) \cap [-5,\infty)$

SOLUTION   The first interval is the set $\{x : -3 < x\}$, which does not include the left endpoint and which has no right endpoint. The second interval is the set $\{x : -5 \leq x\}$, which includes the left endpoint and which has no right endpoint. The set of numbers that are in both these sets equals $\{x : -3 < x\}$, as can be seen in the figure below:

Thus $(-3,\infty) \cap [-5,\infty) = (-3,\infty)$.

CHAPTER SUMMARY

To check that you have mastered the most important concepts and skills covered in this chapter, make sure that you can do each item in the following list:

- Explain the correspondence between the system of real numbers and the real line.
- Simplify algebraic expressions using the commutative, associative, and distributive properties.
- List the order of algebraic operations.
- Explain how parentheses are used to alter the order of algebraic operations.
- Use the algebraic identities involving additive inverses and multiplicative inverses.

- Manipulate inequalities.
- Use interval notation for open intervals, closed intervals, and half-open intervals.
- Use interval notation involving $-\infty$ and ∞, with the understanding that $-\infty$ and ∞ are not real numbers.
- Write inequalities involving an absolute value without using an absolute value.
- Compute the union of intervals.

To review a chapter, go through the list above to find items that you do not know how to do, then reread the material in the chapter about those items. Then try to answer the chapter review questions below without looking back at the chapter.

CHAPTER REVIEW QUESTIONS

1. Explain how the points on the real line correspond to the set of real numbers.

2. Show that $7 - 6\sqrt{2}$ is an irrational number.

3. What is the commutative property for addition?

4. What is the commutative property for multiplication?

5. What is the associative property for addition?

6. What is the associative property for multiplication?

7. Expand $(t + w)^2$.

8. Expand $(u - v)^2$.

9. Expand $(x - y)(x + y)$.

10. Expand $(a + b)(x - y - z)$.

11. Expand $(a + b - c)^2$.

12. Simplify the expression $\dfrac{\frac{1}{t-b} - \frac{1}{t}}{b}$.

13. Find all real numbers x such that $|3x - 4| = 5$.

14. Give an example of two numbers x and y such that $|x + y|$ does not equal $|x| + |y|$.

15. Suppose $0 < a < b$ and $0 < c < d$. Explain why $ac < bd$.

16. Write the set $\{t : |t - 3| < \frac{1}{4}\}$ as an interval.

17. Write the set $\{w : |5w + 2| < \frac{1}{3}\}$ as an interval.

18. Explain why the sets $\{x : |8x - 5| < 2\}$ and $\{t : |5 - 8t| < 2\}$ are the same set.

19. Write $[-5, 6) \cup [-1, 9)$ as an interval.

20. Write $(-\infty, 4] \cup (3, 8]$ as an interval.

21. Explain why $[7, \infty]$ is not an interval of real numbers.

22. Write the set $\{t : |2t + 7| \geq 5\}$ as a union of two intervals.

23. Is the set of all real numbers x such that $x^2 > 3$ an interval?

Functions and Their Graphs

Functions lie at the heart of modern mathematics. We begin this chapter by introducing the notion of a function along with the domain and range of a function. Then we discuss the coordinate plane, which can be thought of as a two-dimensional analogue of the real line.

Although functions are algebraic objects, often we can understand a function better by viewing its graph. In the third section of this chapter, we will see how algebraic transformations of a function change the graph.

The last three sections of this chapter focus on the composition of functions and on inverse functions. Although the early part of this chapter may be review, pay special attention to these sections on composition and inverse functions. Inverse functions will be key tools in later chapters of this book, for example in our treatment of logarithms.

1.1 | *Functions*

SECTION OBJECTIVES

By the end of this section you should

- understand the concept of a function;
- understand the notation used to represent a function;
- be able to determine the domain and range of a function.

Definition and Examples

Although we do not need to do so in this book, functions can be defined more generally to deal with objects other than real numbers.

Functions and their domains

A **function** associates every number in some set of real numbers, called the **domain** of the function, with another real number.

We usually denote functions by letters such as f, g, and h. If f is a function and x is a number in the domain of f, then the number that f associates with x is denoted by $f(x)$ and is called the value of f at x.

EXAMPLE 1

The use of informal language when discussing functions is acceptable if the meaning is clear. For example, a textbook or your instructor might refer to "the function x^2" or "the function $f(x) = x^2$".

Both these phrases are shorthand for the more formally correct "the function f defined by $f(x) = x^2$".

Suppose a function f is defined by the formula

$$f(x) = x^2$$

for every real number x. Evaluate each of the following:

(a) $f(3)$ (b) $f(-\tfrac{1}{2})$ (c) $f(1+t)$ (d) $f\left(\dfrac{x+5}{\pi}\right)$

SOLUTION Here the domain of f is the set of real numbers, and f is the function that associates every real number with its square. To evaluate f at any number, we simply square that number, as shown by the solutions below:

(a) $f(3) = 3^2 = 9$

(b) $f(-\tfrac{1}{2}) = (-\tfrac{1}{2})^2 = \tfrac{1}{4}$

(c) $f(1+t) = (1+t)^2 = 1 + 2t + t^2$

(d) $f\left(\dfrac{x+5}{\pi}\right) = \left(\dfrac{x+5}{\pi}\right)^2 = \dfrac{x^2 + 10x + 25}{\pi^2}$

A function need not be defined by a single algebraic expression, as shown by the following example.

EXAMPLE 2

Suppose a function g (with domain the set of real numbers) is defined as follows:

$$g(x) = \begin{cases} 3x & \text{if } x < 0 \\ \sqrt{2} & \text{if } x = 0 \\ x^2 + 7 & \text{if } x > 0. \end{cases}$$

(a) Evaluate $g(-2)$.   (b) Evaluate $g(0)$.   (c) Evaluate $g(4)$.

SOLUTION

(a) Because $-2 < 0$, we have $g(-2) = 3 \cdot (-2) = -6$.

(b) The definition of g explicitly states that $g(0) = \sqrt{2}$.

(c) Because $4 > 0$, we have $g(4) = 4^2 + 7 = 16 + 7 = 23$.

The next example shows that sometimes finding a single algebraic expression can be more complicated than using the flexibility offered by the notion of a function.

Give an example of a function h whose domain is the set of positive numbers and such that $h(1) = 10$, $h(3) = 2$, and $h(9) = 26$.

EXAMPLE 3

SOLUTION   The hard way to find a function h with the required properties is to search for a function defined by a single algebraic expression. The easy way to come up with an example is to define h to have the desired values at 1, 3, and 9 and to be something simple at other values. For example, h could be defined as follows:

$$h(x) = \begin{cases} 10 & \text{if } x = 1 \\ 2 & \text{if } x = 3 \\ 26 & \text{if } x = 9 \\ 0 & \text{if } x \text{ is a positive number other than 1, 3, or 9.} \end{cases}$$

The function h defined by

$$h(x) = x^2 - 8x + 17$$

for all positive numbers x provides another correct solution in this example (as you can verify). However, finding this algebraic expression requires serious effort.

Instead of 0, we could have used any number to define $h(x)$ when x is a positive number other than 1, 3, or 9, or we could have done something slightly more complicated such as defining $h(x)$ to be x^4 when x is a positive number other than 1, 3, or 9.

You might sometimes find it useful to think of a function f as a machine that when given an input x produces an output $f(x)$.

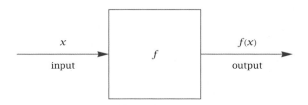

This machine might work using a formula, or it might work in a more mysterious fashion, in which case it is sometimes called a "black box".

For example, if f is the function whose domain is the interval $[-4, 6]$, with f defined by the formula $f(x) = x^2$ for every x in the interval $[-4, 6]$, then giving input 3 to this machine produces output 9. The same input must always produce the same output; thus inputting 3 to this machine at a later time must again produce the output 9. Although each input has a unique output, a given output may arise from more than one input. For example, the inputs -3 and 3 both produce the output 9 for this function.

What if the number 8 is input to the machine described in the paragraph above? Because 8 is not in the domain of this function f, the machine cannot produce an output for this input; the machine should produce an error message stating that 8 is not an allowable input.

Equality of Functions

Consider the function f such that

The variable used when defining a function is irrelevant.

$$f(x) = 3x$$

for every real number x. There is no particular x here. The symbol x is simply a placeholder to indicate that f associates any number with 3 times that number. We could have defined the same function f by using the formula $f(y) = 3y$ for every real number y. Or we could have used the formula $f(t) = 3t$ for every real number t. All these formulas show that $f(2) = 6$ and that $f(2w + 5) = 3(2w + 5)$.

Here is what it means for two functions to be equal:

Equality of functions

Two functions are **equal** if and only if they have the same domain and the same value at every number in that domain.

EXAMPLE 4

The domain of a function matters because two functions with different domains are not equal as functions, even if they are defined by the same formula.

Suppose f is the function whose domain is the set of real numbers, with f defined on this domain by the formula
$$f(x) = x^2.$$
Suppose g is the function whose domain is the set of positive numbers, with g defined on this domain by the formula
$$g(x) = x^2.$$
Are f and g equal functions?

SOLUTION   Note that, for example, $f(-3) = 9$, but the expression $g(-3)$ makes no sense because $g(x)$ has not been defined when x is negative. Because f and g have different domains, these two functions are not equal.

The next example shows that considering only the formula defining a function can be deceptive.

EXAMPLE 5

Suppose f and g are functions whose domain is the set consisting of the two numbers $\{1, 2\}$, with f and g defined on this domain by the formula
$$f(x) = x^2 \quad \text{and} \quad g(x) = 3x - 2.$$
Are f and g equal functions?

SOLUTION   Here f and g have the same domain—the set $\{1, 2\}$. Thus it is at least possible that f equals g. Because f and g have different formulas, the natural inclination is to assume that f is not equal to g. However,

$$f(1) = 1^2 = 1, \quad g(1) = 3 \cdot 1 - 2 = 1 \quad \text{and} \quad f(2) = 2^2 = 4, \quad g(2) = 3 \cdot 2 - 2 = 4.$$

Thus $f(1) = g(1)$ and $f(2) = g(2)$. Because f and g have the same value at every number in their domain $\{1, 2\}$, the functions f and g are equal.

The Domain of a Function

Although the domain of a function is a formal part of characterizing the function, often we are loose about the domain of a function. Usually the domain is clear from the context or from a formula defining a function. Use the following informal rule when the domain is not specified:

Distinguishing between f and $f(x)$ is usually worthwhile and helps lead to better understanding. Use f to denote a function and $f(x)$ to denote the value of a function f at a number x.

Domain not specified

If a function is defined by a formula, with no domain specified, then the domain is assumed to be the set of all real numbers for which the formula makes sense and produces a real number.

The next three examples illustrate this rule.

Find the domain of the function f defined by

$$f(x) = (3x - 1)^2.$$

EXAMPLE 6

SOLUTION   No domain has been specified, but the formula above makes sense for all real numbers x. Thus unless the context indicates otherwise, we assume that the domain for this function is the set of real numbers.

The following example shows that avoiding division by 0 can determine the domain of a function.

Find the domain of the function h defined by

$$h(x) = \frac{x^2 + 3x + 7}{x - 4}.$$

EXAMPLE 7

SOLUTION   No domain has been specified, but the formula above does not make sense when $x = 4$, which would lead to division by 0. Thus unless the context indicates otherwise, we assume that the domain for this function is the set $\{x : x \neq 4\}$.

The following example illustrates the requirement of the informal rule that the formula must produce a real number.

EXAMPLE 8

Find the domain of the function g defined by

$$g(x) = \sqrt{x - 3}.$$

SOLUTION   No domain has been specified, but the formula above produces a real number only for numbers x greater than or equal to 3. Thus unless the context indicates otherwise, we assume that the domain for this function is the interval $[3, \infty)$.

Functions via Tables

x	$f(x)$
2	3
7	$\sqrt{2}$
13	-4

If the domain of a function consists of only finitely many numbers, then all the values of a function can be listed in a table. Here, for example, is a table for a function f whose domain consists of the three numbers $\{2, 7, 13\}$. For this function we have $f(2) = 3$, $f(7) = \sqrt{2}$, and $f(13) = -4$; this table constitutes a complete description of the function f.

If the domain of a function consists of infinitely many numbers, then no finite table can list all the values of the function. However, a table listing some values of a function can often be useful in understanding the behavior of the function. For example, consider the function f defined by

$$f(x) = \frac{\sqrt{1 + x} - 1}{x},$$

where the domain of this function is the set of positive numbers. The formula defining f makes no sense when $x = 0$, but we can use a table to see the behavior of $f(x)$ for some small values of x:

These values of $f(x)$ were calculated by a computer and rounded off to five digits after the decimal point.

x	$f(x)$
0.1	0.48809
0.01	0.49876
0.001	0.49988
0.0001	0.49999

$\frac{\sqrt{1+x}-1}{x}$ *for some small values of x.*

The table above makes it appear that $f(x)$ gets close to $\frac{1}{2}$ as x gets close to 0 (as indeed does happen).

The Range of a Function

Another set associated with a function, along with the domain, is the range. The range of a function is the set of all values taken on by the function. Here is the precise definition:

Range

> The **range** of a function f is the set of all numbers y such that $f(x) = y$ for at least one x in the domain of f.

EXAMPLE 9

Suppose f is defined by $f(x) = x^2$.

(a) What is the range of f if the domain of f is the interval $[1, 3]$?

(b) What is the range of f if the domain of f is the interval $[-2, 3]$?

(c) What is the range of f if the domain of f is the set of positive numbers?

(d) What is the range of f if the domain of f is the set of negative numbers?

(e) What is the range of f if the domain of f is the set of real numbers?

SOLUTION

(a) If the domain of f is the interval $[1, 3]$, then the range of f is the interval $[1, 9]$.

(b) If the domain of f is the interval $[-2, 3]$, then the range of f is the interval $[0, 9]$. Note that for each number y in the interval $(0, 4]$, there are two numbers x in the domain of f such that $f(x) = y$; those two possible choices for x are $\sqrt{y}$ and $-\sqrt{y}$.

(c) If the domain of f is the set of positive numbers, then the range of f is the set of positive numbers.

(d) If the domain of f is the set of negative numbers, then the range of f is the set of positive numbers.

(e) If the domain of f is the set of real numbers, then the range of f is the set of nonnegative numbers. Note that for each number $y \neq 0$, there are two numbers x in the domain of f such that $f(x) = y$; those two possible choices for x are $\sqrt{y}$ and $-\sqrt{y}$.

A real number is called **nonnegative** *if it is not negative. Thus a number is nonnegative if it is either 0 or positive.*

Domain and range from a table

> Suppose a function has only finitely many numbers in its domain and all the values of the function are displayed in a table. Then
>
> - the domain of the function is the set of numbers that appear in the left column of the table;
>
> - the range of the function is the set of numbers that appear in the right column of the table.

EXAMPLE 10

Suppose f is the function completely determined by the table in the margin.

(a) What is the domain of f?

(b) What is the range of f?

x	$f(x)$
1	6
2	6
3	-7
5	6

SOLUTION

(a) The left column of the table contains the numbers 1, 2, 3, and 5. Thus the domain of f is the set $\{1, 2, 3, 5\}$.

(b) The right column of the table contains only two distinct numbers, -7 and 6. Thus the range of f is the set $\{-7, 6\}$.

To say that a number y is in the range of a function f means that the equation $f(x) = y$ has at least one solution x in the domain of f. The next two examples illustrate this idea.

EXAMPLE 11

Suppose the domain of f is the interval $[2, 5]$, with f defined on this interval by the equation $f(x) = 3x + 1$. Is 19 in the range of f?

SOLUTION   We need to determine whether the equation

$$3x + 1 = 19$$

has at least one solution x in the interval $[2, 5]$. The only solution to the equation above is $x = 6$, which is not in $[2, 5]$, the domain of f. Thus 19 is not in the range of f.

For a number y to be in the range of a function f, there is no requirement that the equation $f(x) = y$ have a unique solution x in the domain of f. The requirement is that there be at least one solution. The next example shows that multiple solutions can easily arise.

EXAMPLE 12

Suppose the domain of g is the interval $[1, 20]$, with g defined on this interval by the equation $g(x) = |x - 5|$. Is 2 in the range of g?

SOLUTION   We need to determine whether the equation

This equation implies that $x - 5 = 2$ or $x - 5 = -2$.

$$|x - 5| = 2$$

has at least one solution x in the interval $[1, 20]$. The equation above has two solutions, $x = 7$ and $x = 3$, both of which are in the domain of g. Thus 2 is in the range of g.

EXERCISES

For Exercises 1–8, assume that f and g are functions completely defined by the following tables:

x	$f(x)$
3	13
4	-5
6	$\frac{3}{5}$
7.3	-5

x	$g(x)$
3	3
8	$\sqrt{7}$
8.4	$\sqrt{7}$
12.1	$-\frac{2}{7}$

1. Evaluate $f(6)$.

2. Evaluate $g(8)$.

3. What is the domain of f?

4. What is the domain of g?

5. What is the range of f?

6. What is the range of g?

7. Find two different values of x such that $f(x) = -5$.

8. Find two different values of x such that $g(x) = \sqrt{7}$.

9. Find all functions (displayed as tables) whose domain is the set $\{2, 9\}$ and whose range is the set $\{4, 6\}$.

10. Find all functions (displayed as tables) whose domain is the set $\{5, 8\}$ and whose range is the set $\{1, 3\}$.

11. Find all functions (displayed as tables) whose domain is $\{1, 2, 4\}$ and whose range is $\{-2, 1, \sqrt{3}\}$.

12. Find all functions (displayed as tables) whose domain is $\{-1, 0, \pi\}$ and whose range is $\{-3, \sqrt{2}, 5\}$.

13. Find all functions (displayed as tables) whose domain is $\{3, 5, 9\}$ and whose range is $\{2, 4\}$.

14. Find all functions (displayed as tables) whose domain is $\{0, 2, 8\}$ and whose range is $\{6, 9\}$.

For Exercises 15–26, assume that

$$f(x) = \frac{x + 2}{x^2 + 1}$$

for every real number x. Evaluate and simplify each of the following expressions.

15. $f(0)$

16. $f(1)$

17. $f(-1)$

18. $f(-2)$

19. $f(2a)$

20. $f\left(\frac{b}{3}\right)$

21. $f(2a + 1)$

22. $f(3a - 1)$

23. $f(x^2 + 1)$

24. $f(2x^2 + 3)$

25. $f\left(\frac{a}{b} - 1\right)$

26. $f\left(\frac{2a}{b} + 3\right)$

For Exercises 27–32, assume that

$$g(x) = \frac{x - 1}{x + 2}.$$

27. Find a number b such that $g(b) = 4$.

28. Find a number b such that $g(b) = 3$.

29. Evaluate and simplify the expression $\frac{g(x) - g(2)}{x - 2}$.

30. Evaluate and simplify the expression $\frac{g(x) - g(3)}{x - 3}$.

31. Evaluate and simplify the expression $\frac{g(a + t) - g(a)}{t}$.

32. Evaluate and simplify the expression $\frac{g(x + b) - g(x - b)}{2b}$.

For Exercises 33–40, assume that f is the function defined by

$$f(x) = \begin{cases} 2x + 9 & \text{if } x < 0 \\ 3x - 10 & \text{if } x \ge 0. \end{cases}$$

33. Evaluate $f(1)$.

34. Evaluate $f(2)$.

35. Evaluate $f(-3)$.

36. Evaluate $f(-4)$.

37. Evaluate $f(|x| + 1)$.

38. Evaluate $f(|x - 5| + 2)$.

39. Find two different values of x such that $f(x) = 0$.

40. Find two different values of x such that $f(x) = 4$.

For Exercises 41–44, find a number b such that the function f equals the function g.

41. The function f has domain the set of positive numbers and is defined by $f(x) = 5x^2 - 7$; the function g has domain (b, ∞) and is defined by $g(x) = 5x^2 - 7$.

42. The function f has domain the set of numbers with absolute value less than 4 and is defined by $f(x) = \frac{3}{x+5}$; the function g has domain the interval $(-b, b)$ and is defined by $g(x) = \frac{3}{x+5}$.

43. Both f and g have domain $\{3, 5\}$, with f defined on this domain by the formula $f(x) = x^2 - 3$ and g defined on this domain by the formula $g(x) = \frac{18}{x} + b(x - 3)$.

44. Both f and g have domain $\{-3, 4\}$, with f defined on this domain by the formula $f(x) = 3x + 5$ and g defined on this domain by the formula $g(x) = 15 + \frac{8}{x} + b(x - 4)$.

For Exercises 45-50, a formula has been given defining a function f but no domain has been specified. Find the domain of each function f, assuming that the domain is the set of real numbers for which the formula makes sense and produces a real number.

45. $f(x) = \frac{2x+1}{3x-4}$

46. $f(x) = \frac{4x-9}{7x+5}$

47. $f(x) = \frac{\sqrt{x-5}}{x-7}$

48. $f(x) = \frac{\sqrt{2x+3}}{x-6}$

49. $f(x) = \sqrt{|x-6|-1}$

50. $f(x) = \sqrt{|x+5|-3}$

For Exercises 51-56, suppose h is defined by

$$h(t) = |t| + 1.$$

51. What is the range of h if the domain of h is the interval $(1, 4]$?

52. What is the range of h if the domain of h is the interval $[-8, -3)$?

53. What is the range of h if the domain of h is the interval $[-3, 5]$?

54. What is the range of h if the domain of h is the interval $[-8, 2]$?

55. What is the range of h if the domain of h is the set of positive numbers?

56. What is the range of h if the domain of h is the set of negative numbers?

PROBLEMS

Some problems require considerably more thought than the exercises. Unlike exercises, problems usually have more than one correct answer.

57. Give an example of a function whose domain is $\{2, 5, 7\}$ and whose range is $\{-2, 3, 4\}$.

58. Give an example of a function whose domain is $\{3, 4, 7, 9\}$ and whose range is $\{-1, 0, 3\}$.

59. Find two different functions whose domain is $\{3, 8\}$ and whose range is $\{-4, 1\}$.

60. Explain why there does not exist a function whose domain is $\{-1, 0, 3\}$ and whose range is $\{3, 4, 7, 9\}$.

61. Give an example of a function f whose domain is the set of real numbers and such that the values of $f(-1)$, $f(0)$, and $f(2)$ are given by the following table:

x	$f(x)$
-1	$\sqrt{2}$
0	$\frac{17}{3}$
2	-5

62. Suppose the only information you know about a function f is that the domain of f is the set of real numbers and that $f(1) = 1$, $f(2) = 4$, $f(3) = 9$, and $f(4) = 16$. What can you say about the value of $f(5)$?
[*Hint:* The answer to this problem is not "25". The shortest correct answer is just one word.]

63. Give an example of two different functions f and g, both of which have the set of real numbers as their domain, such that $f(x) = g(x)$ for every rational number x.

64. Give an example of a function whose domain equals the set of real numbers and whose range equals the set $\{-1, 0, 1\}$.

65. Give an example of a function whose domain equals the set of real numbers and whose range equals the set of integers.

66. Give an example of a function whose domain equals $[0, 1]$ and whose range equals $(0, 1)$.

67. Give an example of a function whose domain equals $(0, 1)$ and whose range equals $[0, 1]$.

68. Give an example of a function whose domain is the set of positive integers and whose range is the set of positive even integers.

69. Give an example of a function whose domain is the set of positive even integers and whose range is the set of positive odd integers.

70. Give an example of a function whose domain is the set of integers and whose range is the set of positive integers.

71. Give an example of a function whose domain is the set of positive integers and whose range is the set of integers.

WORKED-OUT SOLUTIONS *to Odd-numbered Exercises*

Do not read these worked-out solutions before first struggling to do the exercises yourself. Otherwise you risk the danger of mimicking the techniques shown here without understanding the ideas.

Best way to learn: Carefully read the section of the textbook, then do all the odd-numbered exercises (even if they have not been assigned) and check your answers here. If you get stuck on an exercise, reread the section of the textbook—then try the exercise again. If you are still stuck, then look at the worked-out solution here.

For Exercises 1–8, assume that *f* and *g* are functions completely defined by the following tables:

x	f(x)
3	13
4	−5
6	$\frac{3}{5}$
7.3	−5

x	g(x)
3	3
8	$\sqrt{7}$
8.4	$\sqrt{7}$
12.1	$-\frac{2}{7}$

1. Evaluate $f(6)$.

   SOLUTION Looking at the table, we see that $f(6) = \frac{3}{5}$.

3. What is the domain of f?

   SOLUTION The domain of f is the set of numbers in the first column of the table defining f. Thus the domain of f is the set $\{3, 4, 6, 7.3\}$.

5. What is the range of f?

   SOLUTION The range of f is the set of numbers that appear in the second column of the table defining f. Numbers that appear more than once in the second column need to be listed only once when finding the range. Thus the range of f is the set $\{13, -5, \frac{3}{5}\}$.

7. Find two different values of x such that $f(x) = -5$.

   SOLUTION Looking at the table, we see that $f(4) = -5$ and $f(7.3) = -5$.

9. Find all functions (displayed as tables) whose domain is the set $\{2, 9\}$ and whose range is the set $\{4, 6\}$.

   SOLUTION Because we seek functions f whose domain is the set $\{2, 9\}$, the first column of the table for any such function must have 2 appear

once and must have 9 appear once. In other words, the table must start like this

x	f(x)
2	
9	

or this

x	f(x)
9	
2	

The order of the rows in a table that define a function do not matter. For convenience, we choose the first possibility above.

Because the range must be the set $\{4, 6\}$, the second column must contain 4 and 6. There are only two slots in which to put these numbers in the first table above, and thus each one must appear exactly once in the second column. Thus there are only two functions whose domain is the set $\{2, 9\}$ and whose range is the set $\{4, 6\}$; these functions are given by the following two tables:

x	f(x)
2	4
9	6

x	f(x)
2	6
9	4

The first function above is the function f defined by $f(2) = 4$ and $f(9) = 6$; the second function above is the function f defined by $f(2) = 6$ and $f(9) = 4$.

11. Find all functions (displayed as tables) whose domain is $\{1, 2, 4\}$ and whose range is $\{-2, 1, \sqrt{3}\}$.

   SOLUTION Because we seek functions f whose domain is $\{1, 2, 4\}$, the first column of the table for any such function must have 1 appear once, must have 2 appear once, and must have 4 appear once. The order of the rows in a table that define a function do not matter. For convenience, we put the first column in numerical order 1, 2, 4.

Because the range must be $\{-2, 1, \sqrt{3}\}$, the second column must contain -2, 1, and $\sqrt{3}$. There are only three slots in which to put these three numbers, and thus each one must appear exactly once in the second column. There are six ways in which these three numbers can be ordered. Thus the six functions whose domain is $\{1, 2, 4\}$ and whose range is $\{-2, 1, \sqrt{3}\}$ are given by the following tables:

x	$f(x)$
1	-2
2	1
4	$\sqrt{3}$

x	$f(x)$
1	-2
2	$\sqrt{3}$
4	1

x	$f(x)$
1	1
2	-2
4	$\sqrt{3}$

x	$f(x)$
1	1
2	$\sqrt{3}$
4	-2

x	$f(x)$
1	$\sqrt{3}$
2	-2
4	1

x	$f(x)$
1	$\sqrt{3}$
2	1
4	-2

13. Find all functions (displayed as tables) whose domain is $\{3, 5, 9\}$ and whose range is $\{2, 4\}$.

SOLUTION   Because we seek functions f whose domain is $\{3, 5, 9\}$, the first column of the table for any such function must have 3 appear once, must have 5 appear once, and must have 9 appear once. The order of the rows in a table that define a function do not matter. For convenience, we put the first column in numerical order 3, 5, 9.

Because the range must be $\{2, 4\}$, the second column must contain 2 and 4. There are three slots in which to put these three numbers, and thus one of them must be repeated once. There are six ways to do this. Thus the six functions whose domain is $\{3, 5, 9\}$ and whose range is $\{2, 4\}$ are given by the following tables:

x	$f(x)$
3	2
5	2
9	4

x	$f(x)$
3	2
5	4
9	2

x	$f(x)$
3	4
5	2
9	2

x	$f(x)$
3	4
5	4
9	2

x	$f(x)$
3	4
5	2
9	4

x	$f(x)$
3	2
5	4
9	4

For Exercises 15-26, assume that

$$f(x) = \frac{x + 2}{x^2 + 1}$$

for every real number x. Evaluate and simplify each of the following expressions.

15. $f(0)$

SOLUTION $f(0) = \frac{0+2}{0^2+1} = \frac{2}{1} = 2$

17. $f(-1)$

SOLUTION $f(-1) = \dfrac{-1 + 2}{(-1)^2 + 1} = \dfrac{1}{1 + 1} = \dfrac{1}{2}$

19. $f(2a)$

SOLUTION $f(2a) = \dfrac{2a + 2}{(2a)^2 + 1} = \dfrac{2a + 2}{4a^2 + 1}$

21. $f(2a + 1)$

SOLUTION

$$f(2a + 1) = \frac{(2a + 1) + 2}{(2a + 1)^2 + 1} = \frac{2a + 3}{4a^2 + 4a + 2}$$

23. $f(x^2 + 1)$

SOLUTION

$$f(x^2 + 1) = \frac{(x^2 + 1) + 2}{(x^2 + 1)^2 + 1} = \frac{x^2 + 3}{x^4 + 2x^2 + 2}$$

25. $f\left(\frac{a}{b} - 1\right)$

SOLUTION   We have

$$f\left(\frac{a}{b} - 1\right) = \frac{\left(\frac{a}{b} - 1\right) + 2}{\left(\frac{a}{b} - 1\right)^2 + 1} = \frac{\frac{a}{b} + 1}{\frac{a^2}{b^2} - 2\frac{a}{b} + 2}$$

$$= \frac{ab + b^2}{a^2 - 2ab + 2b^2},$$

where the last expression was obtained by multiplying the numerator and denominator of the previous expression by b^2.

For Exercises 27-32, assume that

$$g(x) = \frac{x - 1}{x + 2}.$$

27. Find a number b such that $g(b) = 4$.

SOLUTION   We want to find a number b such that

$$\frac{b - 1}{b + 2} = 4.$$

Multiply both sides of the equation above by $b + 2$, getting

$$b - 1 = 4b + 8.$$

Now solve this equation for b, getting $b = -3$.

29. Evaluate and simplify the expression $\frac{g(x)-g(2)}{x-2}$.

SOLUTION We begin by evaluating the numerator:

$$
\begin{aligned}
g(x) - g(2) &= \frac{x-1}{x+2} - \frac{1}{4} \\
&= \frac{4(x-1) - (x+2)}{4(x+2)} \\
&= \frac{4x - 4 - x - 2}{4(x+2)} \\
&= \frac{3x - 6}{4(x+2)} \\
&= \frac{3(x-2)}{4(x+2)}.
\end{aligned}
$$

Thus

$$
\begin{aligned}
\frac{g(x)-g(2)}{x-2} &= \frac{3(x-2)}{4(x+2)} \cdot \frac{1}{x-2} \\
&= \frac{3}{4(x+2)}.
\end{aligned}
$$

31. Evaluate and simplify the expression $\frac{g(a+t)-g(a)}{t}$.

SOLUTION We begin by computing the numerator:

$$
\begin{aligned}
& g(a+t) - g(a) \\
&= \frac{(a+t)-1}{(a+t)+2} - \frac{a-1}{a+2} \\
&= \frac{(a+t-1)(a+2) - (a-1)(a+t+2)}{(a+t+2)(a+2)} \\
&= \frac{3t}{(a+t+2)(a+2)}.
\end{aligned}
$$

Thus

$$
\frac{g(a+t)-g(a)}{t} = \frac{3}{(a+t+2)(a+2)}.
$$

For Exercises 33-40, assume that f is the function defined by

$$
f(x) = \begin{cases} 2x + 9 & \text{if } x < 0 \\ 3x - 10 & \text{if } x \geq 0. \end{cases}
$$

33. Evaluate $f(1)$.

SOLUTION Because $1 \geq 0$, we have

$$f(1) = 3 \cdot 1 - 10 = -7.$$

35. Evaluate $f(-3)$.

SOLUTION Because $-3 < 0$, we have

$$f(-3) = 2(-3) + 9 = 3.$$

37. Evaluate $f(|x| + 1)$.

SOLUTION Because $|x| + 1 \geq 1 > 0$, we have

$$f(|x| + 1) = 3(|x| + 1) - 10 = 3|x| - 7.$$

39. Find two different values of x such that $f(x) = 0$.

SOLUTION If $x < 0$, then $f(x) = 2x + 9$. We want to find x such that $f(x) = 0$, which means that we need to solve the equation $2x + 9 = 0$ and hope that the solution satisfies $x < 0$. Subtracting 9 from both sides of $2x + 9 = 0$ and then dividing both sides by 2 gives $x = -\frac{9}{2}$. This value of x satisfies the inequality $x < 0$, and we do indeed have $f(-\frac{9}{2}) = 0$.

If $x \geq 0$, then $f(x) = 3x - 10$. We want to find x such that $f(x) = 0$, which means that we need to solve the equation $3x - 10 = 0$ and hope that the solution satisfies $x \geq 0$. Adding 10 to both sides of $3x - 10 = 0$ and then dividing both sides by 3 gives $x = \frac{10}{3}$. This value of x satisfies the inequality $x \geq 0$, and we do indeed have $f(\frac{10}{3}) = 0$.

For Exercises 41-44, find a number b such that the function f equals the function g.

41. The function f has domain the set of positive numbers and is defined by $f(x) = 5x^2 - 7$; the

function g has domain (b, ∞) and is defined by $g(x) = 5x^2 - 7$.

SOLUTION For two functions to be equal, they must at least have the same domain. Because the domain of f is the set of positive numbers, which equals the interval $(0, \infty)$, we must have $b = 0$.

43. Both f and g have domain $\{3, 5\}$, with f defined on this domain by the formula $f(x) = x^2 - 3$ and g defined on this domain by the formula $g(x) = \frac{18}{x} + b(x - 3)$.

SOLUTION Note that
$$f(3) = 3^2 - 3 = 6 \quad \text{and} \quad f(5) = 5^2 - 3 = 22.$$
Also,
$$g(3) = \tfrac{18}{3} + b(3 - 3) = 6 \quad \text{and} \quad g(5) = \tfrac{18}{5} + 2b.$$
Thus regardless of the choice of b, we have $f(3) = g(3)$. To make the function f equal the function g, we must also have $f(5) = g(5)$, which means that we must have
$$22 = \tfrac{18}{5} + 2b.$$
Solving this equation for b, we get $b = \frac{46}{5}$.

For Exercises 45–50, a formula has been given defining a function f but no domain has been specified. Find the domain of each function f, assuming that the domain is the set of real numbers for which the formula makes sense and produces a real number.

45. $f(x) = \frac{2x+1}{3x-4}$

SOLUTION The formula above does not make sense when $3x - 4 = 0$, which would lead to division by 0. The equation $3x - 4 = 0$ is equivalent to $x = \frac{4}{3}$. Thus the domain of f is the set of real numbers not equal to $\frac{4}{3}$. In other words, the domain of f equals $\{x : x \neq \frac{4}{3}\}$, which could also be written as $(-\infty, \frac{4}{3}) \cup (\frac{4}{3}, \infty)$.

47. $f(x) = \frac{\sqrt{x-5}}{x-7}$

SOLUTION The formula above does not make sense when $x < 5$ because we cannot take the square root of a negative number. The formula above also does not make sense when $x = 7$, which would lead to division by 0. Thus the domain of f is the set of real numbers

greater than or equal to 5 and not equal to 7. In other words, the domain of f equals $\{x : x \geq 5 \text{ and } x \neq 7\}$, which could also be written as $[5, 7) \cup (7, \infty)$.

49. $f(x) = \sqrt{|x - 6| - 1}$

SOLUTION Because we cannot take the square root of a negative number, we must have $|x - 6| - 1 \geq 0$. This inequality is equivalent to $|x - 6| \geq 1$, which means that $x - 6 \geq 1$ or $x - 6 \leq -1$. Adding 6 to both sides of these inequalities, we see that the formula above makes sense only when $x \geq 7$ or $x \leq 5$. In other words, the domain of f equals $\{x : x \leq 5 \text{ or } x \geq 7\}$, which could also be written as $(-\infty, 5] \cup [7, \infty)$.

For Exercises 51–56, suppose h is defined by
$$h(t) = |t| + 1.$$

51. What is the range of h if the domain of h is the interval $(1, 4]$?

SOLUTION For each number t in the interval $(1, 4]$, we have $h(t) = t + 1$. Thus the range of h is obtained by adding 1 to each number in the interval $(1, 4]$. This implies that the range of h is the interval $(2, 5]$.

53. What is the range of h if the domain of h is the interval $[-3, 5]$?

SOLUTION For each number t in the interval $[-3, 0)$, we have $h(t) = -t + 1$, and for each number t in the interval $[0, 5]$ we have $h(t) = t + 1$. Thus the range of h consists of the numbers obtained by multiplying each number in the interval $[-3, 0)$ by -1 and then adding 1 (this produces the interval $(1, 4]$), along with the numbers obtained by adding 1 to each number in the interval $[0, 5]$ (this produces the interval $[1, 6]$). This implies that the range of h is the interval $[1, 6]$.

55. What is the range of h if the domain of h is the set of positive numbers?

SOLUTION For each positive number t we have $h(t) = t + 1$. Thus the range of h is the set obtained by adding 1 to each positive number. Hence the range of h is the interval $(1, \infty)$.

1.2   *The Coordinate Plane and Graphs*

SECTION OBJECTIVES

By the end of this section you should

- understand the coordinate plane;
- understand the relationship between a function and its graph;
- be able to determine the domain and range of a function from its graph;
- be able to use the vertical line test to determine if a set is the graph of some function.

The Coordinate Plane

Recall that the real line is constructed by starting with a horizontal line, picking an arbitrary point on it that is labeled 0, picking an arbitrary point to the right of 0 that is labeled 1, and then labeling other points using the scale determined by 0 and 1 (see Section 0.1 to review the construction of the real line). The coordinate plane is constructed in a similar fashion, but using a horizontal and a vertical line rather than just a horizontal line.

The coordinate plane

- The **coordinate plane** is constructed by starting with a horizontal line and a vertical line in a plane. These lines are called the **coordinate axes**.

- The intersection point of the coordinate axes is called the **origin**; it receives a label of 0 on both axes.

- On the horizontal axis, pick an arbitrary point to the right of the origin and label it 1. Then label other points on the horizontal axis using the scale determined by the origin and 1.

- Similarly, on the vertical axis, pick an arbitrary point above the origin and label it 1. Then label other points on the vertical axis using the scale determined by the origin and 1.

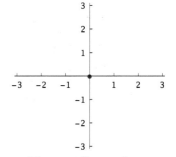

The coordinate plane, with a blue dot at the origin.

Sometimes it is important to use the same scale on both axes, as in the figure above. Other times it may be more convenient to use two different scales on the two axes.

Just as we used the real line to help visualize real numbers, we can use the coordinate plane to help visualize functions. A function can be visualized by considering its graph, which we will define after discussing the coordinates of a point.

A point in the plane is identified with its coordinates, which are written as an ordered pair of numbers surrounded by parentheses.

The plane with this system of labeling points is often called the **Cartesian plane** *in honor of the French mathematician-philosopher René Descartes (1596–1650), who described this technique in his 1637 book* Discourse on Method.

Coordinates

- The first coordinate indicates the horizontal distance from the origin, with positive numbers corresponding to points to the right of the origin and negative numbers corresponding to points to the left of the origin.

- The second coordinate indicates the vertical distance from the origin, with positive numbers corresponding to points above the origin and negative numbers corresponding to points below the origin.

EXAMPLE 1

Locate on a coordinate plane the following points:

(a) $(2, 1)$;   (b) $(-1, 2.5)$;   (c) $(-2.5, -2.5)$;   (d) $(3, -2)$.

SOLUTION

(a) The point $(2, 1)$ can be located by starting at the origin, moving 2 units to the right along the horizontal axis, and then moving up 1 unit; see the figure below.

The notation $(-1, 2.5)$ could denote either the point with coordinates $(-1, 2.5)$ or the open interval $(-1, 2.5)$. You should be able to tell from the context which meaning is intended.

(b) The point $(-1, 2.5)$ can be located by starting at the origin, moving 1 unit to the left along the horizontal axis, and then moving up 2.5 units; see the figure below.

(c) The point $(-2.5, 2.5)$ can be located by starting at the origin, moving 2.5 units to the left along the horizontal axis, and then moving down 2.5 units; see the figure below.

(d) The point $(3, -2)$ can be located by starting at the origin, moving 3 units to the right along the horizontal axis, and then moving down 2 units; see the figure below.

These coordinates are sometimes called **rectangular coordinates** *because each point's coordinates are determined by a rectangle, as shown in this figure.*

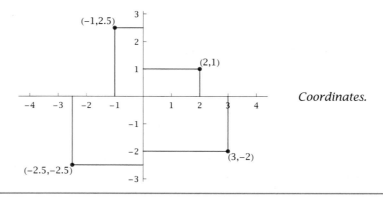

Coordinates.

The horizontal axis is often called the **x-axis** and the vertical axis is often called the **y-axis**. In this case, the coordinate plane can be called the xy-plane. However, other variables can also be used, depending on the problem at hand.

If the horizontal axis has been labeled the x-axis, then the first coordinate of a point is often called the **x-coordinate**. Similarly, if the vertical axis has been labeled the y-axis, then the second coordinate is often called the **y-coordinate**. The potential confusion of this terminology becomes apparent when we want to consider a point whose coordinates are (y, x); here y is the x-coordinate and x is the y-coordinate. Furthermore, always calling the first coordinate the x-coordinate will lead to confusion when the horizontal axis is labeled with another variable such as t or θ.

Regardless of the names of the axes, remember that the first coordinate corresponds to horizontal distance from the origin and the second coordinate corresponds to vertical distance from the origin.

The Graph of a Function

A function can often be visualized by its graph, which we now define:

> ### The graph of a function
>
> The **graph** of a function f is the set of points of the form $(x, f(x))$ as x varies over the domain of f.

Suppose the domain of f is the set of four numbers $\{1, 2, 3, 4\}$, with f defined by the table shown here. Draw the graph of f.

EXAMPLE 2

x	$f(x)$
1	2
2	3
3	−1
4	1

SOLUTION
Each number x in the domain of f generates a point $(x, f(x))$ on the graph of f. The number 1 is in the domain of f; it generates the point $(1, f(1))$, which equals $(1, 2)$, on the graph of f. Similarly, the number 2 generates the point $(2, 3)$ on the graph of f, the number 3 generates the point $(3, -1)$ on the graph of f, and the number 4 generates the point $(4, 1)$ on the graph of f.

For this particular function f, the domain consists of only the four numbers 1, 2, 3, 4. Thus the graph of f consists of the four points $(1, 2)$, $(2, 3)$, $(3, -1)$, and $(4, 1)$, as shown here.

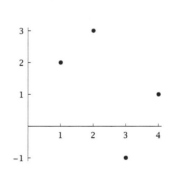

In the next chapter we will learn how to graph linear and quadratic functions, so we will not take up those topics here.

This figure shows the graph of the function f whose domain is $[-4, 4]$, with f defined by $f(x) = |x|$. Note that this graph has a corner at the origin.

To consider a more complicated example, let f be the function whose domain is the interval $[1, 4]$, with f defined on this domain by the formula

$$f(x) = \frac{4(5x - x^2 - 2)}{x^2 + 2}.$$

Because the domain of f contains infinitely many numbers, no table can list all the values of f. To get an idea about the graph of f, we can evaluate f

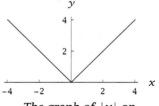

The graph of $|x|$ on the interval $[-4, 4]$.

at sufficiently many numbers and then plot the corresponding points on the coordinate plane. For example, using a computer to evaluate f at values of x in steps of 0.1 gives this table. Here the values of $f(x)$ have been rounded off to two digits after the decimal point; to save space only the first three values and last two values have been listed.

x	$f(x)$
1.0	2.67
1.1	2.85
1.2	2.98
$\vdots$	$\vdots$
3.9	0.53
4.0	0.44

Plotting the 31 points determined by this table, meaning first $(1.0, 2.67)$, then $(1.1, 2.85)$, and so on, gives the partial graph of f shown below on the left. This figure already gives us a good idea of the shape of the graph of f.

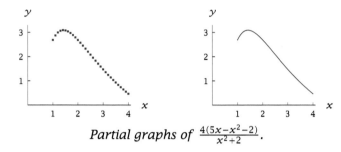

Partial graphs of $\frac{4(5x-x^2-2)}{x^2+2}$.

The computer-generated graph shown above on the right appears to be a smooth curve, but it actually consists of a finite but large number of points. The table that generated this figure contains many more points than the figure above on the left. The dots representing the points are too small to see individually, thus fooling our eyes into seeing an unbroken curve.

A better image of the graph of f can be obtained by plotting more points than in the figure above on the left. The figure above on the right was generated by a computer, which used enough points to leave no visible gaps.

If we define f with the same formula as above, but change the domain to the interval $[-4, 4]$, then the graph becomes too large if we keep the same scale on both axes (because on the interval $[-4, 4]$, the values of f range from about -11 to about 3). Thus sometimes for convenience we use different scales on the two axes, as in the graph below. Note that in the graph below, the distance from 3 to the origin is much shorter on the vertical axis than on the horizontal axis.

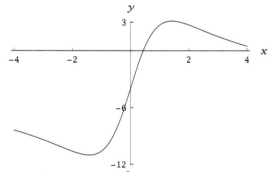

The graph of $\frac{4(5x-x^2-2)}{x^2+2}$ *on a larger interval.*

Using different scales on the axes changes the shape of the curve. Specifically, the part of the last graph on the interval $[1, 4]$ appears flatter than the prior graph of the same function on that interval.

Determining a Function from Its Graph

Sometimes the only information available about a function comes from its graph. The next example is our first attempt to use the graph of a function to learn about the function.

EXAMPLE 3

Suppose all we know about a function f is the sketch of its graph shown here.

(a) Is 0.5 in the domain of f?

(b) Is 2.5 in the domain of f?

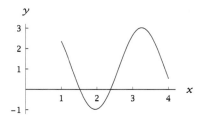

SOLUTION   Recall that the graph of f consists of all points of the form $(b, f(b))$ as b varies over the domain of f. Thus the line $x = b$ intersects the graph of f if and only if b is in the domain of f. The figure below, in addition to the graph of f, contains the lines $x = 0.5$ and $x = 2.5$:

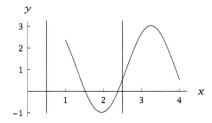

The vertical lines that intersect the graph correspond to numbers in the domain.

(a) As can be seen above, the line $x = 0.5$ does not intersect the graph of f. Thus 0.5 is not in the domain of f.

(b) The line $x = 2.5$ does intersect the graph of f. Thus 2.5 is in the domain of f.

The technique used above can be summarized as follows (here we assume that the horizontal axis has been labeled the x-axis):

> ### Determining the domain from the graph
>
> A number b is in the domain of a function f if and only if the line $x = b$ intersects the graph of f.

If the only information available about a function is a sketch of its graph, then use caution. However, do not be afraid to draw reasonable conclusions that would be valid unless something weird is happening.

Caution must be used when obtaining information from the graph of a function. For example, it appears that the domain of the function f in the previous example is the interval $[1, 4]$. We need to use the word "appear" because a graph can give only a good approximation of the domain. The actual domain of f might be $(1, 4)$ or $[1, 4.001]$ or an even more unusual set such as all numbers in the interval $[1, 4]$ except $\sqrt{2}$ and 2.5; our eyes could not detect such subtle differences from a sketch of the graph.

The graph of a function can be used to find approximate values of the function, as illustrated in the next example.

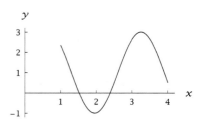

EXAMPLE 4

Estimate the value of $f(3)$, where f is the function whose graph is shown here.

SOLUTION   To evaluate $f(3)$ from the graph, draw a vertical line segment from the point 3 on the x-axis until it intersects the graph. The length of that line segment will equal $f(3)$, as shown below on the left:

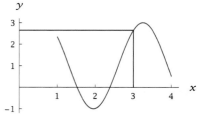

Vertical line segment has length $f(3)$.   *$f(3)$ is approximately 2.6.*

Usually the easiest way to estimate the length of the vertical line segment shown above on the left is to draw a horizontal line from the graph intersection point to the y-axis. The point where that horizontal line intersects the y-axis then gives the length of the vertical line segment. Applying this procedure to the figure on the left gives the figure on the right.

From the figure on the right, we see that $f(3)$ is a bit more than halfway between 2 and 3. Thus 2.6 is a good estimate of $f(3)$, based on this graph.

The following summary of the procedure used in the example above can be used more generally for approximating the values of a function from its graph:

Here we assume that the horizontal axis has been labeled the x-axis and the vertical axis has been labeled the y-axis.

Finding values of a function from its graph

To evaluate $f(b)$ given only the graph of f,

(a) find the point where the vertical line $x = b$ intersects the graph of f;

(b) draw a horizontal line from that point to the y-axis;

(c) the intersection of that horizontal line with the y-axis gives the value of $f(b)$.

Which Sets Are Graphs of Functions?

Not every curve in the plane is the graph of some function, as illustrated in the following example.

Is this curve the graph of some function?

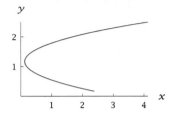

EXAMPLE 5

SOLUTION   If this curve were the graph of some function f, then we could find the value of $f(1)$ by seeing where the line $x = 1$ intersects the curve. However, as can be seen in the figure below, the line $x = 1$ intersects the curve in two points. The definition of a function requires that $f(1)$ be a single number, not a pair of numbers. Thus this curve is not the graph of any function.

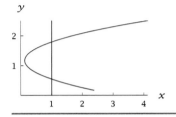

The line $x = 1$ intersects the curve in two points. Thus this curve is not the graph of a function.

More generally, any set in the coordinate plane that intersects some vertical line in more than one point cannot be the graph of a function. Conversely, a set in the plane that intersects each vertical line in at most one point is the graph of some function f, with the values of f determined as in the previous subsection.

The condition for a set of points in the coordinate plane to be the graph of some function can be summarized as follows:

> ### Vertical line test
>
> A set of points in the coordinate plane is the graph of some function if and only if every vertical line intersects the set in at most one point.

Determining the Range of a Function from Its Graph

Recall that the range of a function is the set of all values taken on by the function. The values taken on by a function occur as the second coordinates of points on the graph of a function. Thus the range of a function can be determined by the horizontal lines that intersect the graph of the function.

Suppose f is the function with domain $[1, 4]$ whose graph is shown here.

(a) Is 1.5 in the range of f?

(b) Is 4 in the range of f?

(c) Make a reasonable guess of the range of f.

EXAMPLE 6

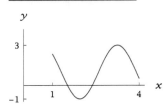

SOLUTION

(a) As can be seen below, the line $y = 1.5$ intersects the graph of f in three points. Thus 1.5 is in the range of f.

This figure shows that the equation $f(x) = 1.5$ has three solutions x in the domain of f. We need one or more such solutions for 1.5 to be in the range of f.

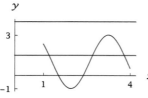

The horizontal lines that intersect the graph correspond to numbers in the range.

(b) As can be seen above, the line $y = 4$ does not intersect the graph of f. In other words, the equation $f(x) = 4$ has no solutions x in the domain of f. Thus 4 is not in the range of f.

(c) By drawing horizontal lines, we can see that the range of this function appears to be the interval $[-1, 3]$. The actual range of this function might be slightly different—we would not be able to notice the difference from the sketch of the graph if the range were actually equal to the interval $[-1.02, 3.001]$.

The following characterization summarizes the procedure for determining the range of a function from its graph (here we assume that the vertical axis has been labeled the y-axis):

Determining the range from the graph

A number c is in the range of a function f if and only if the horizontal line $y = c$ intersects the graph of f.

EXERCISES

For Exercises 1–8, give the coordinates of the specified point using the figure below:

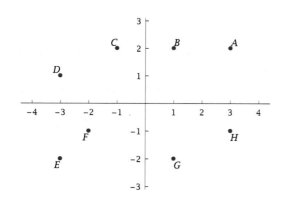

1. A
2. B
3. C
4. D
5. E
6. F
7. G
8. H

9. Sketch a coordinate plane showing the following four points, their coordinates, and the rectangles determined by each point (as in Example 1): $(1, 2), (-2, 2), (-3, -1), (2, -3)$.

10. Sketch a coordinate plane showing the following four points, their coordinates, and the rectangles determined by each point (as in Example 1): $(2.5, 1), (-1, 3), (-1.5, -1.5), (1, -3)$.

11. Sketch the graph of the function f whose domain is the set of five numbers $\{-2, -1, 0, 1, 2\}$ and whose values are defined by the following table:

x	$f(x)$
-2	1
-1	3
0	-1
1	-2
2	3

12. Sketch the graph of the function f whose domain is the set of five numbers $\{-1, 0, 1, 2, 4\}$ and whose values are defined by the following table:

x	$f(x)$
-1	-2
0	2
1	0
2	1
4	-1

For Exercises 13-18, assume that g and h are the functions completely defined by the tables below:

x	$g(x)$		x	$h(x)$
-3	-1		-4	2
-1	1		-2	-3
1	2.5		2	-1.5
3	-2		3	1

13. What is the domain of g?

14. What is the domain of h?

15. What is the range of g?

16. What is the range of h?

17. Draw the graph of g.

18. Draw the graph of h.

19. Shown below is the graph of a function f.

    (a) What is the domain of f?

    (b) What is the range of f?

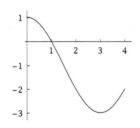

20. Shown below is the graph of a function f.

    (a) What is the domain of f?

    (b) What is the range of f?

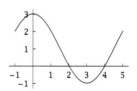

For Exercises 21-32, assume that f is the function with domain $[-4, 4]$ whose graph is shown below:

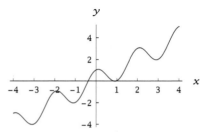

The graph of f.

21. Estimate the value of $f(-4)$.

22. Estimate the value of $f(-3)$.

23. Estimate the value of $f(-2)$.

24. Estimate the value of $f(-1)$.

25. Estimate the value of $f(2)$.

26. Estimate the value of $f(0)$.

27. Estimate the value of $f(4)$.

28. Estimate the value of $f(3)$.

29. Estimate a number b such that $f(b) = 4$.

30. Estimate a negative number b such that $f(b) = 0.5$.

31. How many values of x satisfy the equation $f(x) = \frac{1}{2}$?

32. How many values of x satisfy the equation $f(x) = -3.5$?

For Exercises 33–44, assume that g is the function with domain [−4, 4] whose graph is shown below:

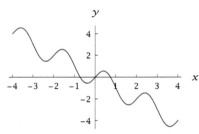

The graph of g.

33. Estimate the value of $g(-4)$.
34. Estimate the value of $g(-3)$.

35. Estimate the value of $g(-2)$.
36. Estimate the value of $g(-1)$.
37. Estimate the value of $g(2)$.
38. Estimate the value of $g(1)$.
39. Estimate the value of $g(2.5)$.
40. Estimate the value of $g(1.5)$.
41. Estimate a number b such that $g(b) = 3.5$.
42. Estimate a number b such that $g(b) = -3.5$.
43. How many values of x satisfy the equation $g(x) = -2$?
44. How many values of x satisfy the equation $g(x) = 0$?

PROBLEMS

45. Sketch the graph of a function whose domain equals the interval $[1, 3]$ and whose range equals the interval $[-2, 4]$.

46. Sketch the graph of a function whose domain is the interval $[0, 4]$ and whose range is the set of two numbers $\{2, 3\}$.

47. Explain why no function has a graph that is a circle.

WORKED-OUT SOLUTIONS *to Odd-numbered Exercises*

For Exercises 1–8, give the coordinates of the specified point using the figure below:

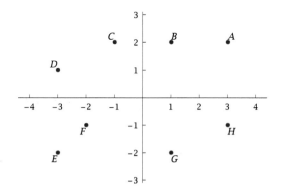

1. *A*

SOLUTION To get to the point A starting at the origin, we must move 3 units right and 2 units up. Thus A has coordinates $(3, 2)$.

Numbers obtained from a figure should be considered approximations. Thus the actual coordinates of A might be $(3.01, 1.98)$.

3. *C*

SOLUTION To get to the point C starting at the origin, we must move 1 unit left and 2 units up. Thus C has coordinates $(-1, 2)$.

5. *E*

SOLUTION To get to the point E starting at the origin, we must move 3 units left and 2 units down. Thus E has coordinates $(-3, -2)$.

7. *G*

SOLUTION To get to the point G starting at the origin, we must move 1 unit right and 2 units down. Thus G has coordinates $(1, -2)$.

9. Sketch a coordinate plane showing the following four points, their coordinates, and the rectangles determined by each point (as in Example 1): $(1,2)$, $(-2,2)$, $(-3,-1)$, $(2,-3)$.

SOLUTION

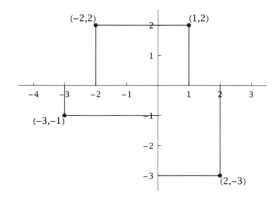

11. Sketch the graph of the function f whose domain is the set of five numbers $\{-2,-1,0,1,2\}$ and whose values are defined by the following table:

x	$f(x)$
-2	1
-1	3
0	-1
1	-2
2	3

SOLUTION

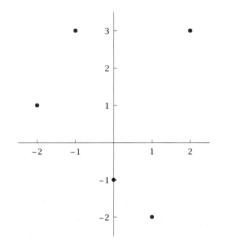

For Exercises 13-18, assume that g and h are the functions completely defined by the tables below:

x	$g(x)$		x	$h(x)$
-3	-1		-4	2
-1	1		-2	-3
1	2.5		2	-1.5
3	-2		3	1

13. What is the domain of g?

   SOLUTION   The domain of g is the set of numbers in the first column of the table defining g. Thus the domain of g is the set $\{-3,-1,1,3\}$.

15. What is the range of g?

   SOLUTION   The range of g is the set of numbers that appear in the second column of the table defining g. Thus the range of g is the set $\{-1,1,2.5,-2\}$.

17. Draw the graph of g.

   SOLUTION   The graph of g consists of the four points with coordinates $(-3,-1)$, $(-1,1)$, $(1,2.5)$, $(3,-2)$, as shown below:

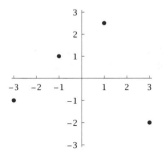

19. Shown below is the graph of a function f.

   (a) What is the domain of f?
   (b) What is the range of f?

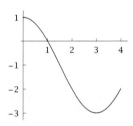

SOLUTION

(a) From the figure, it appears that the domain of f is $[0, 4]$.

The word "appears" is used here because a figure cannot provide precision. The actual domain of f might be $[0, 4.001]$ or $[0, 3.99]$ or $(0, 4)$.

(b) From the figure, it appears that the range of f is $[-3, 1]$.

For Exercises 21–32, assume that f is the function with domain $[-4, 4]$ whose graph is shown below:

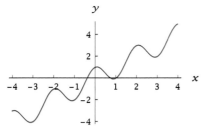

y

x

The graph of f.

21. Estimate the value of $f(-4)$.

SOLUTION   To estimate the value of $f(-4)$, draw a vertical line from the point -4 on the x-axis to the graph, as shown below:

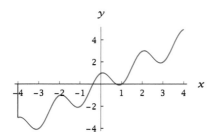

Then draw a horizontal line from where the vertical line intersects the graph to the y-axis:

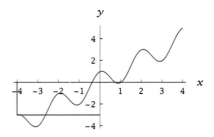

The intersection of the horizontal line with the y-axis gives the value of $f(-4)$. Thus we see that $f(-4) \approx -3$ (the symbol $\approx$ means "is approximately equal to", which is the best that can be done when using a graph).

23. Estimate the value of $f(-2)$.

SOLUTION   To estimate the value of $f(-2)$, draw a vertical line from the point -2 on the x-axis to the graph, as shown below:

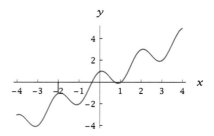

Then draw a horizontal line from where the vertical line intersects the graph to the y-axis:

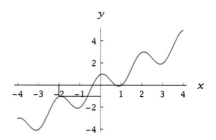

The intersection of the horizontal line with the y-axis gives the value of $f(-2)$. Thus we see that $f(-2) \approx -1$.

25. Estimate the value of $f(2)$.

    SOLUTION   To estimate the value of $f(2)$, draw a vertical line from the point 2 on the x-axis to the graph, as shown below:

    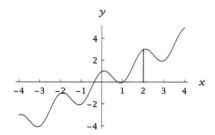

    Then draw a horizontal line from where the vertical line intersects the graph to the y-axis:

    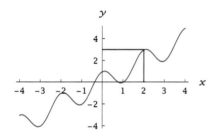

    The intersection of the horizontal line with the y-axis gives the value of $f(2)$. Thus we see that $f(2) \approx 3$.

27. Estimate the value of $f(4)$.

    SOLUTION   To estimate the value of $f(4)$, draw a vertical line from the point 4 on the x-axis to the graph, as shown below:

    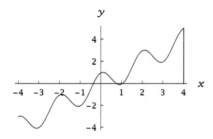

    Then draw a horizontal line from where the vertical line intersects the graph to the y-axis:

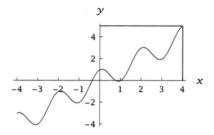

The intersection of the horizontal line with the y-axis gives the value of $f(4)$. Thus we see that $f(4) \approx 5$.

29. Estimate a number b such that $f(b) = 4$.

    SOLUTION   Draw the horizontal line $y = 4$, as shown below:

    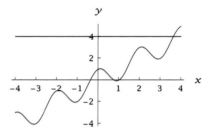

    Then draw a vertical line from where this horizontal line intersects the graph to the x-axis:

    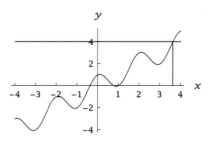

    The intersection of the vertical line with the x-axis gives the value of b such that $f(b) = 4$. Thus we see that $b \approx 3.6$.

31. How many values of x satisfy the equation $f(x) = \frac{1}{2}$?

    SOLUTION   Draw the horizontal line $y = \frac{1}{2}$, as shown below. This horizontal line intersects the graph in three points. Thus there exist three values of x such that $f(x) = \frac{1}{2}$.

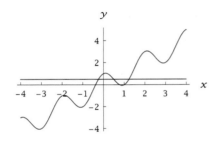

The intersection of the horizontal line with the y-axis gives the value of $g(-4)$. Thus we see that $g(-4) \approx 4$.

35. Estimate the value of $g(-2)$.

SOLUTION   To estimate the value of $g(-2)$, draw a vertical line from the point -2 on the x-axis to the graph, as shown below:

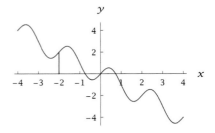

For Exercises 33–44, assume that g is the function with domain [−4, 4] whose graph is shown below:

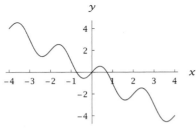

The graph of g.

Then draw a horizontal line from where the vertical line intersects the graph to the y-axis:

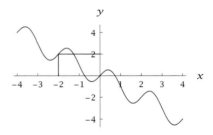

33. Estimate the value of $g(-4)$.

SOLUTION   To estimate the value of $g(-4)$, draw a vertical line from the point -4 on the x-axis to the graph, as shown below:

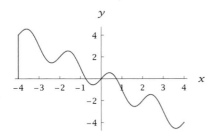

The intersection of the horizontal line with the y-axis gives the value of $g(-2)$. Thus we see that $g(-2) \approx 2$.

37. Estimate the value of $g(2)$.

SOLUTION   To estimate the value of $g(2)$, draw a vertical line from the point 2 on the x-axis to the graph, as shown below:

Then draw a horizontal line from where the vertical line intersects the graph to the y-axis:

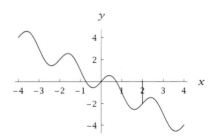

Then draw a horizontal line from where the vertical line intersects the graph to the y-axis:

The intersection of the horizontal line with the y-axis gives the value of $g(2)$. Thus we see that $g(2) \approx -2$.

39. Estimate the value of $g(2.5)$.

SOLUTION   To estimate the value of $g(2.5)$, draw a vertical line from the point 2.5 on the x-axis to the graph, as shown below:

Then draw a horizontal line from where the vertical line intersects the graph to the y-axis:

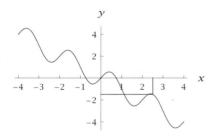

The intersection of the horizontal line with the y-axis gives the value of $g(2.5)$. Thus we see that $g(2.5) \approx -1.5$.

41. Estimate a number b such that $g(b) = 3.5$.

SOLUTION   Draw the horizontal line $y = 3.5$, as shown below:

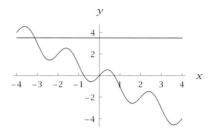

Then draw a vertical line from where this horizontal line intersects the graph to the x-axis:

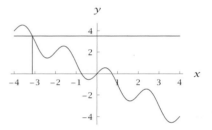

The intersection of the vertical line with the x-axis gives the value of b such that $g(b) = 3.5$. Thus we see that $b \approx -3.1$.

43. How many values of x satisfy the equation $g(x) = -2$?

SOLUTION   Draw the horizontal line $y = -2$, as shown here. This horizontal line intersects the graph in three points. Thus there exist three values of x such that $g(x) = -2$.

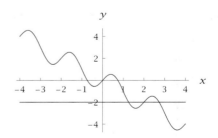

1.3 | *Function Transformations and Graphs*

SECTION OBJECTIVES

By the end of this section you should

- understand which function transformations shift the graph up, down, left, or right;

- understand which function transformations stretch the graph vertically or horizontally;

- understand which function transformations reflect the graph through the horizontal or vertical axis;

- be able to determine the domain, range, and graph of a transformed function.

In this section we investigate various transformations of functions and learn the effect of such transformations on the domain, range, and graph of a function. To illustrate these ideas, throughout this section we will use the function f defined by $f(x) = x^2$, with the domain of f being the interval $[-1, 1]$. Thus the graph of f is part of a familiar parabola.

In Section 6.5 we will revisit many of the ideas in this section, using trigonometric functions as the examples.

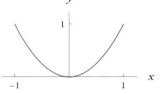

The graph of $f(x) = x^2$, with domain $[-1, 1]$. The range of f is $[0, 1]$.

Shifting a Graph Up or Down

This example illustrates the procedure for shifting up the graph of a function:

EXAMPLE 1

Define a function g by

$$g(x) = f(x) + 1,$$

where f is the function defined by $f(x) = x^2$, with the domain of f the interval $[-1, 1]$.

(a) Find the domain of g.   (c) Sketch the graph of g.

(b) Find the range of g.

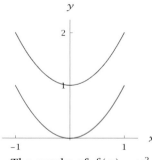

The graphs of $f(x) = x^2$ (blue) and $g(x) = x^2 + 1$ (red), each with domain $[-1, 1]$.

SOLUTION

(a) The formula defining g shows that $g(x)$ is defined precisely when $f(x)$ is defined. In other words, the domain of g equals the domain of f. Thus the domain of g is the interval $[-1, 1]$.

(b) Recall that the range of g is the set of values taken on by $g(x)$ as x varies over the domain of g. Because $g(x)$ equals $f(x) + 1$, we see that the range of g is obtained by adding 1 to each number in the range of f. Thus the range of g is the interval $[1, 2]$.

(c) A typical point on the graph of f has the form (x, x^2), where x is in the interval $[-1, 1]$. Because $g(x) = x^2 + 1$, a typical point on the graph of g has the form $(x, x^2 + 1)$, where x is in the interval $[-1, 1]$. Thus the graph of g is obtained by shifting the graph of f up 1 unit, as shown here.

Shifting the graph of a function down follows a similar pattern, with a minus sign replacing the plus sign, as shown in the following example.

Define a function h by
$$h(x) = f(x) - 1,$$
where f is the function defined by $f(x) = x^2$, with the domain of f the interval $[-1, 1]$.

(a) Find the domain of h.

(b) Find the range of h.

(c) Sketch the graph of h.

EXAMPLE 2

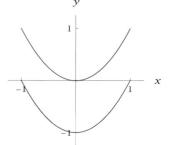

SOLUTION

(a) The formula above shows that $h(x)$ is defined precisely when $f(x)$ is defined. In other words, the domain of h equals the domain of f. Thus the domain of h is the interval $[-1, 1]$.

(b) Because $h(x)$ equals $f(x) - 1$, we see that the range of h is obtained by subtracting 1 from each number in the range of f. Thus the range of h is the interval $[-1, 0]$.

(c) Because $h(x) = x^2 - 1$, a typical point on the graph of h has the form $(x, x^2 - 1)$, where x is in the interval $[-1, 1]$. Thus the graph of h is obtained by shifting the graph of f down 1 unit, as shown here.

The graphs of $f(x) = x^2$ (blue) and $h(x) = x^2 - 1$ (red), each with domain $[-1, 1]$.

We could have used any positive number a instead of 1 in these examples when defining $g(x)$ as $f(x) + 1$ and defining $h(x)$ as $f(x) - 1$. Similarly, there is nothing special about the particular function f that we used. Thus the following results hold in general:

Shifting a graph up or down

Suppose f is a function and $a > 0$. Define functions g and h by
$$g(x) = f(x) + a \quad \text{and} \quad h(x) = f(x) - a.$$

Then

- the graph of g is obtained by shifting the graph of f up a units;

- the graph of h is obtained by shifting the graph of f down a units.

Shifting a Graph Right or Left

The procedure for shifting the graph of a function to the right is illustrated by the following example:

| EXAMPLE 3 | Define a function g by |

$$g(x) = f(x - 1),$$

where f is the function defined by $f(x) = x^2$, with the domain of f the interval $[-1, 1]$.

(a) Find the domain of g. (c) Sketch the graph of g.

(b) Find the range of g.

SOLUTION

(a) The formula defining g shows that $g(x)$ is defined precisely when $f(x - 1)$ is defined, which means that $x - 1$ must be in the interval $[-1, 1]$, which means that x must be in the interval $[0, 2]$. Thus the domain of g is the interval $[0, 2]$.

(b) Because $g(x)$ equals $f(x - 1)$, we see that the values taken on by g are the same as the values taken on by f. Thus the range of g equals the range of f, which is the interval $[0, 1]$.

Example 2 with $h(x) = x^2 - 1$ *differs from this example with* $g(x) = (x - 1)^2$. *In the earlier example, the graph was shifted down; in this example, the graph is shifted right. The domains and ranges also behave differently in these two examples.*

(c) Note that $g(x) = (x - 1)^2$ for each x in the interval $[0, 2]$. For each point (x, x^2) on the graph of f, the point $(x + 1, x^2)$ is on the graph of g (because $g(x + 1) = x^2$). Thus the graph of g is obtained by shifting the graph of f right 1 unit:

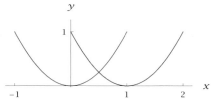

The graphs of $f(x) = x^2$ (blue, with domain $[-1, 1]$) and $g(x) = (x - 1)^2$ (red, with domain $[0, 2]$). The graph of g is obtained by shifting the graph of f right 1 unit.

Suppose we define a function h by

$$h(x) = f(x + 1),$$

where f is again the function defined by $f(x) = x^2$, with the domain of f the interval $[-1, 1]$. Then everything works as in the example above, except that the domain and graph of h are obtained by shifting the domain and graph of f left 1 unit (instead of right 1 unit as in the example above).

More generally, we could have used any positive number b instead of 1 in these examples when defining $g(x)$ as $f(x - 1)$ and defining $h(x)$ as $f(x + 1)$. Similarly, there is nothing special about the particular function f that we used. Thus the following results hold in general:

Shifting a graph right or left

Suppose f is a function and $b > 0$. Define functions g and h by

$$g(x) = f(x - b) \quad \text{and} \quad h(x) = f(x + b).$$

Then

- the graph of g is obtained by shifting the graph of f right b units;

- the graph of h is obtained by shifting the graph of f left b units.

Instead of memorizing the conclusions in all the result boxes in this section, try to understand how these conclusions arise. Then you can figure out what you need depending on the problem at hand.

Stretching a Graph Vertically or Horizontally

The procedure for stretching the graph of a function vertically is illustrated by the following example:

Define a function g by
$$g(x) = 2f(x),$$
where f is the function defined by $f(x) = x^2$, with the domain of f the interval $[-1, 1]$.

(a) Find the domain of g.   (c) Sketch the graph of g.

(b) Find the range of g.

EXAMPLE 4

SOLUTION

(a) The formula defining g shows that $g(x)$ is defined precisely when $f(x)$ is defined. In other words, the domain of g equals the domain of f. Thus the domain of g is the interval $[-1, 1]$.

(b) Because $g(x)$ equals $2f(x)$, we see that the range of g is obtained by multiplying each number in the range of f by 2. Thus the range of g is the closed interval $[0, 2]$.

(c) Note that $g(x) = 2x^2$ for each x in the interval $[-1, 1]$. For each point (x, x^2) on the graph of f, the point $(x, 2x^2)$ is on the graph of g. Thus the graph of g is obtained by vertically stretching the graph of f by a factor of 2, as shown here.

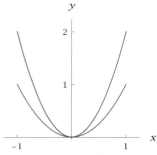

The graphs of $f(x) = x^2$ (blue) and $g(x) = 2x^2$ (red), each with domain $[-1, 1]$.

Before getting to the next example, we need to deal with a bit of terminology. In the example above, the graph of g was obtained by vertically stretching the graph of f by a factor of 2. Similarly, if we had instead defined $g(x)$ to equal $3f(x)$, then we would vertically stretch the graph of f by a factor of 3 to get the graph of g.

But what if we had defined $g(x)$ to equal $\frac{1}{2}f(x)$? In that case the graph of g would consist of the points of the form $(x, \frac{x^2}{2})$, where x is in the interval $[-1, 1]$. In this case it is reasonable to say that the graph of g is obtained by vertically stretching the graph of f by a factor of $\frac{1}{2}$. This may seem a little

Perhaps the word "shrink" would be more appropriate here. strange, because the word "stretch" often has the connotation of something getting larger. However, we will find it convenient to use the word "stretch" in the wider sense of multiplying by some positive number, which might be less than 1.

The next example shows the procedure for horizontally stretching the graph of a function.

EXAMPLE 5

Define a function h by
$$h(x) = f(2x),$$
where f is the function defined by $f(x) = x^2$, with the domain of f the interval $[-1, 1]$.

(a) Find the domain of h.   (c) Sketch the graph of h.

(b) Find the range of h.

SOLUTION

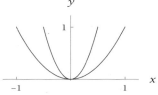

The graphs of $f(x) = x^2$ (blue, with domain $[-1, 1]$) and $h(x) = (2x)^2$ (red, with domain $[-\frac{1}{2}, \frac{1}{2}]$).

(a) The formula defining h shows that $h(x)$ is defined precisely when $f(2x)$ is defined, which means that $2x$ must be in the interval $[-1, 1]$, which means that x must be in the interval $[-\frac{1}{2}, \frac{1}{2}]$. Thus the domain of h is the interval $[-\frac{1}{2}, \frac{1}{2}]$.

(b) Because $h(x)$ equals $f(2x)$, we see that the values taken on by h are the same as the values taken on by f. Thus the range of h equals the range of f, which is the interval $[0, 1]$.

(c) Note that $h(x) = (2x)^2$ for each x in the interval $[-\frac{1}{2}, \frac{1}{2}]$. For each point (x, x^2) on the graph of f, the point $(\frac{x}{2}, x^2)$ is on the graph of h (because $h(\frac{x}{2}) = x^2$). Thus the graph of h is obtained by horizontally stretching the graph of f by a factor of $\frac{1}{2}$, as shown here.

We could have used any positive number c instead of 2 in these examples when defining $g(x)$ as $2f(x)$ and defining $h(x)$ as $f(2x)$. Similarly, there is nothing special about the particular function f that we used. Thus the following results hold in general:

Stretching a graph vertically or horizontally

Suppose f is a function and $c > 0$. Define functions g and h by

$$g(x) = cf(x) \quad \text{and} \quad h(x) = f(cx).$$

Then

- the graph of g is obtained by vertically stretching the graph of f by a factor of c;

- the graph of h is obtained by horizontally stretching the graph of f by a factor of $\frac{1}{c}$.

Reflecting a Graph in the Horizontal or Vertical Axis

The procedure for reflecting the graph of a function through the horizontal axis is illustrated by the following example:

Define a function g by

$$g(x) = -f(x),$$

where f is the function defined by $f(x) = x^2$, with the domain of f the interval $[-1, 1]$.

(a) Find the domain of g. (c) Sketch the graph of g.

(b) Find the range of g.

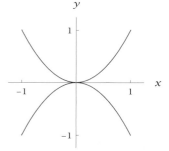

SOLUTION

(a) The formula defining g shows that $g(x)$ is defined precisely when $f(x)$ is defined. In other words, the domain of g equals the domain of f. Thus the domain of g is the interval $[-1, 1]$.

(b) Because $g(x)$ equals $-f(x)$, we see that the values taken on by g are the negatives of the values taken on by f. Thus the range of g is the interval $[-1, 0]$.

(c) Note that $g(x) = -x^2$ for each x in the interval $[-1, 1]$. For each point (x, x^2) on the graph of f, the point $(x, -x^2)$ is on the graph of g. Thus the graph of g is the reflection of the graph of f through the horizontal axis, as shown here.

The graphs of $f(x) = x^2$ (blue) and $g(x) = -x^2$ (red), each with domain $[-1, 1]$.

The procedure for reflecting the graph of a function through the vertical axis is illustrated by the following example. To show the ideas more clearly, in the next example we change the domain of f to the interval $[\frac{1}{2}, 1]$.

Define a function h by

$$h(x) = f(-x),$$

where f is the function defined by $f(x) = x^2$, with the domain of f the interval $[\frac{1}{2}, 1]$.

(a) Find the domain of h. (c) Sketch the graph of h.

(b) Find the range of h.

SOLUTION

(a) The formula defining h shows that $h(x)$ is defined precisely when $f(-x)$ is defined, which means that $-x$ must be in the interval $[\frac{1}{2}, 1]$, which means that x must be in the interval $[-1, -\frac{1}{2}]$. Thus the domain of h is the interval $[-1, -\frac{1}{2}]$.

(b) Because $h(x)$ equals $f(-x)$, we see that the values taken on by h are the same as the values taken on by f. Thus the range of h equals the range of f, which is the interval $[\frac{1}{4}, 1]$.

(c) Note that $h(x) = (-x)^2 = x^2$ for each x in the interval $[-1, -\frac{1}{2}]$. For each point (x, x^2) on the graph of f, the point $(-x, x^2)$ is on the graph of h (because $h(-x) = x^2$). Thus the graph of h is the reflection of the graph of f through the vertical axis:

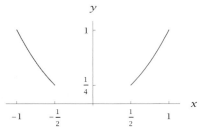

The graphs of $f(x) = x^2$ (blue, with domain $[\frac{1}{2}, 1]$)
and $h(x) = (-x)^2 = x^2$ (red, with domain $[-1, -\frac{1}{2}]$).
The graph of h is the reflection of the graph of f through the vertical axis.

The following results hold for an arbitrary function f:

Reflecting a graph in the horizontal or vertical axis

The domain of g is the same as the domain of f, but the domain of h is obtained by multiplying each number in the domain of f by -1.

Suppose f is a function. Define functions g and h by

$$g(x) = -f(x) \quad \text{and} \quad h(x) = f(-x).$$

Then

- the graph of g is the reflection of the graph of f through the horizontal axis;

- the graph of h is the reflection of the graph of f through the vertical axis.

We have now learned about function transformations that can shift a graph (up, down, left, or right), stretch a graph (vertically or horizontally), or reflect a graph (through the horizontal or vertical axis). These transformations can be combined. For example, suppose g is defined by $g(x) = 2f(x) + 1$. Then the graph of g would be obtained by vertically stretching the graph of f by a factor of 2 and then shifting up 1 unit.

Pay attention to the order of the operations when dealing with multiple function transformations, as explained here and then demonstrated in the next example.

Multiple function transformations

To obtain the graph of a function defined by multiple function transformations, apply the transformations in the same order as the corresponding operations when evaluating the function.

Suppose f is a function and functions g and h are defined by

EXAMPLE 8

$$g(x) = -2f(x) + 1 \quad \text{and} \quad h(x) = -2(f(x) + 1).$$

(a) Describe how the graph of g is obtained from the graph of f.

(b) Describe how the graph of h is obtained from the graph of f.

SOLUTION

(a) To compute $g(x)$ from $f(x)$, we first multiply $f(x)$ by 2, then take the additive inverse, then add 1. Using the same order, the graph of g is thus obtained by vertically stretching the graph of f by a factor of 2, then reflecting through the horizontal axis, and then shifting up 1 unit.

(b) To compute $h(x)$ from $f(x)$, we first add 1 to $f(x)$, then multiply by 2, then take the additive inverse. Using the same order, the graph of h is thus obtained by shifting the graph of f up 1 unit, then vertically stretching by a factor of 2, then reflecting through the horizontal axis.

Even and Odd Functions

Suppose $f(x) = x^2$ for every real number x. Notice that

$$f(-x) = (-x)^2 = x^2 = f(x).$$

Later in the book we will encounter several other important functions that satisfy the equation $f(-x) = f(x)$. This property is sufficiently important that we give it a name:

Even functions

A function f is called **even** if

$$f(-x) = f(x)$$

for every x in the domain of f.

In order for the equation $f(-x) = f(x)$ to hold for every x in the domain of f, the expression $f(-x)$ must make sense. In other words, $-x$ must be in the domain of f for every x in the domain of f. For example, a function whose domain is the interval $[-3, 5]$ cannot possibly be an even function, but a function whose domain is the interval $(-4, 4)$ may or may not be an even function.

As we have already observed, x^2 is an even function. Here is another simple example:

EXAMPLE 9

Show that the function f defined by $f(x) = |x|$ for every real number x is an even function.

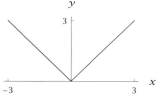

SOLUTION   This function is even because

$$f(-x) = |-x| = |x| = f(x)$$

for every real number x.

The graph of $|x|$ on the interval $[-3, 3]$.

Suppose f is an even function. As we know, reflecting the graph of f through the vertical axis gives the graph of the function h defined by $h(x) = f(-x)$. Because f is even, we actually have $h(x) = f(-x) = f(x)$, which implies that $h = f$. In other words, the reflection of the graph of f through the vertical axis gives us back the graph of f. Thus the graph of an even function is symmetric about the vertical axis. This symmetry can be seen, for example, in the graph shown above of $|x|$ on the interval $[-3, 3]$. Here is the statement of the result in general:

The graph of an even function

A function is even if and only if its graph is the same as the reflection of its graph through the vertical axis.

Consider now the function defined by $f(x) = x^3$ for every real number x. Notice that

$$f(-x) = (-x)^3 = -(x^3) = -f(x).$$

Later in the book we will encounter several other important functions that satisfy the equation $f(-x) = -f(x)$. This property is sufficiently important that we also give it a name:

Odd functions

A function f is called **odd** if

$$f(-x) = -f(x)$$

for every x in the domain of f.

As was the case for even functions, for a function to be odd $-x$ must be in the domain of f for every x in the domain of f, because otherwise there is no possibility that the equation $f(-x) = -f(x)$ can hold for every x in the domain of f.

As we have already observed, x^3 is an odd function. Here is another simple example:

Show that the function f defined by $f(x) = \frac{1}{x}$ for every real number $x \neq 0$ is an odd function.

EXAMPLE 10

SOLUTION   This function is odd because

$$f(-x) = \frac{1}{-x} = -\frac{1}{x} = -f(x)$$

for every real number $x \neq 0$.

Suppose f is an odd function. If x is a number in the domain of f, then $(x, f(x))$ is a point on the graph of f. Because $f(-x) = -f(x)$, the point $(-x, -f(x))$ also is on the graph of f. In other words, for each point $(x, f(x))$ on the graph of f, its reflection through the origin $(-x, -f(x))$ is also on the graph of f. Thus the graph of an odd function is symmetric with respect to the origin. This symmetry can be seen, for example, in the graph shown here of $\frac{1}{x}$ on $[-1, -\frac{1}{2}] \cup [\frac{1}{2}, 1]$. Here is the statement of the result in general:

The graph of $\frac{1}{x}$ on $[-1, -\frac{1}{2}] \cup [\frac{1}{2}, 1]$.

The graph of an odd function

A function is odd if and only if its graph is the same as the reflection of its graph through the origin.

EXERCISES

For Exercises 1–14, assume that f is the function defined on the interval $[1, 2]$ by the formula $f(x) = \frac{4}{x^2}$. Thus the domain of f is the interval $[1, 2]$, the range of f is the interval $[1, 4]$, and the graph of f is shown here.

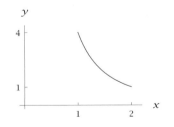

The graph of f.

For each function g described below:

(a) *Sketch the graph of g.*

(b) *Find the domain of g (the endpoints of this interval should be shown on the horizontal axis of your sketch of the graph of g).*

(c) *Give a formula for g.*

(d) *Find the range of g (the endpoints of this interval should be shown on the vertical axis of your sketch of the graph of g).*

1. The graph of g is obtained by shifting the graph of f up 1 unit.

2. The graph of g is obtained by shifting the graph of f up 3 units.

3. The graph of g is obtained by shifting the graph of f down 3 units.

4. The graph of g is obtained by shifting the graph of f down 2 units.

5. The graph of g is obtained by shifting the graph of f left 3 units.

6. The graph of g is obtained by shifting the graph of f left 4 units.

7. The graph of g is obtained by shifting the graph of f right 1 unit.

8. The graph of g is obtained by shifting the graph of f right 3 units.

9. The graph of g is obtained by vertically stretching the graph of f by a factor of 2.

10. The graph of g is obtained by vertically stretching the graph of f by a factor of 3.

11. The graph of g is obtained by horizontally stretching the graph of f by a factor of 2.

12. The graph of g is obtained by horizontally stretching the graph of f by a factor of $\frac{1}{2}$.

13. The graph of g is obtained by reflecting the graph of f through the horizontal axis.

14. The graph of g is obtained by reflecting the graph of f through the vertical axis.

For Exercises 15–46, assume that f is a function whose domain is the interval $[1, 5]$, whose range is the interval $[1, 3]$, and whose graph is the figure below.

The graph of f.

For each given function g:

(a) *Find the domain of g.*

(b) *Find the range of g.*

(c) *Sketch the graph of g.*

15. $g(x) = f(x) + 1$

16. $g(x) = f(x) + 3$

17. $g(x) = f(x) - 3$

18. $g(x) = f(x) - 5$

19. $g(x) = 2f(x)$

20. $g(x) = \frac{1}{2}f(x)$

21. $g(x) = f(x + 2)$

22. $g(x) = f(x + 3)$

23. $g(x) = f(x - 1)$

24. $g(x) = f(x - 2)$

25. $g(x) = f(2x)$

26. $g(x) = f(3x)$

27. $g(x) = f(\frac{x}{2})$

28. $g(x) = f(\frac{5x}{8})$

29. $g(x) = 3 - f(x)$

30. $g(x) = 2 - f(x)$

31. $g(x) = -f(x - 1)$

32. $g(x) = -f(x - 3)$

33. $g(x) = f(x + 1) + 2$

34. $g(x) = f(x + 2) + 1$

35. $g(x) = f(2x) + 1$

36. $g(x) = f(3x) + 2$

37. $g(x) = f(2x + 1)$

38. $g(x) = f(3x + 2)$

39. $g(x) = 2f(\frac{x}{2} + 1)$

40. $g(x) = 3f(\frac{2x}{5} + 2)$

41. $g(x) = 2f(\frac{x}{2} + 1) - 3$

42. $g(x) = 3f(\frac{2x}{5} + 2) + 1$

43. $g(x) = 2f(\frac{x}{2} + 3)$

44. $g(x) = 3f(\frac{2x}{5} - 2)$

45. $g(x) = 6 - 2f(\frac{x}{2} + 3)$

46. $g(x) = 1 - 3f(\frac{2x}{5} - 2)$

For Exercises 47–50, suppose f is a function whose domain is the interval $[-5, 5]$ and that

$$f(x) = \frac{x}{x + 3}$$

for every x in the interval $[0, 5]$.

47. Suppose f is an even function. Evaluate $f(-2)$.

48. Suppose f is an even function. Evaluate $f(-3)$.

49. Suppose f is an odd function. Evaluate $f(-2)$.

50. Suppose f is an odd function. Evaluate $f(-3)$.

PROBLEMS

51. The result box following Example 2 could have been made more complete by including explicit information about the domain and range of the functions g and h. For example, the more complete result box might have looked like the one shown here:

Shifting a graph up or down

Suppose f is a function and $a > 0$. Define functions g and h by

$$g(x) = f(x) + a \quad \text{and} \quad h(x) = f(x) - a.$$

Then

- g and h have the same domain as f;
- the range of g is obtained by adding a to every number in the range of f;
- the range of h is obtained by subtracting a from every number in the range of f;
- the graph of g is obtained by shifting the graph of f up a units;
- the graph of h is obtained by shifting the graph of f down a units.

Construct similar complete result boxes, including explicit information about the domain and range of the functions g and h, for each of the other three result boxes in this section that deal with function transformations.

52. (a) True or false: Just as every integer is either even or odd, every function whose domain is the set of integers is either an even function or an odd function.

    (b) Explain your answer to part (a). This means that if the answer is "true", then you should explain why every function whose domain is the set of integers is either an even function or an odd function; if the answer is "false", then you should give an example of a function whose domain is the set of integers but that is neither even nor odd.

53. Show that if f is an odd function such that 0 is in the domain of f, then $f(0) = 0$.

54. True or false: If f is an odd function whose domain is the set of real numbers and a function g is defined by

$$g(x) = \begin{cases} f(x) & \text{if } x \geq 0 \\ -f(x) & \text{if } x < 0, \end{cases}$$

then g is an even function. Explain your answer.

55. True or false: If f is an even function whose domain is the set of real numbers and a function g is defined by

$$g(x) = \begin{cases} f(x) & \text{if } x \geq 0 \\ -f(x) & \text{if } x < 0, \end{cases}$$

then g is an odd function. Explain your answer.

56. Show that the sum of two even functions (with the same domain) is an even function.

57. Show that the product of two even functions (with the same domain) is an even function.

58. Show that the product of two odd functions (with the same domain) is an even function.

59. Find the only function whose domain is the set of real numbers and that is both even and odd.

60. (a) True or false: The product of an even function and an odd function (with the same domain) is an odd function.

    (b) Explain your answer to part (a). This means that if the answer is "true", then explain why the product of every even function and every odd function (with the same domain) is an odd function; if the answer is "false", then give an example of an even function f and an odd function g (with the same domain) such that fg is not an odd function.

61. (a) True or false: The sum of an even function and an odd function (with the same domain) is an odd function.

    (b) Explain your answer to part (a). This means that if the answer is "true", then explain why the sum of every even function and every odd function (with the same domain) is an odd function; if the answer is "false", then give an example of an even function f and an odd function g (with the same domain) such that $f + g$ is not an odd function.

WORKED-OUT SOLUTIONS *to Odd-numbered Exercises*

For Exercises 1–14, assume that f is the function defined on the interval $[1, 2]$ by the formula $f(x) = \frac{4}{x^2}$. Thus the domain of f is the interval $[1, 2]$, the range of f is the interval $[1, 4]$, and the graph of f is shown here.

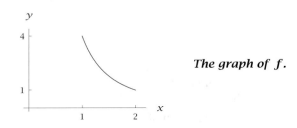

The graph of f.

For each function g described below:

(a) *Sketch the graph of g.*

(b) *Find the domain of g (the endpoints of this interval should be shown on the horizontal axis of your sketch of the graph of g).*

(c) *Give a formula for g.*

(d) *Find the range of g (the endpoints of this interval should be shown on the vertical axis of your sketch of the graph of g).*

1. The graph of g is obtained by shifting the graph of f up 1 unit.

SOLUTION

(a)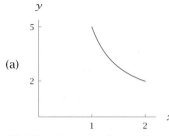

Shifting the graph of f up 1 unit gives this graph.

(b) The domain of g is the same as the domain of f. Thus the domain of g is the interval $[1, 2]$.

(c) Because the graph of g is obtained by shifting the graph of f up 1 unit, we have $g(x) = f(x) + 1$. Thus

$$g(x) = \frac{4}{x^2} + 1$$

for each number x in the interval $[1, 2]$.

(d) The range of g is obtained by adding 1 to each number in the range of f. Thus the range of g is the interval $[2, 5]$.

3. The graph of g is obtained by shifting the graph of f down 3 units.

SOLUTION

(a)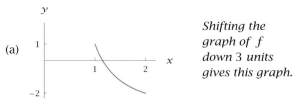

Shifting the graph of f down 3 units gives this graph.

(b) The domain of g is the same as the domain of f. Thus the domain of g is the interval $[1, 2]$.

(c) Because the graph of g is obtained by shifting the graph of f down 3 units, we have $g(x) = f(x) - 3$. Thus

$$g(x) = \frac{4}{x^2} - 3$$

for each number x in the interval $[1, 2]$.

(d) The range of g is obtained by subtracting 3 from each number in the range of f. Thus the range of g is the interval $[-2, 1]$.

5. The graph of g is obtained by shifting the graph of f left 3 units.

SOLUTION

(a)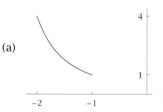

Shifting the graph of f left 3 units gives this graph.

(b) The domain of g is obtained by subtracting 3 from every number in domain of f. Thus the domain of g is the interval $[-2, -1]$.

(c)   Because the graph of g is obtained by shifting the graph of f left 3 units, we have $g(x) = f(x + 3)$. Thus

$$g(x) = \frac{4}{(x + 3)^2}$$

for each number x in the interval $[-2, -1]$.

(d)   The range of g is the same as the range of f. Thus the range of g is the interval $[1, 4]$.

7.   The graph of g is obtained by shifting the graph of f right 1 unit.

SOLUTION

(a)

Shifting the graph of f right 1 unit gives this graph.

(b)   The domain of g is obtained by adding 1 to every number in domain of f. Thus the domain of g is the interval $[2, 3]$.

(c)   Because the graph of g is obtained by shifting the graph of f right 1 unit, we have $g(x) = f(x - 1)$. Thus

$$g(x) = \frac{4}{(x - 1)^2}$$

for each number x in the interval $[2, 3]$.

(d)   The range of g is the same as the range of f. Thus the range of g is the interval $[1, 4]$.

9.   The graph of g is obtained by vertically stretching the graph of f by a factor of 2.

SOLUTION

(a)

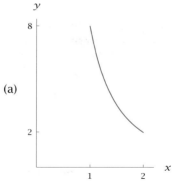

Vertically stretching the graph of f by a factor of 2 gives this graph.

(b)   The domain of g is the same as the domain of f. Thus the domain of g is the interval $[1, 2]$.

(c)   Because the graph of g is obtained by vertically stretching the graph of f by a factor of 2, we have $g(x) = 2f(x)$. Thus

$$g(x) = \frac{8}{x^2}$$

for each number x in the interval $[1, 2]$.

(d)   The range of g is obtained by multiplying every number in the range of f by 2. Thus the range of g is the interval $[2, 8]$.

11.   The graph of g is obtained by horizontally stretching the graph of f by a factor of 2.

SOLUTION

(a)

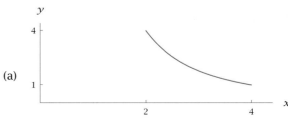

Horizontally stretching the graph of f by a factor of 2 gives this graph.

(b)   The domain of g is obtained by multiplying every number in the domain of f by 2. Thus the domain of g is the interval $[2, 4]$.

(c)   Because the graph of g is obtained by horizontally stretching the graph of f by a factor of 2, we have $g(x) = f(x/2)$. Thus

$$g(x) = \frac{4}{(x/2)^2} = \frac{16}{x^2}$$

for each number x in the interval $[2, 4]$.

(d) The range of g is the same as the range of f. Thus the range of g is the interval $[1, 4]$.

13. The graph of g is obtained by reflecting the graph of f through the horizontal axis.

SOLUTION

(a)

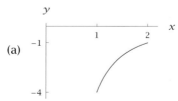

Reflecting the graph of f in the horizontal axis gives this graph.

(b) The domain of g is the same as the domain of f. Thus the domain of g is the interval $[1, 2]$.

(c) Because the graph of g is obtained by reflecting the graph of f through the horizontal axis, we have $g(x) = -f(x)$. Thus

$$g(x) = -\frac{4}{x^2}$$

for each number x in the interval $[1, 2]$.

(d) The range of g is obtained by multiplying every number in the range of f by -1. Thus the range of g is the interval $[-4, -1]$.

For Exercises 15–46, assume that f is a function whose domain is the interval $[1, 5]$, whose range is the interval $[1, 3]$, and whose graph is the figure below.

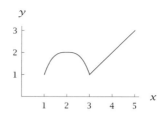

The graph of f.

For each given function g:

   (a) Find the domain of g.

   (b) Find the range of g.

   (c) Sketch the graph of g.

15. $g(x) = f(x) + 1$

SOLUTION

(a) Note that $g(x)$ is defined precisely when $f(x)$ is defined. In other words, the function g has the same domain as f. Thus the domain of g is the interval $[1, 5]$.

(b) The range of g is obtained by adding 1 to every number in the range of f. Thus the range of g is the interval $[2, 4]$.

(c) The graph of g, shown here, is obtained by shifting the graph of f up 1 unit.

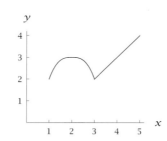

17. $g(x) = f(x) - 3$

SOLUTION

(a) Note that $g(x)$ is defined precisely when $f(x)$ is defined. In other words, the function g has the same domain as f. Thus the domain of g is the interval $[1, 5]$.

(b) The range of g is obtained by subtracting 3 from each number in the range of f. Thus the range of g is the interval $[-2, 0]$.

(c) The graph of g, shown here, is obtained by shifting the graph of f down 3 units.

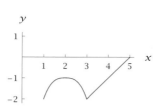

19. $g(x) = 2f(x)$

SOLUTION

(a) Note that $g(x)$ is defined precisely when $f(x)$ is defined. In other words, the function g has the same domain as f. Thus the domain of g is the interval $[1, 5]$.

(b) The range of g is obtained by multiplying each number in the range of f by 2. Thus the range of g is the interval $[2, 6]$.

(c)   The graph of g, shown here, is obtained by vertically stretching the graph of f by a factor of 2.

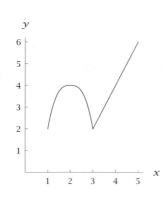

21. $g(x) = f(x + 2)$

SOLUTION

(a)   Note that $g(x)$ is defined when $x + 2$ is in the interval $[1, 5]$, which means that x must be in the interval $[-1, 3]$. Thus the domain of g is the interval $[-1, 3]$.

(b)   The range of g is the same as the range of f. Thus the range of g is the interval $[1, 3]$.

(c)   The graph of g, shown here, is obtained by shifting the graph of f left 2 units.

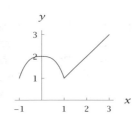

23. $g(x) = f(x - 1)$

SOLUTION

(a)   Note that $g(x)$ is defined when $x - 1$ is in the interval $[1, 5]$, which means that x must be in the interval $[2, 6]$. Thus the domain of g is the interval $[2, 6]$.

(b)   The range of g is the same as the range of f. Thus the range of g is the interval $[1, 3]$.

(c)   The graph of g, shown here, is obtained by shifting the graph of f right 1 unit.

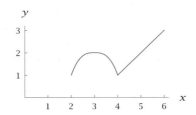

25. $g(x) = f(2x)$

SOLUTION

(a)   Note that $g(x)$ is defined when $2x$ is in the interval $[1, 5]$, which means that x must be in the interval $[\frac{1}{2}, \frac{5}{2}]$. Thus the domain of g is the interval $[\frac{1}{2}, \frac{5}{2}]$.

(b)   The range of g is the same as the range of f. Thus the range of g is the interval $[1, 3]$.

(c)   The graph of g, shown here, is obtained by horizontally stretching the graph of f by a factor of $\frac{1}{2}$.

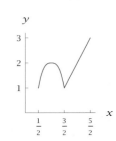

27. $g(x) = f(\frac{x}{2})$

SOLUTION

(a)   Note that $g(x)$ is defined when $\frac{x}{2}$ is in the interval $[1, 5]$, which means that x must be in the interval $[2, 10]$. Thus the domain of g is the interval $[2, 10]$.

(b)   The range of g is the same as the range of f. Thus the range of g is the interval $[1, 3]$.

(c)   The graph of g, shown below, is obtained by horizontally stretching the graph of f by a factor of 2.

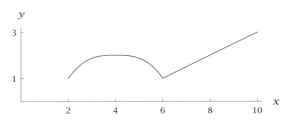

29. $g(x) = 3 - f(x)$

SOLUTION

(a)   Note that $g(x)$ is defined precisely when $f(x)$ is defined. In other words, the function g has the same domain as f. Thus the domain of g is the interval $[1, 5]$.

(b) The range of g is obtained by multiplying each number in the range of f by -1 and then adding 3. Thus the range of g is the interval $[0, 2]$.

(c) The graph of g, shown here, is obtained by reflecting the graph of f through the x-axis, then shifting up by 3 units.

31. $g(x) = -f(x - 1)$

SOLUTION

(a) Note that $g(x)$ is defined when $x - 1$ is in the interval $[1, 5]$, which means that x must be in the interval $[2, 6]$. Thus the domain of g is the interval $[2, 6]$.

(b) The range of g is obtained by multiplying each number in the range of f by -1. Thus the range of g is the interval $[-3, -1]$.

(c) The graph of g, shown here, is obtained by shifting the graph of f right 1 unit, then reflecting through the x-axis.

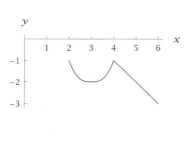

33. $g(x) = f(x + 1) + 2$

SOLUTION

(a) Note that $g(x)$ is defined when $x + 1$ is in the interval $[1, 5]$, which means that x must be in the interval $[0, 4]$. Thus the domain of g is the interval $[0, 4]$.

(b) The range of g is obtained by adding 2 to each number in the range of f. Thus the range of g is the interval $[3, 5]$.

(c) The graph of g, shown here, is obtained by shifting the graph of f left 1 unit, then shifting up by 2 units.

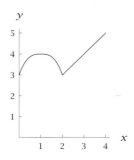

35. $g(x) = f(2x) + 1$

SOLUTION

(a) Note that $g(x)$ is defined when $2x$ is in the interval $[1, 5]$, which means that x must be in the interval $[\frac{1}{2}, \frac{5}{2}]$. Thus the domain of g is the interval $[\frac{1}{2}, \frac{5}{2}]$.

(b) The range of g is obtained by adding 1 to each number in the range of f. Thus the range of g is the interval $[2, 4]$.

(c) The graph of g, shown here, is obtained by horizontally stretching the graph of f by a factor of $\frac{1}{2}$, then shifting up by 1 unit.

37. $g(x) = f(2x + 1)$

SOLUTION

(a) Note that $g(x)$ is defined when $2x + 1$ is in the interval $[1, 5]$, which means that x must be in the interval $[0, 2]$ (find one endpoint of this interval by solving the equation $2x + 1 = 1$; find the other endpoint by solving the equation $2x + 1 = 5$). Thus the domain of g is the interval $[0, 2]$.

(b) The range of g equals the range of f. Thus the range of g is the interval $[1, 3]$.

(c) Define a function h by $h(x) = f(x + 1)$. The graph of h is obtained by shifting the graph of f left 1 unit. Note that $g(x) = h(2x)$. Thus the graph of g is obtained by horizontally stretching the graph of h by a factor of $\frac{1}{2}$.

Putting this together, we see that the graph of g, shown here, is obtained by shifting the graph of f left 1 unit, then horizontally stretching by a factor of $\frac{1}{2}$.

39. $g(x) = 2f(\frac{x}{2} + 1)$

SOLUTION

(a) Note that $g(x)$ is defined when $\frac{x}{2} + 1$ is in the interval $[1, 5]$, which means that x must be in the interval $[0, 8]$ (find one endpoint of this interval by solving the equation $\frac{x}{2} + 1 = 1$; find the other endpoint by solving the equation $\frac{x}{2} + 1 = 5$). Thus the domain of g is the interval $[0, 8]$.

(b) The range of g is obtained by multiplying each number in the range of f by 2. Thus the range of g is the interval $[2, 6]$.

(c) Define a function h by $h(x) = f(x + 1)$. The graph of h is obtained by shifting the graph of f left 1 unit. Note that $g(x) = 2h(\frac{x}{2})$. Thus the graph of g is obtained from the graph of h by stretching horizontally by a factor of 2 and stretching vertically by a factor of 2.

Putting this together, we see that the graph of g, shown below, is obtained by shifting the graph of f left 1 unit, then stretching horizontally by a factor of 2 and stretching vertically by a factor of 2.

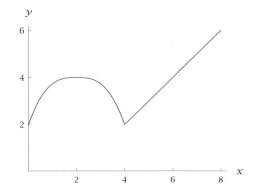

41. $g(x) = 2f(\frac{x}{2} + 1) - 3$

SOLUTION

(a) Note that $g(x)$ is defined when $\frac{x}{2} + 1$ is in the interval $[1, 5]$, which means that x must be in the interval $[0, 8]$ (find one endpoint of this interval by solving the equation $\frac{x}{2} + 1 = 1$; find the other endpoint by solving the equation $\frac{x}{2} + 1 = 5$). Thus the domain of g is the interval $[0, 8]$.

(b) The range of g is obtained by multiplying each number in the range of f by 2 and then subtracting 3. Thus the range of g is the interval $[-1, 3]$.

(c) The graph of g, shown below, is obtained by shifting the graph obtained in the solution to Exercise 39 down 3 units.

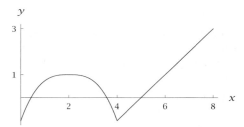

43. $g(x) = 2f(\frac{x}{2} + 3)$

SOLUTION

(a) Note that $g(x)$ is defined when $\frac{x}{2} + 3$ is in the interval $[1, 5]$, which means that x must be in the interval $[-4, 4]$ (find one endpoint of this interval by solving the equation $\frac{x}{2} + 3 = 1$; find the other endpoint by solving the equation $\frac{x}{2} + 3 = 5$). Thus the domain of g is the interval $[-4, 4]$.

(b) The range of g is obtained by multiplying each number in the range of f by 2. Thus the range of g is the interval $[2, 6]$.

(c) Define a function h by $h(x) = f(x + 3)$. The graph of h is obtained by shifting the graph of f left 3 units. Note that $g(x) = 2h(\frac{x}{2})$. Thus the graph of g is obtained from the graph of h by stretching horizontally by a factor of 2 and stretching vertically by a factor of 2.

Putting this together, we see that the graph of g, shown below, is obtained by shifting the graph of f left 3 units, then stretching horizontally by a factor of 2 and stretching vertically by a factor of 2.

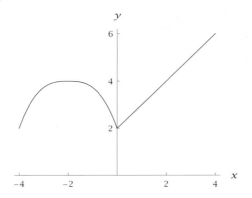

45. $g(x) = 6 - 2f(\frac{x}{2} + 3)$

SOLUTION

(a) Note that $g(x)$ is defined when $\frac{x}{2} + 3$ is in the interval $[1, 5]$, which means that x must be in the interval $[-4, 4]$ (find one endpoint of this interval by solving the equation $\frac{x}{2} + 3 = 1$; find the other endpoint by solving the equation $\frac{x}{2} + 3 = 5$). Thus the domain of g is the interval $[-4, 4]$.

(b) The range of g is obtained by multiplying each number in the range of f by -2 and then adding 6. Thus to find the range of g, consider the equation $z = 6 - 2y$. As y varies over the range of f (which is the interval $[1, 3]$), z will vary over the range of g. When $y = 1$, we see that $z = 4$. When $y = 3$, we see that $z = 0$. Thus the range of g is the interval $[0, 4]$.

(c) The graph of g, shown below, is obtained by reflecting through the x-axis the graph obtained in the solution to Exercise 43, then shifting up by 6 units.

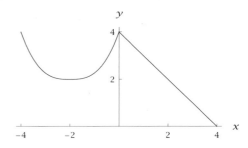

For Exercises 47–50, suppose f is a function whose domain is the interval $[-5, 5]$ and that

$$f(x) = \frac{x}{x + 3}$$

for every x in the interval $[0, 5]$.

47. Suppose f is an even function. Evaluate $f(-2)$.

SOLUTION Because 2 is in the interval $[0, 5]$, we can use the formula above to evaluate $f(2)$. We have

$$f(2) = \frac{2}{2+3} = \frac{2}{5}.$$

Because f is an even function, we have

$$f(-2) = f(2) = \frac{2}{5}.$$

49. Suppose f is an odd function. Evaluate $f(-2)$.

SOLUTION Because f is an odd function, we have

$$f(-2) = -f(2) = -\frac{2}{5}.$$

1.4   *Composition of Functions*

In this section we discuss the composition of functions. This concept, which allows us to write complicated functions in terms of simpler functions, has applications throughout wide areas of mathematics.

Definition of Composition

As an example of how a complicated function can be written in terms of simpler functions, consider the function h defined by

$$h(x) = \sqrt{x + 3}.$$

Thus, for example, $h(2) = \sqrt{5}$. The value of $h(x)$ is computed by carrying out two steps: first add 3 to x, and then take the square root of that sum. These two steps show that we can think of h as being constructed from two simpler functions by defining

$$f(x) = \sqrt{x} \quad \text{and} \quad g(x) = x + 3.$$

Then

$$h(x) = \sqrt{x + 3} = \sqrt{g(x)} = f(g(x)).$$

In the last term above, $f(g(x))$, we evaluate f at $g(x)$. This kind of construction occurs so often that it has been given a name and notation:

> ## *Composition*
>
> If f and g are functions, then the **composition** of f and g, denoted $f \circ g$, is the function defined by
>
> $$(f \circ g)(x) = f(g(x)).$$

In the definition above, we have been careless about specifying the domains of the functions involved. Unless specified otherwise, the domain of $f \circ g$ is the set of numbers x such that $f(g(x))$ makes sense. For $f(g(x))$ to make sense, x must be in the domain of g (so that $g(x)$ will be defined) and $g(x)$ must be in the domain of f (so that $f(g(x))$ will be defined). Thus unless specified otherwise, the domain of $f \circ g$ is the set of numbers x in the domain of g such that $g(x)$ is in the domain of f.

In evaluating $(f \circ g)(x)$, first we evaluate $g(x)$, then we evaluate $f(g(x))$.

EXAMPLE 1

Suppose

$$f(x) = \frac{1}{x-4} \quad \text{and} \quad g(x) = x^2.$$

(a) Evaluate $(f \circ g)(3)$.

(b) Find a formula for the composition $f \circ g$.

(c) What is the domain of $f \circ g$?

SOLUTION

(a) Using the definition of composition, we have

$$(f \circ g)(3) = f(g(3)) = f(3^2) = f(9) = \frac{1}{9-4} = \frac{1}{5}.$$

(b) Using the definition of composition, we have

$$(f \circ g)(x) = f(g(x)) = f(x^2) = \frac{1}{x^2 - 4}.$$

(c) The domains of f and g were not specified, which means we are implicitly assuming that each domain is the set of numbers where the formulas defining these functions make sense. Thus the domain of f equals the set of real numbers except 4, and the domain of g equals the set of real numbers.

From part (b), we see that $f(g(x))$ makes sense provided $x^2 \neq 4$. Thus the domain of $f \circ g$ equals the set of all real numbers except -2 and 2.

Order Matters in Composition

Composition is not commutative. In other words, it is not necessarily true that $f \circ g = g \circ f$, as can be shown by choosing almost any pair of functions. Here is a simple example:

EXAMPLE 2

Suppose

$$f(x) = 1 + x \quad \text{and} \quad g(x) = x^2.$$

(a) Evaluate $(f \circ g)(4)$.

(b) Evaluate $(g \circ f)(4)$.

(c) Find a formula for the composition $f \circ g$.

(d) Find a formula for the composition $g \circ f$.

SOLUTION

The solutions to (a) and (b) show that $(f \circ g)(4) \neq (g \circ f)(4)$ for these functions f and g.

(a) Using the definition of composition, we have

$$(f \circ g)(4) = f(g(4)) = f(4^2) = f(16) = 1 + 16 = 17.$$

(b) Using the definition of composition, we have

$$(g \circ f)(4) = g(f(4)) = g(1 + 4) = g(5) = 5^2 = 25.$$

(c) Using the definition of composition, we have

$$(f \circ g)(x) = f(g(x)) = f(x^2) = 1 + x^2.$$

(d) Using the definition of composition, we have

$$(g \circ f)(x) = g(f(x)) = g(1 + x) = (1 + x)^2 = 1 + 2x + x^2.$$

Never, ever make the mistake of thinking that $(1 + x)^2$ equals $1 + x^2$.

The example above is typical, meaning that for most functions f and g we have $f \circ g \neq g \circ f$. However, the identity function that we now define does commute (with respect to composition) with all other functions.

Identity function

The **identity function** is the function I defined by

$$I(x) = x$$

for every number x.

If f is any function and x is any number in the domain of f, then

$$(f \circ I)(x) = f(I(x)) = f(x) \quad \text{and} \quad (I \circ f)(x) = I(f(x)) = f(x).$$

Thus we have the following result, which explains why I is called the identity function.

The function I is the identity for composition

If f is any function, then $f \circ I = I \circ f = f$.

Decomposing Functions

Computing the composition of two functions is usually a straightforward application of the definition of composition. Less straightforward is the process of starting with a function and writing it as the composition of two simpler functions. The following example illustrates the process.

Suppose

$$T(x) = \left| \frac{x^2 - 3}{x^2 - 7} \right|.$$

Write T as the composition of two simpler functions. In other words, find two functions f and g, each of them simpler than T, such that $T = f \circ g$.

EXAMPLE 3

Typically a function can be decomposed into the composition of other functions in many different ways.

SOLUTION The problem here is that there is no rigorous definition of "simpler". Certainly it is easy to write T as the composition of two functions, because $T = T \circ I$, where I is the identity function, but that decomposition is unlikely to be useful.

Because evaluating an absolute value is the last operation done in computing $T(x)$, one reasonable possibility is to define

$$f(x) = |x| \quad \text{and} \quad g(x) = \frac{x^2 - 3}{x^2 - 7}.$$

You should verify that with these definitions of f and g, we indeed have $T = f \circ g$. Furthermore, both f and g seem to be simpler functions than T.

Because x appears in the formula defining T only in the expression x^2, another reasonable possibility is to define

$$f(x) = \left| \frac{x - 3}{x - 7} \right| \quad \text{and} \quad g(x) = x^2.$$

Again you should verify that with these definitions of f and g, we have $T = f \circ g$. Again, both f and g seem to be simpler functions than T.

Both potential solutions discussed above are correct. Choosing one or the other may depend on the context or on one's taste. Also, see Example 4, where T is decomposed into three simpler functions.

Composing More than Two Functions

Although composition is not commutative, it is associative.

Composition is associative

If f, g, and h are functions, then

$$(f \circ g) \circ h = f \circ (g \circ h).$$

Here we assume that the domains of these functions are such that all these compositions make sense.

To prove the associativity of composition, note that

$$((f \circ g) \circ h)(x) = (f \circ g)(h(x)) = f(g(h(x)))$$

and

$$(f \circ (g \circ h))(x) = f((g \circ h)(x)) = f(g(h(x))).$$

The equations above show that the functions $(f \circ g) \circ h$ and $f \circ (g \circ h)$ have the same value at every number x in their domain. Thus $(f \circ g) \circ h = f \circ (g \circ h)$.

Because composition is associative, we can dispense with the parentheses and simply write $f \circ g \circ h$, which is the function whose value at a number x is $f(g(h(x)))$.

Suppose

EXAMPLE 4

$$T(x) = \left| \frac{x^2 - 3}{x^2 - 7} \right|.$$

Write T as the composition of three simpler functions.

SOLUTION   We want to choose reasonably simple functions f, g, and h such that $T = f \circ g \circ h$. Probably the best choice here is to take

$$f(x) = |x|, \quad g(x) = \frac{x - 3}{x - 7}, \quad h(x) = x^2.$$

With these choices, we have

$$f(g(h(x))) = f(g(x^2)) = f\left(\frac{x^2 - 3}{x^2 - 7}\right) = \left| \frac{x^2 - 3}{x^2 - 7} \right|,$$

as desired.

Here is how to come up with the choices made above for f, g, and h: Because x appears in the formula defining T only in the expression x^2, we start by taking $h(x) = x^2$. To make $(g \circ h)(x)$ equal $\frac{x^2-3}{x^2-7}$, we then take $g(x) = \frac{x-3}{x-7}$. Finally, because evaluating an absolute value is the last operation done in computing $T(x)$, we take $f(x) = |x|$.

EXERCISES

For Exercises 1–10, evaluate the indicated expression assuming that f, g, and h are the functions completely defined by the tables below:

x	$f(x)$
1	4
2	1
3	2
4	2

x	$g(x)$
1	2
2	4
3	1
4	3

x	$h(x)$
1	3
2	3
3	4
4	1

1. $(f \circ g)(1)$

2. $(f \circ g)(3)$

3. $(g \circ f)(1)$

4. $(g \circ f)(3)$

5. $(f \circ f)(2)$

6. $(f \circ f)(4)$

7. $(g \circ g)(4)$

8. $(g \circ g)(2)$

9. $(f \circ g \circ h)(2)$

10. $(h \circ g \circ f)(2)$

For Exercises 11–24, evaluate the indicated expression assuming that

$$f(x) = \sqrt{x}, \quad g(x) = \frac{x + 1}{x + 2}, \quad h(x) = |x - 1|.$$

11. $(f \circ g)(4)$

12. $(f \circ g)(5)$

13. $(g \circ f)(4)$

14. $(g \circ f)(5)$

15. $(f \circ h)(-3)$

16. $(f \circ h)(-15)$

17. $(f \circ g \circ h)(0)$

18. $(h \circ g \circ f)(0)$

19. $(f \circ g)(0.23)$

20. $(f \circ g)(3.85)$

21. $(g \circ f)(0.23)$

22. $(g \circ f)(3.85)$

23. $(h \circ f)(0.3)$

24. $(h \circ f)(0.7)$

In Exercises 25–30, for the given functions f and g find formulas for (a) $f \circ g$ and (b) $g \circ f$. Simplify your results as much as possible.

25. $f(x) = x^2 + 1, \quad g(x) = \dfrac{1}{x}$

26. $f(x) = (x + 1)^2, \quad g(x) = \dfrac{3}{x}$

27. $f(x) = \dfrac{x - 1}{x + 1}, \quad g(x) = x^2 + 2$

28. $f(x) = \dfrac{x + 2}{x - 3}, \quad g(x) = \dfrac{1}{x + 1}$

29. $f(x) = \dfrac{x - 1}{x^2 + 1}, \quad g(x) = \dfrac{x + 3}{x + 4}$

30. $f(x) = \dfrac{x - 2}{x + 3}, \quad g(x) = \dfrac{1}{(x + 2)^2}$

31. Find a number b such that $f \circ g = g \circ f$, where $f(x) = 2x + b$ and $g(x) = 3x + 4$.

32. Find a number c such that $f \circ g = g \circ f$, where $f(x) = 5x - 2$ and $g(x) = cx - 3$.

33. Suppose
$$h(x) = \left(\frac{x^2 + 1}{x - 1} - 1\right)^3.$$

    (a) If $f(x) = x^3$, then find a function g such that $h = f \circ g$.

    (b) If $f(x) = (x - 1)^3$, then find a function g such that $h = f \circ g$.

34. Suppose
$$h(x) = \sqrt{\frac{1}{x^2 + 1} + 2}.$$

    (a) If $f(x) = \sqrt{x}$, then find a function g such that $h = f \circ g$.

    (b) If $f(x) = \sqrt{x + 2}$, then find a function g such that $h = f \circ g$.

35. Suppose
$$h(x) = 2 + \sqrt{\frac{1}{x^2 + 1}}.$$

    (a) If $g(x) = \frac{1}{x^2 + 1}$, then find a function f such that $h = f \circ g$.

    (b) If $g(x) = x^2$, then find a function f such that $h = f \circ g$.

36. Suppose
$$h(x) = \left(\frac{x^2 + 1}{x - 1} - 1\right)^3.$$

    (a) If $g(x) = \frac{x^2 + 1}{x - 1} - 1$, then find a function f such that $h = f \circ g$.

    (b) If $g(x) = \frac{x^2 + 1}{x - 1}$, then find a function f such that $h = f \circ g$.

In Exercises 37–40, find functions f and g, each simpler than the given function h, such that $h = f \circ g$.

37. $h(x) = (x^2 - 1)^2$

38. $h(x) = \sqrt{x^2 - 1}$

39. $h(x) = \dfrac{3}{2 + x^2}$

40. $h(x) = \dfrac{2}{3 + \sqrt{1 + x}}$

In Exercises 41–42, find functions f, g, and h, each simpler than the given function T, such that $T = f \circ g \circ h$.

41. $T(x) = \dfrac{4}{5 + x^2}$

42. $T(x) = \sqrt{4 + x^2}$

PROBLEMS

43. Suppose $f(x) = ax + b$ and $g(x) = cx + d$, where a, b, c, and d are constants. Show that $f \circ g = g \circ f$ if and only if $d(a - 1) = b(c - 1)$.

44. Suppose f and g are functions. Explain why the composition $f \circ g$ can be defined to have the same domain as g precisely when the range of g is contained in the domain of f.

A constant function is a function whose value is the same at every number in its domain. For example, the function f defined by $f(x) = 4$ for every number x is a constant function.

45. Show that if f is a constant function and g is any function, then $f \circ g$ and $g \circ f$ are both constant functions.

46. Give an example of three functions f, g, and h, none of which is a constant function, such that $f \circ g = f \circ h$ but g is not equal to h.

47. Give an example of three functions f, g, and h, none of which is a constant function, such that $f \circ h = g \circ h$ but f is not equal to g.

48. Suppose g is an even function and f is any function such that the composition $f \circ g$ is defined. Show that $f \circ g$ is an even function.

49. Suppose f is an even function and g is an odd function such that the composition $f \circ g$ is defined. Show that $f \circ g$ is an even function.

50. Suppose f and g are both odd functions such that their composition $f \circ g$ is defined. Is the composition $f \circ g$ even, odd, or neither? Explain.

WORKED-OUT SOLUTIONS *to Odd-numbered Exercises*

For Exercises 1-10, evaluate the indicated expression assuming that *f*, *g*, and *h* are the functions completely defined by the tables below:

x	$f(x)$
1	4
2	1
3	2
4	2

x	$g(x)$
1	2
2	4
3	1
4	3

x	$h(x)$
1	3
2	3
3	4
4	1

1. $(f \circ g)(1)$

   SOLUTION $(f \circ g)(1) = f(g(1)) = f(2) = 1$

3. $(g \circ f)(1)$

   SOLUTION $(g \circ f)(1) = g(f(1)) = g(4) = 3$

5. $(f \circ f)(2)$

   SOLUTION $(f \circ f)(2) = f(f(2)) = f(1) = 4$

7. $(g \circ g)(4)$

   SOLUTION $(g \circ g)(4) = g(g(4)) = g(3) = 1$

9. $(f \circ g \circ h)(2)$

   SOLUTION

   $$(f \circ g \circ h)(2) = f(g(h(2)))$$
   $$= f(g(3)) = f(1) = 4$$

For Exercises 11-24, evaluate the indicated expression assuming that

$$f(x) = \sqrt{x}, \quad g(x) = \frac{x+1}{x+2}, \quad h(x) = |x-1|.$$

11. $(f \circ g)(4)$

   SOLUTION

   $$(f \circ g)(4) = f(g(4)) = f\left(\frac{4+1}{4+2}\right) = f\left(\frac{5}{6}\right) = \sqrt{\frac{5}{6}}$$

13. $(g \circ f)(4)$

   SOLUTION

   $$(g \circ f)(4) = g(f(4))$$
   $$= g(\sqrt{4}) = g(2) = \frac{2+1}{2+2} = \frac{3}{4}$$

15. $(f \circ h)(-3)$

   SOLUTION

   $$(f \circ h)(-3) = f(h(-3)) = f(|-3-1|)$$
   $$= f(|-4|) = f(4) = \sqrt{4} = 2$$

17. $(f \circ g \circ h)(0)$

   SOLUTION

   $$(f \circ g \circ h)(0) = f(g(h(0)))$$
   $$= f(g(1)) = f\left(\frac{2}{3}\right) = \sqrt{\frac{2}{3}}$$

19. $(f \circ g)(0.23)$

   SOLUTION

   $$(f \circ g)(0.23) = f(g(0.23)) = f\left(\frac{0.23+1}{0.23+2}\right)$$
   $$\approx f(0.55157) = \sqrt{0.55157} \approx 0.74268$$

21. $(g \circ f)(0.23)$

   SOLUTION

   $$(g \circ f)(0.23) = g(f(0.23)) = g(\sqrt{0.23})$$
   $$\approx g(0.47958) = \frac{0.47958+1}{0.47958+2}$$
   $$\approx 0.59671$$

23. $(h \circ f)(0.3)$

   SOLUTION

   $$(h \circ f)(0.3) = h(f(0.3)) = h(\sqrt{0.3})$$
   $$\approx h(0.547723) = |0.547723 - 1|$$
   $$= |-0.452277| = 0.452277$$

In Exercises 25-30, for the given functions *f* and *g* find formulas for (a) *f* ∘ *g* and (b) *g* ∘ *f*. Simplify your results as much as possible.

25. $f(x) = x^2 + 1$, $g(x) = \dfrac{1}{x}$

SOLUTION

(a)
$$(f \circ g)(x) = f(g(x))$$
$$= f\left(\frac{1}{x}\right)$$
$$= \left(\frac{1}{x}\right)^2 + 1$$
$$= \frac{1}{x^2} + 1$$

(b)
$$(g \circ f)(x) = g(f(x))$$
$$= g(x^2 + 1)$$
$$= \frac{1}{x^2 + 1}$$

27. $f(x) = \dfrac{x - 1}{x + 1}$, $g(x) = x^2 + 2$

SOLUTION

(a)
$$(f \circ g)(x) = f(g(x))$$
$$= f(x^2 + 2)$$
$$= \frac{(x^2 + 2) - 1}{(x^2 + 2) + 1}$$
$$= \frac{x^2 + 1}{x^2 + 3}$$

(b)
$$(g \circ f)(x) = g(f(x))$$
$$= g\left(\frac{x - 1}{x + 1}\right)$$
$$= \left(\frac{x - 1}{x + 1}\right)^2 + 2$$

29. $f(x) = \dfrac{x - 1}{x^2 + 1}$, $g(x) = \dfrac{x + 3}{x + 4}$

SOLUTION

(a) We have

$$(f \circ g)(x) = f(g(x))$$
$$= f\left(\frac{x + 3}{x + 4}\right)$$
$$= \frac{\frac{x+3}{x+4} - 1}{\left(\frac{x+3}{x+4}\right)^2 + 1}$$
$$= \frac{(x + 3)(x + 4) - (x + 4)^2}{(x + 3)^2 + (x + 4)^2}$$
$$= \frac{x^2 + 7x + 12 - x^2 - 8x - 16}{x^2 + 6x + 9 + x^2 + 8x + 16}$$
$$= \frac{-x - 4}{2x^2 + 14x + 25}.$$

In going from the third line above to the fourth line, both numerator and denominator were multiplied by $(x + 4)^2$.

(b) We have

$$(g \circ f)(x) = g(f(x))$$
$$= g\left(\frac{x - 1}{x^2 + 1}\right)$$
$$= \frac{\frac{x-1}{x^2+1} + 3}{\frac{x-1}{x^2+1} + 4}$$
$$= \frac{x - 1 + 3(x^2 + 1)}{x - 1 + 4(x^2 + 1)}$$
$$= \frac{3x^2 + x + 2}{4x^2 + x + 3}.$$

In going from the third line above to the fourth line, both numerator and denominator were multiplied by $x^2 + 1$.

31. Find a number b such that $f \circ g = g \circ f$, where $f(x) = 2x + b$ and $g(x) = 3x + 4$.

SOLUTION   We will compute $(f \circ g)(x)$ and $(g \circ f)(x)$, then set those two expressions equal to each other and solve for b. We begin with $(f \circ g)(x)$:

$$(f \circ g)(x) = f(g(x)) = f(3x + 4)$$
$$= 2(3x + 4) + b = 6x + 8 + b.$$

Next we compute $(g \circ f)(x)$:

$$(g \circ f)(x) = g(f(x)) = g(2x + b)$$
$$= 3(2x + b) + 4 = 6x + 3b + 4.$$

Looking at the expressions for $(f \circ g)(x)$ and $(g \circ f)(x)$, we see that they will equal each other if

$$8 + b = 3b + 4.$$

Solving this equation for b, we get $b = 2$.

33. Suppose

$$h(x) = \left(\frac{x^2 + 1}{x - 1} - 1\right)^3.$$

(a) If $f(x) = x^3$, then find a function g such that $h = f \circ g$.

(b) If $f(x) = (x - 1)^3$, then find a function g such that $h = f \circ g$.

SOLUTION

(a) We want the following equation to hold: $h(x) = f(g(x))$. Replacing h and f with the formulas for them, we have

$$\left(\frac{x^2 + 1}{x - 1} - 1\right)^3 = (g(x))^3.$$

Looking at the equation above, we see that we want to choose

$$g(x) = \frac{x^2 + 1}{x - 1} - 1.$$

(b) We want the following equation to hold: $h(x) = f(g(x))$. Replacing h and f with the formulas for them, we have

$$\left(\frac{x^2 + 1}{x - 1} - 1\right)^3 = (g(x) - 1)^3.$$

Looking at the equation above, we see that we want to choose

$$g(x) = \frac{x^2 + 1}{x - 1}.$$

35. Suppose

$$h(x) = 2 + \sqrt{\frac{1}{x^2 + 1}}.$$

(a) If $g(x) = \frac{1}{x^2+1}$, then find a function f such that $h = f \circ g$.

(b) If $g(x) = x^2$, then find a function f such that $h = f \circ g$.

SOLUTION

(a) We want the following equation to hold: $h(x) = f(g(x))$. Replacing h and g with the formulas for them, we have

$$2 + \sqrt{\frac{1}{x^2 + 1}} = f\left(\frac{1}{x^2 + 1}\right).$$

Looking at the equation above, we see that we want to choose $f(x) = 2 + \sqrt{x}$.

(b) We want the following equation to hold: $h(x) = f(g(x))$. Replacing h and g with the formulas for them, we have

$$2 + \sqrt{\frac{1}{x^2 + 1}} = f(x^2).$$

Looking at the equation above, we see that we want to choose

$$f(x) = 2 + \sqrt{\frac{1}{x + 1}}.$$

In Exercises 37–40, find functions f and g, each simpler than the given function h, such that $h = f \circ g$.

37. $h(x) = (x^2 - 1)^2$

SOLUTION   The last operation performed in the computation of $h(x)$ is squaring. Thus the most natural way to write h as a composition of two functions f and g is to choose $f(x) = x^2$, which then suggests that we choose $g(x) = x^2 - 1$.

39. $h(x) = \dfrac{3}{2 + x^2}$

SOLUTION   The last operation performed in the computation of $h(x)$ is dividing 3 by a certain expression. Thus the most natural way to write h as a composition of two functions f and g is to choose $f(x) = \frac{3}{x}$, which then requires that we choose $g(x) = 2 + x^2$.

In Exercises 41–42, find functions f, g, and h, each simpler than the given function T, such that $T = f \circ g \circ h$.

41. $T(x) = \dfrac{4}{5 + x^2}$

SOLUTION   A good solution is to take

$$f(x) = \frac{4}{x}, \quad g(x) = 5 + x, \quad h(x) = x^2.$$

1.5 Inverse Functions

SECTION OBJECTIVES

By the end of this section you should

- understand the concept of an inverse function;
- understand which functions have inverses;
- be able to find a formula for an inverse function (when possible).

The Inverse Problem

The concept of an inverse function will play a key role throughout much of this book and in other mathematics courses that you might take. To motivate this concept, we begin with some simple examples.

Suppose f is the function defined by $f(x) = 3x$. Given a value of x, we can find the value of $f(x)$ by using the formula defining f. For example, taking $x = 5$, we see that $f(5)$ equals 15.

In the inverse problem, we are given the value of $f(x)$ and asked to find the value of x. The following example illustrates the idea of the inverse problem:

EXAMPLE 1   Suppose f is the function defined by

$$f(x) = 3x.$$

(a) Find x such that $f(x) = 6$.

(b) Find x such that $f(x) = 300$.

(c) For each number y, find a number x such that $f(x) = y$.

SOLUTION

(a) Solving the equation $3x = 6$ for x, we get $x = 2$.

(b) Solving the equation $3x = 300$ for x, we get $x = 100$.

(c) Solving the equation $3x = y$ for x, we get $x = \frac{y}{3}$.

Inverse functions will be defined more precisely after we work through some examples.

For each number y, part (c) of the example above asks for the number x such that $f(x) = y$. That number x is called $f^{-1}(y)$ (pronounced "f inverse of y"). The example above shows that if $f(x) = 3x$, then $f^{-1}(6) = 2$ and $f^{-1}(300) = 100$ and, more generally, $f^{-1}(y) = \frac{y}{3}$ for every number y.

To see how inverse functions can arise in real-world problems, suppose you know that a temperature of x degrees Celsius corresponds to $\frac{9}{5}x + 32$ degrees Fahrenheit (we will derive this formula in Example 4 in Section 2.1). In other words, you know that the function f that converts the Celsius temperature scale to the Fahrenheit temperature scale is given by the formula

$$f(x) = \tfrac{9}{5}x + 32.$$

For example, because $f(20) = 68$, this formula shows that 20 degrees Celsius corresponds to 68 degrees Fahrenheit.

If you are given a temperature on the Fahrenheit scale and asked to convent it to Celsius, then you are facing the problem of finding the inverse of the function above, as shown in the following example.

EXAMPLE 2

The Fahrenheit temperature scale was invented in the 18th century by the German physicist and engineer Daniel Gabriel Fahrenheit.

(a)   Convert 95 degrees Fahrenheit to the Celsius scale.

(b)   For each temperature y on the Fahrenheit scale, what is the corresponding temperature on the Celsius scale?

SOLUTION   Let
$$f(x) = \tfrac{9}{5}x + 32.$$
Thus x degrees Celsius corresponds to $f(x)$ degrees Fahrenheit.

(a)   We need to find x such that $f(x) = 95$. Solving the equation $\tfrac{9}{5}x + 32 = 95$ for x, we get $x = 35$. Thus 35 degrees Celsius corresponds to 95 degrees Fahrenheit.

(b)   For each number y, we need to find x such that $f(x) = y$. Solving the equation $\tfrac{9}{5}x + 32 = y$ for x, we get $x = \tfrac{5}{9}(y - 32)$. Thus $\tfrac{5}{9}(y - 32)$ degrees Celsius corresponds to y degrees Fahrenheit.

In the example above we have $f(x) = \tfrac{9}{5}x + 32$. For each number y, part (b) of the example above asks for the number x such that $f(x) = y$. We call that number $f^{-1}(y)$. Part (a) of the example above shows that $f^{-1}(95) = 35$; part (b) shows more generally that

$$f^{-1}(y) = \tfrac{5}{9}(y - 32).$$

In this example, the function f converts from Celsius to Fahrenheit, and the function f^{-1} goes in the other direction, converting from Fahrenheit to Celsius.

One-to-one Functions

To see the difficulties that can arise with inverse problems, consider the function f, with domain the set of real numbers, defined by the formula

$$f(x) = x^2.$$

Suppose we are told that x is a number such that $f(x) = 16$, and we are asked to find the value of x. Of course $f(4) = 16$, but also $f(-4) = 16$. Thus with the information given we have no way to determine a unique value of x such that $f(x) = 16$. Hence in this case an inverse function does not exist.

The difficulty with the lack of a unique solution to an inverse problem can often be fixed by changing the domain. For example, consider the function g, with domain the set of positive numbers, defined by the formula

$$g(x) = x^2.$$

When studying trigonometric functions in Chapter 5, we will use this technique of restricting the domain to obtain an inverse function.

Note that g is defined by the same formula as f in the previous paragraph, but these two functions are not the same because they have different domains. Now if we are told that x is a number in the domain of g such that $g(x) = 16$ and we are asked to find x, we can assert that $x = 4$. More generally, given any positive number y, we can ask for the number x in the domain of g such that $g(x) = y$. This number x, which depends on y, is denoted $g^{-1}(y)$, and is given by the formula

$$g^{-1}(y) = \sqrt{y}.$$

We saw earlier that the function f defined by $f(x) = x^2$ (and with domain equal to the set of real numbers) does not have an inverse because, in particular, the equation $f(x) = 16$ has more than one solution. A function is called **one-to-one** if this situation does not arise.

As we will soon see, functions that are one-to-one are precisely the functions that have inverses.

One-to-one

A function f is called **one-to-one** if for each number y in the range of f there is exactly one number x in the domain of f such that $f(x) = y$.

For example, the function f, with domain the set of real numbers, defined by $f(x) = x^2$ is not one-to-one because there are two numbers x in the domain of f such that $f(x) = 16$ (we could have used any positive number instead of 16 to show that f is not one-to-one). In contrast, the function g, with domain the set of positive numbers, defined by $g(x) = x^2$ is one-to-one.

The Definition of an Inverse Function

We are now ready to give the formal definition of an inverse function.

Definition of f^{-1}

Suppose f is a one-to-one function.

- If y is in the range of f, then $f^{-1}(y)$ is defined to be the number x such that $f(x) = y$.

- The function f^{-1} is called the **inverse function** of f.

EXAMPLE 3

Suppose $f(x) = 2x + 3$.

(a) Evaluate $f^{-1}(11)$.

(b) Find a formula for $f^{-1}(y)$.

SOLUTION

(a) To evaluate $f^{-1}(11)$, we must find the number x such that $f(x) = 11$. In other words, we must solve the equation $2x + 3 = 11$. The solution to this equation is $x = 4$. Thus $f^{-1}(11) = 4$.

(b) Fix a number y. To find a formula for $f^{-1}(y)$, we must find the number x such that $f(x) = y$. In other words, we must solve the equation

$$2x + 3 = y$$

for x. The solution to this equation is $x = \frac{y-3}{2}$. Thus $f^{-1}(y) = \frac{y-3}{2}$.

Let's examine the definition of f^{-1} more closely. Suppose f is a one-to-one function and y is in the range of f. Because y is in the range of f, there exists a number x in the domain of f such that $f(x) = y$. Because f is a one-to-one function, there is only one such x. This value of x is declared to be $f^{-1}(y)$. This relationship can be summarized as follows:

The inverse function is not defined for a function that is not one-to-one.

> **Relationship between f and f^{-1}**
>
> Suppose f is a one-to-one function and x and y are numbers. Then
>
> $$f(x) = y \quad \text{if and only if} \quad f^{-1}(y) = x.$$

Thus, for example, if f is a one-to-one function, then $f(2) = 3$ if and only if $f^{-1}(3) = 2$.

If f is a one-to-one function, then for each y in the range of f we have a uniquely defined number $f^{-1}(y)$. Thus f^{-1} is itself indeed a function.

Think of f^{-1} as undoing whatever f does. This list gives some examples of a function f and its inverse f^{-1}.

f	f^{-1}
$f(x) = x + 2$	$f^{-1}(y) = y - 2$
$f(x) = 3x$	$f^{-1}(y) = \frac{y}{3}$
$f(x) = x^2$	$f^{-1}(y) = \sqrt{y}$
$f(x) = \sqrt{x}$	$f^{-1}(y) = y^2$

The first entry in the list above shows that if f is the function that adds 2 to a number, then f^{-1} is the function that subtracts 2 from a number. The second entry in the list above shows that if f is the function that multiplies a number by 3, then f^{-1} is the function that divides a number by 3.

Similarly, the third entry in the list above shows that if f is the function that squares a number, then f^{-1} is the function that takes the square root of a number (here the domain of f is assumed to be the nonnegative numbers, so that we have a one-to-one function).

Finally, the fourth entry in the list above shows that if f is the function that takes the square root of a number, then f^{-1} is the function that squares a number (here the domain of f is assumed to be the nonnegative numbers, because the square root of a negative number is not defined as a real number).

The procedure for finding a formula for an inverse function can be described as follows:

Finding a formula for an inverse function

Suppose f is a one-to-one function. To find a formula for $f^{-1}(y)$, solve the equation $f(x) = y$ for x in terms of y.

The Celsius temperature scale is named in honor of the 18th century Swedish astronomer Anders Celsius, who originally proposed a temperature scale with 0 as the boiling point of water and 100 as the freezing point. Later this was reversed, giving us the familiar scale in which higher numbers correspond to hotter temperatures.

For example, we already used this procedure with the formula for converting from the Celsius temperature scale to the Fahrenheit scale. In that case, we had $f(x) = \frac{9}{5}x + 32$. We solved the equation

$$\tfrac{9}{5}x + 32 = y$$

for x, getting

$$x = \tfrac{5}{9}(y - 32),$$

which then gave the formula $f^{-1}(y) = \frac{5}{9}(y - 32)$.

The Domain and Range of an Inverse Function

The domain and range of a one-to-one function are nicely related to the domain and range of its inverse. To understand this relationship, consider a one-to-one function f. Note that $f^{-1}(y)$ is defined precisely when y is in the range of f. Thus the domain of f^{-1} equals the range of f.

Similarly, because f^{-1} reverses the action of f, a moment's thought shows that the range of f^{-1} equals the domain of f. We can summarize the relationship between the domains and ranges of functions and their inverses as follows:

Domain and range of an inverse function

If f is a one-to-one function, then

- the domain of f^{-1} equals the range of f;

- the range of f^{-1} equals the domain of f.

EXAMPLE 4

Suppose the domain of f is the interval $[0, 2]$, with f defined on this domain by the equation $f(x) = x^2$.

(a) What is the range of f?

(b) Find a formula for the inverse function f^{-1}.

(c) What is the domain of the inverse function f^{-1}?

(d) What is the range of the inverse function f^{-1}?

SOLUTION

(a) The range of f is the interval $[0, 4]$ because that interval is equal to the set of squares of numbers in the interval $[0, 2]$.

(b) Suppose y is in the range of f, which is the interval $[0, 4]$. To find a formula for $f^{-1}(y)$, we have to solve for x the equation $f(x) = y$. In other words, we have to solve the equation $x^2 = y$ for x. The solution x must be in the domain of f, which is $[0, 2]$, and in particular x must be nonnegative. Thus we have $x = \sqrt{y}$. In other words, $f^{-1}(y) = \sqrt{y}$.

This example illustrates how the inverse function interchanges the domain and range of the original function.

(c) The domain of the inverse function f^{-1} is the interval $[0, 4]$, which is the range of f.

(d) The range of the inverse function f^{-1} is the interval $[0, 2]$, which is the domain of f.

The Composition of a Function and Its Inverse

The following example will help motivate our next result.

Suppose f is the function whose domain is the set of real numbers, with f defined by $f(x) = x + 2$.

EXAMPLE 5

(a) Find a formula for $f \circ f^{-1}$.

(b) Find a formula for $f^{-1} \circ f$.

SOLUTION   As we have seen, $f^{-1}(y) = y - 2$. Thus we have the following:

(a) $(f \circ f^{-1})(y) = f(f^{-1}(y)) = f(y - 2) = (y - 2) + 2 = y$

(b) $(f^{-1} \circ f)(x) = f^{-1}(f(x)) = f^{-1}(x + 2) = (x + 2) - 2 = x$

Similar equations hold for the composition of any one-to-one function and its inverse:

The composition of a function and its inverse

Suppose f is a one-to-one function. Then

- $f(f^{-1}(y)) = y$ for every y in the range of f;
- $f^{-1}(f(x)) = x$ for every x in the domain of f.

To see why these results hold, first suppose y is a number in the range of f. Let $x = f^{-1}(y)$. Then $f(x) = y$. Thus

$$f(f^{-1}(y)) = f(x) = y,$$

as claimed above.

To verify the second conclusion in the box above, suppose x is a number in the domain of f. Let $y = f(x)$ Then $f^{-1}(y) = x$. Thus

$$f^{-1}(f(x)) = f^{-1}(y) = x,$$

as claimed.

The function I is the identity for the operation of composition, in the sense that $f \circ I = I \circ f = f$ for every function f.

Recall that I is the identity function defined by $I(x) = x$ (where we have left the domain vague), or we could equally well define I by the equation $I(y) = y$. The results in the box above could be expressed by the equations

$$f \circ f^{-1} = I \quad \text{and} \quad f^{-1} \circ f = I.$$

Here the I in the first equation above has domain equal to the range of f (which equals the domain of f^{-1}), and the I in the second equation above has the same domain as f. The equations above explain why the terminology "inverse" is used for the inverse function: f^{-1} is the inverse of f under composition in the sense that the composition of f and f^{-1} in either order gives the identity function.

Suppose you need to compute the inverse of a function f. As discussed earlier, to find a formula for f^{-1} you need to solve the equation $f(x) = y$ for x in terms of y. Once you have obtained a formula for f^{-1}, a good way to check that you have the correct formula is to verify one or both of the equations in the box above.

EXAMPLE 6

Suppose $f(x) = \frac{9}{5}x + 32$, which is the formula for converting the Celsius temperature scale to the Fahrenheit scale. We computed earlier that the inverse to this function is given by the formula $f^{-1}(y) = \frac{5}{9}(y - 32)$. Check that this is correct by verifying that $f(f^{-1}(y)) = y$ for every real number y.

SOLUTION   To check that we have the right formula for f^{-1}, we compute as follows:

$$f(f^{-1}(y)) = f\left(\tfrac{5}{9}(y - 32)\right)$$
$$= \tfrac{9}{5}\left(\tfrac{5}{9}(y - 32)\right) + 32$$
$$= (y - 32) + 32$$
$$= y.$$

Thus $f(f^{-1}(y)) = y$, which means that our formula for f^{-1} is correct. If our computation of $f(f^{-1}(y))$ had simplified to anything other than y, we would know that we had made a mistake in computing f^{-1}.

To be doubly safe that we are not making an algebraic manipulation error, we could also verify in the example above that $f^{-1}(f(x)) = x$ for every real number x. However, one check is usually good enough.

Comments about Notation

The notation $y = f(x)$ leads naturally to the notation $f^{-1}(y)$. Recall, however, that in defining a function the variable is simply a placeholder. Thus we could use other letters, including x, as the variable for the inverse function. For example, consider the function f, with domain equal to the set of positive numbers, defined by the equation

$$f(x) = x^2.$$

As we have seen, the inverse function is given by the formula

$$f^{-1}(y) = \sqrt{y}.$$

However, the inverse function could also be characterized by the formula

$$f^{-1}(x) = \sqrt{x}.$$

Other letters could also be used as the placeholder. For example, we might also characterize the inverse function by the formula

$$f^{-1}(t) = \sqrt{t}.$$

The notation f^{-1} for the inverse of a function (which means the inverse under composition) should not be confused with the multiplicative inverse $\frac{1}{f}$. In other words, $f^{-1} \neq \frac{1}{f}$. However, if the exponent -1 is placed anywhere other than immediately after a function symbol, then it should probably be interpreted as a multiplicative inverse.

Do not confuse $f^{-1}(y)$ with $f(y)^{-1}$.

Suppose $f(x) = x^2 - 1$, with the domain of f being the set of positive numbers.

(a) Evaluate $f^{-1}(8)$.

(b) Evaluate $f(8)^{-1}$.

EXAMPLE 7

SOLUTION

(a) To evaluate $f^{-1}(8)$, we must find a positive number x such that $f(x) = 8$. In other words, we must solve the equation $x^2 - 1 = 8$. The solution to this equation is $x = 3$. Thus $f^{-1}(8) = 3$.

(b)

$$f(8)^{-1} = \frac{1}{f(8)} = \frac{1}{8^2 - 1} = \frac{1}{63}$$

EXERCISES

For Exercises 1–8, check your answer by evaluating the appropriate function at your answer.

1. Suppose $f(x) = 4x + 6$. Evaluate $f^{-1}(5)$.

2. Suppose $f(x) = 7x - 5$. Evaluate $f^{-1}(-3)$.

3. Suppose $g(x) = \dfrac{x + 2}{x + 1}$. Evaluate $g^{-1}(3)$.

4. Suppose $g(x) = \dfrac{x - 3}{x - 4}$. Evaluate $g^{-1}(2)$.

5. Suppose $f(x) = 3x + 2$. Find a formula for f^{-1}.

6. Suppose $f(x) = 8x - 9$. Find a formula for f^{-1}.

7. Suppose $h(t) = \dfrac{1 + t}{2 - t}$. Find a formula for h^{-1}.

8. Suppose $h(t) = \dfrac{2 - 3t}{4 + 5t}$. Find a formula for h^{-1}.

9. Suppose $f(x) = 2 + \dfrac{x - 5}{x + 6}$.
   (a) Evaluate $f^{-1}(4)$.
   (b) Evaluate $f(4)^{-1}$.

10. Suppose $h(x) = 3 - \dfrac{x + 4}{x - 7}$.
   (a) Evaluate $h^{-1}(9)$.
   (b) Evaluate $h(9)^{-1}$.

11. Suppose $h(x) = 5x^2 + 7$, where the domain of h is the set of positive numbers. Find a formula for h^{-1}.

12. Suppose $h(x) = 3x^2 - 4$, where the domain of h is the set of positive numbers. Find a formula for h^{-1}.

For each of the functions f given in Exercises 13–22:
   (a) *Find the domain of f.*
   (b) *Find the range of f.*
   (c) *Find a formula for f^{-1}.*
   (d) *Find the domain of f^{-1}.*
   (e) *Find the range of f^{-1}.*

You can check your solutions to part (c) by verifying that $f^{-1} \circ f = I$ and $f \circ f^{-1} = I$ (recall that I is the function defined by $I(x) = x$).

13. $f(x) = 3x + 5$

14. $f(x) = 2x - 7$

15. $f(x) = \dfrac{1}{3x + 2}$

16. $f(x) = \dfrac{4}{5x - 3}$

17. $f(x) = \dfrac{2x}{x + 3}$

18. $f(x) = \dfrac{3x - 2}{4x + 5}$

19. $f(x) = \begin{cases} 3x & \text{if } x < 0 \\ 4x & \text{if } x \geq 0 \end{cases}$

20. $f(x) = \begin{cases} 2x & \text{if } x < 0 \\ x^2 & \text{if } x \geq 0 \end{cases}$

21. $f(x) = x^2 + 8$, where the domain of f equals $(0, \infty)$.

22. $f(x) = 2x^2 + 5$, where the domain of f equals $(0, \infty)$.

23. 🖩 Suppose $f(x) = x^5 + 2x^3$. Which of the numbers listed below equals $f^{-1}(8.10693)$?

$$1.1, \quad 1.2, \quad 1.3, \quad 1.4$$

   [*For this particular function, it is not possible to find a formula for $f^{-1}(y)$.*]

24. 🖩 Suppose $f(x) = 3x^5 + 4x^3$. Which of the numbers listed below equals $f^{-1}(0.28672)$?

$$0.2, \quad 0.3, \quad 0.4, \quad 0.5$$

   [*For this particular function, it is not possible to find a formula for $f^{-1}(y)$.*]

In 2006 the U. S. federal income tax for a single person with taxable income t dollars (this is the net income after allowable deductions) was $f(t)$ dollars, where f is the function defined as follows:

$$f(t) = \begin{cases} 0.1t & \text{if } 0 \leq t \leq 7550 \\ 0.15t - 377.5 & \text{if } 7550 < t \leq 30650 \\ 0.25t - 3442.5 & \text{if } 30650 < t \leq 74200 \\ 0.28t - 5668.5 & \text{if } 74200 < t \leq 154800 \\ 0.33t - 13408.5 & \text{if } 154800 < t \leq 336550 \\ 0.35t - 20139.5 & \text{if } 336550 < t. \end{cases}$$

Use the information above for Exercises 25–26.

25. 🖩 What is the taxable income of a single person who paid $10,000 in federal taxes?

26. 🖩 What is the taxable income of a single person who paid $20,000 in federal taxes?

27. Suppose $g(x) = x^7 + x^3$. Evaluate

$$\left(g^{-1}(4)\right)^7 + \left(g^{-1}(4)\right)^3 + 1.$$

28. Suppose $g(x) = 8x^9 + 7x^3$. Evaluate

$$8\left(g^{-1}(5)\right)^9 + 7\left(g^{-1}(5)\right)^3 - 3.$$

PROBLEMS

29. Suppose f is the function whose domain is the set of real numbers, with f defined on this domain by the formula

$$f(x) = |x + 6|.$$

Explain why f is not a one-to-one function.

30. Suppose g is the function whose domain is the interval $[-2, 2]$, with g defined on this domain by the formula

$$g(x) = (5x^2 + 3)^{7777}.$$

Explain why g is not a one-to-one function.

31. Consider the function h whose domain is the interval $[-4, 4]$, with h defined on this domain by the formula

$$h(x) = (2 + x)^2.$$

Does h have an inverse? If so, find it, along with its domain and range. If not, explain why not.

32. Consider the function h whose domain is the interval $[-3, 3]$, with h defined on this domain by the formula

$$h(x) = (3 + x)^2.$$

Does h have an inverse? If so, find it, along with its domain and range. If not, explain why not.

33. Suppose f is a one-to-one function. Explain why the inverse of the inverse of f equals f. In other words, explain why

$$(f^{-1})^{-1} = f.$$

34. The function f defined by

$$f(x) = x^5 + x^3$$

is one-to-one (here the domain of f is the set of real numbers). Compute $f^{-1}(y)$ for four different values of y of your choice.
[*For this particular function, it is not possible to find a formula for* $f^{-1}(y)$.]

35. Suppose f is a function whose domain equals $\{2, 4, 7, 8, 9\}$ and whose range equals $\{-3, 0, 2, 6, 7\}$. Explain why f is a one-to-one function.

36. Suppose f is a function whose domain equals $\{2, 4, 7, 8, 9\}$ and whose range equals $\{-3, 0, 2, 6\}$. Explain why f is not a one-to-one function.

37. Show that the composition of two one-to-one functions is a one-to-one function.
[*Here you need to assume that the two functions have range and domain such that their composition makes sense.*]

38. Give an example to show that the sum of two one-to-one functions is not necessarily a one-to-one function.

39. Give an example to show that the product of two one-to-one functions is not necessarily a one-to-one function.

40. Give an example of a function f such that the domain of f and the range of f both equal the set of integers, but f is not a one-to-one function.

41. Give an example of a one-to-one function whose domain equals the set of integers and whose range equals the set of positive integers.

WORKED-OUT SOLUTIONS *to Odd-numbered Exercises*

For Exercises 1–8, check your answer by evaluating the appropriate function at your answer.

1. Suppose $f(x) = 4x + 6$. Evaluate $f^{-1}(5)$.

    SOLUTION We need to find a number x such that $f(x) = 5$. In other words, we need to solve

the equation

$$4x + 6 = 5.$$

This equation has solution $x = -\frac{1}{4}$. Thus $f^{-1}(5) = -\frac{1}{4}$.

CHECK To check that $f^{-1}(5) = -\frac{1}{4}$, we need to verify that $f(-\frac{1}{4}) = 5$. We have

$$f(-\tfrac{1}{4}) = 4(-\tfrac{1}{4}) + 6 = 5,$$

as desired.

3. Suppose $g(x) = \dfrac{x+2}{x+1}$. Evaluate $g^{-1}(3)$.

SOLUTION We need to find a number x such that $g(x) = 3$. In other words, we need to solve the equation

$$\frac{x+2}{x+1} = 3.$$

Multiplying both sides of this equation by $x + 1$ gives the equation

$$x + 2 = 3x + 3,$$

which has solution $x = -\tfrac{1}{2}$. Thus $g^{-1}(3) = -\tfrac{1}{2}$.

CHECK To check that $g^{-1}(3) = -\tfrac{1}{2}$, we need to verify that $g(-\tfrac{1}{2}) = 3$. We have

$$g(-\tfrac{1}{2}) = \frac{-\tfrac{1}{2} + 2}{-\tfrac{1}{2} + 1} = \frac{\tfrac{3}{2}}{\tfrac{1}{2}} = 3,$$

as desired.

5. Suppose $f(x) = 3x + 2$. Find a formula for f^{-1}.

SOLUTION For each number y, we need to find a number x such that $f(x) = y$. In other words, we need to solve the equation

$$3x + 2 = y$$

for x in terms of y. Subtracting 2 from both sides of the equation above and then dividing both sides by 3 gives

$$x = \frac{y-2}{3}.$$

Thus

$$f^{-1}(y) = \frac{y-2}{3}$$

for every number y.

CHECK To check that $f^{-1}(y) = \frac{y-2}{3}$, we need to verify that $f(\frac{y-2}{3}) = y$. We have

$$f(\tfrac{y-2}{3}) = 3(\frac{y-2}{3}) + 2 = y,$$

as desired.

7. Suppose $h(t) = \dfrac{1+t}{2-t}$. Find a formula for h^{-1}.

SOLUTION For each number y, we need to find a number t such that $h(t) = y$. In other words, we need to solve the equation

$$\frac{1+t}{2-t} = y$$

for t in terms of y. Multiplying both sides of this equation by $2 - t$ and the collecting all the terms with t on one side gives

$$t + yt = 2y - 1.$$

Rewriting the left side as $(1 + y)t$ and then dividing both sides by $1 + y$ gives

$$t = \frac{2y-1}{1+y}.$$

Thus

$$h^{-1}(y) = \frac{2y-1}{1+y}$$

for every number $y \neq -1$.

CHECK To check that $h^{-1}(y) = \frac{2y-1}{1+y}$, we need to verify that $h(\frac{2y-1}{1+y}) = y$. We have

$$h(\tfrac{2y-1}{1+y}) = \frac{1 + \frac{2y-1}{1+y}}{2 - \frac{2y-1}{1+y}}.$$

Multiplying numerator and denominator of the expression on the right by $1 + y$ gives

$$h(\tfrac{2y-1}{1+y}) = \frac{1 + y + 2y - 1}{2 + 2y - 2y + 1} = \frac{3y}{3} = y,$$

as desired.

9. Suppose $f(x) = 2 + \dfrac{x-5}{x+6}$.

(a) Evaluate $f^{-1}(4)$.

(b) Evaluate $f(4)^{-1}$.

SOLUTION

(a) We need to find a number x such that $f(x) = 4$. In other words, we need to solve the equation

$$2 + \frac{x-5}{x+6} = 4.$$

Subtracting 2 from both sides and then multiplying both sides by $x + 6$ gives the equation

$$x - 5 = 2x + 12,$$

which has solution $x = -17$. Thus $f^{-1}(4) = -17$.

(b) Note that

$$f(4) = 2 + \frac{4-5}{4+6} = \frac{20}{10} - \frac{1}{10} = \frac{19}{10}.$$

Thus $f(4)^{-1} = \frac{10}{19}$.

11. Suppose $h(x) = 5x^2 + 7$, where the domain of h is the set of positive numbers. Find a formula for h^{-1}.

SOLUTION   For each number y, we need to find a number x such that $h(x) = y$. In other words, we need to solve the equation

$$5x^2 + 7 = y$$

for x in terms of y. Subtracting 7 from both sides of the equation above and then dividing both sides by 5 and taking square roots gives

$$x = \sqrt{\frac{y-7}{5}},$$

where we chose the positive square root because x is required to be a positive number. Thus

$$h^{-1}(y) = \sqrt{\frac{y-7}{5}}$$

for every number $y > 7$ (the restriction that $y > 7$ is required to insure that we get a positive number when evaluating the formula above).

For each of the functions f given in Exercises 13–22:

   (a) *Find the domain of f.*

   (b) *Find the range of f.*

   (c) *Find a formula for f^{-1}.*

   (d) *Find the domain of f^{-1}.*

   (e) *Find the range of f^{-1}.*

You can check your solutions to part (c) by verifying that $f^{-1} \circ f = I$ and $f \circ f^{-1} = I$ (recall that I is the function defined by $I(x) = x$).

13. $f(x) = 3x + 5$

   SOLUTION

(a) The expression $3x + 5$ makes sense for all real numbers x. Thus the domain of f is the set of real numbers.

(b) To find the range of f, we need to find the numbers y such that

$$y = 3x + 5$$

for some x is the domain of f. In other words, we need to find the values of y such that the equation above can be solved for a real number x. Solving the equation above for x, we get

$$x = \frac{y-5}{3}.$$

The expression above on the right makes sense for every real number y. Thus the range of f is the set of real numbers.

(c) The expression above shows that f^{-1} is given by the formula

$$f^{-1}(y) = \frac{y-5}{3}.$$

(d) The domain of f^{-1} equals the range of f. Thus the domain of f^{-1} is the set of real numbers.

(e) The range of f^{-1} equals the domain of f. Thus the range of f^{-1} is the set of real numbers.

15. $f(x) = \dfrac{1}{3x + 2}$

   SOLUTION

(a) The expression $\frac{1}{3x+2}$ makes sense except when $3x + 2 = 0$. Solving this equation for x gives $x = -\frac{2}{3}$. Thus the domain of f is the set $\{x : x \neq -\frac{2}{3}\}$.

(b) To find the range of f, we need to find the numbers y such that

$$y = \frac{1}{3x + 2}$$

for some x is the domain of f. In other words, we need to find the values of y such that the equation above can be solved for a real number $x \neq -\frac{2}{3}$. To solve this equation for x, multiply both sides by $3x + 2$, getting

$$3xy + 2y = 1.$$

Now subtract $2y$ from both sides, then divide by $3y$, getting

$$x = \frac{1 - 2y}{3y}.$$

The expression above on the right makes sense for every real number $y \neq 0$ and produces a number $x \neq -\frac{2}{3}$ (because the equation $-\frac{2}{3} = \frac{1-2y}{3y}$ leads to nonsense, as you can verify if you try to solve it for y). Thus the range of f is the set $\{y : y \neq 0\}$.

(c)   The expression above shows that f^{-1} is given by the formula

$$f^{-1}(y) = \frac{1 - 2y}{3y}.$$

(d)   The domain of f^{-1} equals the range of f. Thus the domain of f^{-1} is the set $\{y : y \neq 0\}$.

(e)   The range of f^{-1} equals the domain of f. Thus the range of f^{-1} is the set $\{x : x \neq -\frac{2}{3}\}$.

17. $f(x) = \dfrac{2x}{x + 3}$

SOLUTION

(a)   The expression $\frac{2x}{x+3}$ makes sense except when $x = -3$. Thus the domain of f is the set $\{x : x \neq -3\}$.

(b)   To find the range of f, we need to find the numbers y such that

$$y = \frac{2x}{x + 3}$$

for some x is the domain of f. In other words, we need to find the values of y such that the equation above can be solved for a real number $x \neq -3$. To solve this equation for x, multiply both sides by $x + 3$, getting

$$xy + 3y = 2x.$$

Now subtract xy from both sides, getting

$$3y = 2x - xy = x(2 - y).$$

Dividing by $2 - y$ gives

$$x = \frac{3y}{2 - y}.$$

The expression above on the right makes sense for every real number $y \neq 2$ and produces a number $x \neq -3$ (because the equation $-3 = \frac{3y}{2-y}$ leads to nonsense, as you can verify if you try to solve it for y). Thus the range of f is the set $\{y : y \neq 2\}$.

(c)   The expression above shows that f^{-1} is given by the formula

$$f^{-1}(y) = \frac{3y}{2 - y}.$$

(d)   The domain of f^{-1} equals the range of f. Thus the domain of f^{-1} is the set $\{y : y \neq 2\}$.

(e)   The range of f^{-1} equals the domain of f. Thus the range of f^{-1} is the set $\{x : x \neq -3\}$.

19. $f(x) = \begin{cases} 3x & \text{if } x < 0 \\ 4x & \text{if } x \geq 0 \end{cases}$

SOLUTION

(a)   The expression defining $f(x)$ makes sense for all real numbers x. Thus the domain of f is the set of real numbers.

(b)   To find the range of f, we need to find the numbers y such that $y = f(x)$ for some real number x. From the definition of f, we see that if $y < 0$, then $y = f(\frac{y}{3})$, and if $y \geq 0$, then $y = f(\frac{y}{4})$. Thus every real number y is in the range of f. In other words, the range of f is the set of real numbers.

(c)   From the paragraph above, we see that f^{-1} is given by the formula

$$f^{-1}(y) = \begin{cases} \frac{y}{3} & \text{if } y < 0 \\ \frac{y}{4} & \text{if } y \geq 0. \end{cases}$$

(d)   The domain of f^{-1} equals the range of f. Thus the domain of f^{-1} is the set of real numbers.

(e)   The range of f^{-1} equals the domain of f. Thus the range of f^{-1} is the set of real numbers.

21. $f(x) = x^2 + 8$, where the domain of f equals $(0, \infty)$.

SOLUTION

(a)   As part of the definition of the function f, the domain has been specified to be the interval $(0, \infty)$, which is the set of positive numbers.

(b)   To find the range of f, we need to find the numbers y such that

$$y = x^2 + 8$$

for some x is the domain of f. In other words, we need to find the values of y such that the equation above can be solved for a positive number x. To solve this equation for x, subtract 8 from both sides and then take square roots of both sides, getting

$$x = \sqrt{y - 8},$$

where we chose the positive square root of $y - 8$ because x is required to be a positive number.

The expression above on the right makes sense and produces a positive number x for every number $y > 8$. Thus the range of f is the interval $(8, \infty)$.

(c) The expression above shows that f^{-1} is given by the formula

$$f^{-1}(y) = \sqrt{y - 8}.$$

(d) The domain of f^{-1} equals the range of f. Thus the domain of f^{-1} is the interval $(8, \infty)$.

(e) The range of f^{-1} equals the domain of f. Thus the range of f^{-1} is the interval $(0, \infty)$, which is the set of positive numbers.

23. ✐ Suppose $f(x) = x^5 + 2x^3$. Which of the numbers listed below equals $f^{-1}(8.10693)$?

$$1.1, \quad 1.2, \quad 1.3, \quad 1.4$$

SOLUTION First we test whether or not $f^{-1}(8.10693)$ equals 1.1 by checking whether or not $f(1.1)$ equals 8.10693. Using a calculator, we find that

$$f(1.1) = 4.27251,$$

which means that $f^{-1}(8.10693) \neq 1.1$.

Next we test whether or not $f^{-1}(8.10693)$ equals 1.2 by checking whether or not $f(1.2)$ equals 8.10693. Using a calculator, we find that

$$f(1.2) = 5.94432,$$

which means that $f^{-1}(8.10693) \neq 1.2$.

Next we test whether or not $f^{-1}(8.10693)$ equals 1.3 by checking whether or not $f(1.3)$ equals 8.10693. Using a calculator, we find that

$$f(1.3) = 8.10693,$$

which means that $f^{-1}(8.10693) = 1.3$.

In 2006 the U. S. federal income tax for a single person with taxable income t dollars (this is the net income after allowable deductions) was $f(t)$ dollars, where f is the function defined as follows:

$$f(t) = \begin{cases} 0.1t & \text{if } 0 \le t \le 7550 \\ 0.15t - 377.5 & \text{if } 7550 < t \le 30650 \\ 0.25t - 3442.5 & \text{if } 30650 < t \le 74200 \\ 0.28t - 5668.5 & \text{if } 74200 < t \le 154800 \\ 0.33t - 13408.5 & \text{if } 154800 < t \le 336550 \\ 0.35t - 20139.5 & \text{if } 336550 < t. \end{cases}$$

Use the information above for Exercises 25–26.

25. ✐ What is the taxable income of a single person who paid \$10,000 in federal taxes?

SOLUTION We need to evaluate $f^{-1}(10000)$. Letting $t = f^{-1}(10000)$, this means that we need to solve the equation $f(t) = 10000$ for t. Determining which formula to apply requires a bit of experimentation. Using the definition of f, we can calculate that $f(7550) = 755$, $f(30650) = 4220$, and $f(74200) = 15107.5$. Because 10000 is between 4220 and 15107.5, this means that t is between 30650 and 74200. Thus $f(t) = 0.25t - 3442.5$. Solving the equation

$$0.25t - 3442.5 = 10000$$

for t, we get $t = 53770$. Thus a single person whose federal tax bill was \$10,000 had a taxable income of \$53,770.

27. Suppose $g(x) = x^7 + x^3$. Evaluate

$$\left(g^{-1}(4)\right)^7 + \left(g^{-1}(4)\right)^3 + 1.$$

SOLUTION We are asked to evaluate $g\left(g^{-1}(4)\right) + 1$. Because $g\left(g^{-1}(4)\right) = 4$, the quantity above equals 5.

1.6 | *A Graphical Approach to Inverse Functions*

SECTION OBJECTIVES

By the end of this section you should

- be able to sketch the graph of f^{-1} from the graph of f;

- be able to use the horizontal line test to determine whether a function has an inverse;

- understand the relationship between a table of values of f and a table of values of f^{-1};

- understand the concepts of increasing function and decreasing function.

The Graph of an Inverse Function

Consider the function f whose domain equals $[0, 2]$, with f defined by $f(x) = x^2$. The graph of f, shown below in blue, is part of the familiar parabola defined by the curve $y = x^2$. The range of f is the interval $[0, 4]$. The inverse function f^{-1} has domain $[0, 4]$, with $f^{-1}(x) = \sqrt{x}$; its graph is shown below in red. Notice that the graphs of f and f^{-1} are symmetric with respect to the line $y = x$, meaning that we could obtain either graph by reflecting the other graph through this line.

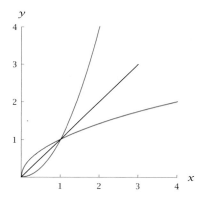

The graph of x^2 (blue) and the graph of its inverse $\sqrt{x}$ (red) are symmetric about the line $y = x$ (black).

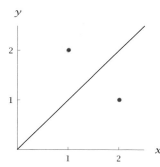

The point $(2, 1)$ (blue) and its reflection $(1, 2)$ (red) through the line $y = x$.

The relationship noted above between the graph of x^2 and the graph of its inverse $\sqrt{x}$ holds in general for the graph of any one-to-one function and the graph of its inverse. Suppose, for example, that the point $(2, 1)$ is on the graph of some one-to-one function f. This means that $f(2) = 1$, which is equivalent to the equation $f^{-1}(1) = 2$, which means that $(1, 2)$ is on the graph of f^{-1}. As can be seen in the figure shown here, the point $(1, 2)$ can be obtained by reflecting the point $(2, 1)$ through the line $y = x$.

More generally, a point (a, b) is on the graph of a one-to-one function f if and only if (b, a) is on the graph of its inverse function f^{-1}. In other words, the graph of f^{-1} can be obtained by interchanging the first and second coordinates of each point on the graph of f. Interchanging first and second coordinates amounts to a reflection through the line $y = x$.

Our discussion of the relationship between the graph of a function and the graph of its inverse can be summarized as follows:

> ### *The graph of a function and its inverse*
>
> - The graph of a function and the graph of its inverse are symmetric with respect to the line $y = x$.
>
> - Each graph can be obtained from the other by reflection through the line $y = x$.

Sometimes an explicit formula cannot be found for f^{-1} because the equation $f(x) = y$ cannot be solved for x even though f is a one-to-one function. However, even in such cases we can obtain the graph of f^{-1} from the graph of f by reflection through the line $y = x$, as shown in the example below.

Suppose f is the function with domain $[0, 1]$ defined by $f(x) = \frac{1}{2}x^5 + \frac{3}{2}x^3$. Sketch the graph of f^{-1}.

EXAMPLE 1

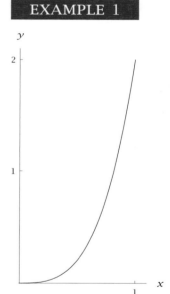

The graph of
$f(x) = \frac{1}{2}x^5 + \frac{3}{2}x^3.$

SOLUTION   The graph of f is shown here in the margin; it was produced by a computer program that can graph a function if given a formula for the function.

Even though f is a one-to-one function, neither humans nor computers can solve the equation

$$\tfrac{1}{2}x^5 + \tfrac{3}{2}x^3 = y$$

for x in terms of y. Thus in this case there is no formula for f^{-1} that a computer can use to produce the graph of f^{-1}.

However, we can find the graph of f^{-1} by reflecting the graph of f through the line $y = x$, as shown below:

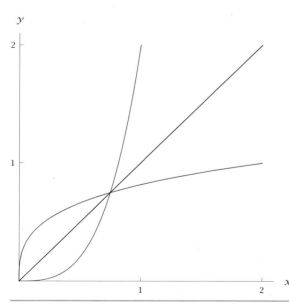

The graph of
$f(x) = \frac{1}{2}x^5 + \frac{3}{2}x^3$ (blue)
and the graph of its inverse
(red), which is obtained by
reflection through the line
$y = x$.

Inverse Functions via Tables

For functions whose domain consists of only finitely many numbers, tables provide good insight into the notion of an inverse function.

EXAMPLE 2

x	$f(x)$
$\sqrt{2}$	3
8	-5
17	6
18	1

Suppose f is the function whose domain is the four numbers $\{\sqrt{2}, 8, 17, 18\}$, with the values of f given in the table shown here in the margin.

(a) What is the range of f?

(b) Explain why f is a one-to-one function.

(c) What is the table for the function f^{-1}?

SOLUTION

(a) The range of f is the set of numbers appearing in the second column of the table defining f. Thus the range of f is the set $\{3, -5, 6, 1\}$.

(b) A function is one-to-one if and only if each number in its range corresponds to only one number in the domain. This means that a function defined by a table is one-to-one if and only if no number is repeated in the second column of the table defining the function. Because the second column of the table above contains no repetitions, we conclude that f is a one-to-one function.

y	$f^{-1}(y)$
3	$\sqrt{2}$
-5	8
6	17
1	18

(c) Suppose we want to evaluate $f^{-1}(3)$. This means that we need to find a number x such that $f(x) = 3$. Looking in the table above at the column labeled $f(x)$, we see that $f(\sqrt{2}) = 3$. Thus $f^{-1}(3) = \sqrt{2}$, which means that in the table for f^{-1} the positions of $\sqrt{2}$ and 3 should be interchanged from their positions in the table for f. More generally, the table for f^{-1} is obtained by interchanging the columns in the table for f, producing the table shown here.

The ideas used in the example above apply to any function defined by a table, as summarized below.

> ### Inverse functions via tables
>
> Suppose f is a function defined by a table. Then:
>
> - f is one-to-one if and only if the table defining f has no repetitions in the second column.
>
> - If f is one-to-one, then the table for f^{-1} is obtained by interchanging the columns of the table defining f.

Graphical Interpretation of One-to-One

The graph of a function can be used to determine whether or not the function is one-to-one (and thus whether or not the function has an inverse). The example below illustrates the idea.

Suppose f is the function with domain $[1,4]$ whose graph is shown here in the margin. Is f a one-to-one function?

EXAMPLE 3

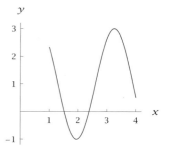

SOLUTION   For f to be one-to-one, for each number y there must be at most one number x such that $f(x) = y$. Draw the line $y = 2$ on the same coordinate plane as the graph, as shown below.

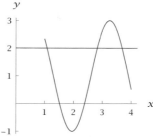

As can be seen here, the line $y = 2$ intersects the graph of f in three points. Thus there are three numbers x in the domain of f such that $f(x) = 2$. Hence f is not a one-to-one function.

The method used in the example above can be used with the graph of any function. Here is the formal statement of the resulting test:

Horizontal line test

A function is one-to-one if and only if every horizontal line intersects the graph of the function in at most one point.

The functions that have inverses are precisely the one-to-one functions. Thus the horizontal line test can be used to determine whether or not a function has an inverse.

When using the horizontal line test, be careful about its correct interpretation: If you find even one horizontal line that intersects the graph in more than one point, then the function is not one-to-one. However, finding one horizontal line that intersects the graph in at most one point does not imply anything concerning whether or not the function is one-to-one. For the function to be one-to-one, *every* horizontal line must intersect the graph in at most one point.

Suppose f is the function with domain $[-2,2]$ whose graph is shown here in the margin. Is f a one-to-one function?

EXAMPLE 4

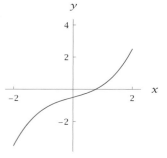

SOLUTION   For f to be one-to-one, each horizontal line must intersect the graph of f in at most one point. The figure below shows the graph of f along with the horizontal lines $y = 1$ and $y = 3$.

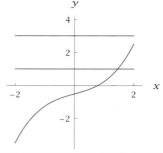

As can be seen here, the line $y = 1$ intersects the graph of f in one point, and the line $y = 3$ intersects the graph in zero points. Furthermore, we can see from the figure that each horizontal line will intersect the graph in at most one point. Hence f is a one-to-one function.

Increasing and Decreasing Functions

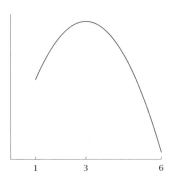

The domain of the function shown here is the interval $[1,6]$. On the interval $[1,3]$, the graph of this function gets higher from left to right; thus we say that this function is **increasing** on the interval $[1,3]$. On the interval $[3,6]$, the graph of this function gets lower from left to right; thus we say that this function is **decreasing** on the interval $[3,6]$. Here are the formal definitions:

Increasing on an interval

A function f is called **increasing** on an interval if $f(a) < f(b)$ whenever $a < b$ and a, b are in the interval.

Decreasing on an interval

A function f is called **decreasing** on an interval if $f(a) > f(b)$ whenever $a < b$ and a, b are in the interval.

EXAMPLE 5

The function f whose graph is shown here has domain $[-1,6]$.

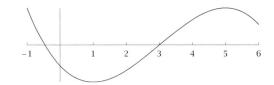

(a) Find the largest interval on which f is increasing.

(b) Find the largest interval on which f is decreasing.

(c) Find the largest interval containing 6 on which f is decreasing.

SOLUTION

(a) As can be seen from the graph above, $[1,5]$ is the largest interval on which f is increasing.

(b) As can be seen from the graph above, $[-1,1]$ is the largest interval on which f is decreasing.

(c) As can be seen from the graph above, $[5,6]$ is the largest interval containing 6 on which f is decreasing.

Sometimes the terms "increasing" and "decreasing" are used without referring to an interval, as explained here.

A function is called **increasing** if its graph gets higher from left to right on its entire domain. Here is the formal definition:

Increasing functions

A function f is called **increasing** if $f(a) < f(b)$ whenever $a < b$ and a, b are in the domain of f.

Similarly, a function is called **decreasing** if its graph gets lower from left to right on its entire domain, as defined below:

> ### Decreasing functions
>
> A function f is called **decreasing** if $f(a) > f(b)$ whenever $a < b$ and a, b are in the domain of f.

Shown below are the graphs of three functions; each function is graphed on its entire domain.

EXAMPLE 6

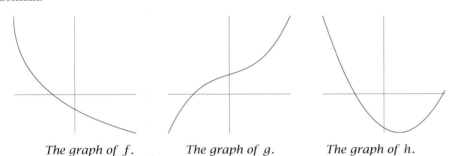

The graph of f.   The graph of g.   The graph of h.

(a) Is f increasing, decreasing, or neither?

(b) Is g increasing, decreasing, or neither?

(c) Is h increasing, decreasing, or neither?

SOLUTION

(a) The graph of f gets lower from left to right on its entire domain. Thus f is decreasing.

(b) The graph of g gets higher from left to right on its entire domain. Thus g is increasing.

(c) The graph of h gets lower from left to right on part of its domain and gets higher from left to right on another part of its domain. Thus h is neither increasing nor decreasing.

Every horizontal line intersects the graph of an increasing function in at most one point, and similarly for the graph of a decreasing function. Thus we have the following result:

> ### Increasing and decreasing functions are one-to-one
>
> - Every increasing function is one-to-one.
>
> - Every decreasing function is one-to-one.

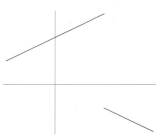

The graph of a one-to-one function that is neither increasing nor decreasing.

The result above raises the question of whether every one-to-one function must be increasing or decreasing. The graph shown here answers this question. Specifically, this function is one-to-one because each horizontal line intersects the graph in at most one point. However, this function is neither increasing nor decreasing.

The graph in the example shown here is not one connected piece—you cannot sketch it without lifting your pencil from the paper. A one-to-one function whose graph consists of just one connected piece must be either increasing or decreasing. However, a rigorous explanation of why this result holds requires tools from calculus.

Suppose f is an increasing function and a and b are numbers in the domain of f with $a < b$. Thus $f(a) < f(b)$. Recall that $f(a)$ and $f(b)$ are numbers in the domain of f^{-1}. We have

$$f^{-1}(f(a)) < f^{-1}(f(b))$$

because $f^{-1}(f(a)) = a$ and $f^{-1}(f(b)) = b$. The inequality above shows that f^{-1} is an increasing function.

In other words, we have just shown that the inverse of an increasing function is increasing. The figure of a function and its inverse in Example 1 illustrates this result graphically. A similar result holds for decreasing functions.

> ### Inverses of increasing and decreasing functions
>
> - The inverse of an increasing function is increasing.
>
> - The inverse of a decreasing function is decreasing.

EXERCISES

For Exercises 1–24 suppose f and g are functions, each of whose domain consists of four numbers, with f and g defined by the tables below:

x	$f(x)$
1	4
2	5
3	2
4	3

x	$g(x)$
2	3
3	2
4	4
5	1

1. What is the domain of f?
2. What is the domain of g?
3. What is the range of f?
4. What is the range of g?
5. Sketch the graph of f.
6. Sketch the graph of g.
7. Give the table of values for f^{-1}.
8. Give the table of values for g^{-1}.
9. What is the domain of f^{-1}?
10. What is the domain of g^{-1}?
11. What is the range of f^{-1}?
12. What is the range of g^{-1}?
13. Sketch the graph of f^{-1}.
14. Sketch the graph of g^{-1}.
15. Give the table of values for $f^{-1} \circ f$.
16. Give the table of values for $g^{-1} \circ g$.
17. Give the table of values for $f \circ f^{-1}$.
18. Give the table of values for $g \circ g^{-1}$.

19. Give the table of values for $f \circ g$.

20. Give the table of values for $g \circ f$.

21. Give the table of values for $(f \circ g)^{-1}$.

22. Give the table of values for $(g \circ f)^{-1}$.

23. Give the table of values for $g^{-1} \circ f^{-1}$.

24. Give the table of values for $f^{-1} \circ g^{-1}$.

For Exercises 25–36, use the following graphs:

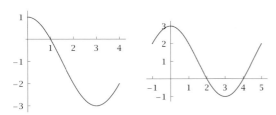

The graph of f.   **The graph of g.**

Here f has domain $[0, 4]$ and g has domain $[-1, 5]$.

25. What is the largest interval contained in the domain of f on which f is increasing?

26. What is the largest interval contained in the domain of g on which g is increasing?

27. Let F denote the function obtained from f by restricting the domain to the interval in Exercise 25. What is the domain of F^{-1}?

28. Let G denote the function obtained from g by restricting the domain to the interval in Exercise 26. What is the domain of G^{-1}?

29. With F as in Exercise 27, what is the range of F^{-1}?

30. With G as in Exercise 28, what is the range of G^{-1}?

31. What is the largest interval contained in the domain of f on which f is decreasing?

32. What is the largest interval contained in the domain of g on which g is decreasing?

33. Let H denote the function obtained from f by restricting the domain to the interval in Exercise 31. What is the domain of H^{-1}?

34. Let J denote the function obtained from g by restricting the domain to the interval in Exercise 32. What is the domain of J^{-1}?

35. With H as in Exercise 33, what is the range of H^{-1}?

36. With J as in Exercise 34, what is the range of J^{-1}?

PROBLEMS

37. Suppose f is the function whose domain is the interval $[-2, 2]$, with f defined by the following formula:

$$f(x) = \begin{cases} -\frac{x}{3} & \text{if } -2 \le x < 0 \\ 2x & \text{if } 0 \le x \le 2. \end{cases}$$

   (a) Sketch the graph of f.

   (b) Explain why the graph of f shows that f is not a one-to-one function.

   (c) Give an explicit example of two distinct numbers a and b such that $f(a) = f(b)$.

38. Draw the graph of a function that is increasing on the interval $[-2, 0]$ and decreasing on the interval $[0, 2]$.

39. Draw the graph of a function that is decreasing on the interval $[-2, 1]$ and increasing on the interval $[1, 5]$.

40. Give an example of an increasing function whose domain is the interval $[0, 1]$ but whose range does not equal the interval $[f(0), f(1)]$.

41. Show that the sum of two increasing functions is increasing.

42. Give an example of two increasing functions whose product is not increasing.
    [*Hint:* There are no such examples where both functions are positive everywhere.]

43. Give an example of two decreasing functions whose product is increasing.

44. Show that the composition of two increasing functions is increasing.

45. Explain why it is important as a matter of social policy that the income tax function f used for Exercises 25–26 of Section 1.5 be an increasing function.

46. Explain why an even function whose domain contains a nonzero number cannot be a one-to-one function.

47. The solutions to Exercises 21 and 23 are the same, suggesting that

$$(f \circ g)^{-1} = g^{-1} \circ f^{-1}.$$

Explain why the equation above holds whenever f and g are one-to-one functions such that the range of g equals the domain of f.

WORKED-OUT SOLUTIONS *to Odd-numbered Exercises*

For Exercises 1–24 suppose f and g are functions, each of whose domain consists of four numbers, with f and g defined by the tables below:

x	$f(x)$
1	4
2	5
3	2
4	3

x	$g(x)$
2	3
3	2
4	4
5	1

1. What is the domain of f?

    SOLUTION   The domain of f equals the set of numbers in the left column of the table defining f. Thus the domain of f equals $\{1, 2, 3, 4\}$.

3. What is the range of f?

    SOLUTION   The range of f equals the set of numbers in the right column of the table defining f. Thus the range of f equals $\{2, 3, 4, 5\}$.

5. Sketch the graph of f.

    SOLUTION   The graph of f consists of all points of the form $(x, f(x))$ as x varies over the domain of f. Thus the graph of f, shown below, consists of the four points $(1, 4)$, $(2, 5)$, $(3, 2)$, and $(4, 3)$.

7. Give the table of values for f^{-1}.

    SOLUTION   The table for the inverse of a function is obtained by interchanging the two columns of the table for the function (after which one can, if desired, reorder the rows, as has been done below):

y	$f^{-1}(y)$
2	3
3	4
4	1
5	2

9. What is the domain of f^{-1}?

    SOLUTION   The domain of f^{-1} equals the range of f. Thus the domain of f^{-1} is the set $\{2, 3, 4, 5\}$.

11. What is the range of f^{-1}?

    SOLUTION   The range of f^{-1} equals the domain of f. Thus the range of f^{-1} is the set $\{1, 2, 3, 4\}$.

13. Sketch the graph of f^{-1}.

    SOLUTION   The graph of f^{-1} consists of all points of the form $(x, f^{-1}(x))$ as x varies over the domain of f^{-1}. Thus the graph of f^{-1}, shown below, consists of the four points $(4, 1)$, $(5, 2)$, $(2, 3)$, and $(3, 4)$.

15. Give the table of values for $f^{-1} \circ f$.

    SOLUTION We know that $f^{-1} \circ f$ is the identity function on the domain of f; thus no computations are necessary. However, because this function f has only four numbers in its domain, it may be instructive to compute $(f^{-1} \circ f)(x)$ for each value of x in the domain of f. Here is that computation:

    $$(f^{-1} \circ f)(1) = f^{-1}(f(1)) = f^{-1}(4) = 1$$

    $$(f^{-1} \circ f)(2) = f^{-1}(f(2)) = f^{-1}(5) = 2$$

    $$(f^{-1} \circ f)(3) = f^{-1}(f(3)) = f^{-1}(2) = 3$$

    $$(f^{-1} \circ f)(4) = f^{-1}(f(4)) = f^{-1}(3) = 4$$

    Thus, as expected, the table of values for $f^{-1} \circ f$ is as shown below:

x	$(f^{-1} \circ f)(x)$
1	1
2	2
3	3
4	4

17. Give the table of values for $f \circ f^{-1}$.

    SOLUTION We know that $f \circ f^{-1}$ is the identity function on the range of f (which equals the domain of f^{-1}); thus no computations are necessary. However, because this function f has only four numbers in its range, it may be instructive to compute $(f \circ f^{-1})(y)$ for each value of y in the range of f. Here is that computation:

$$(f \circ f^{-1})(2) = f(f^{-1}(2)) = f(3) = 2$$

$$(f \circ f^{-1})(3) = f(f^{-1}(3)) = f(4) = 3$$

$$(f \circ f^{-1})(4) = f(f^{-1}(4)) = f(1) = 4$$

$$(f \circ f^{-1})(5) = f(f^{-1}(5)) = f(2) = 5$$

Thus, as expected, the table of values for $f \circ f^{-1}$ is as shown here.

y	$(f \circ f^{-1})(y)$
2	2
3	3
4	4
5	5

19. Give the table of values for $f \circ g$.

    SOLUTION We need to compute $(f \circ g)(x)$ for every x in the domain of g. Here is that computation:

    $$(f \circ g)(2) = f(g(2)) = f(3) = 2$$

    $$(f \circ g)(3) = f(g(3)) = f(2) = 5$$

    $$(f \circ g)(4) = f(g(4)) = f(4) = 3$$

    $$(f \circ g)(5) = f(g(5)) = f(1) = 4$$

    Thus the table of values for $f \circ g$ is as shown here.

x	$(f \circ g)(x)$
2	2
3	5
4	3
5	4

21. Give the table of values for $(f \circ g)^{-1}$.

    SOLUTION The table of values for $(f \circ g)^{-1}$ is obtained by interchanging the two columns of the table for $(f \circ g)$ (after which one can, if desired, reorder the rows, as has been done below).

    Thus the table for $(f \circ g)^{-1}$ is as shown here.

y	$(f \circ g)^{-1}(y)$
2	2
3	4
4	5
5	3

23. Give the table of values for $g^{-1} \circ f^{-1}$.

    SOLUTION We need to compute $(g^{-1} \circ f^{-1})(y)$ for every y in the domain of f^{-1}. Here is that computation:

$$(g^{-1} \circ f^{-1})(2) = g^{-1}(f^{-1}(2)) = g^{-1}(3) = 2$$

$$(g^{-1} \circ f^{-1})(3) = g^{-1}(f^{-1}(3)) = g^{-1}(4) = 4$$

$$(g^{-1} \circ f^{-1})(4) = g^{-1}(f^{-1}(4)) = g^{-1}(1) = 5$$

$$(g^{-1} \circ f^{-1})(5) = g^{-1}(f^{-1}(5)) = g^{-1}(2) = 3$$

Thus the table of values for $g^{-1} \circ f^{-1}$ is as shown here.

y	$(g^{-1} \circ f^{-1})(y)$
2	2
3	4
4	5
5	3

For Exercises 25–36, use the following graphs:

The graph of f.

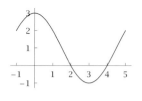

The graph of g.

Here f has domain $[0, 4]$ and g has domain $[-1, 5]$.

25. What is the largest interval contained in the domain of f on which f is increasing?

SOLUTION   As can be seen from the graph, $[3, 4]$ is the largest interval on which f is increasing.

As usual when obtaining information solely from graphs, this answer (as well as the answers to the other parts of this exercise) should be considered an approximation. An expanded graph at a finer scale might show that $[2.99, 4]$ or $[3.01, 4]$ would be a more accurate answer than $[3, 4]$.

27. Let F denote the function obtained from f by restricting the domain to the interval in Exercise 25. What is the domain of F^{-1}?

SOLUTION   The domain of F^{-1} equals the range of F. Because F is the function f with domain restricted to the interval $[3, 4]$, we see from the graph above that the range of F is the interval $[-3, -2]$. Thus the domain of F^{-1} is the interval $[-3, -2]$.

29. With F as in Exercise 27, what is the range of F^{-1}?

SOLUTION   The range of F^{-1} equals the domain of F. Thus the range of F^{-1} is the interval $[3, 4]$.

31. What is the largest interval contained in the domain of f on which f is decreasing?

SOLUTION   As can be seen from the graph, $[0, 3]$ is the largest interval on which f is decreasing.

33. Let H denote the function obtained from f by restricting the domain to the interval in Exercise 31. What is the domain of H^{-1}?

SOLUTION   The domain of H^{-1} equals the range of H. Because H is the function f with domain restricted to the interval $[0, 3]$, we see from the graph above that the range of H is the interval $[-3, 1]$. Thus the domain of H^{-1} is the interval $[-3, 1]$.

35. With H as in Exercise 33, what is the range of H^{-1}?

SOLUTION   The range of H^{-1} equals the domain of H. Thus the range of H^{-1} is the interval $[0, 3]$.

CHAPTER SUMMARY

To check that you have mastered the most important concepts and skills covered in this chapter, make sure that you can do each item in the following list:

- Explain the concept of a function, including its domain.
- Define the range of a function.
- Locate points on the coordinate plane.
- Explain the relationship between a function and its graph.
- Determine the domain and range of a function from its graph.
- Use the vertical line test to determine if a set is the graph of some function.
- Determine whether a function transformation shifts the graph up, down, left, or right.
- Determine whether a function transformation stretches the graph vertically or horizontally.
- Determine whether a function transformation reflects the graph vertically or horizontally.
- Determine the domain, range, and graph of a transformed function.

- Compute the composition of two functions.
- Write a complicated function as the composition of simpler functions.
- Explain the concept of an inverse function.
- Explain which functions have inverses.
- Find a formula for an inverse function (when possible).
- Sketch the graph of f^{-1} from the graph of f.
- Use the horizontal line test to determine whether a function has an inverse.
- Construct a table of values of f^{-1} from a table of values of f.
- Recognize from a graph whether a function is increasing or decreasing or neither on an interval.

To review a chapter, go through the list above to find items that you do not know how to do, then reread the material in the chapter about those items. Then try to answer the chapter review questions below without looking back at the chapter.

CHAPTER REVIEW QUESTIONS

1. Suppose f is a function. Explain what it means to say that $\frac{3}{2}$ is in the domain of f.

2. Suppose f is a function. Explain what it means to say that $\frac{3}{2}$ is in the range of f.

3. Give an example of a function whose domain consists of five numbers and whose range consists of three numbers.

4. Explain how to find the domain of a function from its graph.

5. Explain how to find the range of a function from its graph.

6. Explain how to use the vertical line test to determine whether or not a set in the plane is the graph of some function.

7. Sketch a curve in the coordinate plane that is not the graph of any function.

For Questions 8–15, assume that f is the function defined on the interval $[1, 3]$ by the formula

$$f(x) = \frac{1}{x^2 - 3x + 3}.$$

The domain of f is the interval $[1, 3]$, the range of f is the interval $[\frac{1}{3}, \frac{4}{3}]$, and the graph of f is shown below.

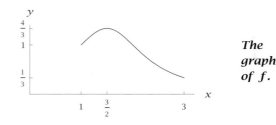

The graph of f.

For each function g described below:

(a) *Sketch the graph of g.*

(b) *Find the domain of g (the endpoints of this interval should be shown on the horizontal axis of your sketch of the graph of g).*

(c) *Give a formula for g.*

(d) *Find the range of g (the endpoints of this interval should be shown on the vertical axis of your sketch of the graph of g).*

8. The graph of g is obtained by shifting the graph of f up 2 units.

9. The graph of g is obtained by shifting the graph of f down 2 units.

10. The graph of g is obtained by shifting the graph of f left 2 units.

11. The graph of g is obtained by shifting the graph of f right 2 units.

12. The graph of g is obtained by vertically stretching the graph of f by a factor of 3.

13. The graph of g is obtained by horizontally stretching the graph of f by a factor of 2.

14. The graph of g is obtained by reflecting the graph of f through the horizontal axis.

15. The graph of g is obtained by reflecting the graph of f through the vertical axis.

16. Suppose f is a function with domain $[1, 3]$ and range $[2, 5]$. Define functions g and h by

$$g(x) = 3f(x) \quad \text{and} \quad h(x) = f(4x).$$

(a) What is the domain of g?

(b) What is the range of g?

(c) What is the domain of h?

(d) What is the range of h?

17. Show that the sum of two odd functions (with the same domain) is an odd function.

18. Define the composition of two functions.

19. Suppose $f(x) = \frac{x^2+3}{5x^2-9}$. Find two functions g and h, each simpler than f, such that $f = g \circ h$.

For Questions 20–23, suppose

$$h(x) = |2x + 3| + x^2 \quad \text{and} \quad f(x) = 3x - 5.$$

20. Evaluate $(h \circ f)(3)$.

21. Evaluate $(f \circ h)(-4)$.

22. Find a formula for $h \circ f$.

23. Find a formula for $f \circ h$.

24. Explain how to use the horizontal line test to determine whether or not a function is one-to-one.

25. Suppose $f(x) = \frac{2x+1}{3x-4}$. Evaluate $f^{-1}(-5)$.

26. Suppose $g(x) = 3 + \frac{x}{2x-3}$. Find a formula for g^{-1}.

27. Suppose f is a one-to-one function. Explain the relationship between the graph of f and the graph of f^{-1}.

28. Suppose f is a one-to-one function. Explain the relationship between the domain and range of f and the domain and range of f^{-1}.

29. Explain the different meanings of the notations $f^{-1}(x)$ and $f(x)^{-1}$.

30. The function f defined by

$$f(x) = x^5 + 2x^3 + 2$$

is one-to-one (here the domain of f is the set of real numbers). Compute $f^{-1}(y)$ for four different values of y of your choice.

31. Draw the graph of a function that is decreasing on the interval $[1, 2]$ and increasing on the interval $[2, 5]$.

32. Make up a table that defines a one-to-one function whose domain consists of five numbers. Then sketch the graph of this function and its inverse.

This detail from **The School of Athens** *(painted by Raphael around 1510) depicts Euclid explaining geometry.*

Linear, Quadratic, Polynomial, and Rational Functions

In this chapter we focus on four important special classes of functions. The main themes of the last chapter—transformations of functions, composition of functions, and inverses of functions—appear in this chapter in the context of these special classes of functions.

Linear functions form our first special class of functions. Lines and their slopes, although simple concepts, have immense importance.

After dealing with linear functions and lines, we will turn to the quadratic functions, our second class of special functions. The graph of a quadratic function is a parabola. We will see how to find the vertex of a parabola, how to perform the useful algebraic operation of completing the square, and how to solve quadratic equations.

Then we will take a brief diversion to review the algebra of integer exponents in preparation for dealing with the polynomial functions, which form our third special class of functions. From polynomials we will move on to rational functions, our fourth special class of functions.

This chapter concludes with two optional sections—one discusses complex numbers (needed to solve arbitrary quadratic equations) and one discusses systems of equations and matrices.

2.1 | *Linear Functions and Lines*

SECTION OBJECTIVES

By the end of this section you should

- understand the concept of the slope of a line;
- be able to find the equation of a line given its slope and a point on it;
- be able to find the equation of a line given two points on it;
- understand why parallel lines have the same slope;
- be able to find the equation of a line perpendicular to a given line and containing a given point.

Slope

Consider a line in the coordinate plane, along with four points (x_1, y_1), (x_2, y_2), (x_3, y_3), and (x_4, y_4) on the line. Draw two right triangles with horizontal and vertical edges as in the figure below:

In this figure, each side of the larger triangle has twice the length of the corresponding side of the smaller triangle.

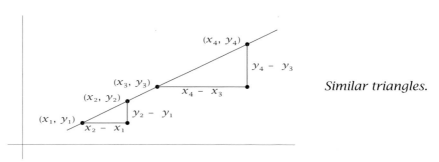

Similar triangles.

The two right triangles in the figure above are similar because their angles are equal. Thus the ratios of the corresponding sides of the two triangles above are equal. Specifically, taking the ratio of the vertical side and horizontal side for each triangle, we have

$$\frac{y_2 - y_1}{x_2 - x_1} = \frac{y_4 - y_3}{x_4 - x_3}.$$

The equation above states that for any pair of points (x_1, y_1) and (x_2, y_2) on the line, the ratio $\frac{y_2 - y_1}{x_2 - x_1}$ does not depend on the particular pair of points chosen on the line. If we choose another pair of points on the line, say (x_3, y_3) and (x_4, y_4) instead of (x_1, y_1) and (x_2, y_2), then the difference of second coordinates divided by the difference of first coordinates remains the same, as shown by the equation above.

Thus the ratio $\frac{y_2 - y_1}{x_2 - x_1}$ is a constant depending only on the line and not on the particular points (x_1, y_1) and (x_2, y_2) chosen on the line. This constant is called the **slope** of the line.

Slope

If (x_1, y_1) and (x_2, y_2) are any two points on a line, with $x_1 \neq x_2$, then the **slope** of the line is

$$\frac{y_2 - y_1}{x_2 - x_1}.$$

Find the slope of the line containing the points $(2, 1)$ and $(5, 3)$.

EXAMPLE 1

SOLUTION   The line containing $(2, 1)$ and $(5, 3)$ is shown here. The slope of this line is $\frac{3-1}{5-2}$, which equals $\frac{2}{3}$.

A line with positive slope slants up from left to right; a line with negative slope slants down from left to right. Lines whose slopes have larger absolute value are steeper than lines whose slopes have smaller absolute value. This figure shows some lines and their slopes; the same scale has been used on both axes.

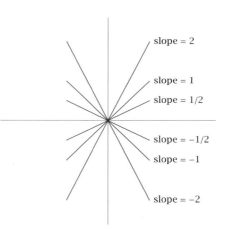

In the figure above, the horizontal axis has slope 0, as does every horizontal line. Vertical lines, including the vertical axis, do not have a slope, because a vertical line does not contain two points (x_1, y_1) and (x_2, y_2) with $x_1 \neq x_2$.

The Equation of a Line

Consider a line with slope m, and suppose (x_1, y_1) is a point on this line. Let (x, y) denote a typical point on the line, as shown here.

Because this line has slope m, we have

$$\frac{y - y_1}{x - x_1} = m.$$

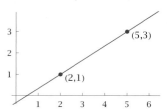

A line with slope m.

Multiplying both sides of the equation above by $x - x_1$, we get the following formula:

The equation of a line, given its slope and one point on it

The symbol m is often used to denote the slope of a line.

The line in the xy-plane that has slope m and contains the point (x_1, y_1) is given by the equation

$$y - y_1 = m(x - x_1).$$

The equation above can be solved for y to get an equation for the line in the form $y = mx + b$, where m and b are constants.

EXAMPLE 2

Find the equation of the line in the xy-plane that has slope 4 and contains the point $(2, 3)$.

SOLUTION   In this case the equation displayed above becomes

$$y - 3 = 4(x - 2).$$

Adding 3 to both sides and simplifying, we get

$$y = 4x - 5.$$

Always perform this kind of check to determine if an error has been made.

As a check, if we take $x = 2$ in the equation above, we get $y = 3$. Thus the point $(2, 3)$ is indeed on this line.

Suppose we want to find the equation of the line containing two specific points. We can reduce this problem to a problem we have already solved by computing the slope of the line and then using the formula in the box above. Specifically, suppose we want to find the equation of the line containing the points (x_1, y_1) and (x_2, y_2), where $x_1 \neq x_2$. This line has slope $(y_2 - y_1)/(x_2 - x_1)$. Thus the formula above gives the following result:

The equation of a line, given two points on it

The line in the xy-plane that contains the points (x_1, y_1) and (x_2, y_2), where $x_1 \neq x_2$, is given by the equation

$$y - y_1 = \left(\frac{y_2 - y_1}{x_2 - x_1} \right)(x - x_1).$$

EXAMPLE 3

Find the equation of the line in the xy-plane that contains the points $(2, 1)$ and $(5, 3)$ (this line is shown with Example 1).

SOLUTION   In this case the equation above becomes

$$y - 1 = \left(\frac{3 - 1}{5 - 2} \right)(x - 2).$$

Solving this equation for y, we get

$$y = \tfrac{2}{3}x - \tfrac{1}{3}.$$

As a check, if we take $x = 2$ in the equation above, we get $y = 1$, and if we take $x = 5$ in the equation above, we get $y = 3$; thus the points $(2, 1)$ and $(5, 3)$ are indeed on this line.

Suppose we want to find the equation of the line in the xy-plane with slope m that intersects the y-axis at the point $(0, b)$. Because $(0, b)$ is a point on the line, we can use the formula for the equation of a line given its slope and one point on it. In this case, that equation becomes

The point where a line intersects the y-axis is often called the y-intercept.

$$y - b = m(x - 0).$$

Solving this equation for y, we have the following result:

> ### The equation of a line, given its slope and vertical axis intersection
>
> The line in the xy-plane with slope m that intersects the y-axis at $(0, b)$ is given by the equation
> $$y = mx + b.$$

If a line contains the origin, then $b = 0$ in the equation above. For example, the line in the xy-plane that has slope 2 and contains the origin is given by the equation $y = 2x$. The figure below Example 1 shows several lines containing the origin.

We have seen that a line in the xy-plane with slope m is characterized by the equation $y = mx + b$, where b is some constant. To restate this conclusion in terms of functions, let f be the function defined by $f(x) = mx + b$, where m and b are constants. Then the graph of f is a line with slope m. Functions of this form are so important that they have a name— linear functions:

Differential calculus focuses on approximating an arbitrary function on a small part of its domain by a linear function. Thus you will frequently encounter linear functions in future mathematics courses.

> ### Linear functions
>
> A **linear function** is a function f of the form
> $$f(x) = mx + b,$$
> where m and b are constants.

Find the function f such that $f(x)$ equals the temperature on the Fahrenheit scale corresponding to temperature x on the Celsius scale.

EXAMPLE 4

This thermometer shows Celsius degrees on the left, Fahrenheit degrees on the right.

SOLUTION Changing from one system of units to another system of units is modeled by a linear function. Thus f has the form $f(x) = mx + b$ for some constants m and b.

To find m and b, we recall that the freezing temperature of water equals 0 degrees Celsius and 32 degrees Fahrenheit; also, the boiling point of water equals 100 degrees Celsius and 212 degrees Fahrenheit. Thus

$$f(0) = 32 \quad \text{and} \quad f(100) = 212.$$

But $f(0) = b$, and thus $b = 32$. Now we know that $f(x) = mx + 32$. Hence $f(100) = 100m + 32$. Setting this last quantity equal to 212 and then solving for m shows that $m = \frac{9}{5}$. Thus

$$f(x) = \frac{9}{5}x + 32.$$

A special type of linear function is obtained when considering functions of the form $f(x) = mx + b$ with $m = 0$:

The graph of $f(x) = \frac{9}{5}x + 32$ on the interval $[-10, 110]$.

> ## Constant functions
>
> A **constant function** is a function f of the form
>
> $$f(x) = b,$$
>
> where b is a constant.

The graph of a constant function is a horizontal line.

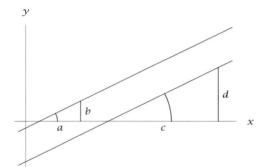

The graph of the constant function f defined by $f(x) = 2$ on the interval $[1, 4]$.

Parallel Lines

Consider two parallel lines in the coordinate plane, as shown in the figure below:

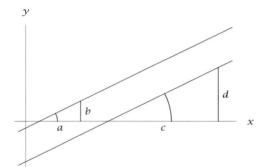

Parallel lines.

Because the two lines are parallel, the corresponding angles in the two triangles above are equal (as shown by the arcs in the figure above), and thus the two right triangles are similar. This implies that

$$\frac{b}{a} = \frac{d}{c}.$$

Because $\frac{b}{a}$ is the slope of the top line and $\frac{d}{c}$ is the slope of the bottom line, we conclude that these parallel lines have the same slope.

The logic used in the paragraph above is reversible. Specifically, suppose instead of starting with the assumption that the two lines in the figure above are parallel, we start with the assumption that the two lines have the same slope. This implies that $\frac{b}{a} = \frac{d}{c}$, which implies that the two right triangles in the figure above are similar. This then implies that the two lines make equal angles with the horizontal axis, as shown by the arcs in the figure, which implies that the two lines are parallel.

The figure and reasoning given above do not work if both lines are horizontal or both lines are vertical. But horizontal lines all have slope 0, and the slope is not defined for vertical lines. Thus we can summarize our characterization of parallel lines as follows:

Parallel lines

Two nonvertical lines in the coordinate plane are parallel if and only if they have the same slope.

The phrase "if and only if", when connecting two statements, means that the two statements are either both true or both false. For example, $x + 1 > 6$ if and only if $x > 5$.

For example, the lines in the xy-plane given by the equations

$$y = 4x - 5 \quad \text{and} \quad y = 4x + 18$$

are parallel because they have the same slope (which equals 4). As another example, the lines in the xy-plane given by the equations

$$y = 6x + 5 \quad \text{and} \quad y = 7x + 5$$

are not parallel because their slopes are not equal—the first line has slope 6 and the second line has slope 7.

Sometimes seeing a second explanation for an important result can help lead to better understanding. We used geometry to derive the conclusion in the box above. The same result can also be derived algebraically. To do that, first we need to examine the procedure for finding the intersection of two lines, which is illustrated by the following example.

Find the intersection of the lines in the xy-plane given by the equations

$$y = 4x - 5 \quad \text{and} \quad y = -3x + 7.$$

EXAMPLE 5

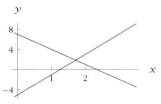

The lines
$y = 4x - 5$ *(blue) and*
$y = -3x + 7$ *(red).*

SOLUTION The figure here is good enough to give an estimate of the coordinates of the point of intersection of the two lines, but to find the exact coordinates we need to use algebra.

To find the intersection of the two lines, we need to find a point (x, y) that satisfies both the equations above. The simplest way to solve this system of two simultaneous equations is to notice that the left side of both equations equals y; thus the right sides must be equal. Setting the two right sides equal to each other, we get the equation

$$4x - 5 = -3x + 7.$$

Solving this equation for x gives $x = \frac{12}{7}$. Then this value of x can be substituted in the first equation $y = 4x - 5$, giving $y = \frac{13}{7}$. As a check that we have not made an error, we can substitute $x = \frac{12}{7}$ into our second equation $y = -3x + 7$, again getting $y = \frac{13}{7}$ (getting a different value of y would indicate that an error has been made somewhere).

Thus the two lines intersect at the point $(\frac{12}{7}, \frac{13}{7})$, which is consistent with the figure above.

The next several paragraphs give an algebraic explanation for the characterization of parallel lines, as compared to the geometric explanation that we saw earlier.

Suppose we have two distinct lines in the xy-plane given by the equations

$$y = m_1 x + b_1 \quad \text{and} \quad y = m_2 x + b_2.$$

Two distinct lines in the coordinate plane are parallel if and only if they do not intersect. Thus to determine whether or not these lines are parallel, we can determine algebraically whether or not they intersect. To do this, we set the two right sides of the equations above equal to each other, getting

$$m_1 x + b_1 = m_2 x + b_2.$$

This equation is equivalent to the equation

$$(m_1 - m_2)x = b_2 - b_1.$$

First suppose $m_1 = m_2$. Then the equation above becomes $0x = b_1 - b_2$. Because $b_1 \neq b_2$ (otherwise the two lines would not be distinct), this equation has no solutions. Thus the two lines do not intersect and hence they are parallel.

Now suppose $m_1 \neq m_2$. Then we can divide both sides of the displayed equation above by $m_1 - m_2$, getting a solution to the equation, which leads to a point of intersection of the two lines. Thus if $m_1 \neq m_2$, then the lines are not parallel.

We have shown algebraically that the two lines are parallel if and only if $m_1 = m_2$. In other words, the two lines are parallel if and only if they have the same slope.

Perpendicular Lines

Our next goal is to show that two lines with slopes m_1 and m_2 are perpendicular if and only if $m_1 m_2 = -1$. If $m_1 m_2 = -1$, then either m_1 or m_2

is negative. Thus before beginning our treatment of perpendicular lines, we take a brief detour to make clear the geometry of a line with negative slope.

A line with negative slope slants down from left to right. The figure below shows a line with negative slope; to avoid clutter the coordinate axes are not shown:

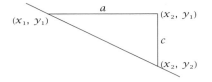

A line with slope $-\frac{c}{a}$.

In the figure above, a is the length of the horizontal line segment and c is the length of the vertical line segment. Of course a and c are positive numbers, because lengths are positive. In terms of the coordinates as shown in the figure above, we have $a = x_2 - x_1$ and $c = y_1 - y_2$. The slope of this line equals $(y_2 - y_1)/(x_2 - x_1)$, which equals $-c/a$.

Now consider two perpendicular lines, as shown in blue in the figure here, where again to avoid clutter the coordinate axes are not shown. In addition to the two perpendicular lines in blue, the figure shows the horizontal line segment PS and the vertical line segment QT, which intersect at S.

We assume that the angle PQT is θ degrees. To check that the other three labeled angles in the figure are labeled correctly, first note that the triangle QPT is a right triangle, one of whose angles is θ degrees. Thus the angle PTQ is $90 - \theta$ degrees, as shown in the figure. Consideration of the right triangle PST now shows that angle TPS is θ degrees, as labeled. This then implies that angle QPS is $90 - \theta$ degrees, as shown in the figure.

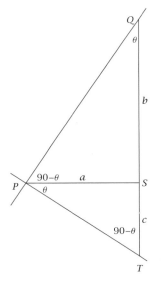

This figure contains three right triangles: QPT, PSQ, and TSP.

Let a denote the length of the line segment PS, let b denote the length of the line segment QS, and let c denote the length of the line segment ST, as shown in the figure.

The line containing the points P and Q has slope b/a, as can be seen from the figure. Furthermore, as can be seen from our brief discussion of lines with negative slope, the line containing the points P and T has slope $-c/a$. To find a relationship between the slopes of these two lines, we will find a formula connecting a, b, and c.

Consider the right triangles PSQ and TSP in the figure. These triangles have the same angles, and thus they are similar. Thus the ratios of corresponding sides are equal. Specifically, we have

$$\frac{b}{a} = \frac{a}{c}.$$

Multiplying both sides of this equation by $-c/a$, we get

$$\left(\frac{b}{a}\right) \cdot \left(-\frac{c}{a}\right) = -1.$$

As we have already seen, the first quantity on the left above is the slope of the line containing the points P and Q, and the second quantity is the slope of the line containing the points P and T. Thus we can conclude that the product of the slopes of these two perpendicular lines equals -1.

The logic used above is reversible. Specifically, suppose instead of starting with the assumption that the two lines in blue are perpendicular, we start with the assumption that the product of their slopes equals -1. This implies that $\frac{b}{a} = \frac{a}{c}$, which implies that the two right triangles PSQ and TSP are similar; thus these two triangles have the same angles. This implies that the angles are labeled correctly in the figure above (assuming that we start by declaring that angle PQS measures θ degrees). This then implies that angle QPT measures $90°$. Thus the two lines in blue are perpendicular.

In conclusion, we have derived the following characterization of perpendicular lines:

Numbers m_1 and m_2 such that $m_1 m_2 = -1$ are sometimes called **negative reciprocals** *of each other.*

Perpendicular lines

Two nonvertical lines are perpendicular if and only if the product of their slopes equals -1.

EXAMPLE 6

Show that the lines in the xy-plane given by the equations

$$y = 4x - 5 \quad \text{and} \quad y = -\tfrac{1}{4}x + 18$$

are perpendicular.

SOLUTION The first line has slope 4; the second line has slope $-\frac{1}{4}$. The product of these slopes is $4 \cdot (-\frac{1}{4})$, which equals -1. Because the product of the two slopes equals -1, the two lines are perpendicular.

To show that two lines are perpendicular, we only need to know the slopes of the lines, not their full equations. The following example illustrates this point.

EXAMPLE 7

Show that the line containing the points $(1, 2)$ and $(3, 7)$ is perpendicular to the line containing the points $(9, 3)$ and $(4, 5)$.

SOLUTION The line containing $(1, 2)$ and $(3, 7)$ has slope $\frac{7-2}{3-1}$, which equals $\frac{5}{2}$. Also, the line containing $(9, 3)$ and $(4, 5)$ has slope $\frac{5-3}{4-9}$, which equals $-\frac{2}{5}$. Because the product $\frac{5}{2} \cdot (-\frac{2}{5})$ equals -1, the two lines are perpendicular.

EXERCISES

1. What are the coordinates of the unlabeled vertex of the smaller of the two right triangles in the figure at the beginning of this section?

2. What are the coordinates of the unlabeled vertex of the larger of the two right triangles in the figure at the beginning of this section?

3. Find the slope of the line that contains the points $(3, 4)$ and $(7, 13)$.

4. Find the slope of the line that contains the points $(2, 11)$ and $(6, -5)$.

5. Find a number t such that the line containing the points $(1, t)$ and $(3, 7)$ has slope 5.

6. Find a number c such that the line containing the points $(c, 4)$ and $(-2, 9)$ has slope -3.

7. Find the equation of the line in the xy-plane with slope 2 that contains the point $(7, 3)$.

8. Find the equation of the line in the xy-plane with slope -4 that contains the point $(-5, -2)$.

9. Find the equation of the line that contains the points $(2, -1)$ and $(4, 9)$.

10. Find the equation of the line that contains the points $(-3, 2)$ and $(-5, 7)$.

11. Find a number t such that the point $(3, t)$ is on the line containing the points $(7, 6)$ and $(14, 10)$.

12. Find a number t such that the point $(-2, t)$ is on the line containing the points $(5, -2)$ and $(10, -8)$.

13. Find a number c such that the point $(c, 13)$ is on the line containing the points $(-4, -17)$ and $(6, 33)$.

14. Find a number c such that the point $(c, -19)$ is on the line containing the points $(2, 1)$ and $(4, 9)$.

15. Find a number t such that the point $(t, 2t)$ is on the line containing the points $(3, -7)$ and $(5, -15)$.

16. Find a number t such that the point $(t, \frac{t}{2})$ is on the line containing the points $(2, -4)$ and $(-3, -11)$.

17. Let $f(x)$ be the number of seconds in x days. Find a formula for $f(x)$.

18. Let $f(x)$ be the number of seconds in x weeks. Find a formula for $f(x)$.

19. Let $f(x)$ be the number of inches in x miles. Find a formula for $f(x)$.

20. Let $f(x)$ be the number of miles in x feet. Find a formula for $f(x)$.

21. Let $f(x)$ be the number of kilometers in x miles. Find a formula for $f(x)$.
    [*The exact conversion between the English measurement system and the metric system is given by the equation* 1 *inch* = 2.54 *centimeters*.]

22. Let $f(x)$ be the number of miles in x meters. Find a formula for $f(x)$.

23. Let $f(x)$ be the number of inches in x centimeters. Find a formula for $f(x)$.

24. Let $f(x)$ be the number of meters in x feet. Find a formula for $f(x)$.

25. Find the equation of the line in the xy-plane that contains the point $(3, 2)$ and that is parallel to the line $y = 4x - 1$.

26. Find the equation of the line in the xy-plane that contains the point $(-4, -5)$ and that is parallel to the line $y = -2x + 3$.

27. Find the equation of the line that contains the point $(2, 3)$ and that is parallel to the line containing the points $(7, 1)$ and $(5, 6)$.

28. Find the equation of the line that contains the point $(-4, 3)$ and that is parallel to the line containing the points $(3, -7)$ and $(6, -9)$.

29. Find a number t such that the line containing the points $(t, 2)$ and $(3, 5)$ is parallel to the line containing the points $(-1, 4)$ and $(-3, -2)$.

30. Find a number t such that the line containing the points $(-3, t)$ and $(2, -4)$ is parallel to the line containing the points $(5, 6)$ and $(-2, 4)$.

31. Find the intersection in the xy-plane of the lines $y = 5x + 3$ and $y = -2x + 1$.

32. Find the intersection in the xy-plane of the lines $y = -4x + 5$ and $y = 5x - 2$.

33. Find a number b such that the three lines in the xy-plane given by the equations $y = 2x + b$, $y = 3x - 5$, and $y = -4x + 6$ have a common intersection point.

34. Find a number m such that the three lines in the xy-plane given by the equations $y = mx + 3$, $y = 4x + 1$, and $y = 5x + 7$ have a common intersection point.

35. Find the equation of the line in the xy-plane that contains the point $(4, 1)$ and that is perpendicular to the line whose equation is $y = 3x + 5$.

36. Find the equation of the line in the xy-plane that contains the point $(-3, 2)$ and that is perpendicular to the line whose equation is $y = -5x + 1$.

37. Find a number t such that the line in the xy-plane containing the points $(t, 4)$ and $(2, -1)$ is perpendicular to the line $y = 6x - 7$.

38. Find a number t such that the line in the xy-plane containing the points $(-3, t)$ and $(4, 3)$ is perpendicular to the line $y = -5x + 999$.

39. Find a number t such that the line containing the points $(4, t)$ and $(-1, 6)$ is perpendicular to the line that contains the points $(3, 5)$ and $(1, -2)$.

40. Find a number t such that the line containing the points $(t, -2)$ and $(-3, 5)$ is perpendicular to the line that contains the points $(4, 7)$ and $(1, 11)$.

PROBLEMS

Some problems require considerably more thought than the exercises.
Unlike exercises, problems usually have more than one correct answer.

41. Show that the points $(-84, -14)$, $(21, 1)$, and $(98, 12)$ lie on a line.

42. Show that the points $(-8, -65)$, $(1, 52)$, and $(3, 77)$ do not lie on a line.

43. Change just one of the six numbers in the problem above so that the resulting three points do lie on a line.

44. Show that for every number t, the point $(5 - 3t, 7 - 4t)$ is on the line containing the points $(2, 3)$ and $(5, 7)$.

45. Show that the composition of two linear functions is a linear function.

46. Show that if f and g are linear functions, then the graphs of $f \circ g$ and $g \circ f$ have the same slope.

47. Show that a linear function is increasing if and only if the slope of its graph is positive.

48. Show that a linear function is decreasing if and only if the slope of its graph is negative.

49. Show that every nonconstant linear function is a one-to-one function.

50. Show that if f is the linear function defined by $f(x) = mx + b$, where $m \neq 0$, then the inverse function f^{-1} is defined by the formula $f^{-1}(y) = \frac{1}{m}y - \frac{b}{m}$.

51. Show that the linear function f defined by $f(x) = mx + b$ is an odd function if and only if $b = 0$.

52. Show that the linear function f defined by $f(x) = mx + b$ is an even function if and only if $m = 0$.

53. We used the similar triangles to show that the product of the slopes of two perpendicular lines equals -1. The steps below outline an alternative proof that avoids the use of similar triangles but uses more algebra instead. Use the figure below, which is the same as the figure used earlier except that there is now no need to label the angles.

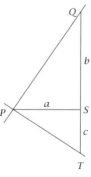

QP is perpendicular to PT.

(a) Apply the Pythagorean Theorem to triangle PSQ to find the length of the line segment PQ in terms of a and b.

(b) Apply the Pythagorean Theorem to triangle PST to find the length of the line segment PT in terms of a and c.

(c) Apply the Pythagorean Theorem to triangle QPT to find the length of the line segment QT in terms of the lengths of the line segments of PQ and PT calculated in the first two parts of this problem.

(d) As can be seen from the figure, the length of the line segment QT equals $b + c$. Thus set the formula for length of the line segment QT, as calculated in the previous part of this problem, equal to $b + c$, and solve the resulting equation for c in terms of a and b.

(e) Use the result in the previous part of this problem to show that the slope of the line containing P and Q times the slope of the line containing P and T equals -1.

54. Show that the graphs of two linear functions f and g are perpendicular if and only if the graph of $f \circ g$ has slope -1.

WORKED-OUT SOLUTIONS *to Odd-numbered Exercises*

Do not read these worked-out solutions before first struggling to do the exercises yourself. Otherwise you risk the danger of mimicking the techniques shown here without understanding the ideas.

Best way to learn: Carefully read the section of the textbook, then do all the odd-numbered exercises (even if they have not been assigned) and check your answers here. If you get stuck on an exercise, reread the section of the textbook—then try the exercise again. If you are still stuck, then look at the worked-out solution here.

1. What are the coordinates of the unlabeled vertex of the smaller of the two right triangles in the figure at the beginning of this section?

   SOLUTION Drawing vertical and horizontal lines from the point in question to the coordinate axes shows that the coordinates of the point are (x_2, y_1).

3. Find the slope of the line that contains the points $(3, 4)$ and $(7, 13)$.

   SOLUTION The line containing the points $(3, 4)$ and $(7, 13)$ has slope

   $$\frac{13 - 4}{7 - 3},$$

   which equals $\frac{9}{4}$.

5. Find a number t such that the line containing the points $(1, t)$ and $(3, 7)$ has slope 5.

   SOLUTION The slope of the line containing the points $(1, t)$ and $(3, 7)$ equals

   $$\frac{7 - t}{3 - 1},$$

   which equals $\frac{7-t}{2}$. We want this slope to equal 5. Thus we must find a number t such that

   $$\frac{7 - t}{2} = 5.$$

   Solving this equation for t, we get $t = -3$.

7. Find the equation of the line in the xy-plane with slope 2 that contains the point $(7, 3)$.

   SOLUTION If (x, y) denotes a typical point on the line with slope 2 that contains the point $(7, 3)$, then

   $$\frac{y - 3}{x - 7} = 2.$$

   Multiplying both sides of this equation by $x - 7$ and then adding 3 to both sides gives the equation

   $$y = 2x - 11.$$

   CHECK The line whose equation is $y = 2x - 11$ has slope 2. We should also check that the point $(7, 3)$ is on this line. In other words, we need to verify the alleged equation

$$3 \overset{?}{=} 2 \cdot 7 - 11.$$

Simple arithmetic shows that this is indeed true.

9. Find the equation of the line that contains the points $(2, -1)$ and $(4, 9)$.

SOLUTION The line that contains the points $(2, -1)$ and $(4, 9)$ has slope

$$\frac{9 - (-1)}{4 - 2},$$

which equals 5. Thus if (x, y) denotes a typical point on this line, then

$$\frac{y - 9}{x - 4} = 5.$$

Multiplying both sides of this equation by $x - 4$ and then adding 9 to both sides gives the equation

$$y = 5x - 11.$$

CHECK We need to check that both $(2, -1)$ and $(4, 9)$ are on the line whose equation is $y = 5x - 11$. In other words, we need to verify the alleged equations

$$-1 \overset{?}{=} 5 \cdot 2 - 11 \quad \text{and} \quad 9 \overset{?}{=} 5 \cdot 4 - 11.$$

Simple arithmetic shows that both alleged equations are indeed true.

11. Find a number t such that the point $(3, t)$ is on the line containing the points $(7, 6)$ and $(14, 10)$.

SOLUTION First we find the equation of the line containing the points $(7, 6)$ and $(14, 10)$. To do this, note that the line containing those two points has slope

$$\frac{10 - 6}{14 - 7},$$

which equals $\frac{4}{7}$. Thus if (x, y) denotes a typical point on this line, then

$$\frac{y - 6}{x - 7} = \frac{4}{7}.$$

Multiplying both sides of this equation by $x - 7$ and then adding 6 gives the equation

$$y = \tfrac{4}{7}x + 2.$$

Now we can find a number t such that the point $(3, t)$ is on the line given by the equation above. To do this, in the equation above replace x by 3 and y by t, getting

$$t = \tfrac{4}{7} \cdot 3 + 2.$$

Performing the arithmetic to compute the right side, we get $t = \frac{26}{7}$.

CHECK We should check that all three points $(7, 6)$, $(14, 10)$, and $(3, \frac{26}{7})$ are on the line $y = \frac{4}{7}x + 2$. In other words, we need to verify the alleged equations

$$6 \overset{?}{=} \tfrac{4}{7} \cdot 7 + 2, \quad 10 \overset{?}{=} \tfrac{4}{7} \cdot 14 + 2, \quad \tfrac{26}{7} \overset{?}{=} \tfrac{4}{7} \cdot 3 + 2.$$

Simple arithmetic shows that all three alleged equations are indeed true.

13. Find a number c such that the point $(c, 13)$ is on the line containing the points $(-4, -17)$ and $(6, 33)$.

SOLUTION First we find the equation of the line containing the points $(-4, -17)$ and $(6, 33)$. To do this, note that the line containing those two points has slope

$$\frac{33 - (-17)}{6 - (-4)},$$

which equals 5. Thus if (x, y) denotes a typical point on this line, then

$$\frac{y - 33}{x - 6} = 5.$$

Multiplying both sides of this equation by $x - 6$ and then adding 33 gives the equation

$$y = 5x + 3.$$

Now we can find a number c such that the point $(c, 13)$ is on the line given by the equation above. To do this, in the equation above replace x by c and y by 13, getting

$$13 = 5c + 3.$$

Solving this equation for c, we get $c = 2$.

CHECK We should check that the three points $(-4, -17)$, $(6, 33)$, and $(2, 13)$ are all on the line whose equation is $y = 5x + 3$. In other words, we need to verify the alleged equations

$$-17 \stackrel{?}{=} 5 \cdot (-4) + 3, \quad 33 \stackrel{?}{=} 5 \cdot 6 + 3, \quad 13 \stackrel{?}{=} 5 \cdot 2 + 2.$$

Simple arithmetic shows that all three alleged equations are indeed true.

15. Find a number t such that the point $(t, 2t)$ is on the line containing the points $(3, -7)$ and $(5, -15)$.

SOLUTION First we find the equation of the line containing the points $(3, -7)$ and $(5, -15)$. To do this, note that the line containing those two points has slope

$$\frac{-7 - (-15)}{3 - 5},$$

which equals -4. Thus if (x, y) denotes a point on this line, then

$$\frac{y - (-7)}{x - 3} = -4.$$

Multiplying both sides of this equation by $x - 3$ and then subtracting 7 gives the equation

$$y = -4x + 5.$$

Now we can find a number t such that the point $(t, 2t)$ is on the line given by the equation above. To do this, in the equation above replace x by t and y by $2t$, getting

$$2t = -4t + 5.$$

Solving this equation for t, we get $t = \frac{5}{6}$.

CHECK We should check that the three points $(3, -7)$, $(5, -15)$, and $(\frac{5}{6}, 2 \cdot \frac{5}{6})$ are all on the line whose equation is $y = -4x + 5$. In other words, we need to verify the alleged equations

$$-7 \stackrel{?}{=} -4 \cdot 3 + 5, \quad -15 \stackrel{?}{=} -4 \cdot 5 + 5, \quad \frac{5}{3} \stackrel{?}{=} -4 \cdot \frac{5}{6} + 5.$$

Simple arithmetic shows that all three alleged equations are indeed true.

17. Let $f(x)$ be the number of seconds in x days. Find a formula for $f(x)$.

SOLUTION Each minute has 60 seconds, and each hour has 60 minutes. Thus each hour has 60×60 seconds, or 3600 seconds. Each day has

24 hours; thus each day has 24×3600 seconds, or 86400 seconds. Thus

$$f(x) = 86400x.$$

19. Let $f(x)$ be the number of inches in x miles. Find a formula for $f(x)$.

SOLUTION Each foot has 12 inches, and each mile has 5280 feet. Thus each mile has 5280×12 inches, or 63360 inches. Thus

$$f(x) = 63360x.$$

21. Let $f(x)$ be the number of kilometers in x miles. Find a formula for $f(x)$.

SOLUTION Multiplying both sides of the equation

$$1 \text{ inch} = 2.54 \text{ centimeters}$$

by 12 gives

$$1 \text{ foot} = 12 \times 2.54 \text{ centimeters}$$
$$= 30.48 \text{ centimeters}.$$

Multiplying both sides of the equation above by 5280 gives

$$1 \text{ mile} = 5280 \times 30.48 \text{ centimeters}$$
$$= 160934.4 \text{ centimeters}$$
$$= 1609.344 \text{ meters}$$
$$= 1.609344 \text{ kilometers}.$$

Multiplying both sides of the equation above by a number x shows that x miles = $1.609344x$ kilometers. In other words,

$$f(x) = 1.609344x.$$

[*The formula above is exact. However, the approximation $f(x) = 1.61x$ is often used.*]

23. Let $f(x)$ be the number of inches in x centimeters. Find a formula for $f(x)$.

SOLUTION Dividing both sides of the equation $1 \text{ inch} = 2.54 \text{ centimeters}$ by 2.54 gives

$$1 \text{ centimeter} = \frac{1}{2.54} \text{ inches.}$$

Multiplying both sides of the equation above by a number x shows that x centimeters = $\frac{x}{2.54}$ inches. In other words,

$$f(x) = \frac{x}{2.54}.$$

25. Find the equation of the line in the xy-plane that contains the point $(3, 2)$ and that is parallel to the line $y = 4x - 1$.

SOLUTION   The line in the xy-plane whose equation is $y = 4x - 1$ has slope 4. Thus each line parallel to it also has slope 4 and hence has the form

$$y = 4x + b$$

for some constant b.

Thus we need to find a constant b such that the point $(3, 2)$ is on the line given by the equation above. Replacing x by 3 and replacing y by 2 in the equation above, we have

$$2 = 4 \cdot 3 + b.$$

Solving this equation for b, we get $b = -10$. Thus the line that we seek is described by the equation

$$y = 4x - 10.$$

27. Find the equation of the line that contains the point $(2, 3)$ and that is parallel to the line containing the points $(7, 1)$ and $(5, 6)$.

SOLUTION   The line containing the points $(7, 1)$ and $(5, 6)$ has slope

$$\frac{6 - 1}{5 - 7},$$

which equals $-\frac{5}{2}$. Thus each line parallel to it also has slope $-\frac{5}{2}$ and hence has the form

$$y = -\frac{5}{2}x + b$$

for some constant b.

Thus we need to find a constant b such that the point $(2, 3)$ is on the line given by the equation above. Replacing x by 2 and replacing y by 3 in the equation above, we have

$$3 = -\frac{5}{2} \cdot 2 + b.$$

Solving this equation for b, we get $b = 8$. Thus the line that we seek is described by the equation

$$y = -\frac{5}{2}x + 8.$$

29. Find a number t such that the line containing the points $(t, 2)$ and $(3, 5)$ is parallel to the line containing the points $(-1, 4)$ and $(-3, -2)$.

SOLUTION   The line containing the points $(-1, 4)$ and $(-3, -2)$ has slope

$$\frac{4 - (-2)}{-1 - (-3)},$$

which equals 3. Thus each line parallel to it also has slope 3.

The line containing the points $(t, 2)$ and $(3, 5)$ has slope

$$\frac{5 - 2}{3 - t},$$

which equals $\frac{3}{3-t}$. From the paragraph above, we want this slope to equal 3. In other words, we need to solve the equation

$$\frac{3}{3 - t} = 3.$$

Dividing both sides of the equation above by 3 and then multiplying both sides by $3 - t$ gives the equation $1 = 3 - t$. Thus $t = 2$.

31. Find the intersection in the xy-plane of the lines $y = 5x + 3$ and $y = -2x + 1$.

SOLUTION   Setting the two right sides of the equations above equal to each other, we get

$$5x + 3 = -2x + 1.$$

To solve this equation for x, add $2x$ to both sides and then subtract 3 from both sides, getting $7x = -2$. Thus $x = -\frac{2}{7}$.

To find the value of y at the intersection point, we can plug the value $x = -\frac{2}{7}$ into either of the equations of the two lines. Choosing the first equation, we have $y = -5 \cdot \frac{2}{7} + 3$, which implies that $y = \frac{11}{7}$. Thus the two lines intersect at the point $(-\frac{2}{7}, \frac{11}{7})$.

CHECK   As a check, we can substitute the value $x = -\frac{2}{7}$ into the equation for the second line and see if that also gives the value $y = \frac{11}{7}$. In other words, we need to verify the alleged equation

$$\frac{11}{7} \overset{?}{=} -2(-\frac{2}{7}) + 1.$$

Simple arithmetic shows that this is true. Thus we indeed have the correct solution.

33. Find a number b such that the three lines in the xy-plane given by the equations $y = 2x + b$, $y = 3x - 5$, and $y = -4x + 6$ have a common intersection point.

   SOLUTION   The unknown b appears in the first equation; thus our first step will be to find the point of intersection of the last two lines. To do this, we set the right sides of the last two equations equal to each other, getting

$$3x - 5 = -4x + 6.$$

   To solve this equation for x, add $4x$ to both sides and then add 5 to both sides, getting $7x = 11$. Thus $x = \frac{11}{7}$. Substituting this value of x into the equation $y = 3x - 5$, we get

$$y = 3 \cdot \tfrac{11}{7} - 5.$$

   Thus $y = -\frac{2}{7}$.

   At this stage, we have shown that the lines given by the equations $y = 3x - 5$ and $y = -4x + 6$ intersect at the point $(\frac{11}{7}, -\frac{2}{7})$. We want the line given by the equation $y = 2x + b$ also to contain this point. Thus we set $x = \frac{11}{7}$ and $y = -\frac{2}{7}$ in this equation, getting

$$-\tfrac{2}{7} = 2 \cdot \tfrac{11}{7} + b.$$

   Solving this equation for b, we get $b = -\frac{24}{7}$.

   CHECK   As a check that the line given by the equation $y = -4x + 6$ contains the point $(\frac{11}{7}, -\frac{2}{7})$, we can substitute the value $x = \frac{11}{7}$ into the equation for that line and see if it gives the value $y = -\frac{2}{7}$. In other words, we need to verify the alleged equation

$$-\tfrac{2}{7} \overset{?}{=} -4 \cdot \tfrac{11}{7} + 6.$$

   Simple arithmetic shows that this is true. Thus we indeed found the correct point of intersection.

   We chose the line whose equation is given by $y = -4x + 6$ for this check because the other two lines had been used in direct calculations in our solution.

35. Find the equation of the line in the xy-plane that contains the point $(4, 1)$ and that is perpendicular to the line whose equation is $y = 3x + 5$.

   SOLUTION   The line in the xy-plane whose equation is $y = 3x + 5$ has slope 3. Thus every line perpendicular to it has slope $-\frac{1}{3}$. Hence the equation of the line that we seek has the form

$$y = -\tfrac{1}{3}x + b$$

   for some constant b. We want the point $(4, 1)$ to be on this line. Substituting $x = 4$ and $y = 1$ into the equation above, we have

$$1 = -\tfrac{1}{3} \cdot 4 + b.$$

   Solving this equation for b, we get $b = \frac{7}{3}$. Thus the equation of the line that we seek is

$$y = -\tfrac{1}{3}x + \tfrac{7}{3}.$$

37. Find a number t such that the line in the xy-plane containing the points $(t, 4)$ and $(2, -1)$ is perpendicular to the line $y = 6x - 7$.

   SOLUTION   The line in the xy-plane whose equation is $y = 6x - 7$ has slope 6. Thus every line perpendicular to it has slope $-\frac{1}{6}$. Thus we want the line containing the points $(t, 4)$ and $(2, -1)$ to have slope $-\frac{1}{6}$. In other words, we want

$$\frac{4 - (-1)}{t - 2} = -\frac{1}{6}.$$

   Solving this equation for t, we get $t = -28$.

39. Find a number t such that the line containing the points $(4, t)$ and $(-1, 6)$ is perpendicular to the line that contains the points $(3, 5)$ and $(1, -2)$.

   SOLUTION   The line containing the points $(3, 5)$ and $(1, -2)$ has slope

$$\frac{5 - (-2)}{3 - 1},$$

   which equals $\frac{7}{2}$. Thus every line perpendicular to it has slope $-\frac{2}{7}$. Thus we want the line containing the points $(4, t)$ and $(-1, 6)$ to have slope $-\frac{2}{7}$. In other words, we want

$$\frac{t - 6}{4 - (-1)} = -\frac{2}{7}.$$

   Solving this equation for t, we get $t = \frac{32}{7}$.

2.2 | *Quadratic Functions and Parabolas*

SECTION OBJECTIVES

By the end of this section you should

- be able to use the completing-the-square technique with quadratic expressions;
- be able to find the vertex of a parabola;
- understand how the quadratic formula was discovered;
- be able to solve quadratic equations.

The Vertex of a Parabola

The last section dealt with linear functions. Now we move up one level of complexity to deal with quadratic functions. We begin with the definition:

Quadratic functions

A **quadratic function** is a function f of the form

$$f(x) = ax^2 + bx + c,$$

where a, b, and c are constants, with $a \neq 0$.

The simplest quadratic function is the function f defined by $f(x) = x^2$; this function arises by taking $a = 1$, $b = 0$, and $c = 0$ in the definition above.

Parabolas can be defined geometrically, but for our purposes it is simpler to define a parabola algebraically:

Parabolas

A **parabola** is the graph of a quadratic function.

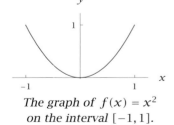

The graph of $f(x) = x^2$ on the interval $[-1, 1]$.

For example, the graph of the quadratic function f defined by $f(x) = x^2$ is the familiar parabola shown here. For this function f we have $f(-x) = f(x)$. In other words, f is an even function, which implies that the graph of f is symmetric about the vertical axis. Note that the vertical axis intersects this parabola at the origin.

As we will soon see, every parabola is symmetric about some line. The point where this line of symmetry intersects the parabola is sufficiently important to deserve its own name:

For example, the vertex of the parabola shown above is the origin.

Vertex

The **vertex** of a parabola is the point where the line of symmetry of the parabola intersects the parabola.

Suppose f, g, and h are defined by

EXAMPLE 1

$$f(x) = -x^2, \quad g(x) = -2x^2, \quad h(x) = -2x^2 + 1.$$

(a) Sketch the graphs of f, g, and h on the interval $[-1, 1]$.

(b) What is the line of symmetry of the graphs of f, g, and h?

(c) Find the vertex of the graph of f, the graph of g, and the graph of h.

(d) What is the maximum value of f? The maximum value of g? The maximum value of h?

SOLUTION

(a) The graph of f is the reflection of the graph of the function x^2 through the horizontal axis. The graph of g is then obtained from the graph of f by stretching vertically by a factor of 2. The graph of h is then obtained from the graph of g by shifting up by 1 unit.

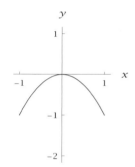

The graph of $-x^2$
on the interval $[-1, 1]$.

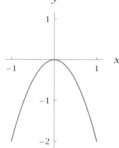

The graph of $-2x^2$
on the interval $[-1, 1]$.

The graph of $-2x^2 + 1$
on the interval $[-1, 1]$.

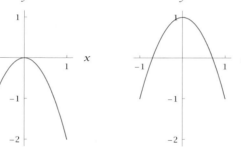

The ancient Greeks discovered that the intersection of a cone and an appropriately positioned plane is a parabola.

(b) As can be seen from the figures above, the line of symmetry for each of the graphs of f, g, and h is the vertical axis.

(c) The figures above show that the vertex of the graph of $-x^2$ is the origin, the vertex of the graph of $-2x^2$ is also the origin, and the vertex of the graph of $-2x^2 + 1$ is the point $(0, 1)$. In each case, the vertex is the intersection of the line of symmetry (which for all three graphs is the vertical axis) with the graph.

(d) As can be seen from the graphs above, the maximum value of f is 0, the maximum value of g is 0, and the maximum value of h is 1. Note that all three functions take on their maximum value when $x = 0$.

Suppose a quadratic function f is defined by $f(x) = ax^2 + c$, where a and c are constants with $a \neq 0$. If $a > 0$, then f takes on its minimum value when $x = 0$ (because ax^2 is positive for all values of x except $x = 0$). Similarly, if $a < 0$, then f takes on its maximum value when $x = 0$ (because ax^2 is negative for all values of x except $x = 0$). In either case, the point $(0, c)$ is the vertex of the graph of f.

For example, the function f defined by $f(x) = 8x^2 + 5$ takes on its minimum value when $x = 0$; the vertex of the graph of f is the point $(0, 5)$.

Completing the Square

We now know how to find the vertex of the graph of quadratic functions of the form $ax^2 + c$. A technique called **completing the square** can be used to put an arbitrary quadratic expression in a form that makes finding the vertex easy. The key to this technique is the simple identity

Be sure that you are thoroughly familiar with this crucial identity.

$$(x + t)^2 = x^2 + 2tx + t^2.$$

The next example illustrates the technique of completing the square.

EXAMPLE 2

Write the expression $x^2 + 6x$ in the form

$$(x + t)^2 + r$$

for some constants t and r.

SOLUTION   When $(x + t)^2$ is expanded to $x^2 + 2tx + t^2$, the $2tx$ term must match the $6x$ term in $x^2 + 6x$. Thus we must have $2t = 6$, and hence we choose $t = 3$.

When $(x + 3)^2$ is expanded, we get $x^2 + 6x + 9$. The x^2 and $6x$ terms match the corresponding terms in the expression $x^2 + 6x$, but the expansion of $(x + 3)^2$ has an extra constant term of 9. Thus to get an equality we subtract 9, obtaining

$$x^2 + 6x = (x + 3)^2 - 9.$$

The general formula for completing the square is shown below. You should not need to memorize this formula. The key point is that the coefficient of the x term will need to be divided by 2, and then the appropriate constant will need to be subtracted to get a correct identity.

Completing the square

$$x^2 + bx = \left(x + \frac{b}{2}\right)^2 - \left(\frac{b}{2}\right)^2$$

For example, if $b = -10$, then the identity above becomes

$$x^2 - 10x = (x - 5)^2 - 25.$$

Note that the term that is subtracted is always positive because $\left(\frac{b}{2}\right)^2$ is positive regardless of whether b is positive or negative, but the $\left(x + \frac{b}{2}\right)^2$ term has a sign that matches the sign of b.

The next example shows the usefulness of completing the square.

EXAMPLE 3

Suppose f is the function defined by

$$f(x) = x^2 + 6x + 11.$$

(a) For what value of x does $f(x)$ attain its minimum value?

(b) Sketch the graph of f on an interval of length 4 centered at the number where f attains its minimum value.

(c) Find the vertex of the graph of f.

SOLUTION

(a) Use the result from the previous example to rewrite $f(x)$ as follows:

$$f(x) = (x^2 + 6x) + 11$$
$$= (x + 3)^2 - 9 + 11$$
$$= (x + 3)^2 + 2$$

Note that the completing the square identity is applied only to the $x^2 + 6x$ part of this expression, and that the constant -9 is then combined with the constant 11.

The last expression shows that f takes on its minimum value when $x = -3$, because $(x + 3)^2$ is positive for all values of x except $x = -3$.

(b) The expression above implies that the graph of f is obtained from the graph of x^2 by shifting left 3 units and then shifting up 2 units. This produces the following graph on the interval $[-5, -1]$, which is the interval of length 4 centered at -3:

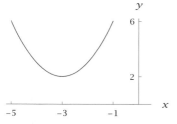

The graph of $x^2 + 6x + 11$ on the interval $[-5, -1]$.

(c) The figure above shows that the vertex of the graph of f is the point $(-3, 2)$. We could have computed this even without the figure by noting that f takes on its minimum value at -3 and that $f(-3) = 2$. Or we could have noted that the graph of f is obtained from the graph of x^2 by shifting left 3 units and then shifting up 2 units, which moves the origin (which is the vertex of the graph of x^2) to the point $(-3, 2)$.

When the coefficient of x^2 is something other than 1, factor out that coefficient from the x^2 and x terms and then use the completing the square identity. The following example illustrates this procedure.

Suppose f is the function defined by

EXAMPLE 4

$$f(x) = -3x^2 + 5x + 1.$$

(a) For what value of x does $f(x)$ attain its maximum value?

(b) Sketch the graph of f on an interval of length 4 centered at the number where f attains its maximum value.

(c) Find the vertex of the graph of f.

SOLUTION

The new expression for f has fractions making it look more cumbersome than the original expression. However, this new expression for f allows us to answer questions about f more easily.

(a) First we factor out the coefficient -3 from the x^2 and x terms and then apply the completing the square identity, rewriting $f(x)$ as follows:

$$f(x) = -3[x^2 - \tfrac{5}{3}x] + 1$$

$$f(x) = -3[(x - \tfrac{5}{6})^2 - \tfrac{25}{36}] + 1$$

$$= -3(x - \tfrac{5}{6})^2 + \tfrac{25}{12} + 1$$

$$= -3(x - \tfrac{5}{6})^2 + \tfrac{37}{12}$$

The last expression shows that f takes on its maximum value when $x = \tfrac{5}{6}$, because $-3(x - \tfrac{5}{6})^2$ is negative for all values of x except $x = \tfrac{5}{6}$.

(b) The expression above for f implies that the graph of f is obtained from the graph of x^2 by shifting right $\tfrac{5}{6}$ units, then stretching vertically by a factor of 3, then reflecting through the horizontal axis, and then shifting up $\tfrac{37}{12}$ units. This produces the following graph on the interval $[-\tfrac{7}{6}, \tfrac{17}{6}]$, which is the interval of length 4 centered at $\tfrac{5}{6}$:

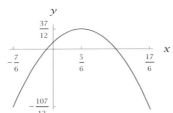

The graph of $-3x^2 + 5x + 1$ on the interval $[-\tfrac{7}{6}, \tfrac{17}{6}]$.

(c) The figure above shows that the vertex of the graph of f is the point $(\tfrac{5}{6}, \tfrac{37}{12})$. We could have computed this even without the figure by noting that f takes on its maximum value at $\tfrac{5}{6}$ and that $f(\tfrac{5}{6}) = \tfrac{37}{12}$. Or we could have noted that the graph of f is obtained from the graph of x^2 by shifting right $\tfrac{5}{6}$ units, then stretching vertically by a factor of 3, then reflecting through the horizontal axis, and then shifting up $\tfrac{37}{12}$ units, which moves the origin (which is the vertex of the graph of x^2) to the point $(\tfrac{5}{6}, \tfrac{37}{12})$.

Notice the relationship in the examples above between the minimum or maximum value of a quadratic function and the vertex of its graph. Specifically, the first coordinate of the vertex of the graph of f is the number where this minimum or maximum value is attained, and the second coordinate of the vertex of the graph of f is the minimum or maximum value of f. This relationship holds for all quadratic functions.

A quadratic function f defined by $f(x) = ax^2 + bx + c$ has a minimum value (but no maximum value) if $a > 0$ and has a maximum value (but no minimum value) if $a < 0$.

Vertex at minimum or maximum value

Suppose f is a quadratic function that takes on its minimum or maximum value at t. Then the point $(t, f(t))$ is the vertex of the graph of f.

The Quadratic Formula

Having worked through some examples, we will now follow the same pattern and complete the square with an arbitrary quadratic function. This will allow us to derive the quadratic formula for solving the equation $f(x) = 0$.

Consider the quadratic function

$$f(x) = ax^2 + bx + c,$$

where $a \neq 0$. Factor out the coefficient a from the first two terms and then complete the square, rewriting $f(x)$ as follows:

$$f(x) = ax^2 + bx + c$$

$$= a\left[x^2 + \frac{b}{a}x\right] + c$$

$$= a\left[\left(x + \frac{b}{2a}\right)^2 - \frac{b^2}{4a^2}\right] + c$$

$$= a\left(x + \frac{b}{2a}\right)^2 - \frac{b^2}{4a} + c$$

$$= a\left(x + \frac{b}{2a}\right)^2 - \frac{b^2 - 4ac}{4a}$$

Suppose now that we want to find the numbers x such that $f(x) = 0$. Setting the last expression for $f(x)$ equal to 0, we have

$$a\left(x + \frac{b}{2a}\right)^2 - \frac{b^2 - 4ac}{4a} = 0,$$

which is equivalent to the equation

$$\left(x + \frac{b}{2a}\right)^2 = \frac{b^2 - 4ac}{4a^2}.$$

Regardless of the value of x, the left side of the last equation is a positive number or 0. Thus if the right side is negative, the equation does not hold for any real number x. In other words, if $b^2 - 4ac < 0$, then the equation $f(x) = 0$ has no real solutions.

If $b^2 - 4ac \geq 0$, then we can take the square root of both sides of the last equation, getting

$$x + \frac{b}{2a} = \pm\frac{\sqrt{b^2 - 4ac}}{2a},$$

which is equivalent to

$$x = \frac{-b \pm \sqrt{b^2 - 4ac}}{2a}.$$

Here $\pm$ is used to indicate that we can choose either the plus sign or minus sign.

By completing the square, we have derived the quadratic formula!

> ### Quadratic formula
>
> Consider the equation
> $$ax^2 + bx + c = 0,$$
>
> where a, b, and c are real numbers with $a \neq 0$.
>
> - If $b^2 - 4ac < 0$, then the equation above has no (real) solutions.
> - If $b^2 - 4ac = 0$, then the equation above has one solution:
> $$x = -\frac{b}{2a}.$$
>
> - If $b^2 - 4ac > 0$, then the equation above has two solutions:
> $$x = \frac{-b \pm \sqrt{b^2 - 4ac}}{2a}.$$

The quadratic formula often is useful in problems that do not initially seem to involve quadratic functions, as illustrated by the following example.

EXAMPLE 5   Find two numbers whose sum equals 7 and whose product equals 8.

SOLUTION   Let's call the two numbers s and t. We want
$$s + t = 7 \quad \text{and} \quad st = 8.$$

Solving the first equation for s, we have $s = 7 - t$. Substituting this expression for s into the second equation gives $(7 - t)t = 8$, which is equivalent to the equation
$$t^2 - 7t + 8 = 0.$$

Using the quadratic formula to solve this equation for t gives
$$t = \frac{7 \pm \sqrt{7^2 - 4 \cdot 8}}{2} = \frac{7 \pm \sqrt{17}}{2}.$$

You should verify that if we had chosen $t = \frac{7-\sqrt{17}}{2}$, then we would have ended up with the same pair of numbers.

Let's choose the solution $t = \frac{7+\sqrt{17}}{2}$. Plugging this value of t into the equation $s = 7-t$ then gives $s = \frac{7-\sqrt{17}}{2}$.

Thus two numbers whose sum equals 7 and whose product equals 8 are $\frac{7-\sqrt{17}}{2}$ and $\frac{7+\sqrt{17}}{2}$.

REMARK   To check that this solution is correct, note that
$$\frac{7 - \sqrt{17}}{2} + \frac{7 + \sqrt{17}}{2} = \frac{14}{2} = 7$$

and
$$\frac{7 - \sqrt{17}}{2} \cdot \frac{7 + \sqrt{17}}{2} = \frac{7^2 - \sqrt{17}^2}{4} = \frac{49 - 17}{4} = \frac{32}{4} = 8.$$

EXERCISES

For Exercises 1–6, find the vertex of the graph of the given function f.

1. $f(x) = 7x^2 - 12$

2. $f(x) = -9x^2 - 5$

3. $f(x) = (x - 2)^2 - 3$

4. $f(x) = (x + 3)^2 + 4$

5. $f(x) = (2x - 5)^2 + 6$

6. $f(x) = (7x + 3)^2 + 5$

For Exercises 7–10, for the given function f:

(a) *Write $f(x)$ in the form $k(x + t)^2 + r$.*

(b) *Find the value of x where $f(x)$ attains its minimum value or its maximum value.*

(c) *Sketch the graph of f on an interval of length 2 centered at the number where f attains its minimum or maximum value.*

(d) *Find the vertex of the graph of f.*

7. $f(x) = x^2 + 7x + 12$

8. $f(x) = 5x^2 + 2x + 1$

9. $f(x) = -2x^2 + 5x - 2$

10. $f(x) = -3x^2 + 5x - 1$

11. Find a constant c such that the graph of $x^2 + 6x + c$ has its vertex on the x-axis.

12. Find a constant c such that the graph of $x^2 + 5x + c$ in the xy-plane has its vertex on the line $y = x$.

13. Find two numbers whose sum equals 10 and whose product equals 7.

14. Find two numbers whose sum equals 6 and whose product equals 4.

15. Find two positive numbers whose difference equals 3 and whose product equals 20.

16. Find two positive numbers whose difference equals 4 and whose product equals 15.

17. Find the minimum value of the function f defined by $f(x) = x^2 - 6x + 2$.

18. Find the minimum value of the function f defined by $f(x) = 3x^2 + 5x + 1$.

19. Find the maximum value of $7 - 2x - x^2$.

20. Find the maximum value of $9 + 5x - 4x^2$.

21. Suppose the graph of f is a parabola with vertex at $(3, 2)$. Suppose $g(x) = 4x + 5$. What are the coordinates of the vertex of the graph of $f \circ g$?

22. Suppose the graph of f is a parabola with vertex at $(-5, 4)$. Suppose $g(x) = 3x - 1$. What are the coordinates of the vertex of the graph of $f \circ g$?

23. Suppose the graph of f is a parabola with vertex at $(3, 2)$. Suppose $g(x) = 4x + 5$. What are the coordinates of the vertex of the graph of $g \circ f$?

24. Suppose the graph of f is a parabola with vertex at $(-5, 4)$. Suppose $g(x) = 3x - 1$. What are the coordinates of the vertex of the graph of $g \circ f$?

25. Suppose the graph of f is a parabola with vertex at (t, s). Suppose $g(x) = ax + b$, where a and b are constants with $a \neq 0$. What are the coordinates of the vertex of the graph of $f \circ g$?

26. Suppose the graph of f is a parabola with vertex at (t, s). Suppose $g(x) = ax + b$, where a and b are constants with $a \neq 0$. What are the coordinates of the vertex of the graph of $g \circ f$?

27. Suppose $h(x) = x^2 + 3x + 4$, with the domain of h being the set of positive numbers. Evaluate $h^{-1}(7)$.

28. Suppose $h(x) = x^2 + 2x - 5$, with the domain of h being the set of positive numbers. Evaluate $h^{-1}(4)$.

For Exercises 29–36, suppose f and g are functions whose domain is the interval $[1, \infty)$, with

$$f(x) = x^2 + 3x + 5 \quad \text{and} \quad g(x) = x^2 + 4x + 7.$$

29. What is the range of f?

30. What is the range of g?

31. Find a formula for f^{-1}.

32. Find a formula for g^{-1}.

33. What is the domain of f^{-1}?

34. What is the domain of g^{-1}?

35. What is the range of f^{-1}?

36. What is the range of g^{-1}?

37. Suppose
$$f(x) = x^2 - 6x + 11.$$
Find the smallest number b such that f is increasing on the interval $[b, \infty)$.

38. Suppose
$$f(x) = x^2 + 8x + 5.$$
Find the smallest number b such that f is increasing on the interval $[b, \infty)$.

PROBLEMS

39. Show that
$$(a + b)^2 = a^2 + b^2$$
if and only if $a = 0$ or $b = 0$.

40. Show that a quadratic function f defined by $f(x) = ax^2 + bx + c$ is an even function if and only if $b = 0$.

41. Show that if f is a nonconstant linear function and g is a quadratic function, then $f \circ g$ and $g \circ f$ are both quadratic functions.

42. Suppose
$$2x^2 + 3x + c > 0$$
for every real number x. Show that $c > \frac{9}{8}$.

43. Suppose
$$3x^2 + bx + 7 > 0$$
for every real number x. Show that $|b| < 2\sqrt{21}$.

44. Suppose
$$at^2 + 5t + 4 > 0$$
for every real number t. Show that $a > \frac{25}{16}$.

45. Suppose
$$f(x) = ax^2 + bx + c,$$
where $a \neq 0$ and $b^2 \geq 4ac$. Verify by direct substitution into the formula above that
$$f\left(\frac{-b + \sqrt{b^2 - 4ac}}{2a}\right) = 0$$
and that
$$f\left(\frac{-b - \sqrt{b^2 - 4ac}}{2a}\right) = 0.$$

46. Suppose $a \neq 0$ and $b^2 \geq 4ac$. Verify by direct calculation that
$$ax^2 + bx + c =$$
$$a\left(x - \frac{-b + \sqrt{b^2 - 4ac}}{2a}\right)\left(x - \frac{-b - \sqrt{b^2 - 4ac}}{2a}\right).$$

47. Suppose $f(x) = ax^2 + bx + c$, where $a \neq 0$. Show that the vertex of the graph of f is the point $\left(-\frac{b}{2a}, \frac{4ac - b^2}{4a}\right)$.

48. Suppose f is a quadratic function such that the equation $f(x) = 0$ has exactly one solution. Show that this solution is the first coordinate of the vertex of the graph of f and that the second coordinate of the vertex equals 0.

49. Suppose f is a quadratic function such that the equation $f(x) = 0$ has two real solutions. Show that the average of these two solutions is the first coordinate of the vertex of the graph of f.

50. Suppose b and c are numbers such that the equation
$$x^2 + bx + c = 0$$
has no real solutions. Explain why the equation
$$x^2 + bx - c = 0$$
has two real solutions.

51. Show that there do not exist two real numbers whose sum equals 7 and whose product equals 13.

WORKED-OUT SOLUTIONS to Odd-numbered Exercises

For Exercises 1–6, find the vertex of the graph of the given function f.

1. $f(x) = 7x^2 - 12$

SOLUTION The value of $7x^2 - 12$ is minimized when $x = 0$. When $x = 0$, the value of $7x^2 - 12$ equals -12. Thus the vertex of the graph of f is $(0, -12)$.

3. $f(x) = (x - 2)^2 - 3$

SOLUTION   The value of $(x - 2)^2 - 3$ is minimized when $x - 2 = 0$, or when $x = 2$. When $x = 2$, the value of $(x - 2)^2 - 3$ equals -3. Thus the vertex of the graph of $(x - 2)^2 - 3$ is $(2, -3)$.

5. $f(x) = (2x - 5)^2 + 6$

SOLUTION   The value of $(2x - 5)^2 + 6$ is minimized when $2x - 5 = 0$, or when $x = \frac{5}{2}$. When $x = \frac{5}{2}$, the value of $(2x - 5)^2 + 6$ equals 6. Thus the vertex of the graph of $(2x - 5)^2 + 6$ is $(\frac{5}{2}, 6)$.

For Exercises 7–10, for the given function f:

   (a) *Write $f(x)$ in the form $k(x + t)^2 + r$.*

   (b) *Find the value of x where $f(x)$ attains its minimum value or its maximum value.*

   (c) *Sketch the graph of f on an interval of length 2 centered at the number where f attains its minimum or maximum value.*

   (d) *Find the vertex of the graph of f.*

7. $f(x) = x^2 + 7x + 12$

SOLUTION

(a) By completing the square, we can write

$$f(x) = x^2 + 7x + 12$$

$$= \left(x + \tfrac{7}{2}\right)^2 - \tfrac{49}{4} + 12$$

$$= \left(x + \tfrac{7}{2}\right)^2 - \tfrac{1}{4}.$$

(b) The expression above shows that the value of $f(x)$ is minimized when $x = -\frac{7}{2}$.

(c) The expression above for f implies that the graph of f is obtained from the graph of x^2 by shifting left $\frac{7}{2}$ units and then shifting down $\frac{1}{4}$ units. This produces the following graph on the interval $[-\frac{9}{2}, -\frac{5}{2}]$, which is the interval of length 2 centered at $-\frac{7}{2}$:

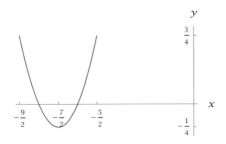

(d) The figure above shows that the vertex of the graph of f is the point $(-\frac{7}{2}, -\frac{1}{4})$. We could have computed this even without the figure by noting that f takes on its minimum value at $-\frac{7}{2}$ and that $f(-\frac{7}{2}) = -\frac{1}{4}$. Or we could have noted that the graph of f is obtained from the graph of x^2 by shifting left $\frac{7}{2}$ units and then shifting down $\frac{1}{4}$ units, which moves the origin (which is the vertex of the graph of x^2) to the point $(-\frac{7}{2}, -\frac{1}{4})$.

9. $f(x) = -2x^2 + 5x - 2$

SOLUTION

(a) By completing the square, we can write

$$f(x) = -2x^2 + 5x - 2$$

$$= -2\left[x^2 - \tfrac{5}{2}x\right] - 2$$

$$= -2\left[\left(x - \tfrac{5}{4}\right)^2 - \tfrac{25}{16}\right] - 2$$

$$= -2\left(x - \tfrac{5}{4}\right)^2 + \tfrac{25}{8} - 2$$

$$= -2\left(x - \tfrac{5}{4}\right)^2 + \tfrac{9}{8}.$$

(b) The expression above shows that the value of $f(x)$ is maximized when $x = \frac{5}{4}$.

(c) The expression above for f implies that the graph of f is obtained from the graph of x^2 by shifting right $\frac{5}{4}$ units, then stretching vertically by a factor of 2, then reflecting through the horizontal axis, and then shifting up $\frac{9}{8}$ units. This produces the following graph on the interval $[\frac{1}{4}, \frac{9}{4}]$, which is the interval of length 2 centered at $\frac{5}{4}$:

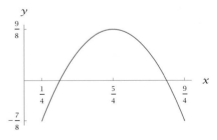

(d) The figure above shows that the vertex of the graph of f is the point $(\frac{5}{4}, \frac{9}{8})$. We could have computed this even without the figure by noting that f takes on its maximum value at $\frac{5}{4}$ and that $f(\frac{5}{4}) = \frac{9}{8}$. Or we could have noted that the graph of f is obtained from the graph of x^2 by shifting right $\frac{5}{4}$ units, then stretching vertically by a factor of 2, then reflecting through the horizontal axis, and then shifting up $\frac{9}{8}$ units, which moves the origin (which is the vertex of the graph of x^2) to the point $(\frac{5}{4}, \frac{9}{8})$.

11. Find a constant c such that the graph of $x^2 + 6x + c$ has its vertex on the x-axis.

SOLUTION   First we find the vertex of the graph of f. To do this, complete the square:

$$x^2 + 6x + c = (x + 3)^2 - 9 + c$$

Thus the value of $x^2 + 6x + c$ is minimized when $x = -3$. When $x = -3$, the value of $x^2 + 6x + c$ equals $-9 + c$. Thus the vertex of $x^2 + 6x + c$ is $(-3, -9 + c)$.

The x-axis consists of the points whose second coordinate equals 0. Thus the vertex of $x^2 + 6x + c$ will be on the x-axis when $-9 + c = 0$, or equivalently when $c = 9$.

13. Find two numbers whose sum equals 10 and whose product equals 7.

SOLUTION   Let's call the two numbers s and t. We want

$$s + t = 10 \quad \text{and} \quad st = 7.$$

Solving the first equation for s, we have $s = 10 - t$. Substituting this expression for s into the second equation gives $(10 - t)t = 7$, which is equivalent to the equation

$$t^2 - 10t + 7 = 0.$$

Using the quadratic formula to solve this equation for t gives

$$t = \frac{10 \pm \sqrt{10^2 - 4 \cdot 7}}{2} = \frac{10 \pm \sqrt{72}}{2}$$

$$= \frac{10 \pm \sqrt{36 \cdot 2}}{2} = 5 \pm 3\sqrt{2}.$$

Let's choose the solution $t = 5 + 3\sqrt{2}$. Plugging this value of t into the equation $s = 10 - t$ then gives $s = 5 - 3\sqrt{2}$.

Thus two numbers whose sum equals 10 and whose product equals 7 are $5 - 3\sqrt{2}$ and $5 + 3\sqrt{2}$.

CHECK   To check that this solution is correct, note that

$$(5 - 3\sqrt{2}) + (5 + 3\sqrt{2}) = 10$$

and

$$(5 - 3\sqrt{2})(5 + 3\sqrt{2}) = 5^2 - 3^2\sqrt{2}^2 = 25 - 9 \cdot 2 = 7.$$

15. Find two positive numbers whose difference equals 3 and whose product equals 20.

SOLUTION   Let's call the two numbers s and t. We want

$$s - t = 3 \quad \text{and} \quad st = 20.$$

Solving the first equation for s, we have $s = t + 3$. Substituting this expression for s into the second equation gives $(t + 3)t = 20$, which is equivalent to the equation

$$t^2 + 3t - 20 = 0.$$

Using the quadratic formula to solve this equation for t gives

$$t = \frac{-3 \pm \sqrt{3^2 + 4 \cdot 20}}{2} = \frac{-3 \pm \sqrt{89}}{2}.$$

Choosing the minus sign in the plus-or-minus expression above would lead to a negative value for t. Because this exercise requires that t be positive, we choose $t = \frac{-3 + \sqrt{89}}{2}$. Plugging this value of t into the equation $s = t + 3$ then gives $s = \frac{3 + \sqrt{89}}{2}$.

Thus two numbers whose difference equals 3 and whose product equals 20 are $\frac{3 + \sqrt{89}}{2}$ and $\frac{-3 + \sqrt{89}}{2}$.

CHECK   To check that this solution is correct, note that

$$\frac{3 + \sqrt{89}}{2} - \frac{-3 + \sqrt{89}}{2} = \frac{6}{2} = 3$$

and

$$\frac{3 + \sqrt{89}}{2} \cdot \frac{-3 + \sqrt{89}}{2} = \frac{\sqrt{89} + 3}{2} \cdot \frac{\sqrt{89} - 3}{2}$$

$$= \frac{\sqrt{89}^2 - 3^2}{4} = \frac{80}{4} = 20.$$

17. Find the minimum value of the function f defined by $f(x) = x^2 - 6x + 2$.

    SOLUTION   By completing the square, we can write

    $$f(x) = x^2 - 6x + 2$$
    $$= (x - 3)^2 - 9 + 2$$
    $$= (x - 3)^2 - 7.$$

    The expression above shows that the minimum value of f is -7 (and that this minimum value occurs when $x = 3$).

19. Find the maximum value of $7 - 2x - x^2$.

    SOLUTION   By completing the square, we can write

    $$7 - 2x - x^2 = -[x^2 + 2x] + 7$$
    $$= -[(x + 1)^2 - 1] + 7$$
    $$= -(x + 1)^2 + 8.$$

    The expression above shows that the maximum value of $7 - 2x - x^2$ is 8 (and that this maximum value occurs when $x = -1$).

21. Suppose the graph of f is a parabola with vertex at $(3, 2)$. Suppose $g(x) = 4x + 5$. What are the coordinates of the vertex of the graph of $f \circ g$?

    SOLUTION   Note that

    $$(f \circ g)(x) = f(g(x)) = f(4x + 5).$$

    Because $f(x)$ attains its minimum or maximum value when $x = 3$, we see from the equation above that $(f \circ g)(x)$ attains its minimum or maximum value when $4x + 5 = 3$. Solving this equation for x, we see that $(f \circ g)(x)$ attains its minimum or maximum value when $x = -\frac{1}{2}$. The equation displayed above shows that this minimum or maximum value of $(f \circ g)(x)$ is the same as the minimum or maximum value of f, which equals 2. Thus the vertex of the graph of $f \circ g$ is $(-\frac{1}{2}, 2)$.

23. Suppose the graph of f is a parabola with vertex at $(3, 2)$. Suppose $g(x) = 4x + 5$. What are the coordinates of the vertex of the graph of $g \circ f$?

    SOLUTION   Note that

    $$(g \circ f)(x) = g(f(x)) = 4f(x) + 5.$$

    Because $f(x)$ attains its minimum or maximum value (which equals 2) when $x = 3$, we see from the equation above that $(g \circ f)(x)$ also attains its minimum or maximum value when $x = 3$. We have

    $$(g \circ f)(3) = g(f(3)) = 4f(3) + 5 = 4 \cdot 2 + 5 = 13.$$

    Thus the vertex of the graph of $g \circ f$ is $(3, 13)$.

25. Suppose the graph of f is a parabola with vertex at (t, s). Suppose $g(x) = ax + b$, where a and b are constants with $a \neq 0$. What are the coordinates of the vertex of the graph of $f \circ g$?

    SOLUTION   Note that

    $$(f \circ g)(x) = f(ax + b).$$

    Because $f(x)$ attains its minimum or maximum value when $x = t$, we see from the equation above that $(f \circ g)(x)$ attains its minimum or maximum value when $ax + b = t$. Thus $(f \circ g)(x)$ attains its minimum or maximum value when $x = \frac{t-b}{a}$. The equation displayed above shows that this minimum or maximum value of $(f \circ g)(x)$ is the same as the minimum or maximum value of f, which equals s. Thus the vertex of the graph of $f \circ g$ is $(\frac{t-b}{a}, s)$.

27. Suppose $h(x) = x^2 + 3x + 4$, with the domain of h being the set of positive numbers. Evaluate $h^{-1}(7)$.

    SOLUTION   We need to find a positive number x such that $h(x) = 7$. In other words, we need to find a positive solution to the equation

    $$x^2 + 3x + 4 = 7,$$

    which is equivalent to the equation

    $$x^2 + 3x - 3 = 0.$$

    The quadratic formula shows that the equation above has solutions

    $$x = \frac{-3 + \sqrt{21}}{2} \quad \text{and} \quad x = \frac{-3 - \sqrt{21}}{2}.$$

    Because the domain of h is the set of positive numbers, the value of x that we seek must be positive. The second solution above is negative; thus it can be discarded, giving $h^{-1}(7) = \frac{-3 + \sqrt{21}}{2}$.

CHECK To check that $h^{-1}(7) = \frac{-3+\sqrt{21}}{2}$, we must verify that $h\left(\frac{-3+\sqrt{21}}{2}\right) = 7$. We have

$$h\left(\tfrac{-3+\sqrt{21}}{2}\right) = \left(\tfrac{-3+\sqrt{21}}{2}\right)^2 + 3\left(\tfrac{-3+\sqrt{21}}{2}\right) + 4$$

$$= \tfrac{15-3\sqrt{21}}{2} + \tfrac{-9+3\sqrt{21}}{2} + 4$$

$$= 7,$$

as desired.

For Exercises 29–36, suppose f and g are functions whose domain is the interval $[1, \infty)$, with

$$f(x) = x^2 + 3x + 5 \quad \text{and} \quad g(x) = x^2 + 4x + 7.$$

29. What is the range of f?

SOLUTION To find the range of f, we need to find the numbers y such that

$$y = x^2 + 3x + 5$$

for some x is the domain of f. In other words, we need to find the values of y such that the equation above can be solved for a number $x \geq 1$. To solve this equation for x, subtract y from both sides, getting the equation

$$x^2 + 3x + (5 - y) = 0.$$

Using the quadratic equation to solve this equation for x, we get

$$x = \frac{-3 \pm \sqrt{3^2 - 4(5 - y)}}{2} = \frac{-3 \pm \sqrt{4y - 11}}{2}.$$

Choosing the negative sign in the equation above would give a negative value for x, which is not possible because x is required to be in the domain of f, which is the interval $[1, \infty)$. Thus we must have

$$x = \frac{-3 + \sqrt{4y - 11}}{2}.$$

Because x is required to be in the domain of f, which is the interval $[1, \infty)$, we must have

$$\frac{-3 + \sqrt{4y - 11}}{2} \geq 1.$$

Multiplying both sides of this inequality by 2 and then adding 3 to both sides gives the inequality

$$\sqrt{4y - 11} \geq 5.$$

Thus $4y - 11 \geq 25$, which implies that $4y \geq 36$, which implies that $y \geq 9$. Thus the range of f is the interval $[9, \infty)$.

31. Find a formula for f^{-1}.

SOLUTION The expression derived in the solution to Exercise 29 shows that f^{-1} is given by the formula

$$f^{-1}(y) = \frac{-3 + \sqrt{4y - 11}}{2}.$$

33. What is the domain of f^{-1}?

SOLUTION The domain of f^{-1} equals the range of f. Thus the domain of f^{-1} is the interval $[9, \infty)$.

35. What is the range of f^{-1}?

SOLUTION The range of f^{-1} equals the domain of f. Thus the range of f^{-1} is the interval $[1, \infty)$.

37. Suppose

$$f(x) = x^2 - 6x + 11.$$

Find the smallest number b such that f is increasing on the interval $[b, \infty)$.

SOLUTION The graph of f is a parabola shaped like this:

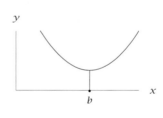

The largest interval on which f is increasing is $[b, \infty)$, where b is the first coordinate of the vertex of the graph of f.

As can be seen from the figure above, the smallest number b such that f is increasing on the interval $[b, \infty)$ is the first coordinate of the vertex of the graph of f. To find this number, we complete the square:

$$x^2 - 6x + 11 = (x - 3)^2 - 9 + 11$$

$$= (x - 3)^2 + 2.$$

The equation above shows that the first coordinate of the vertex of the parabola is 3. Thus we take $b = 3$.

2.3 *Integer Exponents*

SECTION OBJECTIVES

By the end of this section you should

- understand why x^0 is defined to equal 1 (for $x \neq 0$);

- understand why x^{-m} is defined to equal $\frac{1}{x^m}$ (for m a positive integer and $x \neq 0$);

- be able to manipulate and simplify expressions involving integer exponents.

Exponentiation by Positive Integers

Multiplication by a positive integer is repeated addition, in the sense that if x is a real number and m is a positive integer, then mx equals the sum with x repeated m times:

$$mx = \underbrace{x + x + \cdots + x}_{x \text{ repeated } m \text{ times}}.$$

Just as multiplication by a positive integer is defined as repeated addition, **exponentiation** by a positive integer is defined as repeated multiplication:

Exponentiation by a positive integer

If x is a real number and m is a positive integer, then x^m is defined to be the product with x repeated m times:

$$x^m = \underbrace{x \cdot x \cdot \cdots \cdot x}_{x \text{ repeated } m \text{ times}}.$$

Here are three important special cases of this definition:

$$0^m = 0,$$
$$1^m = 1,$$
$$x^1 = x.$$

For example,

$$2^3 = 2 \cdot 2 \cdot 2 = 8.$$

If m is a positive integer, then we can define a function f by

$$f(x) = x^m.$$

We can gain some insight into the behavior of x^m by looking at the graph of this function for various values of m.

For $m = 1$, the graph of the function defined by $f(x) = x$ is a line through the origin with slope 1. For $m = 2$, the graph of the function defined by $f(x) = x^2$ is the familiar parabola with vertex at the origin, as shown here.

The graphs of x^3, x^4, x^5, and x^6 are shown below, separated into two groups according to their shape. Note that x^3 and x^5 are increasing functions, but x^4 and x^6 are decreasing on the interval $(-\infty, 0]$ and increasing on the interval $[0, \infty)$.

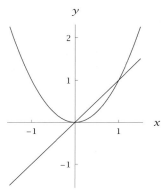

The graphs of x (blue) and x^2 (red) on $[-1.5, 1.5]$.

Although the graphs of x^4 and x^6 have a parabola-type shape, these graphs are not true parabolas.

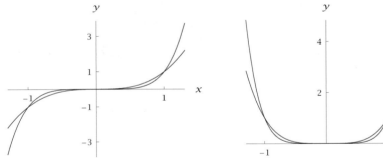

The graphs of x^3 (blue) and x^5 (red) on $[-1.3, 1.3]$.

The graphs of x^4 (blue) and x^6 (red) on $[-1.3, 1.3]$.

We have now seen graphs of x^m for $m = 1, 2, 3, 4, 5, 6$. For larger odd values of m, the graph of x^m has roughly the same shape as the graphs of x^3 and x^5; for larger even values of m, the graph of x^m has roughly the same shape as the graphs of x^2, x^4, and x^6.

Properties of Exponentiation

The properties of exponentiation by positive integers follow from the definition of exponentiation as repeated multiplication. For example, suppose x is a real number and m and n are positive integers. Then

$$x^m x^n = \underbrace{x \cdot x \cdot \,\cdots\, \cdot x}_{x \text{ repeated } m \text{ times}} \cdot \underbrace{x \cdot x \cdot \,\cdots\, \cdot x}_{x \text{ repeated } n \text{ times}}.$$

Because x is repeated a total of $m + n$ times in the product above, we have

$$x^m x^n = x^{m+n}.$$

*The expression x^m is called the mth **power** of x.*

Taking $n = m$ in the equation above, we see that $x^m x^m = x^{m+m}$, which can be rewritten as $(x^m)^2 = x^{2m}$. More generally, continuing with our assumption that x is a real number and m and n are positive integers, the definition of exponentiation shows that

$$(x^m)^n = \underbrace{x^m \cdot x^m \cdot \,\cdots\, \cdot x^m}_{x^m \text{ repeated } n \text{ times}}.$$

Each x^m on the right side of the equation above equals the product with x repeated m times, and x^m is repeated n times. Thus x is repeated a total of mn times in the product above, which shows that

$$(x^m)^n = x^{mn}.$$

Consider now two real numbers x and y, along with a positive integer m. Then

$$(xy)^m = \underbrace{(xy) \cdot (xy) \cdot \ \cdots \ \cdot (xy)}_{(xy) \text{ repeated } m \text{ times}}.$$

Because of the associativity and commutativity of multiplication, the product above can be rearranged to show that

$$(xy)^m = \underbrace{x \cdot x \cdot \ \cdots \ \cdot x}_{x \text{ repeated } m \text{ times}} \cdot \underbrace{y \cdot y \cdot \ \cdots \ \cdot y}_{y \text{ repeated } m \text{ times}}.$$

Thus we see that

$$(xy)^m = x^m y^m.$$

We can summarize our discussion by stating that exponentiation by positive integers obeys the following rules. Soon we will extend these rules to exponentiation by integers that are not necessarily positive.

> ## Properties of exponentiation by positive integers
>
> Suppose x and y are numbers and m and n are positive integers. Then
>
> $$x^m x^n = x^{m+n},$$
>
> $$(x^m)^n = x^{mn},$$
>
> $$x^m y^m = (xy)^m.$$

Defining x^0

To begin the process of extending the definition of exponentiation, consider how x^0 might be defined. Recall that if x is a real number and m and n are positive integers, then

$$x^m x^n = x^{m+n}.$$

We would like to choose the definition of x^0 so that the equation above holds even if $m = 0$. In other words, we would like to define x^0 so that

$$x^0 x^n = x^{0+n}.$$

Rewriting this equation as

$$x^0 x^n = x^n,$$

we see that if $x \neq 0$, then we have no choice but to define x^0 to equal 1.

The paragraph above shows how we should define x^0 for $x \neq 0$, but what happens when $x = 0$? Unfortunately, finding a definition for 0^0 that preserves other exponentiation properties turns out to be impossible. Two conflicting tendencies point to different possible definitions for 0^0:

We have defined x^m as the product of x repeated m times. This definition makes sense only when m is a positive integer. To define x^m for other values of m, we will choose definitions in such a way that the properties listed above for exponentiation by a positive integer continue to hold.

- The equation $x^0 = 1$, valid for all $x \neq 0$, suggests that we should define 0^0 to equal 1.

- The equation $0^m = 0$, valid for all positive integers m, suggests that we should define 0^0 to equal 0.

If we choose to define 0^0 to equal 1, as suggested by the first point above, then we violate the equation $0^m = 0$ suggested by the second point. If we choose to define 0^0 to equal 0, as suggested by the second point above, then we violate the equation $x^0 = 1$ suggested by the first point. Either way, we cannot maintain the consistency of our algebraic properties involving exponentiation.

To solve this dilemma, we leave 0^0 undefined rather than choose a definition that will violate some of our algebraic properties. Mathematics takes a similar position with respect to division by 0: The equations $x \cdot \frac{y}{x} = y$ and $0 \cdot \frac{y}{x} = 0$ cannot both be satisfied if $x = 0$ and $y = 1$ regardless of how we define $\frac{1}{0}$. Thus $\frac{1}{0}$ is left undefined.

In summary, here is our definition of x^0:

For example, $4^0 = 1$.

Definition of x^0

- If $x \neq 0$, then $x^0 = 1$.

- The expression 0^0 is undefined.

Exponentiation by Negative Integers

As with the definition of exponentiation by zero, we will let consistency with previous algebraic properties force upon us the definition of exponentiation by negative integers.

At this stage, we have defined x^m whenever $x \neq 0$ and m is a positive integer or zero. We now turn our attention to defining exponentiation by negative integers.

Recall that if $x \neq 0$ and m and n are nonnegative integers, then

$$x^m x^n = x^{m+n}.$$

We would like to choose the definition of exponentiation by negative integers so that the equation above holds whenever m and n are integers (including the possibility that one or both of m and n might be negative). In the equation above, if we take $n = -m$, we get

$$x^m x^{-m} = x^{m+(-m)}.$$

Because $x^0 = 1$, this equation can be rewritten as

$$x^m x^{-m} = 1.$$

Thus we see that we have no choice but to define x^{-m} to equal the multiplicative inverse of x^m.

Exponentiation by a negative integer

If $x \neq 0$ and m is a positive integer, then x^{-m} is defined to be the multiplicative inverse of x^m:

$$x^{-m} = \frac{1}{x^m}.$$

To avoid division by 0, we cannot allow x to equal 0 in this definition. Thus if m is a positive integer, then 0^{-m} is undefined.

Evaluate 2^{-3}.

SOLUTION
$$2^{-3} = \frac{1}{2^3} = \frac{1}{8}$$

EXAMPLE 1

We can gain some insight into the behavior of the function x^m, for m a negative integer, by looking at its graph. We begin with the graph of x^{-1}, which equals $\frac{1}{x}$. As can be seen from the figure here, the absolute value of $\frac{1}{x}$ is large for values of x near 0. Conversely, $\frac{1}{x}$ is near 0 for x with large absolute value. The function $\frac{1}{x}$ is decreasing on $(-\infty, 0)$ and on $(0, \infty)$. The curve $y = \frac{1}{x}$ has its own name: this shape is called a **hyperbola**.

The graph shown below of x^{-2}, which equals $\frac{1}{x^2}$, should be compared with the graph of $\frac{1}{x}$ above. The most striking difference is that the graph of $\frac{1}{x^2}$ lies entirely above the x-axis. Another difference is that the function $\frac{1}{x^2}$ is increasing on the interval $(-\infty, 0)$; in contrast, the function $\frac{1}{x}$ is decreasing on the interval $(-\infty, 0)$. Both functions are decreasing on the interval $(0, \infty)$.

In general, if m is a positive integer, then the graph of $\frac{1}{x^m}$ behaves like the graph of $\frac{1}{x}$ if m is odd and like the graph of $\frac{1}{x^2}$ if m is even. Larger values of m correspond to functions whose graphs get closer to the x-axis more rapidly for large values of x and closer to the vertical axis more rapidly for values of x near 0.

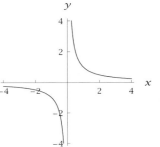

The graph of $\frac{1}{x}$ on $[-4, -\frac{1}{4}] \cup [\frac{1}{4}, 4]$.

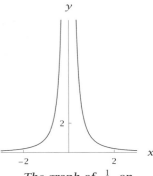

The graph of $\frac{1}{x^2}$ on $[-3, -\frac{1}{3}] \cup [\frac{1}{3}, 3]$.

Manipulations with Powers

For $x \neq 0$, we have now defined x^m for all integer values of m. All of our previous identities involving exponentiation with positive integers hold for arbitrary integers. For example,

$$x^m x^n = x^{m+n}$$

for all integers m and n and all $x \neq 0$. We have already verified this identity when m and n are positive integers. As an example of the kind of verification needed in the other cases, suppose both m and n are negative integers. Then there exist positive integers p and q such that $m = -p$ and $n = -q$. Now

$$x^m x^n = x^{-p} x^{-q} = \frac{1}{x^p} \frac{1}{x^q} = \frac{1}{x^{p+q}} = x^{-(p+q)} = x^{-p+(-q)} = x^{m+n},$$

as desired. For a complete verification we must also check all the other cases, for example when m is a positive integer and n is a negative integer. These cases, and the verification that the other identities also hold for arbitrary integers, are left to the reader.

A useful identity involving fractions states that

$$\frac{x^m}{x^n} = x^{m-n}$$

for all nonzero x and all integers m and n. To verify this identity, we can use other identities, as follows:

$$\frac{x^m}{x^n} = x^m \frac{1}{x^n} = x^m x^{-n} = x^{m+(-n)} = x^{m-n}.$$

The box below lists the key properties of integer exponents. In the next chapter, we will extend these properties to real exponents that are not necessarily integers.

Algebraic properties of exponents

Suppose x and y are nonzero numbers and m and n are integers. Then

$$x^m x^n = x^{m+n},$$

$$x^m y^m = (xy)^m,$$

$$(x^m)^n = x^{mn},$$

$$x^0 = 1,$$

$$x^{-m} = \frac{1}{x^m},$$

$$\frac{x^m}{x^n} = x^{m-n},$$

$$\frac{x^m}{y^m} = \left(\frac{x}{y}\right)^m.$$

The following example illustrates the ideas we have been discussing:

EXAMPLE 2

To manipulate fractions that involve powers, keep in mind that an exponent changes sign when we move it from the numerator to the denominator or from the denominator to the numerator.

Simplify the expression

$$\left(\frac{(x^{-3}y^4)^2}{x^{-9}y^3}\right)^2.$$

SOLUTION   First we will simplify the expression inside the large parentheses, and then we square that expression. To simplify the expression inside the large parentheses, first we simplify the numerator. We have

$$(x^{-3}y^4)^2 = x^{-6}y^8.$$

The expression inside the large parentheses is thus equal to

$$\frac{x^{-6}y^8}{x^{-9}y^3}.$$

Now bring the terms in the denominator to the numerator, changing the signs of the exponents, getting

$$\frac{x^{-6}y^8}{x^{-9}y^3} = x^{-6}x^9y^8y^{-3} = x^{-6+9}y^{8-3} = x^3y^5.$$

Thus the expression inside the large parentheses equals x^3y^5. Squaring that expression, we get

$$\left(\frac{(x^{-3}y^4)^2}{x^{-9}y^3}\right)^2 = x^6y^{10}.$$

EXERCISES

For Exercises 1–6, evaluate the given expression. Do not use a calculator.

1. $2^5 - 5^2$

2. $4^3 - 3^4$

3. $\dfrac{3^{-2}}{2^{-3}}$

4. $\dfrac{2^{-6}}{6^{-2}}$

5. $\left(\frac{2}{3}\right)^{-4}$

6. $\left(\frac{5}{4}\right)^{-3}$

The numbers in Exercises 7–14 are too large to be handled by a calculator. These exercises require an understanding of the concepts.

7. Write 9^{3000} as a power of 3.

8. Write 27^{4000} as a power of 3.

9. Write 5^{4000} as a power of 25.

10. Write 2^{3000} as a power of 8.

11. Write $2^5 \cdot 8^{1000}$ as a power of 2.

12. Write $5^3 \cdot 25^{2000}$ as a power of 5.

13. Write $2^{100} \cdot 4^{200} \cdot 8^{300}$ as a power of 2.

14. Write $3^{500} \cdot 9^{200} \cdot 27^{100}$ as a power of 3.

For Exercises 15–20, simplify the given expression by writing it as a power of a single variable.

15. $x^5(x^2)^3$

16. $y^4(y^3)^5$

17. $y^4(y^2(y^5)^2)^3$

18. $x(x^4(x^3)^2)^5$

19. $t^4(t^3(t^{-2})^5)^4$

20. $w^3(w^4(w^{-3})^6)^2$

21. Write $\dfrac{8^{1000}}{2^5}$ as a power of 2.

22. Write $\dfrac{25^{2000}}{5^3}$ as a power of 5.

23. Find integers m and n such that $2^m \cdot 5^n = 16000$.

24. Find integers m and n such that $2^m \cdot 5^n = 0.0032$.

For Exercises 25–32, simplify the given expression.

25. $\dfrac{(x^2)^3 y^8}{x^5(y^4)^3}$

26. $\dfrac{x^{11}(y^3)^2}{(x^3)^5(y^2)^4}$

27. $\dfrac{(x^{-2})^3 y^8}{x^{-5}(y^4)^{-3}}$

28. $\dfrac{x^{-11}(y^3)^{-2}}{(x^{-3})^5(y^2)^4}$

29. $\dfrac{(x^2 y^4)^3}{(x^5 y^2)^{-4}}$

30. $\dfrac{(x^2 y^4)^{-3}}{(x^5 y^{-2})^4}$

31. $\left(\dfrac{(x^2 y^{-5})^{-4}}{(x^5 y^{-2})^{-3}}\right)^2$

32. $\left(\dfrac{(x^{-3} y^5)^{-4}}{(x^{-5} y^{-2})^{-3}}\right)^{-2}$

For Exercises 33–40, find a formula for $f \circ g$ given the indicated functions f and g.

33. $f(x) = x^2$, $g(x) = x^3$

34. $f(x) = x^5$, $g(x) = x^4$

35. $f(x) = 4x^2$, $g(x) = 5x^3$

36. $f(x) = 3x^5$, $g(x) = 2x^4$

37. $f(x) = 4x^{-2}$, $g(x) = 5x^3$

38. $f(x) = 3x^{-5}$, $g(x) = 2x^4$

39. $f(x) = 4x^{-2}$, $g(x) = -5x^{-3}$

40. $f(x) = 3x^{-5}$, $g(x) = -2x^{-4}$

For Exercises 41-50, sketch the graph of the given function f on the interval $[-1.3, 1.3]$.

41. $f(x) = x^3 + 1$

42. $f(x) = x^4 + 2$

43. $f(x) = x^4 - 1.5$

44. $f(x) = x^3 - 0.5$

45. $f(x) = 2x^3$

46. $f(x) = 3x^4$

47. $f(x) = -2x^4$

48. $f(x) = -3x^3$

49. $f(x) = -2x^4 + 3$

50. $f(x) = -3x^3 + 4$

For Exercises 51-60, sketch the graph of the given function f on the domain $[-3, -\frac{1}{3}] \cup [\frac{1}{3}, 3]$.

51. $f(x) = \dfrac{1}{x} + 1$

52. $f(x) = \dfrac{1}{x^2} + 2$

53. $f(x) = \dfrac{1}{x^2} - 2$

54. $f(x) = \dfrac{1}{x} - 3$

55. $f(x) = \dfrac{2}{x}$

56. $f(x) = \dfrac{3}{x^2}$

57. $f(x) = -\dfrac{2}{x^2}$

58. $f(x) = -\dfrac{3}{x}$

59. $f(x) = -\dfrac{2}{x^2} + 3$

60. $f(x) = -\dfrac{3}{x} + 4$

PROBLEMS

61. Suppose m is a positive integer. Explain why 10^m, when written out in the usual decimal notation, is the digit 1 followed by m 0's.

62. (a) Verify that $2^4 = 4^2$.

   (b) Part (a) might lead someone to guess that exponentiation is commutative. However, for most choices of integers m and n, the inequality $m^n \neq n^m$ holds. For example, show that $2^3 \neq 3^2$ (which shows that exponentiation is not commutative).

63. (a) Verify that $\left(2^2\right)^2 = 2^{\left(2^2\right)}$.

   (b) Part (a) might lead someone to guess that exponentiation is associative. However, show that $\left(3^3\right)^3 \neq 3^{\left(3^3\right)}$ (which shows that exponentiation is not associative).

For the next two problems, suppose m is an integer and f is the function defined by $f(x) = x^m$.

64. Show that if m is an odd number, then f is an odd function.

65. Show that if m is an even number, then f is an even function.

66. Suppose m and n are integers. Define functions f and g by $f(x) = x^m$ and $g(x) = x^n$. Explain why

$$(f \circ g)(x) = x^{mn}.$$

67. Suppose x is a real number and m, n, and p are positive integers. Explain why

$$x^{m+n+p} = x^m x^n x^p.$$

68. Suppose x is a real number and m, n, and p are positive integers. Explain why

$$\left((x^m)^n\right)^p = x^{mnp}.$$

69. Suppose x, y, and z are real numbers and m is a positive integer. Explain why

$$x^m y^m z^m = (xyz)^m.$$

70. Suppose x and y are real numbers, with $y \neq 0$, and m is a positive integer. Explain why

$$\frac{x^m}{y^m} = \left(\frac{x}{y}\right)^m.$$

71. Complete the verification begun in this section that

$$x^m x^n = x^{m+n}$$

for all $x \neq 0$ and all integers m and n. *[We have already verified the identities in this problem and the next two problems when m and n are positive integers. The point of these problems is to verify these identities when one (or both) of m and n is negative or zero.]*

72. Show that if $x \neq 0$ and m and n are integers, then

$$(x^m)^n = x^{mn}.$$

73. Show that if x and y are nonzero real numbers and m is an integer, then

$$(xy)^m = x^m y^m.$$

74. Show that if $x \neq 0$, then

$$|x^n| = |x|^n$$

for all integers n.

Fermat's Last Theorem states that if n is an integer greater than 2, then there do not exist positive integers x, y, and z such that

$$x^n + y^n = z^n.$$

Fermat's Last Theorem was not proved until 1994, although mathematicians had been trying to find a proof for centuries.

75. Use Fermat's Last Theorem to show that if n is an integer greater than 2, then there do not exist positive rational numbers x and y such that

$$x^n + y^n = 1.$$

[*Hint:* Use proof by contradiction: Assume that there exist rational numbers $x = \frac{m}{p}$ and $y = \frac{q}{r}$ such that $x^n + y^n = 1$; then show that this assumption leads to a contradiction of Fermat's Last Theorem.]

76. Use Fermat's Last Theorem to show that if n is an integer greater than 2, then there do not exist positive rational numbers x, y, and z such that

$$x^n + y^n = z^n.$$

[*The equation $3^2 + 4^2 = 5^2$ shows the necessity of the hypothesis that $n > 2$.*]

WORKED-OUT SOLUTIONS *to Odd-numbered Exercises*

For Exercises 1–6, evaluate the given expression. Do not use a calculator.

1. $2^5 - 5^2$

   SOLUTION $\quad 2^5 - 5^2 = 32 - 25 = 7$

3. $\dfrac{3^{-2}}{2^{-3}}$

   SOLUTION $\quad \dfrac{3^{-2}}{2^{-3}} = \dfrac{2^3}{3^2} = \dfrac{8}{9}$

5. $\left(\frac{2}{3}\right)^{-4}$

   SOLUTION $\quad \left(\frac{2}{3}\right)^{-4} = \left(\frac{3}{2}\right)^4 = \frac{3^4}{2^4} = \frac{81}{16}$

The numbers in Exercises 7–14 are too large to be handled by a calculator. These exercises require an understanding of the concepts.

7. Write 9^{3000} as a power of 3.

   SOLUTION $\quad 9^{3000} = (3^2)^{3000} = 3^{6000}$

9. Write 5^{4000} as a power of 25.

   SOLUTION
   $$5^{4000} = 5^{2 \cdot 2000}$$
   $$= (5^2)^{2000}$$
   $$= 25^{2000}$$

11. Write $2^5 \cdot 8^{1000}$ as a power of 2.

SOLUTION $\quad 2^5 \cdot 8^{1000} = 2^5 \cdot (2^3)^{1000}$
$$= 2^5 \cdot 2^{3000}$$
$$= 2^{3005}$$

13. Write $2^{100} \cdot 4^{200} \cdot 8^{300}$ as a power of 2.

SOLUTION

$$2^{100} \cdot 4^{200} \cdot 8^{300} = 2^{100} \cdot (2^2)^{200} \cdot (2^3)^{300}$$
$$= 2^{100} \cdot 2^{400} \cdot 2^{900}$$
$$= 2^{1400}$$

For Exercises 15–20, simplify the given expression by writing it as a power of a single variable.

15. $x^5(x^2)^3$

   SOLUTION $\quad x^5(x^2)^3 = x^5 x^6 = x^{11}$

17. $y^4\left(y^2(y^5)^2\right)^3$

   SOLUTION

   $$y^4\left(y^2(y^5)^2\right)^3 = y^4(y^2 y^{10})^3$$
   $$= y^4(y^{12})^3$$
   $$= y^4 y^{36}$$
   $$= y^{40}$$

19. $t^4(t^3(t^{-2})^5)^4$

SOLUTION

$$
\begin{aligned}
t^4(t^3(t^{-2})^5)^4 &= t^4(t^3 t^{-10})^4 \\
&= t^4(t^{-7})^4 \\
&= t^4 t^{-28} \\
&= t^{-24}
\end{aligned}
$$

21. Write $\dfrac{8^{1000}}{2^5}$ as a power of 2.

SOLUTION $\quad \dfrac{8^{1000}}{2^5} = \dfrac{(2^3)^{1000}}{2^5}$

$$
\begin{aligned}
&= \dfrac{2^{3000}}{2^5} \\
&= 2^{2995}
\end{aligned}
$$

23. Find integers m and n such that $2^m \cdot 5^n = 16000$.

SOLUTION Note that

$$
\begin{aligned}
16000 &= 16 \cdot 1000 \\
&= 2^4 \cdot 10^3 \\
&= 2^4 \cdot (2 \cdot 5)^3 \\
&= 2^4 \cdot 2^3 \cdot 5^3 \\
&= 2^7 \cdot 5^3.
\end{aligned}
$$

Thus if we want to find integers m and n such that $2^m \cdot 5^n = 16000$, we should choose $m = 7$ and $n = 3$.

For Exercises 25–32, simplify the given expression.

25. $\dfrac{(x^2)^3 y^8}{x^5 (y^4)^3}$

SOLUTION $\quad \dfrac{(x^2)^3 y^8}{x^5 (y^4)^3} = \dfrac{x^6 y^8}{x^5 y^{12}}$

$$
\begin{aligned}
&= \dfrac{x^{6-5}}{y^{12-8}} \\
&= \dfrac{x}{y^4}
\end{aligned}
$$

27. $\dfrac{(x^{-2})^3 y^8}{x^{-5} (y^4)^{-3}}$

SOLUTION

$$
\begin{aligned}
\dfrac{(x^{-2})^3 y^8}{x^{-5} (y^4)^{-3}} &= \dfrac{x^{-6} y^8}{x^{-5} y^{-12}} \\
&= \dfrac{y^{8+12}}{x^{6-5}} \\
&= \dfrac{y^{20}}{x}
\end{aligned}
$$

29. $\dfrac{(x^2 y^4)^3}{(x^5 y^2)^{-4}}$

SOLUTION

$$
\begin{aligned}
\dfrac{(x^2 y^4)^3}{(x^5 y^2)^{-4}} &= \dfrac{x^6 y^{12}}{x^{-20} y^{-8}} \\
&= x^{6+20} y^{12+8} \\
&= x^{26} y^{20}
\end{aligned}
$$

31. $\left(\dfrac{(x^2 y^{-5})^{-4}}{(x^5 y^{-2})^{-3}} \right)^2$

SOLUTION

$$
\begin{aligned}
\left(\dfrac{(x^2 y^{-5})^{-4}}{(x^5 y^{-2})^{-3}} \right)^2 &= \dfrac{(x^2 y^{-5})^{-8}}{(x^5 y^{-2})^{-6}} \\
&= \dfrac{x^{-16} y^{40}}{x^{-30} y^{12}} \\
&= x^{30-16} y^{40-12} \\
&= x^{14} y^{28}
\end{aligned}
$$

For Exercises 33–40, find a formula for $f \circ g$ given the indicated functions f and g.

33. $f(x) = x^2, g(x) = x^3$

SOLUTION

$$(f \circ g)(x) = f(g(x)) = f(x^3) = (x^3)^2 = x^6$$

35. $f(x) = 4x^2, g(x) = 5x^3$

SOLUTION

$$
\begin{aligned}
(f \circ g)(x) &= f(g(x)) = f(5x^3) \\
&= 4(5x^3)^2 = 4 \cdot 5^2 (x^3)^2 = 100x^6
\end{aligned}
$$

37. $f(x) = 4x^{-2}$, $g(x) = 5x^3$

SOLUTION

$$(f \circ g)(x) = f(g(x)) = f(5x^3)$$

$$= 4(5x^3)^{-2} = 4 \cdot 5^{-2}(x^3)^{-2} = \tfrac{4}{25}x^{-6}$$

39. $f(x) = 4x^{-2}$, $g(x) = -5x^{-3}$

SOLUTION

$$(f \circ g)(x) = f(g(x)) = f(-5x^{-3})$$

$$= 4(-5x^{-3})^{-2} = 4(-5)^{-2}(x^{-3})^{-2} = \tfrac{4}{25}x^6$$

For Exercises 41–50, sketch the graph of the given function f on the interval [−1.3, 1.3].

41. $f(x) = x^3 + 1$

SOLUTION Shift the graph of x^3 up 1 unit, getting this graph:

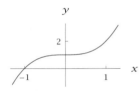

The graph of $x^3 + 1$.

43. $f(x) = x^4 - 1.5$

SOLUTION Shift the graph of x^4 down 1.5 units, getting this graph:

The graph of $x^4 - 1.5$.

45. $f(x) = 2x^3$

SOLUTION Vertically stretch the graph of x^3 by a factor of 2, getting this graph:

The graph of $2x^3$.

47. $f(x) = -2x^4$

SOLUTION Vertically stretch the graph of x^4 by a factor of 2 and then reflect through the x-axis, getting this graph:

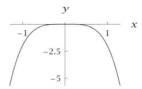

The graph of $-2x^4$.

49. $f(x) = -2x^4 + 3$

SOLUTION Vertically stretch the graph of x^4 by a factor of 2, then reflect through the x-axis, and then shift up by 3 units, getting this graph:

The graph of $-2x^4 + 3$.

For Exercises 51–60, sketch the graph of the given function f on the domain $[-3, -\frac{1}{3}] \cup [\frac{1}{3}, 3]$.

51. $f(x) = \dfrac{1}{x} + 1$

SOLUTION Shift the graph of $\frac{1}{x}$ up 1 unit, getting this graph:

The graph of $\frac{1}{x} + 1$.

53. $f(x) = \dfrac{1}{x^2} - 2$

SOLUTION Shift the graph of $\frac{1}{x^2}$ down 2 units, getting this graph:

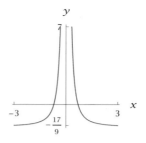

The graph of
$\frac{1}{x^2} - 2.$

55. $f(x) = \dfrac{2}{x}$

SOLUTION   Vertically stretch the graph of $\frac{1}{x}$ by a factor of 2, getting this graph:

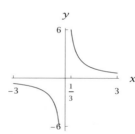

The graph of $\frac{2}{x}$.

57. $f(x) = -\dfrac{2}{x^2}$

SOLUTION   Vertically stretch the graph of $\frac{1}{x^2}$ by a factor of 2 and then reflect through the x-axis, getting this graph:

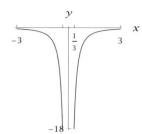

The graph of $-\frac{2}{x^2}$.

59. $f(x) = -\dfrac{2}{x^2} + 3$

SOLUTION   Vertically stretch the graph of $\frac{1}{x^2}$ by a factor of 2, then reflect through the x-axis, and then shift up by 3 units, getting this graph:

The graph of
$-\frac{2}{x^2} + 3.$

2.4 *Polynomials*

SECTION OBJECTIVES

By the end of this section you should

- understand the connection between factorization and the zeros of a polynomial;
- be able to do algebraic manipulations with polynomials;
- be able to determine the behavior of $p(x)$ when p is a polynomial and $|x|$ is large.

The polynomials form the most important class of functions that you will deal with in calculus. Earlier in this chapter we studied linear functions and quadratic functions, which are among the simplest polynomials. In this section we will deal with more general polynomials. We begin with the definition of a polynomial.

Polynomials

A **polynomial** is a function p of the form

$$p(x) = a_0 + a_1x + a_2x^2 + \cdots + a_nx^n,$$

where n is a nonnegative integer and $a_0, a_1, a_2, \ldots, a_n$ are constants.

Because the expression defining a polynomial makes sense for every real number, you should assume that the domain of a polynomial is the set of real numbers unless another domain has been specified.

For example, the function p defined by

$$p(x) = 3 - 7x^5 + 2x^6$$

is a polynomial. Here, in terms of the definition above, we have $a_0 = 3$, $a_1 = a_2 = a_3 = a_4 = 0$, $a_5 = -7$, and $a_6 = 2$.

The Degree of a Polynomial

The highest power that appears in the expression defining a polynomial plays a key role in determining the behavior of the polynomial. Thus the following definition is useful:

Degree of a polynomial

Suppose p is a polynomial defined by

$$p(x) = a_0 + a_1x + a_2x^2 + \cdots + a_nx^n.$$

If $a_n \neq 0$, then we say that p has **degree** n. The degree of p is denoted by $\deg p$.

*The numbers $a_0, a_1, a_2, \ldots, a_n$ are called the **coefficients** of the polynomial p.*

EXAMPLE 1

(a)   Give an example of a polynomial of degree 0. Describe its graph.

(b)   Give an example of a polynomial of degree 1. Describe its graph.

(c)   Give an example of a polynomial of degree 2. Describe its graph.

(d)   Give an example of a polynomial of degree 7.

SOLUTION

The constant poly-nomial p defined by $p(x) = 0$ for every number x has no nonzero coefficients. Thus the degree of this polynomial is undefined. Sometimes it is convenient to write $\deg 0 = -\infty$ to avoid trivial exceptions to various results.

(a)   The polynomial p defined by
$$p(x) = 4$$
is a polynomial of degree 0. Its graph is a horizontal line.

(b)   The polynomial p defined by
$$p(x) = 2 + x$$
is a polynomial of degree 1. Its graph is a nonhorizontal line.

(c)   The polynomial p defined by
$$p(x) = -3 - 5x^2$$
is a polynomial of degree 2. Its graph is a parabola.

(d)   The polynomial p defined by
$$p(x) = 13 + 12x - x^3 - 9x^4 + 3x^7$$
has degree 7.

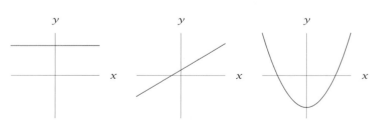

The graph of a polynomial of degree 0 (left), a polynomial of degree 1 (center), and a polynomial of degree 2 (right).

The Algebra of Polynomials

Two polynomials can be added or subtracted, producing another polynomial. Specifically, if p and q are polynomials then the polynomial $p + q$ is defined by

$$(p + q)(x) = p(x) + q(x)$$

and the polynomial $p - q$ is defined by

$$(p - q)(x) = p(x) - q(x).$$

Suppose p and q are polynomials defined by

EXAMPLE 2

$$p(x) = 2 - 7x^2 + 5x^3 \quad \text{and} \quad q(x) = 1 + 9x + x^2 + 5x^3.$$

(a) What is deg p?

(b) What is deg q?

(c) Find a formula for $p + q$.

(d) What is $\deg(p + q)$?

(e) Find a formula for $p - q$.

(f) What is $\deg(p - q)$?

SOLUTION

Polynomial addition is commutative and associative. In other words, $p + q = q + p$ and $(p+q)+r = p+(q+r)$ for all polynomials p, q, and r.

(a) The term with highest power that appears in the expression defining p is $5x^3$. Thus deg $p = 3$.

(b) The term with highest power that appears in the expression defining q is $5x^3$. Thus deg $p = 3$.

(c) Adding together the expressions defining p and q, we have

$$(p + q)(x) = 3 + 9x - 6x^2 + 10x^3.$$

(d) The term with highest power that appears in the expression above for $p + q$ is $10x^3$. Thus $\deg(p + q) = 3$.

(e) Subtracting the expression defining q from the expression defining p, we have

$$(p - q)(x) = 1 - 9x - 8x^2.$$

(f) The term with highest power that appears in the expression above for $p - q$ is $-8x^2$. Thus $\deg(p - q) = 2$.

More generally, we have the following result:

> ### Degree of the sum and difference of two polynomials
>
> If p and q are nonzero polynomials, then
>
> $$\deg(p + q) \leq \text{maximum}\{\deg p, \deg q\}$$
>
> and
>
> $$\deg(p - q) \leq \text{maximum}\{\deg p, \deg q\}.$$

This result holds because neither $p + q$ nor $p - q$ can contain a power larger than the largest power that appears in p or q.

Due to cancellation, the degree of $p + q$ or the degree of $p - q$ can be less than the maximum of the degree of p and the degree of q, as shown in the example above.

Two polynomials can be multiplied together, producing another polynomial. Specifically, if p and q are polynomials, then the polynomial pq is defined by

$$(pq)(x) = p(x) \cdot q(x).$$

EXAMPLE 3

Suppose p and q are polynomials defined by

$$p(x) = 2 - 3x^2 \quad \text{and} \quad q(x) = 4x + 7x^5.$$

(a) What is $\deg p$?

(b) What is $\deg q$?

Polynomial multiplication is commutative and associative. In other words, $pq = qp$ and $(pq)r = p(qr)$ for all polynomials $p, q,$ and r.

(c) Find a formula for pq.

(d) What is $\deg(pq)$?

SOLUTION

(a) The term with highest power that appears in the expression defining p is $-3x^2$. Thus $\deg p = 2$.

(b) The term with highest power that appears in the expression defining q is $7x^5$. Thus $\deg q = 5$.

(c) $(pq)(x) = (2 - 3x^2)(4x + 7x^5) = 8x - 12x^3 + 14x^5 - 21x^7$

(d) The term with highest power that appears in the expression above for pq is $-21x^7$. Thus $\deg(pq) = 7$.

More generally, we have the following result:

> ### Degree of the product of two polynomials
>
> If p and q are nonzero polynomials, then
>
> $$\deg(pq) = \deg p + \deg q.$$

This equality holds because when the highest power term $x^{\deg p}$ in p is multiplied by the highest power term $x^{\deg q}$ in q, we get $x^{\deg p + \deg q}$.

Zeros and Factorization of Polynomials

The zeros of a function are also sometimes called the **roots** *of the function.*

> ### Zeros of a function
>
> A number r is called a **zero** of a function p if $p(r) = 0$.

For example, if $p(x) = 3 - 4x$, then $\frac{3}{4}$ is a zero of p because

$$p(\tfrac{3}{4}) = 3 - 4 \cdot \tfrac{3}{4} = 0.$$

Suppose p is a function and r is a zero of p. Then $p(r) = 0$ and thus $(r, 0)$ is on the graph of p. Because the second coordinate of $(r, 0)$ is 0, we conclude that each zero of p corresponds to a point where the graph of p intersects the horizontal axis.

If p is a polynomial of degree 1 with $p(x) = ax + b$, then p has exactly one zero, which equals $-\frac{b}{a}$, as we see by solving the equation $p(x) = 0$.

The quadratic formula (see Section 2.2) can be used to find the zeros of a polynomial of degree 2. If $p(x) = ax^2 + bx + c$ with $a \neq 0$, then the quadratic formula produces the solutions of the equation $p(x) = 0$, giving us the following information:

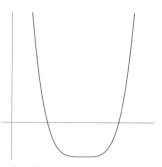

The function whose graph is shown here has two zeros, corresponding to the two points where the graph intersects the horizontal axis.

- p has no (real) zeros if $b^2 - 4ac < 0$;

- p has one zero equal to $-\frac{b}{2a}$ if $b^2 - 4ac = 0$;

- p has two zeros, which equal $\frac{-b + \sqrt{b^2 - 4ac}}{2a}$ and $\frac{-b - \sqrt{b^2 - 4ac}}{2a}$, if $b^2 - 4ac > 0$.

The polynomial p defined by $p(x) = x^2 + 1$ gives a simple example of a polynomial of degree 2 that has no (real) zeros. In this case, the equation $p(x) = 0$ leads to the equation $x^2 = -1$, which has no real solutions because the square of a real number cannot be negative.

Complex numbers were invented to provide solutions to the equation $x^2 = -1$, but in this book we deal mostly with real numbers.

Just as there is a quadratic formula to find the zeros of a polynomial of degree 2, there is a cubic formula to find the zeros of a polynomial of degree 3 and a quartic formula to find the zeros of a polynomial of degree 4. However, these complicated formulas are not of great practical value, and most mathematicians do not know these formulas (although they know of their existence).

No one knows a formula to find the zeros of a polynomial of degree 5 or higher. Remarkably, mathematicians have proved that no such formula exists. Thus our lack of knowledge of such a formula cannot be solved by increased cleverness. However, numerical techniques can be used to give very good approximations to the zeros of polynomials of degree 5 or higher. For example, no one will ever be able to give a formula for a zero of the polynomial p defined by

Note that sometimes we write polynomials starting with the lowest degree terms and sometimes we write polynomials starting with the highest degree terms.

$$p(x) = x^5 + 3x^2 - 6.$$

However, numerical techniques can be used to show that there is a zero of this polynomial very close to 1.15135. Furthermore, advanced mathematical techniques can be used to show that this polynomial has no other (real) zeros.

Find the (real) zeros of the polynomial p of degree 4 defined by

EXAMPLE 4

$$p(x) = (x - 2)(x - 5)(x^2 + 1).$$

SOLUTION   Because $p(x)$ is explicitly written as the product of three terms, we see that $p(x) = 0$ if and only if $x - 2 = 0$ or $x - 5 = 0$ or $x^2 + 1 = 0$. The first condition is equivalent to the equation $x = 2$, the second condition is equivalent to the equation $x = 5$, and the third condition does not hold for any real number x. Thus 2 and 5 are the (real) zeros of p.

The following result shows that the problem of finding the zeros of a polynomial is really the same problem as finding its linear factors.

The next section will provide an explanation of why this result holds.

Factorization of a polynomial using zeros

Suppose p is a nonzero polynomial with at least one (real) zero. Then

- there exist real numbers $r_1, r_2, \ldots, r_m$ and a polynomial G such that G has no (real) zeros and

$$p(x) = (x - r_1)(x - r_2) \ldots (x - r_m)G(x)$$

  for every real number x;

- each of the numbers $r_1, r_2, \ldots, r_m$ is a zero of p;

- p has no zeros other than $r_1, r_2, \ldots, r_m$.

The cubic formula, which was discovered in the 16th century, is presented below for your amusement only. Do not memorize it.

The polynomial G in the result above might be a constant polynomial of degree 0. For example, suppose

$$p(x) = x^3 - 4x^2 - 7x + 10,$$

which can also be expressed in the form

$$p(x) = (x + 2)(x - 1)(x - 5).$$

Consider the cubic polynomial $p(x) = ax^3 + bx^2 + cx + d$, where $a \neq 0$. Set

$$u = \frac{bc}{6a^2} - \frac{b^3}{27a^3} - \frac{d}{2a}$$

and then set

$$v = u^2 + \left(\frac{c}{3a} - \frac{b^2}{9a^2}\right)^3.$$

Suppose $v \geq 0$. Then

$$-\frac{b}{3a} + \sqrt[3]{u + \sqrt{v}}$$

$$+ \sqrt[3]{u - \sqrt{v}}$$

is a zero of p.

This factorization shows that the zeros of p are -2, 1, and 5. To make this factorization above correspond to the boxed result stated above, we take $m = 3$, $r_1 = -2$, $r_2 = 1$, $r_3 = 5$, and $G(x) = 1$.

In the boxed result above, the numbers $r_1, r_2, \ldots, r_m$ are not necessarily distinct. For example, suppose

$$p(x) = x^4 - 9x^3 + 25x^2 - 27x + 10,$$

which can also be expressed in the form

$$p(x) = (x - 1)(x - 1)(x - 2)(x - 5).$$

This factorization shows that the zeros of p are 1, 2, and 5. To make this factorization above correspond to the boxed result stated above, we take $m = 4$, $r_1 = 1$, $r_2 = 1$, $r_3 = 2$, $r_4 = 5$, and $G(x) = 1$.

A polynomial of degree 1 has exactly one zero (because the equation $ax + b = 0$ has exactly one solution $x = -\frac{b}{a}$). We know from the quadratic formula that a polynomial of degree 2 has at most two zeros. More generally, we have the following result:

> ### Number of zeros of a polynomial
> A nonzero polynomial cannot have more zeros than its degree.

Thus, for example, a polynomial of degree 15 has at most 15 zeros. This result holds because each zero of a polynomial p corresponds to at least one term $x - r_j$ in a factorization of the form

$$p(x) = (x - r_1)(x - r_2)\ldots(x - r_m)G(x).$$

If the polynomial p had more zeros than its degree, then the right side of the equation above would have a higher degree than the left side, which would be a contradiction.

The Behavior of a Polynomial Near $\pm\infty$

We now turn to an investigation of the behavior of a polynomial near ∞ and near $-\infty$. To say that x is near ∞ is just an informal way of saying that x is very large. Similarly, to say that x is near $-\infty$ is just an informal way of saying that x is negative and $|x|$ is very large. The phrase "very large" has no precise meaning; even its informal meaning can depend on the context. Our focus will be on determining whether a polynomial takes on positive or negative values near ∞ and near $-\infty$.

Important: Always remember that neither ∞ nor $-\infty$ is a real number.

Let p be the polynomial defined by

$$p(x) = x^5 - 99999x^4 - 9999x^3 - 999x^2 - 99x - 9.$$

Is $p(x)$ is positive or negative for x near ∞? In other words, if x is very large, is $p(x) > 0$ or is $p(x) < 0$?

EXAMPLE 5

SOLUTION   If x is positive, then the x^5 term in $p(x)$ is also positive but the other terms in $p(x)$ are all negative. If $x > 1$, then x^5 is larger than x^4, but perhaps the $-99999x^4$ term along with the other terms will still make $p(x)$ negative. To get a feeling for the behavior of p, we can collect some evidence by evaluating $p(x)$ for some values of x, as in the table below:

x	$p(x)$
1	-111104
10	-1009989899
100	-9999908999909
1000	-99008999999099009
10000	-899999999099900990009

The evidence in this table indicates that $p(x)$ is negative for positive values of x.

From the table above, it appears that $p(x)$ is negative when x is positive, and more decisively negative for larger values of x, as shown in the graph below.

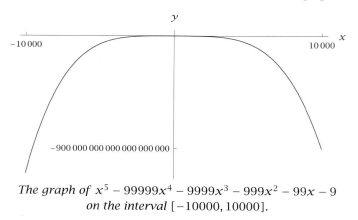

The graph of $x^5 - 99999x^4 - 9999x^3 - 999x^2 - 99x - 9$
on the interval $[-10000, 10000]$.

However, a bit of thought shows that this first impression is wrong. To see this, factor out x^5, the highest-degree term in the expression defining p, getting

$$p(x) = x^5\left(1 - \frac{99999}{x} - \frac{9999}{x^2} - \frac{999}{x^3} - \frac{99}{x^4} - \frac{9}{x^5}\right)$$

for all $x \neq 0$. If x is a very large number, say $x > 10^{10}$, then the five negative terms in the expression above are all very small. Thus if $x > 10^{10}$, then the expression in parentheses above is approximately 1. This means that $p(x)$ behaves like x^5 for very large values of x. In particular, this analysis implies that $p(x)$ is positive for very large values of x, unlike what we expected from the table and graph above.

Indeed, extending the table above to larger values of x and expanding the interval graphed by a factor of 100, we find that $p(x)$ is positive for large values of x:

x	$p(x)$
100000	90000990009990099991
1000000	900000990000999000999900999991
10000000	9900000099900000999900009999900099999991
100000000	999000000999900000999990000999999009999999991

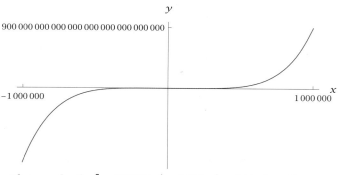

For very large values of x, the polynomial $p(x)$ behaves like x^5. Thus $p(x)$ is positive for x near ∞.

The graph of $x^5 - 99999x^4 - 9999x^3 - 999x^2 - 99x - 9$
on the interval $[-1000000, 1000000]$.

In general, the same trick as used in the example above works with any polynomial:

> ### Behavior of a polynomial near $\pm\infty$
>
> - To determine the behavior of a polynomial near ∞ or near $-\infty$, factor out the term with highest degree.
>
> - If cx^n is the term with highest degree of a polynomial p, then $p(x)$ behaves like cx^n when $|x|$ is very large.

Suppose

$$p(x) = 14 - 888x + 77777x^4 - 5x^6.$$

EXAMPLE 6

(a) Is $p(x)$ positive or negative for x near ∞?

(b) Is $p(x)$ positive or negative for x near $-\infty$?

SOLUTION   The term with highest degree in $p(x)$ is $-5x^6$. Factoring out this term, we have

$$p(x) = -5x^6\Big(1 - \frac{77777}{5x^2} + \frac{888}{5x^5} - \frac{14}{5x^6}\Big).$$

If $|x|$ in very large, then the expression in parentheses above is approximately 1. Thus $p(x)$ behaves like $-5x^6$ when x is near ∞ or when x is near $-\infty$.

(a) If $x > 0$, then $-5x^6$ is negative. Thus $p(x)$ is negative when x is near ∞.

(b) If $x < 0$, then $-5x^6$ is negative. Thus $p(x)$ is negative when x is near $-\infty$.

Suppose p is a polynomial with odd degree. Let cx^n be the term of p with highest degree. Thus n is an odd positive integer and c is a nonzero constant. We know that $p(x)$ behaves like cx^n when $|x|$ is very large. If $c > 0$, this implies that $p(x)$ is positive for x near ∞ and negative for x near $-\infty$. If $c < 0$, then $p(x)$ is negative for x near ∞ and positive for x near $-\infty$.

Either way, we see that the graph of our polynomial p with odd degree contains points above the horizontal axis (where p is positive) and contains points below the horizontal axis (where p is negative). This implies that the graph of p intersects the horizontal axis somewhere; thus p has at least one (real) zero.

The intuitive explanation presented here can be expanded into a rigorous proof, as is done in more advanced mathematics courses.

Suppose the graph of a polynomial p contains a point above the horizontal axis and a point below the horizontal axis, as shown here. A curve connecting these two points must intersect the horizontal axis. In other words, p has a zero.

Thus our examination of the behavior near ∞ and near $-\infty$ of a polynomial with odd degree leads to the following conclusion:

If we work with complex numbers rather than real numbers, then every nonconstant polynomial has a zero. Section 2.6 includes a discussion of this result.

Zeros for polynomials with odd degree

Every polynomial with odd degree has at least one (real) zero.

Some polynomials with even degre have zeros (for example, the polynomial $x^2 - 1$), but other polynomials with even degree do not have zeros (for example, the polynomial $x^2 + 1$).

Graphs of Polynomials

Machines can draw graphs of polynomials better than humans. However, some human thought is usually needed to select on appropriate interval on which to graph a polynomial.

Consider, for example, the polynomial p defined by

$$p(x) = x^4 - 4x^3 - 2x^2 + 13x + 12.$$

If we ask a machine to graph this polynomial on the interval $[-2, 2]$, we obtain the following graph:

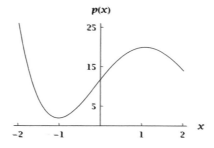

The graph of $x^4 - 4x^3 - 2x^2 + 13x + 12$ on the interval $[-2, 2]$.

Because $p(x)$ behaves like x^4 for very large values of x, we see that the graph above does not depict enough of the features of p. Often you will need to experiment a bit to find an appropriate interval to illustrate the key features of the graph. For this polynomial p, the interval $[-2, 4]$ works well, as shown below:

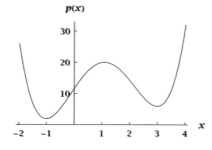

The graph of $x^4 - 4x^3 - 2x^2 + 13x + 12$ on the interval $[-2, 4]$.

The symbol $\approx$ means "approximately equal to".

We see that the graph of p above contains three points that might be thought of as either the top of a peak (at $x \approx 1$) or the bottom of a valley (at $x \approx -1$ and $x \approx 3$). To search for additional peaks and valleys, we might try graphing p on a much larger interval, as follows:

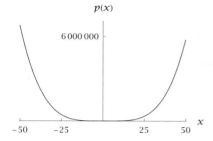

The graph of $x^4 - 4x^3 - 2x^2 + 13x + 12$ on the interval $[-50, 50]$.

The graph above shows no peaks or valleys, even though we know that it contains a total of at least three peaks and valleys. What happened here is that the scale needed to display the graph on the interval $[-50, 50]$ made the peaks and valleys so small that we cannot see them. However, the graph above does look very much like the graph of the function x^4, illustrating how $p(x)$ behaves like x^4 for large values of $|x|$.

The notions of "peak" and "valley" have a clear intuitive meaning. We will leave more rigorous definitions of these concepts to a later course.

The following result is often useful for helping to determine whether any additional peaks or valleys in a graph remain to be discovered:

Peaks and valleys for the graph of a polynomial

The graph of a polynomial p can have a total of at most $\deg p - 1$ peaks and valleys.

Your calculus course will give a good explanation of why this result holds.

For example, the result above implies that the graph of the fourth-degree polynomial $x^4 - 4x^3 - 2x^2 + 13x + 12$ can have a total of at most three peaks and valleys. We discovered a total of three peaks and valleys when graphing this function on the interval $[-2, 4]$. Thus we need not worry that any remaining peaks or valleys are lurking elsewhere.

The result above does not imply that the graph of every fourth-degree polynomial has a total of three peaks and valleys, only that the total number of peaks and valleys cannot be more than three. For example, the graph of the fourth-degree polynomial x^4 has no peaks and only one valley (the graph of x^4 is shown in Section 2.3).

As another example, here is the graph of the polynomial q defined by

$$q(x) = 12x^5 - 77x^4 + 105x^3 + 150x^2 - 360x + 91$$

on the interval $[-1.7, 4]$:

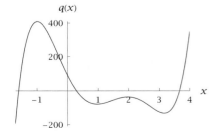

The graph of $12x^5 - 77x^4 + 105x^3 + 150x^2 - 360x + 91$ on the interval $[-1.7, 4]$.

As can be seen above, the graph of q intersects the x-axis at three points (with $x \approx -1.6$, $x \approx 0.3$, and $x \approx 3.7$). Thus q has three zeros, as compared to the potential maximum of five zeros for this fifth-degree polynomial.

We also see that the graph of q has peaks with tops at $x \approx -1$ and $x \approx 2$. Furthermore, q has valleys with bottoms at $x \approx 1$ and $x \approx 3.2$ Thus the graph of q has a total of four peaks and valleys, which is the maximum possible for a fifth-degree polynomial.

Finally, the graph above suggests that $q(x)$ is negative for x near $-\infty$ and positive for x near ∞. Because $q(x)$ behaves like $12x^5$ for $|x|$ very large, we indeed expect $q(x)$ to be negative for x near $-\infty$ and positive for x near ∞. The graph of the same polynomial on a larger interval, shown below, supports this conclusion.

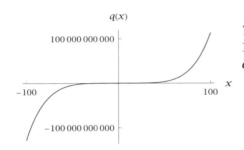

The graph of
$$12x^5 - 77x^4 + 105x^3 + 150x^2 - 360x + 91$$
on the interval $[-100, 100]$.

EXERCISES

Suppose

$$p(x) = x^2 + 5x + 2,$$

$$q(x) = 2x^3 - 3x + 1,$$

$$s(x) = 4x^3 - 2.$$

In Exercises 1-18, write the indicated expression as a sum of terms, each of which is a constant times a power of x.

1. $(p + q)(x)$
2. $(p - q)(x)$
3. $(3p - 2q)(x)$
4. $(4p + 5q)(x)$
5. $(pq)(x)$
6. $(ps)(x)$
7. $(p(x))^2$
8. $(q(x))^2$
9. $(p(x))^2 s(x)$
10. $(q(x))^2 s(x)$
11. $(p \circ q)(x)$
12. $(q \circ p)(x)$
13. $(p \circ s)(x)$
14. $(s \circ p)(x)$
15. $(q \circ (p + s))(x)$
16. $((q + p) \circ s)(x)$
17. $\dfrac{q(2 + x) - q(2)}{x}$
18. $\dfrac{s(1 + x) - s(1)}{x}$

19. Find all real numbers x such that
$$x^6 - 8x^3 + 15 = 0.$$

20. Find all real numbers x such that
$$x^6 - 3x^3 - 10 = 0.$$

21. Find all real numbers x such that
$$x^4 - 2x^2 - 15 = 0.$$

22. Find all real numbers x such that
$$x^4 + 5x^2 - 14 = 0.$$

23. Factor $x^8 - y^8$ as nicely as possible.
24. Factor $x^{16} - y^8$ as nicely as possible.
25. Find a number b such that 3 is a zero of the polynomial p defined by
$$p(x) = 1 - 4x + bx^2 + 2x^3.$$

26. Find a number c such that -2 is a zero of the polynomial p defined by
$$p(x) = 5 - 3x + 4x^2 + cx^3.$$

27. Find a polynomial p of degree 3 such that -1, 2, and 3 are zeros of p and $p(0) = 1$.

28. Find a polynomial p of degree 3 such that -2, -1, and 4 are zeros of p and $p(1) = 2$.

29. Find all choices of b, c, and d such that 1 and 4 are the only zeros of the polynomial p defined by
$$p(x) = x^3 + bx^2 + cx + d.$$

30. Find all choices of b, c, and d such that -3 and 2 are the only zeros of the polynomial p defined by
$$p(x) = x^3 + bx^2 + cx + d.$$

PROBLEMS

31. Show that if p and q are nonzero polynomials with $\deg p < \deg q$, then
$$\deg(p + q) = \deg q.$$

32. Give an example of polynomials p and q such that $\deg(pq) = 8$ and $\deg(p + q) = 5$.

33. Give an example of polynomials p and q such that $\deg(pq) = 8$ and $\deg(p + q) = 2$.

34. Suppose $q(x) = 2x^3 - 3x + 1$.

    (a) Show that the point $(2, 11)$ is on the graph of q.

    (b) Show that the slope of a line containing $(2, 11)$ and a point on the graph of q very close to $(2, 11)$ is approximately 21.

    [*Hint:* Use the result of Exercise 17.]

35. Suppose $s(x) = 4x^3 - 2$.

    (a) Show that the point $(1, 2)$ is on the graph of s.

    (b) Give an estimate for the slope of a line containing $(1, 2)$ and a point on the graph of s very close to $(1, 2)$.

    [*Hint:* Use the result of Exercise 18.]

36. Give an example of polynomials p and q of degree 3 such that $p(1) = q(1)$, $p(2) = q(2)$, and $p(3) = q(3)$, but $p(4) \neq q(4)$.

37. Suppose p and q are polynomials of degree 3 such that $p(1) = q(1)$, $p(2) = q(2)$, $p(3) = q(3)$, and $p(4) = q(4)$. Explain why $p = q$.

38. Verify that
$$(x + y)^3 = x^3 + 3x^2y + 3xy^2 + y^3.$$

39. Verify that
$$x^3 - y^3 = (x - y)(x^2 + xy + y^2).$$

40. Verify that
$$x^3 + y^3 = (x + y)(x^2 - xy + y^2).$$

41. Verify that
$$x^5 - y^5 = (x - y)(x^4 + x^3y + x^2y^2 + xy^3 + y^4).$$

42. Verify that
$$x^4 + 1 = (x^2 + \sqrt{2}x + 1)(x^2 - \sqrt{2}x + 1).$$

43. Write the polynomial $x^4 + 16$ as the product of two polynomials of degree 2.
[*Hint:* Use the result from the previous problem with x replaced by $\frac{x}{2}$.]

44. Show that
$$(a + b)^3 = a^3 + b^3$$
if and only if $a = 0$ or $b = 0$ or $a = -b$.

45. Suppose d is a real number. Show that
$$(d + 1)^4 = d^4 + 1$$
if and only if $d = 0$.

46. Suppose $p(x) = 3x^7 - 5x^3 + 7x - 2$.

    (a) Show that if m is a zero of p, then
    $$\frac{2}{m} = 3m^6 - 5m^2 + 7.$$

    (b) Show that the only possible integer zeros of p are -2, -1, 1, and 2.

    (c) Show that no zero of p is an integer.

47. Suppose a, b, and c are integers and that
$$p(x) = ax^3 + bx^2 + cx + 9.$$
Explain why every zero of p that is an integer is contained in the set $\{-9, -3, -1, 1, 3, 9\}$.

48. Suppose $p(x) = a_0 + a_1 x + \cdots + a_n x^n$, where $a_1, a_2, \ldots, a_n$ are integers. Suppose m is a nonzero integer that is a zero of p. Show that a_0/m is an integer.

49. Give an example of a polynomial of degree 5 that has exactly two zeros.

50. Give an example of a polynomial of degree 8 that has exactly three zeros.

51. Give an example of a polynomial p of degree 4 such that $p(7) = 0$ and $p(x) \geq 0$ for all real numbers x.

52. Give an example of a polynomial p of degree 6 such that $p(0) = 5$ and $p(x) \geq 5$ for all real numbers x.

53. Give an example of a polynomial p of degree 8 such that $p(2) = 3$ and $p(x) \geq 3$ for all real numbers x.

54. Explain why there does not exist a polynomial p of degree 7 such that $p(x) \geq -100$ for every real number x.

55. Explain why the composition of two polynomials is a polynomial.

56. Show that if p and q are nonzero polynomials, then
$$\deg(p \circ q) = (\deg p)(\deg q).$$

57. In the first figure in the solution to Example 5, the graph of the polynomial p clearly lies below the x-axis for x in the interval $[5000, 10000]$. Yet in the second figure in the same solution, the graph of p seems to be on or above the x-axis for all values of p in the interval $[0, 1000000]$. Explain.

WORKED-OUT SOLUTIONS *to Odd-numbered Exercises*

Suppose

$$p(x) = x^2 + 5x + 2,$$

$$q(x) = 2x^3 - 3x + 1,$$

$$s(x) = 4x^3 - 2.$$

In Exercises 1–18, write the indicated expression as a sum of terms, each of which is a constant times a power of x.

1. $(p + q)(x)$

    SOLUTION

    $$(p + q)(x) = (x^2 + 5x + 2) + (2x^3 - 3x + 1)$$
    $$= 2x^3 + x^2 + 2x + 3$$

3. $(3p - 2q)(x)$

    SOLUTION

    $$(3p - 2q)(x) = 3(x^2 + 5x + 2) - 2(2x^3 - 3x + 1)$$
    $$= 3x^2 + 15x + 6 - 4x^3 + 6x - 2$$
    $$= -4x^3 + 3x^2 + 21x + 4$$

5. $(pq)(x)$

    SOLUTION

$$(pq)(x) = (x^2 + 5x + 2)(2x^3 - 3x + 1)$$
$$= x^2(2x^3 - 3x + 1)$$
$$\quad + 5x(2x^3 - 3x + 1) + 2(2x^3 - 3x + 1)$$
$$= 2x^5 - 3x^3 + x^2 + 10x^4 - 15x^2$$
$$\quad + 5x + 4x^3 - 6x + 2$$
$$= 2x^5 + 10x^4 + x^3 - 14x^2 - x + 2$$

7. $\big(p(x)\big)^2$

    SOLUTION

$$\big(p(x)\big)^2 = (x^2 + 5x + 2)(x^2 + 5x + 2)$$
$$= x^2(x^2 + 5x + 2) + 5x(x^2 + 5x + 2)$$
$$\quad + 2(x^2 + 5x + 2)$$
$$= x^4 + 5x^3 + 2x^2 + 5x^3 + 25x^2$$
$$\quad + 10x + 2x^2 + 10x + 4$$
$$= x^4 + 10x^3 + 29x^2 + 20x + 4$$

9. $\big(p(x)\big)^2 s(x)$

    SOLUTION Using the expression that we computed for $\big(p(x)\big)^2$ in the solution to Exercise 7, we have

$(p(x))^2 s(x)$

$$= (x^4 + 10x^3 + 29x^2 + 20x + 4)(4x^3 - 2)$$

$$= 4x^3(x^4 + 10x^3 + 29x^2 + 20x + 4)$$

$$\quad - 2(x^4 + 10x^3 + 29x^2 + 20x + 4)$$

$$= 4x^7 + 40x^6 + 116x^5 + 80x^4 + 16x^3$$

$$\quad - 2x^4 - 20x^3 - 58x^2 - 40x - 8$$

$$= 4x^7 + 40x^6 + 116x^5 + 78x^4$$

$$\quad - 4x^3 - 58x^2 - 40x - 8.$$

11. $(p \circ q)(x)$

SOLUTION

$$(p \circ q)(x) = p(q(x))$$

$$= p(2x^3 - 3x + 1)$$

$$= (2x^3 - 3x + 1)^2 + 5(2x^3 - 3x + 1) + 2$$

$$= (4x^6 - 12x^4 + 4x^3 + 9x^2 - 6x + 1)$$

$$\quad + (10x^3 - 15x + 5) + 2$$

$$= 4x^6 - 12x^4 + 14x^3 + 9x^2 - 21x + 8$$

13. $(p \circ s)(x)$

SOLUTION

$$(p \circ s)(x) = p(s(x))$$

$$= p(4x^3 - 2)$$

$$= (4x^3 - 2)^2 + 5(4x^3 - 2) + 2$$

$$= (16x^6 - 16x^3 + 4) + (20x^3 - 10) + 2$$

$$= 16x^6 + 4x^3 - 4$$

15. $(q \circ (p + s))(x)$

SOLUTION

$$(q \circ (p + s))(x) = q((p + s)(x))$$

$$= q(p(x) + s(x))$$

$$= q(4x^3 + x^2 + 5x)$$

$$= 2(4x^3 + x^2 + 5x)^3 - 3(4x^3 + x^2 + 5x) + 1$$

$$= 2(4x^3 + x^2 + 5x)^2(4x^3 + x^2 + 5x)$$

$$\quad - 12x^3 - 3x^2 - 15x + 1$$

$$= 2(16x^6 + 8x^5 + 41x^4 + 10x^3 + 25x^2)$$

$$\quad \times (4x^3 + x^2 + 5x) - 12x^3 - 3x^2 - 15x + 1$$

$$= 128x^9 + 96x^8 + 504x^7 + 242x^6 + 630x^5$$

$$\quad + 150x^4 + 238x^3 - 3x^2 - 15x + 1$$

17. $\dfrac{q(2 + x) - q(2)}{x}$

SOLUTION

$$\frac{q(2 + x) - q(2)}{x}$$

$$= \frac{2(2 + x)^3 - 3(2 + x) + 1 - (2 \cdot 2^3 - 3 \cdot 2 + 1)}{x}$$

$$= \frac{2x^3 + 12x^2 + 21x}{x}$$

$$= 2x^2 + 12x + 21$$

19. Find all real numbers x such that

$$x^6 - 8x^3 + 15 = 0.$$

SOLUTION   This equation involves x^3 and x^6; thus we make the substitution $x^3 = y$. Squaring both sides of the equation $x^3 = y$ gives $x^6 = y^2$. With these substitutions, the equation above becomes

$$y^2 - 8y + 15 = 0.$$

This new equation can now be solved either by factoring the left side or by using the quadratic formula. Let's factor the left side, getting

$$(y - 3)(y - 5) = 0.$$

Thus $y = 3$ or $y = 5$ (the same result could have been obtained by using the quadratic formula).

Substituting x^3 for y now shows that $x^3 = 3$ or $x^3 = 5$. Thus $x = 3^{1/3}$ or $x = 5^{1/3}$.

21. Find all real numbers x such that
$$x^4 - 2x^2 - 15 = 0.$$

SOLUTION This equation involves x^2 and x^4; thus we make the substitution $x^2 = y$. Squaring both sides of the equation $x^2 = y$ gives $x^4 = y^2$. With these substitutions, the equation above becomes
$$y^2 - 2y - 15 = 0.$$

This new equation can now be solved either by factoring the left side or by using the quadratic formula. Let's use the quadratic formula, getting
$$y = \frac{2 \pm \sqrt{4 + 60}}{2} = \frac{2 \pm 8}{2}.$$
Thus $y = 5$ or $y = -3$ (the same result could have been obtained by factoring).

Substituting x^2 for y now shows that $x^2 = 5$ or $x^2 = -3$. The equation $x^2 = 5$ implies that $x = \sqrt{5}$ or $x = -\sqrt{5}$. The equation $x^2 = -3$ has no solutions in the real numbers. Thus the only solutions to our original equation $x^4 - 2x^2 - 15 = 0$ are $x = \sqrt{5}$ or $x = -\sqrt{5}$.

23. Factor $x^8 - y^8$ as nicely as possible.

SOLUTION
$$x^8 - y^8 = (x^4 - y^4)(x^4 + y^4)$$
$$= (x^2 - y^2)(x^2 + y^2)(x^4 + y^4)$$
$$= (x - y)(x + y)(x^2 + y^2)(x^4 + y^4)$$

25. Find a number b such that 3 is a zero of the polynomial p defined by
$$p(x) = 1 - 4x + bx^2 + 2x^3.$$

SOLUTION Note that

$$p(3) = 1 - 4 \cdot 3 + b \cdot 3^2 + 2 \cdot 3^3$$
$$= 43 + 9b.$$

We want $p(3)$ to equal 0. Thus we solve the equation $0 = 43 + 9b$, getting $b = -\frac{43}{9}$.

27. Find a polynomial p of degree 3 such that -1, 2, and 3 are zeros of p and $p(0) = 1$.

SOLUTION If p is a polynomial of degree 3 and -1, 2, and 3 are zeros of p, then
$$p(x) = c(x + 1)(x - 2)(x - 3)$$

for some constant c. We have $p(0) = c(0 + 1)(0 - 2)(0 - 3) = 6c$. Thus to make $p(0) = 1$ we must choose $c = \frac{1}{6}$. Thus
$$p(x) = \frac{(x + 1)(x - 2)(x - 3)}{6},$$

which by multiplying together the terms in the numerator can also be written in the form
$$p(x) = 1 + \frac{x}{6} - \frac{2x^2}{3} + \frac{x^3}{6}.$$

29. Find all choices of b, c, and d such that 1 and 4 are the only zeros of the polynomial p defined by
$$p(x) = x^3 + bx^2 + cx + d.$$

SOLUTION Because 1 and 4 are zeros of p, there is a polynomial q such that
$$p(x) = (x - 1)(x - 4)q(x).$$

Because p has degree 3, the polynomial q must have degree 1. Thus q has a zero, which must equal 1 or 4 because those are the only zeros of p. Furthermore, the coefficient of x in the polynomial q must equal 1 because the coefficient of x^3 in the polynomial p equals 1.

Thus $q(x) = x - 1$ or $q(x) = x - 4$. In other words, $p(x) = (x - 1)^2(x - 4)$ or $p(x) = (x - 1)(x - 4)^2$. Multiplying out these expressions, we see that $p(x) = x^3 - 6x^2 + 9x - 4$ or $p(x) = x^3 - 9x^2 + 24x - 16$.

Thus $b = -6$, $c = 9$, $d = -4$ or $b = -9$, $c = 24$, $c = -16$.

2.5   *Rational Functions*

Ratios of Polynomials

Just as a rational number is the ratio of two integers, a **rational function** is the ratio of two polynomials:

> ### *Rational functions*
>
> A **rational function** r is a function of the form
>
> $$r(x) = \frac{p(x)}{q(x)},$$
>
> where p and q are polynomials, with $q \neq 0$.

For example, the function r defined by

$$r(x) = \frac{2x^3 + 7x + 1}{x^4 + 3}$$

is a rational function.

Every polynomial is also a rational function because a polynomial can be written as the ratio of itself with the constant polynomial 1.

Unless some other domain has been specified, you should assume that the domain of a rational function is the set of real numbers where the expression defining the rational function makes sense. In the example from the paragraph above, the expression defining r makes sense for every real number; thus the domain of that rational function is the set of real numbers.

Because division by 0 is not defined, the domain of a rational function $\frac{p}{q}$ must exclude all zeros of q, as shown in the following example.

Find the domain of the rational function r defined by

EXAMPLE 1

$$r(x) = \frac{3x^5 + x^4 - 6x^3 - 2}{x^2 - 9}.$$

SOLUTION   The denominator of the expression above is 0 if $x = 3$ or $x = -3$. Thus unless stated otherwise, we would assume that the domain of r is the set of numbers other than 3 and -3. In other words, the domain of r is $(-\infty, -3) \cup (-3, 3) \cup (3, \infty)$.

The Algebra of Rational Functions

Two rational functions can be added or subtracted, producing another rational function. Specifically, if r and s are rational functions then the rational function $r + s$ is defined by

Your algebraic manipulation skills can be sharpened by exercises involving the addition and subtraction of rational functions.

$$(r + s)(x) = r(x) + s(x)$$

and the rational function $r - s$ is defined by

$$(r - s)(x) = r(x) - s(x).$$

The procedure for adding or subtracting rational functions is the same as for adding or subtracting rational numbers—multiply numerator and denominator by the same factor to get common denominators.

EXAMPLE 2

Suppose

$$r(x) = \frac{2x}{x^2 + 1} \quad \text{and} \quad s(x) = \frac{3x + 2}{x^3 + 5}.$$

Write $r + s$ as the ratio of two polynomials.

SOLUTION
$$(r + s)(x) = \frac{2x}{x^2 + 1} + \frac{3x + 2}{x^3 + 5}$$

$$= \frac{(2x)(x^3 + 5)}{(x^2 + 1)(x^3 + 5)} + \frac{(3x + 2)(x^2 + 1)}{(x^2 + 1)(x^3 + 5)}$$

$$= \frac{(2x)(x^3 + 5) + (3x + 2)(x^2 + 1)}{(x^2 + 1)(x^3 + 5)}$$

$$= \frac{2x^4 + 3x^3 + 2x^2 + 13x + 2}{x^5 + x^3 + 5x^2 + 5}$$

Two rational functions can be multiplied or divided, producing another rational function (except that division by the constant rational function 0 is not defined). Specifically, if r and s are rational functions then the rational function rs is defined by

$$(rs)(x) = r(x) \cdot s(x)$$

The quotient $\frac{r}{s}$ is not defined at the zeros of s.

and the rational function $\frac{r}{s}$ is defined by

$$\left(\frac{r}{s}\right)(x) = \frac{r(x)}{s(x)}.$$

The procedure for multiplying or dividing rational functions is the same as for multiplying or dividing rational numbers. In particular, dividing by a rational function $\frac{p}{q}$ is the same as multiplying by $\frac{q}{p}$.

Suppose

$$r(x) = \frac{2x}{x^2 + 1} \quad \text{and} \quad s(x) = \frac{3x + 2}{x^3 + 5}.$$

Write $\frac{r}{s}$ as the ratio of two polynomials.

EXAMPLE 3

SOLUTION

$$\left(\frac{r}{s}\right)(x) = \frac{\dfrac{2x}{x^2 + 1}}{\dfrac{3x + 2}{x^3 + 5}}$$

$$= \frac{2x}{x^2 + 1} \cdot \frac{x^3 + 5}{3x + 2}$$

$$= \frac{2x(x^3 + 5)}{(x^2 + 1)(3x + 2)}$$

$$= \frac{2x^4 + 10x}{3x^3 + 2x^2 + 3x + 2}$$

Note that dividing by $\frac{3x+2}{x^3+5}$ is the same as multiplying by $\frac{x^3+5}{3x+2}$.

Division of Polynomials

Sometimes it is useful to express a rational number as an integer plus a rational number for which the numerator is less than the denominator. For example, $\frac{17}{3}$ can be expressed as $5 + \frac{2}{3}$.

Similarly, sometimes it is useful to express a rational function as a polynomial plus a rational function for which the degree of the numerator is less than the degree of the denominator. For example,

$$\frac{x^5 - 7x^4 + 3x^2 + 6x + 4}{x^2}$$

can easily be expressed as $(x^3 - 7x^2 + 3) + \frac{6x+4}{x^2}$; here the numerator of the rational function $\frac{6x+4}{x^2}$ has degree 1 and the denominator has degree 2.

To consider a less obvious example, suppose we want to express the rational function

$$\frac{x^5 + 6x^3 + 11x + 7}{x^2 + 4}$$

as a polynomial plus a rational function of the form $\frac{ax+b}{x^2+4}$, where a and b are constants. A procedure similar to long division of integers can be used with polynomials. However, mechanistic use of that procedure offers little insight into why it works. The procedure presented here, which is really just long division in slight disguise, has the advantage that its use leads to understanding its validity. The following example illustrates our procedure.

| EXAMPLE 4 | Write |

$$\frac{x^5 + 6x^3 + 11x + 7}{x^2 + 4}$$

in the form $G(x) + \frac{ax+b}{x^2+4}$, where G is a polynomial and a, b are constants.

The idea throughout this procedure is to concentrate on the highest-degree term in the numerator.

SOLUTION   The highest-degree term in the numerator is x^5; the denominator equals $x^2 + 4$. To get an x^5 term from $x^2 + 4$, we multiply $x^2 + 4$ by x^3. Thus we write

$$x^5 = x^3(x^2 + 4) - 4x^3.$$

The $-4x^3$ term above is the adjustment term that cancels the $4x^3$ term that arises when $x^3(x^2 + 4)$ is expanded to $x^5 + 4x^3$. Using the equation above, we write

$$\frac{x^5 + 6x^3 + 11x + 7}{x^2 + 4} = \frac{x^3(x^2 + 4) - 4x^3 + 6x^3 + 11x + 7}{x^2 + 4}$$

$$= x^3 + \frac{2x^3 + 11x + 7}{x^2 + 4}.$$

Again, we concentrate on the highest-degree term in the numerator.

The highest-degree term remaining in the numerator is now $2x^3$. We repeat the technique used above. Specifically, to get a $2x^3$ term from $x^2 + 4$, we multiply $x^2 + 4$ by $2x$. Thus we write

$$2x^3 = 2x(x^2 + 4) - 8x.$$

The $-8x$ term above is the adjustment term that cancels the $8x$ term that arises when $2x(x^2 + 4)$ is expanded to $2x^3 + 8x$. Using the equations above, we write

$$\frac{x^5 + 6x^3 + 11x + 7}{x^2 + 4} = x^3 + \frac{2x^3 + 11x + 7}{x^2 + 4}$$

$$= x^3 + \frac{(2x)(x^2 + 4) - 8x + 11x + 7}{x^2 + 4}$$

$$= x^3 + 2x + \frac{3x + 7}{x^2 + 4}.$$

Thus we have written $\frac{x^5+6x^3+11x+7}{x^2+4}$ in the desired form.

The procedure carried out in the example above can be applied to the ratio of any two polynomials:

Procedure for dividing polynomials

(a) Express the highest-degree term in the numerator as a single term times the denominator, plus whatever adjustment terms are necessary.

(b) Simplify the quotient using the numerator as rewritten in part (a).

(c) Repeat steps (a) and (b) on the remaining rational function until the degree of the numerator is less than the degree of the denominator or the numerator is 0.

The result of the procedure above is the decomposition of a rational function into a polynomial plus a rational function for which the degree of the numerator is less than the degree of the denominator (or the numerator is 0):

Division of polynomials

If p and q are polynomials, with $q \neq 0$, then there exist polynomials G and R such that

$$\frac{p}{q} = G + \frac{R}{q}$$

and $\deg R < \deg q$ or $R = 0$.

The symbol R is used because this term is analogous to the remainder term in division of integers.

Multiplying both sides of the equation in the box above by q gives a useful alternative way to state the conclusion:

Division of polynomials

If p and q are polynomials, with $q \neq 0$, then there exist polynomials G and R such that

$$p = qG + R$$

and $\deg R < \deg q$ or $R = 0$.

As a special case of the result above, fix a real number r and let q be the polynomial defined by $q(x) = x - r$. Because $\deg q = 1$, we will have $\deg R = 0$ or $R = 0$ in the result above; either way, R will be a constant polynomial. In other words, the result above implies that if p is a polynomial, then there exist a polynomial G and a constant c such that

$$p(x) = (x - r)G(x) + c$$

for every real number x. Taking $x = r$ in the equation above, we get $p(r) = c$, and thus the equation above can be rewritten as

$$p(x) = (x - r)G(x) + p(r).$$

Recall that r is called a zero of p if and only if $p(r) = 0$. Thus we have the following result:

Factorization due to a zero

Suppose p is a polynomial and r is a real number. Then r is a zero of p if and only if there exists a polynomial G such that

$$p(x) = (x - r)G(x)$$

for every real number x.

The result above provides justification for one of the results used in the previous section on polynomials. Specifically, suppose p is a nonzero polynomial and r_1 is a zero of p. By the result above, there is a polynomial G_1 such that

$$p(x) = (x - r_1)G_1(x).$$

If G_1 has a (real) zero r_2, then we can apply our result to the polynomial G_1, getting a polynomial G_2 such that $G_1(x) = (x - r_2)G_2(x)$. Substituting this expression for G_1 into the equation above gives

$$p(x) = (x - r_1)(x - r_2)G_2(x).$$

We can continue in this fashion until we end up with a polynomial G_m that has no (real) zeros. We can then rename G_m as G, getting

$$p(x) = (x - r_1)(x - r_2)\ldots(x - r_m)G(x),$$

as claimed in the previous section.

The Behavior of a Rational Function Near $\pm\infty$

We now turn to an investigation of the behavior of a rational function near ∞ and near $-\infty$. Recall that to determine the behavior of a polynomial near ∞ or near $-\infty$, we factored out the term with highest degree. The procedure is the same for rational functions, except that the term of highest degree should be separately factored out of the numerator and the denominator. The next example illustrates this procedure.

EXAMPLE 5

Suppose

$$r(x) = \frac{9x^5 - 2x^3 + 1}{x^8 + x + 1}.$$

Discuss the behavior of $r(x)$ for x near ∞ and for x near $-\infty$.

Remember that neither ∞ nor $-\infty$ is a real number. To say that x is near ∞ is just an informal way of saying that x is very large. Similarly, to say that x is near $-\infty$ is an informal way of saying that x is negative and $|x|$ is very large.

SOLUTION The term of highest degree in the numerator is $9x^5$; the term of highest degree in the denominator is x^8. Factoring out these terms, and considering only values of x near ∞ or near $-\infty$, we have

$$r(x) = \frac{9x^5\left(1 - \frac{2}{9x^2} + \frac{1}{9x^5}\right)}{x^8\left(1 + \frac{1}{x^7} + \frac{1}{x^8}\right)}$$

$$= \frac{9}{x^3} \cdot \frac{\left(1 - \frac{2}{9x^2} + \frac{1}{9x^5}\right)}{\left(1 + \frac{1}{x^7} + \frac{1}{x^8}\right)}$$

$$\approx \frac{9}{x^3}.$$

For $|x|$ very large, $\left(1 - \frac{2}{9x^2} + \frac{1}{9x^5}\right)$ and $\left(1 + \frac{1}{x^7} + \frac{1}{x^8}\right)$ are both very close to 1, which explains how we got the approximation above.

The calculation above indicates that $r(x)$ should behave like $\frac{9}{x^3}$ for x near ∞ or near $-\infty$. In particular, if x is near ∞, then $\frac{9}{x^3}$ is positive but very close to 0; thus $r(x)$ has the same behavior. If x is near $-\infty$, then $\frac{9}{x^3}$ is negative but very close to 0; thus $r(x)$ has the same behavior. As the graph below shows, for this function we do not even need to take $|x|$ particularly large to see this behavior.

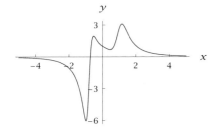

The graph of $\frac{9x^5 - 2x^3 + 1}{x^8 + x + 1}$ on the interval $[-5, 5]$. Note that the values of this function are positive but close to 0 for x near 5, and negative but close to 0 for x near -5.

In general, the same procedure used in the example above works with any rational function:

> ## Behavior of a Rational Function Near $\pm\infty$
>
> To determine the behavior of a rational function near ∞ or near $-\infty$, separately factor out the term with highest degree in the numerator and the denominator.

The next example illustrates the typical behavior of a rational function near $\pm\infty$ when the numerator and denominator have the same degree.

EXAMPLE 6

Suppose

$$r(x) = \frac{3x^6 - 9x^4 + 5}{2x^6 + 4x + 3}.$$

Discuss the behavior of $r(x)$ for x near ∞ and for x near $-\infty$.

SOLUTION   The term of highest degree in the numerator is $3x^6$; the term of highest degree in the denominator is $2x^6$. Factoring out these terms, and considering only values of x near ∞ or near $-\infty$, we have

$$r(x) = \frac{3x^6\left(1 - \frac{3}{x^2} + \frac{5}{3x^6}\right)}{2x^6\left(1 + \frac{2}{x^5} + \frac{3}{2x^6}\right)}$$

$$= \frac{3}{2} \cdot \frac{\left(1 - \frac{3}{x^2} + \frac{5}{3x^6}\right)}{\left(1 + \frac{2}{x^5} + \frac{3}{2x^6}\right)}$$

$$\approx \frac{3}{2}.$$

A computer shows that $r(1000) \approx 1.4999955$, which is very close to the predicted approximation of $\frac{3}{2}$, which equals 1.5.

For $|x|$ very large, $\left(1 - \frac{3}{x^2} + \frac{5}{3x^6}\right)$ and $\left(1 + \frac{2}{x^5} + \frac{3}{2x^6}\right)$ are both very close to 1, which explains how we got the approximation above.

The calculation above indicates that $r(x)$ should equal approximately $\frac{3}{2}$ for x near ∞ or near $-\infty$. As the graph below shows, for this function we do not even need to take $|x|$ particularly large to see this behavior.

The graph of $\frac{3x^6-9x^4+5}{2x^6+4x+3}$ (blue) and the line $y = \frac{3}{2}$ (red) on the interval $[-10, 10]$.

The line $y = \frac{3}{2}$ plays a special role in understanding the behavior of the graph above. Such lines are sufficiently important to have a name. Although the definition below is not precise (because "arbitrarily close" is vague), its meaning should be clear to you.

Asymptote

A line is called an **asymptote** of a graph if the graph becomes and stays arbitrarily close to the line in at least one direction along the line.

For example, the line $y = \frac{3}{2}$ is an asymptote of the graph of $\frac{3x^6-9x^4+5}{2x^6+4x+3}$, as can be seen above. As another example, the x-axis (which is the line $y = 0$) is an asymptote of the graph of $\frac{9x^5-2x^3+1}{x^8+x+1}$, as we saw in Example 5.

The next example illustrates the behavior near $\pm\infty$ of a rational function whose numerator has larger degree than its denominator.

EXAMPLE 7

Suppose
$$r(x) = \frac{4x^{10} - 2x^3 + 3x + 15}{2x^6 + x^5 + 1}.$$
Discuss the behavior of $r(x)$ for x near ∞ and for x near $-\infty$.

SOLUTION The term of highest degree in the numerator is $4x^{10}$; the term of highest degree in the denominator is $2x^6$. Factoring out these terms, and considering only values of x near ∞ or near $-\infty$, we have

A computer shows that $r(1000) \approx 1.999 \times 10^{12}$, which is relatively close to the predicted value of $2 \times (1000)^4 = 2 \times 10^{12}$.

$$r(x) = \frac{4x^{10}\left(1 - \frac{1}{2x^7} + \frac{3}{4x^9} + \frac{15}{4x^{10}}\right)}{2x^6\left(1 + \frac{1}{2x^5} + \frac{1}{2x^6}\right)}$$

$$= 2x^4 \cdot \frac{\left(1 - \frac{1}{2x^7} + \frac{3}{4x^9} + \frac{15}{4x^{10}}\right)}{\left(1 + \frac{1}{2x^5} + \frac{1}{2x^6}\right)}$$

$$\approx 2x^4.$$

For $|x|$ very large, $\left(1 - \frac{1}{2x^7} + \frac{3}{4x^9} + \frac{15}{4x^{10}}\right)$ and $\left(1 + \frac{1}{2x^5} + \frac{1}{2x^6}\right)$ are both very close to 1, which explains how we got the approximation above.

The calculation above indicates that $r(x)$ should behave like $2x^4$ for x near ∞ or near $-\infty$. In particular, $r(x)$ should be positive and large for x near ∞ or near $-\infty$. As the following graph shows, for this function we do not even need to take $|x|$ particularly large to see this behavior.

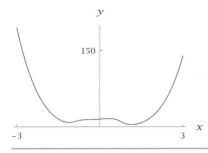

The graph of $\frac{4x^{10}-2x^3+3x+15}{2x^6+x^5+1}$ on the interval $[-3,3]$.

Graphs of Rational Functions

Just as with polynomials, the task of graphing a rational function can be performed better by machines than by humans. We have already seen the graphs of several rational functions and discussed the behavior of rational functions near $\pm\infty$.

The graph of a rational function can look strikingly different from the graph of a polynomial in one important aspect that we have not yet discussed. For example, the figure below shows part of the graph of a rational function.

The graph of $\frac{x^2+5}{x^3-2x^2-x+2}$ on the interval $[-3,3]$, truncated on the vertical axis to the interval $[-25,25]$.

The red lines are the vertical asymptotes of the graph of this rational function. The x-axis is also an asymptote of this graph.

Because the numerator of the rational function $r(x) = \frac{x^2+5}{x^3-2x^2-x+2}$ has degree less than the denominator, $r(x)$ is close to 0 for x near ∞ and for x near $-\infty$. Thus the graph of r is close to the x-axis for large values of $|x|$, as can be seen in the figure above. We encountered a graph with similar behavior near ∞ and $-\infty$ in the previous subsection (see Example 5).

The strikingly different behavior of the graph above as compared to previous graphs that we have seen occurs near $x = -1$, $x = 1$, and $x = 2$, as can be seen in the figure above where those three lines are shown in red. To understand what is happening here, note that the denominator of $r(x) = \frac{x^2+5}{x^3-2x^2-x+2}$ is zero if $x = -1$, $x = 1$, or $x = 2$. Thus the numbers -1, 1, and 2 are not in the domain of r, because division by 0 is not defined.

For values of x very close to $x = -1$, $x = 1$, or $x = 2$, the denominator of r is very close to 0, but the numerator is always at least 5. Dividing a number larger than 5 by a number very close to 0 produces a number with very large absolute value, which explains the behavior of the graph of r near $x = -1$, $x = 1$, and $x = 2$. In other words, the lines $x = -1$, $x = 1$, and $x = 2$ are asymptotes of the graph of $\frac{x^2+5}{x^3-2x^2-x+2}$.

We conclude this section by stating a result about the maximum number of peaks and valleys than can appear in the graph of a rational function.

You will be able to understand why this result holds after you have learned calculus.

Peaks and valleys for the graph of a rational function

The graph of a rational function $\frac{p}{q}$, where p and q are polynomials, can have a total of most $\deg p + \deg q - 1$ peaks and valleys.

EXERCISES

For Exercises 1–4, write the domain of the given function r as a union of intervals.

1. $r(x) = \dfrac{5x^3 - 12x^2 + 13}{x^2 - 7}$

2. $r(x) = \dfrac{x^5 + 3x^4 - 6}{2x^2 - 5}$

3. $r(x) = \dfrac{4x^7 + 8x^2 - 1}{x^2 - 2x - 6}$

4. $r(x) = \dfrac{6x^9 + x^5 + 8}{x^2 + 4x + 1}$

Suppose

$$r(x) = \frac{3x + 4}{x^2 + 1},$$

$$s(x) = \frac{x^2 + 2}{2x - 1},$$

$$t(x) = \frac{5}{4x^3 + 3}.$$

In Exercises 5–22, write the indicated expression as a ratio, with the numerator and denominator each written as a sum of terms of the form cx^m.

5. $(r + s)(x)$

6. $(r - s)(x)$

7. $(s - t)(x)$

8. $(s + t)(x)$

9. $(3r - 2s)(x)$

10. $(4r + 5s)(x)$

11. $(rs)(x)$

12. $(rt)(x)$

13. $\big(r(x)\big)^2$

14. $\big(s(x)\big)^2$

15. $\big(r(x)\big)^2 t(x)$

16. $\big(s(x)\big)^2 t(x)$

17. $(r \circ s)(x)$

18. $(s \circ r)(x)$

19. $(r \circ t)(x)$

20. $(t \circ r)(x)$

21. $\frac{s(1+x)-s(1)}{x}$

22. $\frac{t(x-1)-t(-1)}{x}$

For Exercises 23–28, suppose

$$r(x) = \frac{x + 1}{x^2 + 3} \quad \text{and} \quad s(x) = \frac{x + 2}{x^2 + 5}.$$

23. What is the domain of r?

24. What is the domain of s?

25. Find two distinct numbers x such that $r(x) = \frac{1}{4}$.

26. Find two distinct numbers x such that $s(x) = \frac{1}{8}$.

27. What is the range of r?

28. What is the range of s?

In Exercises 29–34, write each expression in the form $G(x) + \frac{R(x)}{q(x)}$, where q is the denominator of the given expression and G and R are polynomials with $\deg R < \deg q$.

29. $\dfrac{2x + 1}{x - 3}$

30. $\dfrac{4x - 5}{x + 7}$

31. $\dfrac{x^2}{3x - 1}$

32. $\dfrac{x^2}{4x + 3}$

33. $\dfrac{x^6 + 3x^3 + 1}{x^2 + 2x + 5}$

34. $\dfrac{x^6 - 4x^2 + 5}{x^2 - 3x + 1}$

35. Find a constant c such that $r(10^{100}) \approx 6$, where

$$r(x) = \frac{cx^3 + 20x^2 - 15x + 17}{5x^3 + 4x^2 + 18x + 7}.$$

36. Find a constant c such that $r(2^{1000}) \approx 5$, where

$$r(x) = \frac{3x^4 - 2x^3 + 8x + 7}{cx^4 - 9x + 2}.$$

For Exercises 37–40, find the asymptotes of the graph of the given function r.

37. $r(x) = \dfrac{6x^4 + 4x^3 - 7}{2x^4 + 3x^2 + 5}$

38. $r(x) = \dfrac{6x^6 - 7x^3 + 3}{3x^6 + 5x^4 + x^2 + 1}$

39. $r(x) = \dfrac{3x + 1}{x^2 + x - 2}$

40. $r(x) = \dfrac{9x + 5}{x^2 - x - 6}$

PROBLEMS

41. Suppose $s(x) = \dfrac{x^2 + 2}{2x - 1}$.

   (a) Show that the point $(1, 3)$ is on the graph of s.

   (b) Show that the slope of a line containing $(1, 3)$ and a point on the graph of s very close to $(1, 3)$ is approximately -4.

   [*Hint:* Use the result of Exercise 21.]

42. Suppose $t(x) = \dfrac{5}{4x^3 + 3}$.

   (a) Show that the point $(-1, -5)$ is on the graph of t.

   (b) Give an estimate for the slope of a line containing $(-1, -5)$ and a point on the graph of t very close to $(-1, -5)$.

   [*Hint:* Use the result of Exercise 22.]

43. Explain how the result in the previous section for the maximum number of peaks and valleys in the graph of a polynomial is a special case of the result in this section for the maximum number of peaks and valleys in the graph of a rational function.

44. Explain why the composition of a polynomial and a rational function (in either order) is a rational function.

45. Explain why the composition of two rational functions is a rational function.

46. Suppose p is a polynomial and r is a number. Explain why there is a polynomial G such that

$$\frac{p(x) - p(r)}{x - r} = G(x)$$

   for every number $x \neq r$.

WORKED-OUT SOLUTIONS *to Odd-numbered Exercises*

For Exercises 1–4, write the domain of the given function r as a union of intervals.

1. $r(x) = \dfrac{5x^3 - 12x^2 + 13}{x^2 - 7}$

   SOLUTION   Because we have no other information about the domain of r, we assume that the domain of r is the set of numbers where the expression defining r makes sense, which means where the denominator is not 0. The denominator of the expression defining r is 0 if $x = -\sqrt{7}$ or $x = \sqrt{7}$. Thus the domain of r is the set of numbers other than $-\sqrt{7}$ and $\sqrt{7}$. In other words, the domain of r is $(-\infty, -\sqrt{7}) \cup (-\sqrt{7}, \sqrt{7}) \cup (\sqrt{7}, \infty)$.

3. $r(x) = \dfrac{4x^7 + 8x^2 - 1}{x^2 - 2x - 6}$

   SOLUTION   To find where the expression defining r does not make sense, apply the quadratic formula to the equation $x^2 - 2x - 6 = 0$, getting $x = 1 - \sqrt{7}$ or $x = 1 + \sqrt{7}$. Thus the domain of r is the set of numbers other than $1 - \sqrt{7}$ and $1 + \sqrt{7}$. In other words, the domain of r is $(-\infty, 1 - \sqrt{7}) \cup (1 - \sqrt{7}, 1 + \sqrt{7}) \cup (1 + \sqrt{7}, \infty)$.

Suppose

$$r(x) = \frac{3x + 4}{x^2 + 1},$$

$$s(x) = \frac{x^2 + 2}{2x - 1},$$

$$t(x) = \frac{5}{4x^3 + 3}.$$

In Exercises 5–22, write the indicated expression as a ratio, with the numerator and denominator each written as a sum of terms of the form cx^m.

5. $(r + s)(x)$

SOLUTION

$$(r + s)(x) = \frac{3x + 4}{x^2 + 1} + \frac{x^2 + 2}{2x - 1}$$

$$= \frac{(3x + 4)(2x - 1)}{(x^2 + 1)(2x - 1)} + \frac{(x^2 + 2)(x^2 + 1)}{(x^2 + 1)(2x - 1)}$$

$$= \frac{(3x + 4)(2x - 1) + (x^2 + 2)(x^2 + 1)}{(x^2 + 1)(2x - 1)}$$

$$= \frac{6x^2 - 3x + 8x - 4 + x^4 + x^2 + 2x^2 + 2}{2x^3 - x^2 + 2x - 1}$$

$$= \frac{x^4 + 9x^2 + 5x - 2}{2x^3 - x^2 + 2x - 1}$$

7. $(s - t)(x)$

SOLUTION

$$(s - t)(x) = \frac{x^2 + 2}{2x - 1} - \frac{5}{4x^3 + 3}$$

$$= \frac{(x^2 + 2)(4x^3 + 3)}{(2x - 1)(4x^3 + 3)} - \frac{5(2x - 1)}{(2x - 1)(4x^3 + 3)}$$

$$= \frac{(x^2 + 2)(4x^3 + 3) - 5(2x - 1)}{(2x - 1)(4x^3 + 3)}$$

$$= \frac{4x^5 + 8x^3 + 3x^2 - 10x + 11}{8x^4 - 4x^3 + 6x - 3}$$

9. $(3r - 2s)(x)$

SOLUTION

$$(3r - 2s)(x) = 3\left(\frac{3x + 4}{x^2 + 1}\right) - 2\left(\frac{x^2 + 2}{2x - 1}\right)$$

$$= \frac{9x + 12}{x^2 + 1} - \frac{2x^2 + 4}{2x - 1}$$

$$= \frac{(9x + 12)(2x - 1)}{(x^2 + 1)(2x - 1)} - \frac{(2x^2 + 4)(x^2 + 1)}{(x^2 + 1)(2x - 1)}$$

$$= \frac{(9x + 12)(2x - 1) - (2x^2 + 4)(x^2 + 1)}{(x^2 + 1)(2x - 1)}$$

$$= \frac{18x^2 - 9x + 24x - 12 - 2x^4 - 6x^2 - 4}{2x^3 - x^2 + 2x - 1}$$

$$= \frac{-2x^4 + 12x^2 + 15x - 16}{2x^3 - x^2 + 2x - 1}$$

11. $(rs)(x)$

SOLUTION

$$(rs)(x) = \frac{3x + 4}{x^2 + 1} \cdot \frac{x^2 + 2}{2x - 1}$$

$$= \frac{(3x + 4)(x^2 + 2)}{(x^2 + 1)(2x - 1)}$$

$$= \frac{3x^3 + 4x^2 + 6x + 8}{2x^3 - x^2 + 2x - 1}$$

13. $\left(r(x)\right)^2$

SOLUTION

$$\left(r(x)\right)^2 = \left(\frac{3x + 4}{x^2 + 1}\right)^2$$

$$= \frac{(3x + 4)^2}{(x^2 + 1)^2}$$

$$= \frac{9x^2 + 24x + 16}{x^4 + 2x^2 + 1}$$

15. $\left(r(x)\right)^2 t(x)$

SOLUTION   Using the expression that we computed for $\left(r(x)\right)^2$ in the solution to Exercise 13, we have

$$\left(r(x)\right)^2 t(x) = \frac{9x^2 + 24x + 16}{x^4 + 2x^2 + 1} \cdot \frac{5}{4x^3 + 3}$$

$$= \frac{5(9x^2 + 24x + 16)}{(x^4 + 2x^2 + 1)(4x^3 + 3)}$$

$$= \frac{45x^2 + 120x + 80}{4x^7 + 8x^5 + 3x^4 + 4x^3 + 6x^2 + 3}.$$

17. $(r \circ s)(x)$

SOLUTION   We have

$$(r \circ s)(x) = r(s(x))$$

$$= r\left(\frac{x^2 + 2}{2x - 1}\right)$$

$$= \frac{3\left(\frac{x^2+2}{2x-1}\right) + 4}{\left(\frac{x^2+2}{2x-1}\right)^2 + 1}$$

$$= \frac{3\frac{(x^2+2)}{(2x-1)} + 4}{\frac{(x^2+2)^2}{(2x-1)^2} + 1}.$$

Multiplying the numerator and denominator of the expression above by $(2x - 1)^2$ gives

$$(r \circ s)(x) = \frac{3(x^2 + 2)(2x - 1) + 4(2x - 1)^2}{(x^2 + 2)^2 + (2x - 1)^2}$$

$$= \frac{6x^3 + 13x^2 - 4x - 2}{x^4 + 8x^2 - 4x + 5}.$$

19. $(r \circ t)(x)$

SOLUTION   We have

$$(r \circ t)(x) = r(t(x))$$

$$= r\left(\frac{5}{4x^3 + 3}\right)$$

$$= \frac{3\left(\frac{5}{4x^3+3}\right) + 4}{\left(\frac{5}{4x^3+3}\right)^2 + 1}$$

$$= \frac{\frac{15}{4x^3+3} + 4}{\frac{25}{(4x^3+3)^2} + 1}.$$

Multiplying the numerator and denominator of the expression above by $(4x^3 + 3)^2$ gives

$$(r \circ t)(x) = \frac{15(4x^3 + 3) + 4(4x^3 + 3)^2}{25 + (4x^3 + 3)^2}$$

$$= \frac{64x^6 + 156x^3 + 81}{16x^6 + 24x^3 + 34}.$$

21. $\frac{s(1+x)-s(1)}{x}$

SOLUTION   Note that $s(1) = 3$. Thus

$$\frac{s(1 + x) - s(1)}{x} = \frac{\frac{(1+x)^2+2}{2(1+x)-1} - 3}{x}$$

$$= \frac{\frac{x^2+2x+3}{2x+1} - 3}{x}.$$

Multiplying the numerator and denominator of the expression above by $2x + 1$ gives

$$\frac{s(1 + x) - s(1)}{x} = \frac{x^2 + 2x + 3 - 6x - 3}{x(2x + 1)}$$

$$= \frac{x^2 - 4x}{x(2x + 1)}$$

$$= \frac{x - 4}{2x + 1}.$$

For Exercises 23-28, suppose

$$r(x) = \frac{x + 1}{x^2 + 3} \quad and \quad s(x) = \frac{x + 2}{x^2 + 5}.$$

23. What is the domain of r?

SOLUTION   The denominator of the expression defining r is a nonzero number for every real number x, and thus the expression defining r makes sense for every real number x. Because we have no other indication of the domain of r, we thus assume that the domain of r is the set of real numbers.

25. Find two distinct numbers x such that $r(x) = \frac{1}{4}$.

SOLUTION   We need to solve the equation

$$\frac{x + 1}{x^2 + 3} = \frac{1}{4}$$

for x. Multiplying both sides by $x^2 + 3$ and then multiplying both sides by 4 and collecting all the terms on one side, we have

$$x^2 - 4x - 1 = 0.$$

Using the quadratic formula, we get the solutions $x = 2 - \sqrt{5}$ and $x = 2 + \sqrt{5}$.

27. What is the range of r?

SOLUTION   To find the range of r, we must find all numbers y such that

$$\frac{x + 1}{x^2 + 3} = y$$

for at least one number x. Thus we will solve the equation above for x and then determine for which numbers y we get an expression for x that makes sense. Multiplying both sides of the equation above by $x^2 + 3$ and then collecting terms gives

$$yx^2 - x + (3y - 1) = 0.$$

If $y = 0$, then this equation has the solution $x = -1$. If $y \neq 0$, then use the quadratic formula to solve the equation above for x, getting

$$x = \frac{1 + \sqrt{1 + 4y - 12y^2}}{2y}$$

or

$$x = \frac{1 - \sqrt{1 + 4y - 12y^2}}{2y}.$$

These expressions for x make sense precisely when $1 + 4y - 12y^2 \geq 0$. Completing the square, we can rewrite this inequality as

$$-12\left((y - \tfrac{1}{6})^2 - \tfrac{1}{9}\right) \geq 0.$$

Thus we must have $(y - \tfrac{1}{6})^2 \leq \tfrac{1}{9}$, which is equivalent to $-\tfrac{1}{3} \leq y - \tfrac{1}{6} \leq \tfrac{1}{3}$. Adding $\tfrac{1}{6}$ to each side of these inequalities gives $-\tfrac{1}{6} \leq y \leq \tfrac{1}{2}$.

Thus the range of r is the interval $[-\tfrac{1}{6}, \tfrac{1}{2}]$.

In Exercises 29–34, write each expression in the form $G(x) + \frac{R(x)}{q(x)}$, where q is the denominator of the given expression and G and R are polynomials with $\deg R < \deg q$.

29. $\dfrac{2x + 1}{x - 3}$

SOLUTION $\dfrac{2x + 1}{x - 3} = \dfrac{2(x - 3) + 6 + 1}{x - 3}$

$$= 2 + \frac{7}{x - 3}$$

31. $\dfrac{x^2}{3x - 1}$

SOLUTION $\dfrac{x^2}{3x - 1} = \dfrac{\frac{x}{3}(3x - 1) + \frac{x}{3}}{3x - 1}$

$$= \frac{x}{3} + \frac{\frac{x}{3}}{3x - 1}$$

$$= \frac{x}{3} + \frac{\frac{1}{9}(3x - 1) + \frac{1}{9}}{3x - 1}$$

$$= \frac{x}{3} + \frac{1}{9} + \frac{1}{9(3x - 1)}$$

33. $\dfrac{x^6 + 3x^3 + 1}{x^2 + 2x + 5}$

SOLUTION

$$\frac{x^6 + 3x^3 + 1}{x^2 + 2x + 5}$$

$$= \frac{x^4(x^2 + 2x + 5) - 2x^5 - 5x^4 + 3x^3 + 1}{x^2 + 2x + 5}$$

$$= x^4 + \frac{-2x^5 - 5x^4 + 3x^3 + 1}{x^2 + 2x + 5}$$

$$= x^4 + \frac{(-2x^3)(x^2 + 2x + 5)}{x^2 + 2x + 5}$$

$$\quad + \frac{4x^4 + 10x^3 - 5x^4 + 3x^3 + 1}{x^2 + 2x + 5}$$

$$= x^4 - 2x^3 + \frac{-x^4 + 13x^3 + 1}{x^2 + 2x + 5}$$

$$= x^4 - 2x^3 + \frac{(-x^2)(x^2 + 2x + 5)}{x^2 + 2x + 5}$$

$$\quad + \frac{2x^3 + 5x^2 + 13x^3 + 1}{x^2 + 2x + 5}$$

$$= x^4 - 2x^3 - x^2 + \frac{15x^3 + 5x^2 + 1}{x^2 + 2x + 5}$$

$$= x^4 - 2x^3 - x^2$$

$$\quad + \frac{15x(x^2 + 2x + 5) - 30x^2 - 75x + 5x^2 + 1}{x^2 + 2x + 5}$$

$$= x^4 - 2x^3 - x^2 + 15x + \frac{-25x^2 - 75x + 1}{x^2 + 2x + 5}$$

$$= x^4 - 2x^3 - x^2 + 15x$$

$$\quad + \frac{-25(x^2 + 2x + 5) + 50x + 125 - 75x + 1}{x^2 + 2x + 5}$$

$$= x^4 - 2x^3 - x^2 + 15x - 25 + \frac{-25x + 126}{x^2 + 2x + 5}$$

35. Find a constant c such that $r(10^{100}) \approx 6$, where

$$r(x) = \frac{cx^3 + 20x^2 - 15x + 17}{5x^3 + 4x^2 + 18x + 7}.$$

SOLUTION   Because 10^{100} is a very large number, we need to estimate the value of $r(x)$ for very large values of x. The highest-degree term in the numerator of r is cx^3 (unless we choose $c = 0$); the highest-degree term in the denominator of r is $5x^3$. Factoring out these terms and considering only very large values of x, we have

$$r(x) = \frac{cx^3\left(1 + \frac{20}{cx} - \frac{15}{cx^2} + \frac{17}{cx^3}\right)}{5x^3\left(1 + \frac{4}{5x} + \frac{18}{5x^2} + \frac{7}{5x^3}\right)}$$

$$= \frac{c}{5} \cdot \frac{\left(1 + \frac{20}{cx} - \frac{15}{cx^2} + \frac{17}{cx^3}\right)}{\left(1 + \frac{4}{5x} + \frac{18}{5x^2} + \frac{7}{5x^3}\right)}$$

$$\approx \frac{c}{5}.$$

For x very large, $\left(1 + \frac{20}{cx} - \frac{15}{cx^2} + \frac{17}{cx^3}\right)$ and $\left(1 + \frac{4}{5x} + \frac{18}{5x^2} + \frac{7}{5x^3}\right)$ are both very close to 1, which explains how we got the approximation above.

The approximation above shows that $r(10^{100}) \approx \frac{c}{5}$. Hence we want to choose c so that $\frac{c}{5} = 6$. Thus we take $c = 30$.

For Exercises 37–40, find the asymptotes of the graph of the given function r.

37. $r(x) = \dfrac{6x^4 + 4x^3 - 7}{2x^4 + 3x^2 + 5}$

SOLUTION   The denominator of this rational function is never 0, so we only need to worry about the behavior of r near $\pm\infty$. For $|x|$ very large, we have

$$r(x) = \frac{6x^4 + 4x^3 - 7}{2x^4 + 3x^2 + 5}$$

$$= \frac{6x^4\left(1 + \frac{2}{3x} - \frac{7}{6x^4}\right)}{2x^4\left(1 + \frac{3}{2x^2} + \frac{5}{2x^4}\right)}$$

$$\approx 3.$$

Thus the line $y = 3$ is an asymptote of the graph of r, as shown below:

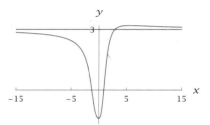

The graph of $\dfrac{6x^4 + 4x^3 - 7}{2x^4 + 3x^2 + 5}$ *on the interval* $[-15, 15]$.

39. $r(x) = \dfrac{3x + 1}{x^2 + x - 2}$

SOLUTION   The denominator of this rational function is 0 when

$$x^2 + x - 2 = 0.$$

Solving this equation either by factoring or using the quadratic formula, we get $x = -2$ or $x = 1$. Because the degree of the numerator is less than the degree of the denominator, the value of this function is close to 0 when $|x|$ is large. Thus the asymptotes of the graph of r are the lines $x = -2$, $x = 1$, and $y = 0$, as shown below:

The graph of $\dfrac{3x + 1}{x^2 + x - 2}$ *on the interval* $[-6, 6]$, *truncated on the vertical axis to the interval* $[-20, 20]$.

2.6 | *Complex Numbers*

SECTION OBJECTIVES

By the end of this section you should

- be able to add, multiply, and divide complex numbers;
- be able to compute the complex conjugate of a complex number;
- be able to use complex numbers to solve quadratic equations;
- understand why nonreal roots of real polynomials come in pairs;
- understand the Fundamental Theorem of Algebra.

The Complex Number System

The real number system provides a powerful context for solving a broad array of problems. Calculus takes place mostly within the real number system. However, some important mathematical problems cannot be solved within the real number system. This section provides an introduction to the complex number system, which is a remarkably useful extension of the real number system.

Consider the equation

$$x^2 = -1.$$

The equation above has no solutions within the system of real numbers, because the square of a real number is either positive or zero.

The symbol i was first used to denote $\sqrt{-1}$ by the Swiss mathematician Leonard Euler in 1777.

Thus mathematicians invented a "number", called i, that provides a solution to the equation above. You can think of i as a symbol with the property that $i^2 = -1$. Numbers such as $2 + 3i$ are called **complex numbers**. We say that 2 is the **real part** of $2 + 3i$ and that 3 is the **imaginary part** of $2 + 3i$. More generally, we have the following definitions:

Complex numbers

- The symbol i has the property that

$$i^2 = -1.$$

- A **complex number** is a number of the form $a + bi$, where a and b are real numbers.

- If $z = a + bi$, where a and b are real numbers, then a is called the **real part** of z and b is called the **imaginary part** of z.

The complex number $4 + 0i$ is considered to be the same as the real number 4. More generally, if a is a real number, then the complex number $a + 0i$ is considered to be the same as the real number a. Thus every real number is also a complex number.

Arithmetic with Complex Numbers

The sum and difference of two complex numbers are defined as follows:

> ### Addition and subtraction of complex numbers
>
> Suppose a, b, c, and d are real numbers. Then
>
> - $(a + bi) + (c + di) = (a + c) + (b + d)i$;
>
> - $(a + bi) - (c + di) = (a - c) + (b - d)i$.

Stating the definition of complex addition in words rather than symbols, we could say that the real part of the sum is the sum of the real parts and the imaginary part of the sum is the sum of the imaginary parts.

(a)   Evaluate $(2 + 3i) + (4 + 5i)$.

(b)   Evaluate $(6 + 3i) - (2 + 8i)$.

EXAMPLE 1

SOLUTION

(a) $(2 + 3i) + (4 + 5i) = (2 + 4) + (3 + 5)i = 6 + 8i$

(b) $(6 + 3i) - (2 + 8i) = (6 - 2) + (3 - 8)i = 4 - 5i$

In the last solution above, note that we have written $4 + (-5)i$ in the equivalent form $4 - 5i$.

The product of two complex numbers is computed by using the property $i^2 = -1$ and by assuming that we can apply the usual properties of arithmetic (commutativity, associativity, and distributive property). The following example illustrates the idea.

Evaluate $(3i)(5i)$.

EXAMPLE 2

SOLUTION   The commutative and associative properties state that order and grouping do not matter. Thus we can rewrite $(3i)(5i)$ as $(3 \cdot 5)(i \cdot i)$ and then complete the calculation as follows:

$$(3i)(5i) = (3 \cdot 5)(i \cdot i) = 15i^2 = 15(-1) = -15.$$

After you become accustomed to working with complex numbers, you will do calculations such as the one above more quickly without the intermediate steps:

$$(3i)(5i) = 15i^2 = -15.$$

The next example shows how to compute a more complicated product of complex numbers. Again, the idea is to use the property $i^2 = -1$ and the usual rules of arithmetic, starting with the distributive property.

EXAMPLE 3

Evaluate $(2 + 3i)(4 + 5i)$.

SOLUTION
$$
\begin{aligned}
(2 + 3i)(4 + 5i) &= 2(4 + 5i) + (3i)(4 + 5i) \\
&= 2 \cdot 4 + 2 \cdot (5i) + (3i) \cdot 4 + (3i) \cdot (5i) \\
&= 8 + 10i + 12i - 15 \\
&= -7 + 22i
\end{aligned}
$$

More generally, we have the following formula for multiplication of complex numbers:

Do not memorize this formula. Instead, when you need to compute the product of complex numbers, just use the property $i^2 = -1$ and the usual rules of arithmetic.

Multiplication of complex numbers

Suppose a, b, c, and d are real numbers. Then

$$(a + bi)(c + di) = (ac - bd) + (ad + bc)i.$$

Do not make the mistake of thinking that the real part of the product of two complex numbers equals the product of the real parts (but see Problem 49 at the end of this section). In this respect, products do not act like sums.

Complex Conjugates and Division of Complex Numbers

Division of a complex number by a real number behaves as you might expect. In keeping with the philosophy that arithmetic with complex numbers should obey the same algebraic rules as arithmetic with real numbers, division by (for example) 3 should be the same as multiplication by $\frac{1}{3}$, and we already know how to do multiplication involving complex numbers. The following simple example illustrates this idea.

EXAMPLE 4

Evaluate $\dfrac{5 + 6i}{3}$.

SOLUTION $\quad \dfrac{5 + 6i}{3} = \dfrac{1}{3}(5 + 6i) = \dfrac{1}{3} \cdot 5 + \dfrac{1}{3}(6i) = \dfrac{5}{3} + 2i$

Thus we see that to divide a complex number by a real number, simply divide the real and imaginary parts of the complex number by the real number to obtain the real and imaginary parts of the quotient.

Division by a nonreal complex number is more complicated. Consider, for example, how to divide a complex number by $2 + 3i$. This should be the same as multiplying by $\frac{1}{2+3i}$, but what is $\frac{1}{2+3i}$? Again using the principle that complex arithmetic should obey the same rules as real arithmetic, $\frac{1}{2+3i}$ is the number such that

$$(2 + 3i)\left(\frac{1}{2 + 3i}\right) = 1.$$

If you are just becoming acquainted with complex numbers, you might guess that $\frac{1}{2+3i}$ equals $\frac{1}{2} + \frac{1}{3}i$ or perhaps $\frac{1}{2} - \frac{1}{3}i$. However, neither of these guesses is correct, because neither $(2 + 3i)(\frac{1}{2} + \frac{1}{3}i)$ nor $(2 + 3i)(\frac{1}{2} - \frac{1}{3}i)$ equals 1 (as you should verify by actually doing the multiplications).

Complex numbers were first used by 16th century Italian mathematicians who were trying to solve cubic equations. Several more centuries passed before most mathematicians became comfortable with using complex numbers.

   Thus we take a slight detour to discuss the complex conjugate, which will be useful in computing the quotient of two complex numbers. Here is the formal definition:

Complex conjugate

Suppose a and b are real numbers. The complex conjugate $a+bi$, denoted $\overline{a + bi}$, is defined by

$$\overline{a + bi} = a - bi.$$

For example,

$$\overline{2 + 3i} = 2 - 3i \quad \text{and} \quad \overline{2 - 3i} = 2 + 3i.$$

The next example hints at the usefulness of complex conjugates. Note the use of the key identity $(x + y)(x - y) = x^2 - y^2$.

Evaluate $(2 + 3i)(\overline{2 + 3i})$.

EXAMPLE 5

SOLUTION
$$\begin{aligned}
(2 + 3i)(\overline{2 + 3i}) &= (2 + 3i)(2 - 3i) \\
&= 2^2 - (3i)^2 \\
&= 4 - (-9) \\
&= 13
\end{aligned}$$

The example above shows that $(2 + 3i)(2 - 3i) = 13$. Dividing both sides of this equation by 13, we see that

$$(2 + 3i)\left(\frac{2}{13} - \frac{3}{13}i\right) = 1.$$

In other words, we now see that

$$\frac{1}{2 + 3i} = \frac{2}{13} - \frac{3}{13}i.$$

Geometric interpretations of the complex number system and complex addition, subtraction, multiplication, division, and complex conjugation will be presented in Section 6.7.

The next example shows the general procedure for dividing by complex numbers. The idea is to multiply by 1, expressed as the ratio of the complex conjugate of the denominator with itself.

EXAMPLE 6

Evaluate $\dfrac{3 + 4i}{2 + 5i}$.

SOLUTION

$$\frac{3 + 4i}{2 + 5i} = \frac{3 + 4i}{2 + 5i} \cdot \frac{2 - 5i}{2 - 5i}$$

$$= \frac{(3 + 4i)(2 - 5i)}{(2 + 5i)(2 - 5i)}$$

$$= \frac{(6 + 20) + (-15 + 8)i}{2^2 + 5^2}$$

$$= \frac{26 - 7i}{29}$$

$$= \frac{26}{29} - \frac{7}{29}i$$

More generally, we have the following formula for division of complex numbers:

Do not memorize this formula. Instead, when you need to compute the quotient of complex numbers, just multiply numerator and denominator by the complex conjugate of the denominator and then compute, as in the example above.

Division of complex numbers

Suppose a, b, c, and d are real numbers, with $c + di \neq 0$. Then

$$\frac{a + bi}{c + di} = \frac{ac + bd}{c^2 + d^2} + \frac{bc - ad}{c^2 + d^2}i.$$

Complex conjugation interacts well with algebraic operations. Specifically, the following properties hold:

Properties of complex conjugation

Suppose w and z are complex numbers. Then

- $\overline{\overline{z}} = z$;

- $\overline{w + z} = \overline{w} + \overline{z}$;

- $\overline{w - z} = \overline{w} - \overline{z}$;

- $\overline{w \cdot z} = \overline{w} \cdot \overline{z}$;

- $\overline{z^n} = (\overline{z})^n$ for every positive integer n;

- $\overline{\left(\dfrac{w}{z}\right)} = \dfrac{\overline{w}}{\overline{z}}$ if $z \neq 0$;

- $\dfrac{z + \overline{z}}{2}$ equals the real part of z;

- $\dfrac{z - \overline{z}}{2i}$ equals the imaginary part of z.

To illustrate the last two properties, suppose $z = 5 + 3i$. Then $\bar{z} = 5 - 3i$. Thus

$$\frac{z + \bar{z}}{2} = \frac{(5 + 3i) + (5 - 3i)}{2} = \frac{10}{2} = 5 = \text{the real part of } z$$

and

$$\frac{z - \bar{z}}{2i} = \frac{(5 + 3i) - (5 - 3i)}{2i} = \frac{6i}{2i} = 3 = \text{the imaginary part of } z.$$

To verify the properties above in general, write the complex numbers w and z in terms of their real and imaginary parts and then compute. The following example illustrates this procedure with one of the properties. The verification of the remaining properties is left to the reader in several of the problems at the end of this section.

Show that if w and z are complex numbers, then $\overline{w + z} = \overline{w} + \overline{z}$.

EXAMPLE 7

SOLUTION Suppose $w = a + bi$ and $z = c + di$, where a, b, c, and d are real numbers. Then

The expression $\bar{z}$ is pronounced "z-bar".

$$\overline{w + z} = \overline{(a + bi) + (c + di)}$$
$$= \overline{(a + c) + (b + d)i}$$
$$= (a + c) - (b + d)i$$
$$= (a - bi) + (c - di)$$
$$= \overline{w} + \overline{z}.$$

Zeros and Factorization of Polynomials, Revisited

In Section 2.2 we saw that the equation $ax^2 + bx + c = 0$ has solutions

$$x = \frac{-b \pm \sqrt{b^2 - 4ac}}{2a}$$

provided $b^2 - 4ac \geq 0$. If we are willing to consider solutions that are complex numbers, then the formula above is valid (with the same derivation) without the restriction that $b^2 - 4ac \geq 0$.

The following example illustrates how the quadratic formula can be used to find complex zeros of quadratic functions.

EXAMPLE 8

Find the complex numbers z such that $z^2 - 2z + 5 = 0$.

Note that $\sqrt{-16}$ simplifies to $\pm 4i$, which is correct because $(\pm 4i)^2 = -16$.

SOLUTION　Using the quadratic formula, we have

$$z = \frac{2 \pm \sqrt{4 - 4 \cdot 5}}{2} = \frac{-2 \pm \sqrt{-16}}{2} = \frac{-2 \pm 4i}{2} = -1 \pm 2i.$$

In the example above, the quadratic polynomial has two zeros, namely $-1 + 2i$ and $-1 - 2i$, that are complex conjugates of each other. This behavior is not a coincidence, even for higher-degree polynomials where the quadratic formula plays no role, as shown by the following example.

EXAMPLE 9

Let p be the polynomial defined by

$$p(z) = z^{12} - 6z^{11} + 13z^{10} + 2z^2 - 12z + 26.$$

Suppose you have been told (accurately) that $3 + 2i$ is a zero of p. Show that $3 - 2i$ is a zero of p.

SOLUTION　We have been told that $p(3 + 2i) = 0$, which can be written as

$$0 = (3 + 2i)^{12} - 6(3 + 2i)^{11} + 13(3 + 2i)^{10} + 2(3 + 2i)^2 - 12(3 + 2i) + 26.$$

We need to verify that $p(3 - 2i) = 0$. This could be done by a long computation that would involve evaluating $(3 - 2i)^{12}$ and the other terms of $p(3 - 2i)$. However, we can get the desired result without calculation by taking the complex conjugate of both sides of the equation above and then using the properties of complex conjugation, getting

$$0 = \overline{(3 + 2i)^{12} - 6(3 + 2i)^{11} + 13(3 + 2i)^{10} + 2(3 + 2i)^2 - 12(3 + 2i) + 26}$$

$$= \overline{(3 + 2i)^{12}} - \overline{6(3 + 2i)^{11}} + \overline{13(3 + 2i)^{10}} + \overline{2(3 + 2i)^2} - \overline{12(3 + 2i)} + \overline{26}$$

$$= (3 - 2i)^{12} - 6(3 - 2i)^{11} + 13(3 - 2i)^{10} + 2(3 - 2i)^2 - 12(3 - 2i) + 26$$

$$= p(3 - 2i).$$

The technique used in the example above can be used more generally to give the following result:

This result states that nonreal zeros of a polynomial with real coefficients come in pairs. In other words, if a and b are real numbers and $a + bi$ is a zero of such a polynomial, then so is $a - bi$.

The complex conjugate of a zero is a zero

Suppose p is a polynomial with real coefficients. If z is a complex number that is a zero of p, then $\overline{z}$ is also a zero of p.

We can think about five increasingly large numbers systems—the positive integers, the integers, the rational numbers, the real numbers, the complex numbers—with each successive number system viewed as an extension of the previous system to allow new kinds of equations to be solved:

- The equation $x + 2 = 0$ leads to the negative number $x = -2$. More generally, the equation $x + m = 0$, where m is a nonnegative integer, leads to the set of integers.

- The equation $5x = 3$ leads to the fraction $x = \frac{3}{5}$. More generally, the equation $nx = m$, where m and n are integers with $n \neq 0$, leads to the set of rational numbers.

- The equation $x^2 = 2$ leads to the irrational numbers $x = \pm\sqrt{2}$. More generally, the notion that the real line contains no holes leads to the set of real numbers.

- The equation $x^2 = -1$ leads to the complex numbers $x = \pm i$. More generally, the quadratic equation $x^2 + bx + c$, where b and c are real numbers, leads to the set of complex numbers.

The progression above makes it reasonable to guess that we need to add new kinds of numbers to solve polynomial equations of higher degree. For example, there is no obvious solution within the complex number system to the equation $x^4 = -1$. Do we need to invent yet another new kind of number to solve this equation? And then yet another new kind of number to solve sixth-degree equations, and so on?

Somewhat surprisingly, rather than a continuing sequence of new kinds of numbers, we can stay within the complex numbers and still be assured that polynomial equations of arbitrary degree have solutions. We will soon state this result more precisely. However, first we turn to the example below, which shows that a solution to the equation $x^4 = -1$ does indeed exist within the complex number system.

Verify that
$$\left(\frac{\sqrt{2}}{2} + \frac{\sqrt{2}}{2}i\right)^4 = -1.$$

EXAMPLE 10

SOLUTION   We have
$$\left(\frac{\sqrt{2}}{2} + \frac{\sqrt{2}}{2}i\right)^2 = \left(\frac{\sqrt{2}}{2}\right)^2 + 2 \cdot \frac{\sqrt{2}}{2} \cdot \frac{\sqrt{2}}{2}i - \left(\frac{\sqrt{2}}{2}\right)^2 = i.$$

Thus
$$\left(\frac{\sqrt{2}}{2} + \frac{\sqrt{2}}{2}i\right)^4 = \left(\left(\frac{\sqrt{2}}{2} + \frac{\sqrt{2}}{2}i\right)^2\right)^2 = i^2 = -1.$$

The next result is so important that it is called the **Fundamental Theorem of Algebra**. The proof of this result requires techniques from advanced mathematics, and thus a proof cannot be given here.

The German mathematician Carl Friedrich Gauss proved the Fundamental Theorem of Algebra in 1799, when he was 22 years old.

> ### Fundamental Theorem of Algebra
>
> Suppose p is a polynomial of degree $n \geq 1$. Then there exist complex numbers $r_1, r_2, \ldots, r_n$ and a constant c such that
>
> $$p(z) = c(z - r_1)(z - r_2) \ldots (z - r_n)$$
>
> for every complex number z.

The complex numbers $r_1, r_2, \ldots, r_n$ in the factorization above are not necessarily distinct. For example, if $p(z) = z^2 - 2z + 1$, then we have $n = 2$, $c = 1$, $r_1 = 1$, and $r_2 = 1$.

The following remarks may help lead to a better understanding of the Fundamental Theorem of Algebra:

- The factorization above shows that $p(r_1) = p(r_2) = \cdots = p(r_n) = 0$. Thus each of the numbers $r_1, r_2, \ldots, r_n$ is a zero of p. Furthermore, p has no other zeros, as can be seen from the factorization above.

- The constant c is the coefficient of z^n in the expression $p(z)$. Thus if z^n has coefficient 1, then $c = 1$.

- In the statement of the Fundamental Theorem of Algebra, we have not specified whether the polynomial p has real coefficients or complex coefficients. The result is true either way. However, even if all the coefficients are real, then the numbers $r_1, r_2, \ldots, r_n$ cannot necessarily be assumed to be real numbers. For example, if $p(z) = z^2 + 1$, then the factorization promised by the Fundamental Theorem of Algebra is $p(z) = (z - i)(z + i)$.

- The Fundamental Theorem of Algebra is an existence theorem. It does not tell us how to find the zeros of p or how to factor p. Thus, for example, although we are assured that the equation $z^6 = -1$ has a solution in the complex number system (because the polynomial $z^6 + 1$ must have a complex zero), the Fundamental Theorem of Algebra does not tell us how to find a solution (but for this specific polynomial, see Problem 43 at the end of this section; also see Section 6.7, which shows how to compute fractional powers using complex numbers).

EXERCISES

For Exercises 1–34, write each expression in the form $a + bi$, where a and b are real numbers.

1. $(4 + 2i) + (3 + 8i)$
2. $(5 + 7i) + (4 + 6i)$
3. $(5 + 3i) - (2 + 9i)$
4. $(9 + 2i) - (6 + 7i)$
5. $(6 + 2i) - (9 - 7i)$
6. $(1 + 3i) - (6 - 5i)$
7. $(2 + 3i)(4 + 5i)$
8. $(5 + 6i)(2 + 7i)$
9. $(2 + 3i)(4 - 5i)$
10. $(5 + 6i)(2 - 7i)$
11. $(4 - 3i)(2 - 6i)$
12. $(8 - 4i)(2 - 3i)$
13. $(3 + 4i)^2$
14. $(6 + 5i)^2$
15. $(5 - 2i)^2$
16. $(4 - 7i)^2$
17. $(4 + \sqrt{3}i)^2$
18. $(5 + \sqrt{6}i)^2$
19. $(\sqrt{5} - \sqrt{7}i)^2$
20. $(\sqrt{11} - \sqrt{3}i)^2$
21. $(2 + 3i)^3$
22. $(4 + 3i)^3$
23. $(1 + \sqrt{3}i)^3$
24. $(\frac{1}{2} - \frac{\sqrt{3}}{2}i)^3$

25. i^{8001}

26. i^{1003}

27. $\overline{8 + 3i}$

28. $\overline{-7 + \frac{2}{3}i}$

29. $\overline{-5 - 6i}$

30. $\overline{\frac{5}{3} - 9i}$

31. $\dfrac{1 + 2i}{3 + 4i}$

32. $\dfrac{5 + 6i}{2 + 3i}$

33. $\dfrac{4 + 3i}{5 - 2i}$

34. $\dfrac{3 - 4i}{6 - 5i}$

35. Find two complex numbers z that satisfy the equation $z^2 + 4z + 6 = 0$.

36. Find two complex numbers z that satisfy the equation $2z^2 + 4z + 5 = 0$.

37. Find a complex number whose square equals $5 + 12i$.

38. Find a complex number whose square equals $21 - 20i$.

39. Find two complex numbers whose sum equals 7 and whose product equals 13.
    [*Compare to Problem 51 in Section 2.2.*]

40. Find two complex numbers whose sum equals 5 and whose product equals 11.

PROBLEMS

41. Write out a table showing the values of i^n with n ranging over the integers from 1 to 12. Describe the pattern that emerges.

42. Verify that
$$(\sqrt{3} + i)^6 = -64.$$

43. Explain why the previous problem implies that
$$\left(\frac{\sqrt{3}}{2} + \frac{1}{2}i\right)^6 = -1.$$

44. Show that addition of complex numbers is commutative, meaning that
$$w + z = z + w$$
for all complex numbers w and z.
[*Hint:* Show that
$$(a + bi) + (c + di) = (c + di) + (a + bi)$$
for all real numbers a, b, c, and d.]

45. Show that addition of complex numbers is associative, meaning that
$$u + (w + z) = (u + w) + z$$
for all complex numbers u, w, and z.

46. Show that multiplication of complex numbers is commutative, meaning that
$$wz = zw$$
for all complex numbers w and z.

47. Show that multiplication of complex numbers is associative, meaning that
$$u(wz) = (uw)z$$
for all complex numbers u, w, and z.

48. Show that addition and multiplication of complex numbers satisfy the distributive property, meaning that
$$u(w + z) = uw + uz$$
for all complex numbers u, w, and z.

49. Suppose w and z are complex numbers such that the real part of wz equals the real part of w times the real part of z. Explain why either w or z must be a real number.

50. Suppose z is a complex number. Show that z is a real number if and only if $z = \overline{z}$.

51. Suppose z is a complex number. Show that $\overline{z} = -z$ if and only if the real part of z equals 0.

52. Show that $\overline{\overline{z}} = z$ for every complex number z.

53. Show that $\overline{w - z} = \overline{w} - \overline{z}$ for all complex numbers w and z.

54. Show that $\overline{w \cdot z} = \overline{w} \cdot \overline{z}$ for all complex numbers w and z.

55. Show that $\overline{z^n} = (\overline{z})^n$ for every complex number z and every positive integer n.

56. Show that if $a + bi \neq 0$, then
$$\frac{1}{a + bi} = \frac{a - bi}{a^2 + b^2}.$$

57. Suppose w and z are complex numbers, with $z \neq 0$. Show that $\overline{\left(\dfrac{w}{z}\right)} = \dfrac{\overline{w}}{\overline{z}}$.

58. Suppose z is a complex number. Show that $\dfrac{z + \bar{z}}{2}$ equals the real part of z.

59. Suppose z is a complex number. Show that $\dfrac{z - \bar{z}}{2i}$ equals the imaginary part of z.

60. Show that if p is a polynomial with real coefficients, then
$$p(\bar{z}) = \overline{p(z)}$$
for every complex number z.

61. Explain why the result in the previous problem implies that if p is a polynomial with real coefficients and z is a complex number that is a zero of p, then $\bar{z}$ is also a zero of p.

62. Suppose f is a quadratic function with real coefficients and no real zeros. Show that the average of the two complex zeros of f is the first coordinate of the vertex of the graph of f.

63. Suppose
$$f(x) = ax^2 + bx + c,$$
where $a \neq 0$ and $b^2 < 4ac$. Verify by direct substitution into the formula above that
$$f\left(\frac{-b + \sqrt{4ac - b^2}\,i}{2a}\right) = 0$$
and
$$f\left(\frac{-b - \sqrt{4ac - b^2}\,i}{2a}\right) = 0.$$

64. Suppose $a \neq 0$ and $b^2 < 4ac$. Verify by direct calculation that
$$ax^2 + bx + c =$$
$$a\left(x - \frac{-b + \sqrt{4ac - b^2}\,i}{2a}\right)\left(x - \frac{-b - \sqrt{4ac - b^2}\,i}{2a}\right).$$

WORKED-OUT SOLUTIONS *to Odd-numbered Exercises*

For Exercises 1–34, write each expression in the form a + bi, where a and b are real numbers.

1. $(4 + 2i) + (3 + 8i)$

SOLUTION
$$(4 + 2i) + (3 + 8i) = (4 + 3) + (2 + 8)i$$
$$= 7 + 10i$$

3. $(5 + 3i) - (2 + 9i)$

SOLUTION
$$(5 + 3i) - (2 + 9i) = (5 - 2) + (3 - 9)i$$
$$= 3 - 6i$$

5. $(6 + 2i) - (9 - 7i)$

SOLUTION
$$(6 + 2i) - (9 - 7i) = (6 - 9) + (2 + 7)i$$
$$= -3 + 9i$$

7. $(2 + 3i)(4 + 5i)$

SOLUTION
$$(2 + 3i)(4 + 5i) = (2 \cdot 4 - 3 \cdot 5) + (2 \cdot 5 + 3 \cdot 4)i$$
$$= -7 + 22i$$

9. $(2 + 3i)(4 - 5i)$

SOLUTION
$$(2 + 3i)(4 - 5i) = (2 \cdot 4 + 3 \cdot 5) + (2 \cdot (-5) + 3 \cdot 4)i$$
$$= 23 + 2i$$

11. $(4 - 3i)(2 - 6i)$

SOLUTION
$$(4 - 3i)(2 - 6i)$$
$$= (4 \cdot 2 - 3 \cdot 6) + (4 \cdot (-6) + (-3) \cdot 2)i$$
$$= -10 - 30i$$

13. $(3 + 4i)^2$

SOLUTION
$$(3 + 4i)^2 = 3^2 + 2 \cdot 3 \cdot 4i + (4i)^2$$
$$= 9 + 24i - 16$$
$$= -7 + 24i$$

15. $(5 - 2i)^2$

SOLUTION

$$(5 - 2i)^2 = 5^2 - 2 \cdot 5 \cdot 2i + (2i)^2$$

$$= 25 - 20i - 4$$

$$= 21 - 20i$$

17. $(4 + \sqrt{3}i)^2$

SOLUTION

$$(4 + \sqrt{3}i)^2 = 4^2 + 2 \cdot 4 \cdot \sqrt{3}i + (\sqrt{3}i)^2$$

$$= 16 + 8\sqrt{3}i - 3$$

$$= 13 + 8\sqrt{3}i$$

19. $(\sqrt{5} - \sqrt{7}i)^2$

SOLUTION

$$(\sqrt{5} - \sqrt{7}i)^2 = \sqrt{5}^2 - 2 \cdot \sqrt{5} \cdot \sqrt{7}i + (\sqrt{7}i)^2$$

$$= 5 - 2\sqrt{35}i - 7$$

$$= -2 - 2\sqrt{35}i$$

21. $(2 + 3i)^3$

SOLUTION   First we compute $(2 + 3i)^2$:

$$(2 + 3i)^2 = 2^2 + 2 \cdot 2 \cdot 3i + (3i)^2$$

$$= 4 + 12i - 9$$

$$= -5 + 12i.$$

Now

$$(2 + 3i)^3 = (2 + 3i)^2(2 + 3i)$$

$$= (-5 + 12i)(2 + 3i)$$

$$= (-10 - 36) + (-15 + 24)i$$

$$= -46 + 9i.$$

23. $(1 + \sqrt{3}i)^3$

SOLUTION   First we compute $(1 + \sqrt{3}i)^2$:

$$(1 + \sqrt{3}i)^2 = 1^2 + 2 \cdot 1 \cdot \sqrt{3}i + (\sqrt{3}i)^2$$

$$= 1 + 2\sqrt{3}i - 3$$

$$= -2 + 2\sqrt{3}i.$$

Now

$$(1 + \sqrt{3}i)^3 = (1 + \sqrt{3}i)^2(1 + \sqrt{3}i)$$

$$= (-2 + 2\sqrt{3}i)(1 + \sqrt{3}i)$$

$$= (-2 - 2\sqrt{3}^2) + (-2\sqrt{3} + 2\sqrt{3})i$$

$$= -8.$$

25. i^{8001}

SOLUTION $i^{8001} = i^{8000}i = (i^2)^{4000}i$

$$= (-1)^{4000}i = i$$

27. $\overline{8 + 3i}$

SOLUTION $\overline{8 + 3i} = 8 - 3i$

29. $\overline{-5 - 6i}$

SOLUTION $\overline{-5 - 6i} = -5 + 6i$

31. $\dfrac{1 + 2i}{3 + 4i}$

SOLUTION $\dfrac{1 + 2i}{3 + 4i} = \dfrac{1 + 2i}{3 + 4i} \cdot \dfrac{3 - 4i}{3 - 4i}$

$$= \dfrac{(1 + 2i)(3 - 4i)}{(3 + 4i)(3 - 4i)}$$

$$= \dfrac{(3 + 8) + (-4 + 6)i}{3^2 + 4^2}$$

$$= \dfrac{11 + 2i}{25}$$

$$= \dfrac{11}{25} + \dfrac{2}{25}i$$

33. $\dfrac{4 + 3i}{5 - 2i}$

SOLUTION

$$\dfrac{4 + 3i}{5 - 2i} = \dfrac{4 + 3i}{5 - 2i} \cdot \dfrac{5 + 2i}{5 + 2i}$$

$$= \dfrac{(4 + 3i)(5 + 2i)}{(5 - 2i)(5 + 2i)}$$

$$= \dfrac{(20 - 6) + (8 + 15)i}{5^2 + 2^2}$$

$$= \dfrac{14 + 23i}{29} = \dfrac{14}{29} + \dfrac{23}{29}i$$

35. Find two complex numbers z that satisfy the equation $z^2 + 4z + 6 = 0$.

    SOLUTION By the quadratic formula, we have

    $$z = \frac{-4 \pm \sqrt{4^2 - 4 \cdot 6}}{2}$$

    $$= \frac{-4 \pm \sqrt{-8}}{2}$$

    $$= \frac{-4 \pm \sqrt{8}i}{2}$$

    $$= \frac{-4 \pm \sqrt{4 \cdot 2}i}{2}$$

    $$= \frac{-4 \pm 2\sqrt{2}i}{2}$$

    $$= -2 \pm \sqrt{2}i.$$

37. Find a complex number whose square equals $5 + 12i$.

    SOLUTION We seek real numbers a and b such that

    $$5 + 12i = (a + bi)^2 = (a^2 - b^2) + 2abi.$$

    The equation above implies that

    $$a^2 - b^2 = 5 \quad \text{and} \quad 2ab = 12.$$

    Solving the last equation for b, we have $b = \frac{6}{a}$. Substituting this value of b in the first equation gives

    $$a^2 - \frac{36}{a^2} = 5.$$

    Multiplying both sides of the equation above by a^2 and then moving all terms to one side produces the equation

    $$0 = (a^2)^2 - 5a^2 - 36.$$

    Think of a^2 as the unknown in the equation above. We can solve for a^2 either by factorization or by using the quadratic formula. For this particular equation, factorization is easy; we have

    $$0 = (a^2)^2 - 5a^2 - 36 = (a^2 - 9)(a^2 + 4).$$

    The equation above shows that we must choose $a^2 = 9$ or $a^2 = -4$. However, the equation $a^2 = -4$ is not satisfied for any real number

a, and thus we must choose $a^2 = 9$, which implies that $a = 3$ or $a = -3$. Choosing $a = 3$, we can now solve for b in the original equation $2ab = 12$, getting $b = 2$.

Thus $3 + 2i$ is our candidate for a solution. Checking, we have

$$(3 + 2i)^2 = 3^2 + 2 \cdot 3 \cdot 2i - 2^2 = 5 + 12i,$$

as desired.

The other correct solution is $-3 - 2i$, which we would have obtained by choosing $a = -3$.

39. Find two complex numbers whose sum equals 7 and whose product equals 13.

    SOLUTION Let's call the two numbers w and z. We want

    $$w + z = 7 \quad \text{and} \quad wz = 13.$$

    Solving the first equation for w, we have $w = 7 - z$. Substituting this expression for w into the second equation gives $(7 - z)z = 13$, which is equivalent to the equation

    $$z^2 - 7z + 13 = 0.$$

    Using the quadratic formula to solve this equation for z gives

    $$z = \frac{7 \pm \sqrt{7^2 - 4 \cdot 13}}{2} = \frac{7 \pm \sqrt{-3}}{2} = \frac{7 \pm \sqrt{3}i}{2}.$$

    Let's choose the solution $z = \frac{7 + \sqrt{3}i}{2}$. Plugging this value of z into the equation $w = 7 - z$ then gives $w = \frac{7 - \sqrt{3}i}{2}$.

    Thus two complex numbers whose sum equals 7 and whose product equals 13 are $\frac{7 - \sqrt{3}i}{2}$ and $\frac{7 + \sqrt{3}i}{2}$.

    CHECK To check that this solution is correct, note that

    $$\frac{7 - \sqrt{3}i}{2} + \frac{7 + \sqrt{3}i}{2} = \frac{14}{2} = 7$$

    and

    $$\frac{7 - \sqrt{3}i}{2} \cdot \frac{7 + \sqrt{3}i}{2} = \frac{7^2 + \sqrt{3}^2}{4}$$

    $$= \frac{49 + 3}{4} = \frac{52}{4} = 13.$$

2.7 *Systems of Equations and Matrices*

SECTION OBJECTIVES

By the end of this section you should

- understand how the solutions to a system of equations in two variables can be interpreted graphically;
- be able to solve a system of equations by substitution, when possible;
- be able to find the solutions to a system of linear equations;
- understand how a system of linear equations can be represented by a matrix;
- understand how the procedure for solving a system of linear equations can be carried out through matrix manipulations.

This section provides only a taste of some topics in systems of equations and matrices. Proper treatment of these subjects requires a full course devoted just to them. The first course in linear algebra focuses on systems of linear equations and matrices.

Solving a System of Equations

A **system of equations** is a collection of equations, usually with two or more variables. A **solution** to a system of equations is an assignment of values to the variables that satisfies all the equations in the system.

For systems of equations with two variables, the following procedure can sometimes be used to estimate the solutions:

No technique exists to produce exact solutions to a system of equations, except in some special cases.

Graphically solving a system of equations with two variables

(a) Label the two coordinate axes in a coordinate plane with the two variables.

(b) Plot the set of points satisfied by each equation.

(c) The solutions to the system of equations correspond to the points where all the plots from the previous step intersect.

The following example illustrates the graphical technique for estimating solutions to a system of equations.

Graphically estimate the solutions to the system of equations

EXAMPLE 1

$$x^2 - y^2 = 1$$
$$2x + y = 4.$$

*The blue curves de-fined by the equation $x^2 - y^2 = 1$ give an example of what is called a **hyperbola**.*

SOLUTION
A computer produced this plot of the points satisfying the two equations. Note that the set of points satisfying the equation $x^2 - y^2 = 1$ (in blue) consists of two curves.

The solution to this system of equations corresponds to the intersection of the two plots. As can be seen from the figure, the two plots intersect at two points.

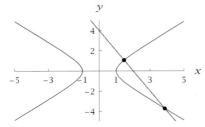

The points satisfying the equation $x^2 - y^2 = 1$ (blue) and $2x + y = 4$ (red).

One of the points of intersection has coordinates that appear to be approximately $(1.5, 1)$, and thus we estimate that one solution to this system of equations is $x \approx 1.5$ and $y \approx 1$. The other point of intersection of the two plots has coordinates that appear to be approximately $(4, -3.75)$, and thus we estimate that another solution to this system of equations is $x \approx 4$ and $y \approx -3.75$.

A better estimate can be obtained by using the computer to zoom in on a region containing one of the solutions. Here we have zoomed in on a region containing the first solution mentioned above. This figure shows that $x \approx 1.45$ and $y \approx 1.1$ is a better estimate than our original approximation. Still better estimates could be obtained by zooming in further.

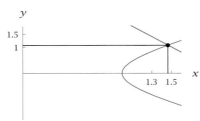

Zooming in on the previous figure.

The ancient Greeks discovered that the intersection of a cone and an appropriately positioned plane is a hyperbola.

One method for finding the exact solutions to a system of equations is called **substitution**. To get started with this procedure, you must be able to solve for one of the variables in terms of the other variables. Substitution works well for some systems of equations, but for other systems of equations it may not be possible to solve for one variable in terms of the other variables.

Solving a system of equations by substitution

(a) Use one of the equations in the system of equations to solve for one of the variables in terms of the other variables.

(b) Substitute the expression obtained in the previous step into the other equations, resulting in a new system of equations with one less variable and one less equation.

(c) Repeat the first two steps until you can solve the remaining system.

(d) Then substitute the values you have found into the previously obtained equations to get the complete solutions.

Use substitution to find exact solutions to the system of equations

EXAMPLE 2

$$x^2 - y^2 = 1$$
$$2x + y = 4.$$

SOLUTION   Solving the second equation for y gives

$$y = 4 - 2x.$$

Substituting this expression for y into the first equation gives

$$x^2 - (4 - 2x)^2 = 1,$$

which can be rewritten as

$$3x^2 - 16x + 17 = 0.$$

Using the quadratic formula to solve the last equation gives

$$x = \frac{8 - \sqrt{13}}{3} \quad \text{or} \quad x = \frac{8 + \sqrt{13}}{3}.$$

Substituting these two values for x into the equation $y = 4 - 2x$ gives the following two exact solutions for the original system of equations:

$$x = \frac{8 - \sqrt{13}}{3}, \ y = \frac{-4 + 2\sqrt{13}}{3} \quad \text{or} \quad x = \frac{8 + \sqrt{13}}{3}, \ y = \frac{-4 - 2\sqrt{13}}{3}.$$

The worked-out solutions to the odd-numbered exercises provide further examples of solving a system of equations by substitution.

Using a calculator to evaluate the exact solutions above shows that we have

$$x \approx 1.46482, \ y \approx 1.07037 \quad \text{or} \quad x \approx 3.86852, \ y \approx -3.73703,$$

which shows that the estimates obtained using the graphical method in Example 1 are reasonable (although imprecise) approximations.

Systems of Linear Equations

We now turn our attention to an important class of equations. To introduce this subject gently, we begin with the definitions of linear equations in two variables and in three variables:

Linear equation in two variables

A **linear equation in two variables** is an equation of the form $ax + by = c$, where a, b, and c are constants.

For example, $5x - 3y = 7$ is a linear equation in two variables; the set of points (x, y) satisfying this equation forms a line in the xy-plane.

206 CHAPTER 2 Linear, Quadratic, Polynomial, and Rational Functions

Linear equation in three variables

A **linear equation in three variables** is an equation of the form

$$ax + by + cz = d,$$

where a, b, c, and d are constants.

For example, $2x + 4y - 9z = 1$ is a linear equation in three variables. Even though the set of points (x, y, z) satisfying this equation forms a plane rather than a line in three-dimensional space, this equation is still called a linear equation because its form is similar to the form of a linear equation in two variables.

The notion of a **linear equation** in any number of variables should now be obvious:

Linear equations

- A **linear equation** has one side consisting of a sum of terms, each of which is a constant times a variable, and the other side is a constant.

- A **system of linear equations** is a system of equations, each of which is a linear equation.

As we will see, a procedure exists for finding the solutions to a system of linear equations. Before getting that procedure, it will be instructive to examine the possible solutions to a linear equation in one variable.

EXAMPLE 3

Suppose a and b are constants. How many solutions are there to the linear equation $ax = b$?

SOLUTION   A quick but incorrect response to this question would be that we must have $x = \frac{b}{a}$ and thus there is exactly one solution to the equation $ax = b$. However, more care is needed to deal with the case where $a = 0$.

For example, suppose $a = 0$ and $b = 1$, in which case our equation becomes $0x = 1$. Clearly this equation is satisfied by no value of x. Thus in this case our equation has no solutions. More generally, if $a = 0$ and $b \neq 0$, then our equation has no solutions.

The other case to consider is where $a = 0$ and $b = 0$. In this case our equation becomes $0x = 0$. Clearly this equation is satisfied by every value of x. Thus in this case our equation has infinitely many solutions.

Even this simple case with only one variable exhibits the behavior shown by larger systems of linear equations.

In summary, the number of solutions depends on a and b:

- If $a \neq 0$, then the equation $ax = b$ has exactly one solution.
- If $a = 0$ and $b \neq 0$, then the equation $ax = b$ has no solutions.
- If $a = 0$ and $b = 0$, then the equation $ax = b$ has infinitely many solutions.

It turns out that every system of linear equations, regardless of the number of variables, has exactly one solution, no solutions, or infinitely many solutions. The next example shows how this conclusion arises with a system of two linear equations in two variables.

Suppose a, b, and c are constants. How many solutions are there to the following system of linear equations?

EXAMPLE 4

$$2x + 3y = 6$$

$$ax + by = c$$

SOLUTION   The graphical method gives the best insight into this question. The set of points that satisfy the equation $2x + 3y = 6$ form the line shown here.

A quick but incorrect response to this question would be that the set of points that satisfy the equation $ax + by = c$ form a line, that two lines intersect at just one point, and thus there is exactly one solution to our system of equations, as shown in the second figure in the margin.

Although the reasoning in the paragraph above is correct most of the time, more care is needed to deal with special cases. One special case occurs, for example, if $a = 0$, $b = 0$, and $c = 1$. In this case, the second equation in our system of equations becomes $0x + 0y = 1$. Clearly this equation is satisfied by no values of x and y. Thus no numbers x and y can satisfy both equations in our system of equations, and hence in this case our system of equations has no solutions.

Another special case occurs, for example, if $a = 4$, $b = 6$, and $c = 7$. In this case the set of points satisfying the second equation (which is $4x + 6y = 7$) is a line parallel to the line corresponding to the first equation. Because these lines are parallel, they do not intersect, as shown in the third figure in the margin. Thus in this case, the system of equations has no solutions.

We can also understand algebraically as well as graphically why the system of equations discussed in the paragraph above has no solutions. If we divide both sides of the equation $4x + 6y = 7$ by 2, the system of equations discussed in the paragraph above becomes

$$2x + 3y = 6$$

$$2x + 3y = 3.5.$$

Because it is impossible for $2x + 3y$ simultaneously to equal 6 and 3.5, there are no numbers x and y satisfying this system of equations. Thus we see algebraically that the system of equations discussed in the paragraph above has no solutions.

Yet another special case occurs, for example, if $a = 6$, $b = 9$, and $c = 18$. In this case, our system of equations is

$$2x + 3y = 6$$

$$6x + 9y = 18.$$

Dividing both sides of the second equation by 3 produces the equation $2x + 3y = 6$, which is the same as the first equation. In other words, in this case the two equations are really the same and the line determined by the second equation is the same as the line determined by the first equation. Thus the intersection of these two lines

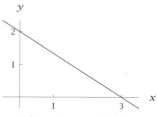

The points satisfying
$2x + 3y = 6.$

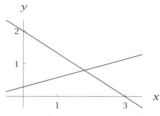

Most lines intersect the first line at exactly one point.

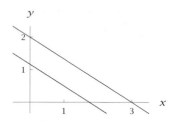

The points satisfying
$2x + 3y = 6$ *(blue) and the points satisfying*
$4x + 6y = 7$ *(red). These parallel lines do not intersect.*

equals the first line, which means that every point on the first line corresponds to a solution of our system of equations. Hence in this case our system of equations has infinitely many solutions.

In Examples 1 and 2 we saw a system of equations that has exactly two solutions, which cannot happen in a system of linear equations.

Finally, we have one more special case to consider. If $a = 0$, $b = 0$, and $c = 0$, then the second equation in our system of equations is $0x + 0y = 0$. This equation is satisfied for all values of x and y and thus in this case the second equation places no restrictions on x and y. The set of solutions to our system of equations in this case corresponds to the line determined by the first equation. Thus in this case our system of equations has infinitely many solutions.

In summary, we have shown that depending on the values of a, b, and c, this system of equations has either exactly one solution, no solutions, or infinitely many solutions.

A procedure called **Gaussian elimination** provides a very fast method for finding solutions to a system of linear equations. The box below describes the basic method of Gaussian elimination for a system of linear equations in which the number of equations equals the number of variables. The basic method shown here breaks down in certain special cases that we discuss later, but it works perfectly with almost all systems of equations in which the number of equations equals the number of variables.

Gaussian elimination is particularly well suited for implementation on a computer.

The basic method described below needs some modifications to deal with the special cases in which it does not work. Those modifications are discussed in the next subsection.

> ### Gaussian elimination for a system of linear equations, basic method
>
> (a) Add multiples of the first equation to the other equations to eliminate the first variable from the other equations.
>
> (b) Add multiples of the second equation to the equations below the second equation to eliminate the second variable from the equations below the second equation.
>
> (c) Continue this process, at each stage starting one equation lower and eliminating the next variable from the equations below.
>
> (d) When the process above can no longer continue, solve for the last variable. Then solve for the second to last variable, then the third to last variable, and so on.

EXAMPLE 5   Find all solutions to the following system of linear equations:

$$x + 2y + 3z = 4$$
$$3x - 3y + 4z = 1$$
$$2x + y - z = 7.$$

SOLUTION The first step in Gaussian elimination is to use the first equation to eliminate the first variable (which here is x) from the other equations. To carry out this procedure, note that the coefficient of x in the second equation is 3. Thus we add -3 times the first equation to the second equation, getting a new second equation: $-9y - 5z = -11$. Similarly, adding -2 times the first equation to the third equation gives a new second equation: $-3y - 7z = -1$. At this stage, our system of linear equations has been changed to the system

$$x + 2y + 3z = 4$$

$$-9y - 5z = -11$$

$$-3y - 7z = -1.$$

The second step in Gaussian elimination is to use the second equation above to eliminate the second variable (which here is y) from the equations below the second equation. To carry out this procedure, note that the coefficient of y in the second equation above is -9 and the coefficient of y in the third equation is -3. Thus we add $-\frac{1}{3}$ times the second equation to the third equation, getting a new third equation: $-\frac{16}{3}z = \frac{8}{3}$. At this stage, our system of linear equations has been changed to the system

Carl Friedrich Gauss on the German 10-mark bill.

$$x + 2y + 3z = 4$$

$$-9y - 5z = -11$$

$$-\frac{16}{3}z = \frac{8}{3}.$$

This process of eliminating variables below an equation cannot continue further. Thus we now solve the last equation in the new system for z and then work our way back up the most recent system of equations (this is called **back substitution**). Specifically, solving the last equation for z, we have $z = -\frac{1}{2}$. Substituting $z = -\frac{1}{2}$ into the second equation in the new system above gives the new equation $-9y + \frac{5}{2} = -11$, which we solve for y, getting $y = \frac{3}{2}$. Finally, substituting $y = \frac{3}{2}$ and $z = -\frac{1}{2}$ into the first equation in the new system above gives the new equation $x + 3 - \frac{3}{2} = 4$, which we solve for x, getting $x = \frac{5}{2}$.

Thus the only solution to our original system of linear equations is $x = \frac{5}{2}$, $y = \frac{3}{2}$, $z = -\frac{1}{2}$. To check that this is indeed a solution to the original system of linear equations, substitute these values for x, y, and z into all three original equations and verify that equalities are indeed obtained.

Matrices and Linear Equations

Matrices

- A **matrix** is a rectangular array of numbers. Usually a matrix is enclosed with straight brackets.

- A horizontal line of numbers within a matrix is called a **row**; a vertical line of numbers within a matrix is called a **column**.

$$\begin{bmatrix} 2 & 3 & 8 \\ -1 & 7 & 4 \end{bmatrix}$$

First row is blue.

$$\begin{bmatrix} 2 & 3 & 8 \\ -1 & 7 & 4 \end{bmatrix}$$

Third column is blue.

$$\begin{bmatrix} 2 & 3 & 8 \\ -1 & 7 & 4 \end{bmatrix}$$

Entry in row 1, column 3 is blue.

Thus

$$\begin{bmatrix} 2 & 3 & 8 \\ -1 & 7 & 4 \end{bmatrix}$$

is a matrix with two rows and three columns. The examples in the margins of this page should help you learn to identify various parts of a matrix.

Matrices have many uses within mathematics and in other fields. In this introductory look at matrices, we focus on their use in solving systems of linear equations.

The main idea in this subject is to represent a system of linear equations as a matrix and then manipulate the matrix. To represent a system of linear equations as a matrix, make the coefficients and the constant term from each equation into one row of the matrix, as shown in the following example.

EXAMPLE 6

Represent the system of linear equations

$$2x + 3y = 7$$

$$5x - 6y = 4$$

as a matrix.

SOLUTION The equation $2x + 3y = 7$ is represented as the row $\begin{bmatrix} 2 & 3 & 7 \end{bmatrix}$ and the equation $5x - 6y = 4$ is represented as the row $\begin{bmatrix} 5 & -6 & 4 \end{bmatrix}$. Thus the system of two linear equations above is represented by the matrix

$$\begin{bmatrix} 2 & 3 & 7 \\ 5 & -6 & 4 \end{bmatrix}.$$

The word "matrix" was first used to mean a rectangular array of numbers by the British mathematician James Sylvester, shown above, around 1850.

Note that in the example above, the coefficients of x in the system of linear equations form the first column $\begin{bmatrix} 2 \\ 5 \end{bmatrix}$ of the matrix and the coefficients of y form the second column $\begin{bmatrix} 3 \\ -6 \end{bmatrix}$ of the matrix. The constant terms form the last column $\begin{bmatrix} 7 \\ 4 \end{bmatrix}$ of the matrix.

When representing a system of linear equations as a matrix, it is important to decide which symbol represents the first variable, which symbol represents the second variable, and so on. Furthermore, once that decision has been made, it is important to maintain consistency in the order of variables. For example, once we decide that x will denote the first variable and y will denote the second variable, then an equation such as $-6y + 5x = 4$ should be rewritten as $5x - 6y = 4$ so that it can be represented as the row $\begin{bmatrix} 5 & -6 & 4 \end{bmatrix}$.

In the next example we go in the other direction, interpreting a matrix as a system of linear equations.

Interpret the matrix

EXAMPLE 7

$$\begin{bmatrix} -8 & 1 & -3 \\ 0 & 2 & 9 \end{bmatrix}$$

as a system of linear equations.

SOLUTION To interpret a matrix as a system of linear equations, we need to have a symbol for the first variable, a symbol for the second variable, and so on. Sometimes the choice of symbols is dictated by the context. When the context does not suggest a choice of symbols, we are free to choose whatever symbols we want. In this case, we will choose x to denote the first variable and y to denote the second variable.

Thus the first row $\begin{bmatrix} -8 & 1 & -3 \end{bmatrix}$ is interpreted as the equation $-8x + y = -3$ and the second row $\begin{bmatrix} 0 & 2 & 9 \end{bmatrix}$ is interpreted as the equation $0x + 2y = 9$, which we rewrite as $2y = 9$. Thus the matrix above is interpreted as the following system of linear equations:

$$-8x + y = -3$$

$$2y = 9.$$

The basic idea of using matrices to solve systems of linear equations is to represent the system of linear equations as a matrix and then perform the operations of Gaussian elimination on the matrix, at least until the stage of back substitution is reached.

The next example illustrates this idea. Furthermore, the next example shows how to deal with one of the special cases where the basic method of Gaussian elimination needs modification to work.

Using matrices to solve systems of linear equations saves considerable time (for humans and computers) by not carrying along the names of the variables in each step.

Use matrix operations to find all solutions to this system of linear equations:

EXAMPLE 8

$$2y + 3z = 5$$

$$x + y + z = 2$$

$$2x - y - 2z = -2.$$

SOLUTION First we represent this system of linear equations as the matrix

$$\begin{bmatrix} 0 & 2 & 3 & 5 \\ 1 & 1 & 1 & 2 \\ 2 & -1 & -2 & -2 \end{bmatrix},$$

where we have made the natural choice of letting the first variable be x, the second variable be y, and the third variable be z.

Now we are ready to perform Gaussian elimination on the matrix. Normally the first step in Gaussian elimination is to add multiples of the first equation to the other equations to eliminate the first variable from the other equations. In terms of matrices, this translates to adding multiples of the first row to the other rows to make the entries in the first column equal to 0 (except for the entry in the first row, first column). However, the entry in the first row, first column of the matrix

*Some books use the term **augmented matrix** to refer to a matrix whose last column consists of the constant terms in a system of equations.*

above equals 0, and thus adding multiples of the first row to the other rows cannot produce additional entries of 0 in the first column.

The solution to this problem is easy. We will simply interchange the first two rows of the matrix above. This operation corresponds to rewriting the order of the equations in our system of linear equations so that the equation $x + y + z = 2$ comes first, with the equation $2y + 3z = 5$ second. Clearly the operation of changing the order of the equations (or equivalently interchanging two rows of the matrix) does not change the solutions to the system of linear equations. After interchanging the first two rows, we now have the matrix

$$\begin{bmatrix} 1 & 1 & 1 & 2 \\ 0 & 2 & 3 & 5 \\ 2 & -1 & -2 & -2 \end{bmatrix}.$$

Now we can proceed with Gaussian elimination. The entry in row 2, column 1 is already 0, so we do not need to do anything to the second row. To make the entry in row 3, column 1 equal to 0 (equivalent to eliminating the first variable x), we add -2 times the first row to the third row (equivalent to adding -2 times one equation to another equation), getting the matrix

$$\begin{bmatrix} 1 & 1 & 1 & 2 \\ 0 & 2 & 3 & 5 \\ 0 & -3 & -4 & -6 \end{bmatrix}.$$

Real-world applications of systems of linear equations can require dozens or hundreds or thousands of variables. Thus efficient techniques, such as Gaussian elimination, must be used.

Now we need to make the entry in row 3, column 2 equal to 0 (equivalent to eliminating y from the third equation). We do this by adding $\frac{3}{2}$ the second row to the third row, getting the matrix

$$\begin{bmatrix} 1 & 1 & 1 & 2 \\ 0 & 2 & 3 & 5 \\ 0 & 0 & \frac{1}{2} & \frac{3}{2} \end{bmatrix}.$$

The last row of the matrix above corresponds to the equation $\frac{1}{2}z = \frac{3}{2}$. Multiplying both sides of this equation by 2 corresponds to multiplying the last row of the matrix above by 2, giving the matrix

$$\begin{bmatrix} 1 & 1 & 1 & 2 \\ 0 & 2 & 3 & 5 \\ 0 & 0 & 1 & 3 \end{bmatrix}.$$

The last row of the matrix above corresponds to the equation $z = 3$. Having solved for the last variable z, we are ready to enter the back substitution phase. The second row of the matrix above corresponds to the equation $2y + 3z = 5$. Substituting $z = 3$ into this equation gives $2y + 9 = 5$, which we easily solve for y, getting $y = -2$.

Finally, the first row of the matrix above corresponds to the equation $x + y + z = 2$. Substituting $y = -2$ and $z = 3$ into this equation gives $x + 1 = 2$, which implies that $x = 1$.

In conclusion, we have shown that the only solution to our original system of equations is $x = 1$, $y = -2$, $z = 3$.

Careful study of the example above will lead to a good understanding of how matrix operations are used to solve systems of linear equations. As can been seen in the example above, only three matrix operations are needed. These three operations are called **elementary row operations**:

Elementary row operations

Each of the following operations on a matrix is called an **elementary row operation:**

- adding a multiple of one row to another row;

- multiplying a row by a nonzero constant;

- interchanging two rows.

The constant 0 is excluded in the second elementary row operation because multiplying both sides of an equation by 0 results in a loss of information. For example, multiplying both sides of the equation $2x = 6$ by 0 produces the useless equation $0x = 0$.

These elementary row operations become easy to understand if you keep in mind that each of them corresponds to an operation on a system of linear equations. Thus the first elementary row operation corresponds to adding a multiple of one equation to another equation. The second elementary row operation corresponds to multiplying an equation by a nonzero constant. The third elementary row operation corresponds to interchanging the order of two equations in a system of linear equations.

Each elementary row operation does not change the set of solutions of the corresponding system of linear equations. Thus performing a series of elementary row operations, as in the example above, does not change the set of solutions. Although a full course (called linear algebra) is needed to deal carefully with these ideas, here is the main idea of using matrices to solve systems of linear equations:

Solving a system of linear equations with elementary row operations

(a) Represent the system of linear equations as a matrix.

(b) Perform elementary row operations on the matrix until back substitution is easy or until the set of solutions becomes obvious.

The next example illustrates one of the special cases that we have not yet encountered.

Use matrix operations to find all solutions to this system of linear equations:

EXAMPLE 9

$$x + y + z = 3$$

$$x + 2y + 3z = 8$$

$$x + 4y + 7z = 10.$$

SOLUTION   First we represent this system of linear equations as the matrix

$$\begin{bmatrix} 1 & 1 & 1 & 3 \\ 1 & 2 & 3 & 8 \\ 1 & 4 & 7 & 10 \end{bmatrix},$$

where we have made the natural choice of letting the first variable be x, the second variable be y, and the third variable be z.

To start Gaussian elimination, we add -1 times the first row to the second row and also add -1 times the first row to the third row, getting the matrix

$$\begin{bmatrix} 1 & 1 & 1 & 3 \\ 0 & 1 & 2 & 5 \\ 0 & 3 & 6 & 7 \end{bmatrix}.$$

Now we make the entry in row 3, column 2 equal to 0 by adding -3 times the second row to the third row, getting the matrix

$$\begin{bmatrix} 1 & 1 & 1 & 3 \\ 0 & 1 & 2 & 5 \\ 0 & 0 & 0 & -8 \end{bmatrix}.$$

The last row of the matrix above corresponds to the equation

$$0x + 0y + 0z = -8.$$

Because the left side of the equation above equals 0 regardless of the values of x, y, and z, we see that there are no values of x, y, and z that satisfy this equation. Thus the original system of linear equations has no solutions.

Some books use determinants to indicate whether a system of linear equations has any solutions. Gaussian elimination is much faster and more efficient than the use of determinants, especially for large systems of linear equations.

We can summarize the experience of the example above as follows:

No solutions

If any stage of Gaussian elimination produces a row consisting of all 0's except for a nonzero entry in the last position, then the corresponding system of linear equations has no solutions.

The next example illustrates yet another special case that we have not yet encountered.

EXAMPLE 10   Use matrix operations to find all solutions to this system of linear equations:

$$x + y + z = 3$$

$$x + 2y + 3z = 8$$

$$x + 4y + 7z = 18.$$

SOLUTION   First we represent this system of linear equations as the matrix

$$\begin{bmatrix} 1 & 1 & 1 & 3 \\ 1 & 2 & 3 & 8 \\ 1 & 4 & 7 & 18 \end{bmatrix},$$

where we have made the natural choice of letting the first variable be x, the second variable be y, and the third variable be z.

To start Gaussian elimination, we add -1 times the first row to the second row and also add -1 times the first row to the third row, getting the matrix

$$\begin{bmatrix} 1 & 1 & 1 & 3 \\ 0 & 1 & 2 & 5 \\ 0 & 3 & 6 & 15 \end{bmatrix}.$$

Now we make the entry in row 3, column 2 equal to 0 by adding -3 times the second row to the third row, getting the matrix

$$\begin{bmatrix} 1 & 1 & 1 & 3 \\ 0 & 1 & 2 & 5 \\ 0 & 0 & 0 & 0 \end{bmatrix}.$$

The last row of the matrix above corresponds to the equation

$$0x + 0y + 0z = 0.$$

This equation is satisfied for all values of x, y, and z. In other words, this equation provides no information, and we can just ignore it.

The second row of the matrix above corresponds to the equation $y + 2z = 5$. Because the variable z cannot be eliminated, we simply solve this equation for y, getting

$$y = 5 - 2z.$$

The first row of the matrix above corresponds to the equation $x + y + z = 3$. Substituting $y = 5 - 2z$ into this equation gives $x + (5 - 2z) + z = 3$, which implies that

$$x = -2 + z.$$

Thus the solutions to our original system of linear equations are given by

$$x = -2 + z, \quad y = 5 - 2z.$$

Some books use Cramer's rule to solve certain systems of linear equations. Cramer's rule is slow and inefficient as compared to Gaussian elimination, especially for large systems of linear equations.

Here z is an arbitrary number, and then x and y are determined by the equations above. For example, taking $z = 0$, we have the solution $x = -2$, $y = 5$, $z = 0$. As another example, taking $z = 1$, we have the solution $x = -1$, $y = 3$, $z = 1$. Our original system of linear equations has one solution for each choice of z, showing that this system of linear equations has infinitely many solutions.

The example above shows that for some systems of linear equations, a complete description of the solutions consists of equations that express some of the variables in terms of the other variables.

Infinitely many solutions

In some systems of linear equations, Gaussian elimination leads to solving for some of the variables in terms of other variables. Such systems of linear equations have infinitely many solutions.

EXERCISES

In Exercises 1–4, find all solutions to the given system of equations.

1. $x^2 - 2y^2 = 3$

   $x + 2y = 1$

2. $x^2 + 3y^2 = 5$

   $x - 3y = 2$

3. $\dfrac{1}{x} - \dfrac{1}{y} = 2$

   $4x + y = 3$

4. $\dfrac{2}{x} - \dfrac{3}{y} = 1$

   $2x + y = -1$

In Exercises 5–8, use Gaussian elimination to find all solutions to the given system of equations. For these exercises, work directly with equations rather than matrices.

5. $x - 4y = 3$

   $3x + 2y = 7$

6. $-x + 2y = 4$

   $2x - 7y = -3$

7. $x + 3y - 2z = 1$

   $2x - 4y + 3z = -5$

   $-3x + 5y - 4z = 0$

8. $x - 2y - 3z = 4$

   $-3x + 2y + 3z = -1$

   $2x + 2y - 3z = -2$

In Exercises 9–12, represent the given system of linear equations as a matrix. Use alphabetical order for the variables.

9. $5x - 3y = 2$

   $4x + 7y = -1$

10. $8x + 6y = -9$

    $10x - \frac{3}{2}y = 2$

11. $8x + 6y - 5z = -9$

    $10x - \frac{3}{2}y + 4z = 2$

    $x + 7y - 3z = 11$

12. $5x - 3y + \sqrt{2}z = 2$

    $4x + 7y - \sqrt{3}z = -1$

    $-x + \frac{1}{3}y + 17z = 6$

In Exercises 13–16, interpret the given matrix as a system of linear equations. Use x for the first variable, y for the second variable, and z for the third variable.

13. $\begin{bmatrix} 5 & -3 & 2 \\ -1 & \frac{1}{3} & 6 \end{bmatrix}$

14. $\begin{bmatrix} -7 & 4 & 23 \\ \frac{7}{3} & 31 & -5 \end{bmatrix}$

15. $\begin{bmatrix} -7 & 4 & 23 & 6 \\ \frac{7}{3} & 31 & -5 & -11 \end{bmatrix}$

16. $\begin{bmatrix} \sqrt{7} & 8 & 12 & -55 \\ 2 & -2\sqrt{3} & 15 & 1 \end{bmatrix}$

In Exercises 17–24, use Gaussian elimination to find all solutions to the given system of equations. For these exercises, work with matrices at least until the back substitution stage is reached.

17. $x - 2y + 3z = -1$

    $3x + 2y - 5z = 3$

    $2x - 5y + 2z = 0$

18. $x + 3y + 2z = 1$

    $2x - 3y + 5z = -2$

    $3x + 4y - 7z = 3$

19. $3y + 2z = 1$

    $x - 3y + 5z = -2$

    $3x + 4y - 7z = 3$

20.
$$2y + 3z = 4$$
$$-x + 4y + 3z = -1$$
$$2x + 5y - 3z = 0$$

21.
$$x + 2y + 4z = -3$$
$$-2x + y + 3z = 1$$
$$-3x + 4y + 10z = 4$$

22.
$$-x - 3y + 5z = 6$$
$$4x + 5y + 6z = 7$$
$$2x - y + 16z = 8$$

23.
$$x + 2y + 4z = -3$$
$$-2x + y + 3z = 1$$
$$-3x + 4y + 10z = -1$$

24.
$$-x - 3y + 5z = 6$$
$$4x + 5y + 6z = 7$$
$$2x - y + 16z = 19$$

25. Find a number b such that the system of linear equations
$$2x + 3y = 4$$
$$3x + by = 7$$
has no solutions.

26. Find a number b such that the system of linear equations
$$3x - 2y = 1$$
$$4x + by = 5$$
has no solutions.

27. Find a number b such that the system of linear equations
$$2x + 3y = 5$$
$$4x + 6y = b$$
has infinitely many solutions.

28. Find a number b such that the system of linear equations
$$3x - 2y = b$$
$$9x - 6y = 5$$
has infinitely many solutions.

PROBLEMS

29. Give an example of a system of three linear equations in two variables that has no solutions.

30. Give an example of a system of three linear equations in two variables that has exactly one solution.

31. Give an example of a system of three linear equations in two variables that has infinitely many solutions.

32. Give an example of a system of two linear equations in three variables that has no solutions.

33. Give an example of a system of two linear equations in three variables that has infinitely many solutions.

34. Give an example of a system of three equations in three variables that has exactly three solutions.

WORKED-OUT SOLUTIONS *to Odd-numbered Exercises*

In Exercises 1–4, find all solutions to the given system of equations.

1.
$$x^2 - 2y^2 = 3$$
$$x + 2y = 1$$

SOLUTION Solve the second equation for x, getting $x = 1 - 2y$. Substitute this value for x into the first equation, getting $(1 - 2y)^2 - 2y^2 = 3$, which can be rewritten as

$$2y^2 - 4y - 2 = 0.$$

Divide both sides of this equation by 2, and then use the quadratic formula to get

$$y = 1 - \sqrt{2} \quad \text{or} \quad y = 1 + \sqrt{2}.$$

Now substitute these values for y into the equation $x = 1 - 2y$, getting the solutions

$$x = -1 + 2\sqrt{2}, \quad y = 1 - \sqrt{2}$$

and

$$x = -1 - 2\sqrt{2}, \quad y = 1 + \sqrt{2}.$$

3. $\dfrac{1}{x} - \dfrac{1}{y} = 2$

$4x + y = 3$

SOLUTION Solve the second equation for y, getting $y = 3 - 4x$. Substitute this value for y into the first equation, getting

$$\frac{1}{x} - \frac{1}{3 - 4x} = 2.$$

Multiply both sides of this equation by $x(3 - 4x)$, getting

$$(3 - 4x) - x = 2x(3 - 4x),$$

which can be rewritten as

$$8x^2 - 11x + 3 = 0.$$

Then use the quadratic formula to get

$$x = \frac{3}{8} \quad \text{or} \quad x = 1.$$

Now substitute these values for x into the equation $y = 3 - 4x$, getting the solutions

$$x = \frac{3}{8}, \quad y = \frac{3}{2}$$

and

$$x = 1, \quad y = -1.$$

In Exercises 5-8, use Gaussian elimination to find all solutions to the given system of equations. For these exercises, work directly with equations rather than matrices.

5. $x - 4y = 3$

$3x + 2y = 7$

SOLUTION Add -3 times the first equation to the second equation, giving the system of linear equations

$$x - 4y = 3$$
$$14y = -2.$$

Solve the second equation for y, getting $y = -\frac{1}{7}$. Substitute this value for y in the first equation, getting the equation $x + \frac{4}{7} = 3$. Thus $x = \frac{17}{7}$. Hence the only solution to this system of linear equations is $x = \frac{17}{7}, y = -\frac{1}{7}$.

7. $x + 3y - 2z = 1$

$2x - 4y + 3z = -5$

$-3x + 5y - 4z = 0$

SOLUTION Add -2 times the first equation to the second equation and add 3 times the first equation to the third equation, giving the system of linear equations

$$x + 3y - 2z = 1$$
$$-10y + 7z = -7$$
$$14y - 10z = 3.$$

Now add $\frac{14}{10}$ (which equals $\frac{7}{5}$) times the second equation to the third equation, giving the system of linear equations

$$x + 3y - 2z = 1$$
$$-10y + 7z = -7$$
$$-\frac{1}{5}z = -\frac{34}{5}.$$

Solve the third equation for z, getting $z = 34$. Substitute this value for z in the second equation, getting the equation $-10y + 7 \cdot 34 = -7$. Thus $y = \frac{49}{2}$. Substitute these values for x and y into the first equation, getting the equation $x + 3 \cdot \frac{49}{2} - 2 \cdot 34 = 1$. Thus $x = -\frac{9}{2}$. Hence the only solution to this system of linear equations is $x = -\frac{9}{2}, y = \frac{49}{2}, z = 34$.

In Exercises 9-12, represent the given system of linear equations as a matrix. Use alphabetical order for the variables.

9. $5x - 3y = 2$

   $4x + 7y = -1$

   SOLUTION The equation $5x - 3y = 2$ is represented as the row $\begin{bmatrix} 5 & -3 & 2 \end{bmatrix}$ and the equation $4x + 7y = -1$ is represented as the row $\begin{bmatrix} 4 & 7 & -1 \end{bmatrix}$. Thus the system of two linear equations above is represented by the matrix

   $$\begin{bmatrix} 5 & -3 & 2 \\ 4 & 7 & -1 \end{bmatrix}.$$

11. $8x + 6y - 5z = -9$

    $10x - \frac{3}{2}y + 4z = 2$

    $x + 7y - 3z = 11$

    SOLUTION The equation $8x + 6y - 5z = -9$ is represented as the row $\begin{bmatrix} 8 & 6 & -5 & -9 \end{bmatrix}$, the equation $10x - \frac{3}{2}y + 4z = 2$ is represented as the row $\begin{bmatrix} 10 & -\frac{3}{2} & 4 & 2 \end{bmatrix}$, and the equation $x + 7y - 3z = 11$ is represented as the row $\begin{bmatrix} 1 & 7 & -3 & 11 \end{bmatrix}$. Thus the system of three linear equations above is represented by the matrix

    $$\begin{bmatrix} 8 & 6 & -5 & -9 \\ 10 & -\frac{3}{2} & 4 & 2 \\ 1 & 7 & -3 & 11 \end{bmatrix}.$$

In Exercises 13-16, interpret the given matrix as a system of linear equations. Use x for the first variable, y for the second variable, and z for the third variable.

13. $\begin{bmatrix} 5 & -3 & 2 \\ -1 & \frac{1}{3} & 6 \end{bmatrix}$

    SOLUTION Interpreting each row as the corresponding equation, we get the following system of linear equations:

    $$5x - 3y = 2$$

    $$-x + \frac{1}{3}y = 6.$$

15. $\begin{bmatrix} -7 & 4 & 23 & 6 \\ \frac{7}{3} & 31 & -5 & -11 \end{bmatrix}$

    SOLUTION Interpreting each row as the corresponding equation, we get the following system of linear equations:

    $$-7x + 4y + 23z = 6$$

    $$\tfrac{7}{3}x + 31y - 5z = -11.$$

In Exercises 17-24, use Gaussian elimination to find all solutions to the given system of equations. For these exercises, work with matrices at least until the back substitution stage is reached.

17. $x - 2y + 3z = -1$

    $3x + 2y - 5z = 3$

    $2x - 5y + 2z = 0$

    SOLUTION First we represent this system of linear equations as the matrix

    $$\begin{bmatrix} 1 & -2 & 3 & -1 \\ 3 & 2 & -5 & 3 \\ 2 & -5 & 2 & 0 \end{bmatrix}.$$

    Add -3 times the first row to the second row and add -2 times the first row to the third row, getting the matrix

    $$\begin{bmatrix} 1 & -2 & 3 & -1 \\ 0 & 8 & -14 & 6 \\ 0 & -1 & -4 & 2 \end{bmatrix}.$$

    Because all the entries in the second row of the matrix above are divisible by 2, we can simplify a bit by multiplying the second row of the matrix above by $\frac{1}{2}$, getting the matrix

    $$\begin{bmatrix} 1 & -2 & 3 & -1 \\ 0 & 4 & -7 & 3 \\ 0 & -1 & -4 & 2 \end{bmatrix}.$$

    To make the arithmetic in the next step a bit simpler, we now interchange the second and third rows, getting the matrix

    $$\begin{bmatrix} 1 & -2 & 3 & -1 \\ 0 & -1 & -4 & 2 \\ 0 & 4 & -7 & 3 \end{bmatrix}.$$

    Now add 4 times the second row to the third row, getting the matrix

$$\begin{bmatrix} 1 & -2 & 3 & -1 \\ 0 & -1 & -4 & 2 \\ 0 & 0 & -23 & 11 \end{bmatrix}.$$

The last row of the matrix above corresponds to the equation $-23z = 11$, and thus $z = -\frac{11}{23}$.

The second row of the matrix above corresponds to the equation $-y - 4z = 2$. Substituting $z = -\frac{11}{23}$ into this equation gives $-y + \frac{44}{23} = 2$, which we can easily solve for y, getting $y = -\frac{2}{23}$.

Finally, the first row of the matrix above corresponds to the equation $x - 2y + 3z = -1$. Substituting $y = -\frac{2}{23}$ and $z = -\frac{11}{23}$ into this equation and then solving for x gives $x = \frac{6}{23}$.

Thus the only solution to our original system of equations is $x = \frac{6}{23}$, $y = -\frac{2}{23}$, $z = -\frac{11}{23}$.

19.
$$3y + 2z = 1$$
$$x - 3y + 5z = -2$$
$$3x + 4y - 7z = 3$$

SOLUTION First we represent this system of linear equations as the matrix

$$\begin{bmatrix} 0 & 3 & 2 & 1 \\ 1 & -3 & 5 & -2 \\ 3 & 4 & -7 & 3 \end{bmatrix}.$$

So that we can begin Gaussian elimination, we interchange the first two rows, getting the matrix

$$\begin{bmatrix} 1 & -3 & 5 & -2 \\ 0 & 3 & 2 & 1 \\ 3 & 4 & -7 & 3 \end{bmatrix}.$$

Add -3 times the first row to the third row, getting the matrix

$$\begin{bmatrix} 1 & -3 & 5 & -2 \\ 0 & 3 & 2 & 1 \\ 0 & 13 & -22 & 9 \end{bmatrix}.$$

Now add $-\frac{13}{3}$ times the second row to the third row, getting the matrix

$$\begin{bmatrix} 1 & -3 & 5 & -2 \\ 0 & 3 & 2 & 1 \\ 0 & 0 & -\frac{92}{3} & \frac{14}{3} \end{bmatrix}.$$

The last row of the matrix above corresponds to the equation $-\frac{92}{3}z = \frac{14}{3}$, and thus $z = -\frac{7}{46}$.

The second row of the matrix above corresponds to the equation $3y + 2z = 1$. Substituting $z = -\frac{7}{46}$ into this equation gives $3y - \frac{7}{23} = 1$, which we can easily solve for y, getting $y = \frac{10}{23}$.

Finally, the first row of the matrix above corresponds to the equation $x - 3y + 5z = -2$. Substituting $y = \frac{10}{23}$ and $z = -\frac{7}{46}$ into this equation and then solving for x gives $x = \frac{3}{46}$.

Thus the only solution to our original system of equations is $x = \frac{3}{46}$, $y = \frac{10}{23}$, $z = -\frac{7}{46}$.

21.
$$x + 2y + 4z = -3$$
$$-2x + y + 3z = 1$$
$$-3x + 4y + 10z = 4$$

SOLUTION First we represent this system of linear equations as the matrix

$$\begin{bmatrix} 1 & 2 & 4 & -3 \\ -2 & 1 & 3 & 1 \\ -3 & 4 & 10 & 4 \end{bmatrix}.$$

Add 2 times the first row to the second row and add 3 times the first row to the third row, getting the matrix

$$\begin{bmatrix} 1 & 2 & 4 & -3 \\ 0 & 5 & 11 & -5 \\ 0 & 10 & 22 & -5 \end{bmatrix}.$$

Now add -2 times the second row to the third row, getting the matrix

$$\begin{bmatrix} 1 & 2 & 4 & -3 \\ 0 & 5 & 11 & -5 \\ 0 & 0 & 0 & 5 \end{bmatrix}.$$

The last row of the matrix above corresponds to the equation

$$0x + 0y + 0z = 5,$$

which is not satisfied by any values of x, y, and z. Thus the original system of linear equations has no solutions.

23. $x + 2y + 4z = -3$

$-2x + y + 3z = 1$

$-3x + 4y + 10z = -1$

SOLUTION   First we represent this system of linear equations as the matrix

$$\begin{bmatrix} 1 & 2 & 4 & -3 \\ -2 & 1 & 3 & 1 \\ -3 & 4 & 10 & -1 \end{bmatrix}.$$

Add 2 times the first row to the second row and add 3 times the first row to the third row, getting the matrix

$$\begin{bmatrix} 1 & 2 & 4 & -3 \\ 0 & 5 & 11 & -5 \\ 0 & 10 & 22 & -10 \end{bmatrix}.$$

Now add -2 times the second row to the third row, getting the matrix

$$\begin{bmatrix} 1 & 2 & 4 & -3 \\ 0 & 5 & 11 & -5 \\ 0 & 0 & 0 & 0 \end{bmatrix}.$$

The last row of the matrix above corresponds to the equation

$$0x + 0y + 0z = 0,$$

which is satisfied for all values of x, y, and z. Thus this equation provides no information, and we can just ignore it.

The second row of the matrix above corresponds to the equation $5y + 11z = -5$. Solving this equation for y, we have

$$y = -1 - \tfrac{11}{5}z.$$

The first row of the matrix above corresponds to the equation $x + 2y + 4z = -3$. Substituting $y = -1 - \tfrac{11}{5}z$ into this equation and then solving for x gives

$$x = -1 + \tfrac{2}{5}z.$$

Thus the solutions to our original equation are given by

$$x = -1 + \tfrac{2}{5}z, \quad y = -1 - \tfrac{11}{5}z,$$

where z is an arbitrary number (in particular, this system of linear equations has infinitely many solutions).

25. Find a number b such that the system of linear equations

$$2x + 3y = 4$$

$$3x + by = 7$$

has no solutions.

SOLUTION   Represent this system of equations as the matrix

$$\begin{bmatrix} 2 & 3 & 4 \\ 3 & b & 7 \end{bmatrix}.$$

Add $-\tfrac{3}{2}$ times the first row to the second row, getting the matrix

$$\begin{bmatrix} 2 & 3 & 4 \\ 0 & b - \tfrac{9}{2} & 1 \end{bmatrix}.$$

The last row corresponds to the equation $(b - \tfrac{9}{2})y = 1$. If we choose $b = \tfrac{9}{2}$, then this becomes the equation $0y = 1$, which has no solutions.

27. Find a number b such that the system of linear equations

$$2x + 3y = 5$$

$$4x + 6y = b$$

has infinitely many solutions.

SOLUTION   Represent this system of equations as the matrix

$$\begin{bmatrix} 2 & 3 & 5 \\ 4 & 6 & b \end{bmatrix}.$$

Add -2 times the first row to the second row, getting the matrix

$$\begin{bmatrix} 2 & 3 & 5 \\ 0 & 0 & b - 10 \end{bmatrix}.$$

The last row corresponds to the equation $0x + 0y = b - 10$. If we choose $b = 10$, then this becomes the equation $0x + 0y = 0$, which is satisfied by all values of x and y, which means that we can ignore it. Thus if $b = 10$, then our system of equations is equivalent to the equation $2x + 3y = 5$, which has infinitely many solutions (obtained by choosing any number y and then setting $x = \tfrac{5-3y}{2}$).

CHAPTER SUMMARY

To check that you have mastered the most important concepts and skills covered in this chapter, make sure that you can do each item in the following list:

- Find the equation of a line given its slope and a point on it.
- Find the equation of a line given two points on it.
- Find the equation of a line parallel to a given line and containing a given point.
- Find the equation of a line perpendicular to a given line and containing a given point.
- Use the completing-the-square technique with quadratic expressions.
- Find the vertex of a parabola.
- Solve quadratic equations.
- Manipulate and simplify expressions involving integer exponents.
- Compute the sum, difference, product, and quotient of two rational functions (and thus of two polynomials).

- Write a rational function as the sum of a polynomial and a rational function whose numerator has smaller degree than its denominator.
- Determine the behavior of a polynomial near $-\infty$ and near ∞.
- Determine the behavior of a rational function near $-\infty$ and near ∞.
- Perform arithmetic involving addition, subtraction, multiplication, division, and complex conjugation of complex numbers.
- Solve a system of equations by substitution.
- Solve a system of linear equations using Gaussian elimination and back substitution.
- Use elementary row operations to solve a system of linear equations.

To review a chapter, go through the list above to find items that you do not know how to do, then reread the material in the chapter about those items. Then try to answer the chapter review questions below without looking back at the chapter.

CHAPTER REVIEW QUESTIONS

1. Explain how to find the slope of a line if given the coordinates of two points on the line.

2. Given the slopes of two lines, how can you determine whether or not the lines are parallel?

3. Given the slopes of two lines, how can you determine whether or not the lines are perpendicular?

4. Find a number t such that the line containing the points $(3, -5)$ and $(-4, t)$ has slope -6.

5. Find the equation of the line in the xy-plane that has slope -4 and contains the point $(3, -7)$.

6. Find the equation of the line in the xy-plane that contains the points $(-6, 1)$ and $(-1, -8)$.

7. Find the equation of the line in the xy-plane that is perpendicular to the line $y = 6x - 7$ and that contains the point $(-2, 9)$.

8. Find the vertex of the graph of the function g defined by

$$g(x) = 5x^2 + 2x + 3.$$

9. Give an example of a quadratic function whose graph has its vertex at the point $(-4, 7)$.

10. Find a number c such that the equation

$$x^2 + cx + 3 = 0$$

has exactly one solution.

11. Find a number x such that
$$\frac{x+1}{x-2} = 3x.$$

12. Write $\dfrac{3^{800} \cdot 9^{30}}{27^7}$ as a power of 3.

13. Write $y^{-5}(y^6(y^3)^4)^2$ as a power of y.

14. Simplify the expression
$$\frac{(t^3 w^5)^{-3}}{(t^{-3} w^2)^4}.$$

15. Explain why 3^0 is defined to equal 1.

16. Explain why 3^{-44} is defined to equal $\frac{1}{3^{44}}$.

17. Sketch the graph of the function f defined by $f(x) = -5x^4 + 7$ on the interval $[-1, 1]$.

18. Sketch the graph of the function f defined by
$$f(x) = -\frac{4}{x} + 6$$
on $[-2, -\frac{1}{2}] \cup [\frac{1}{2}, 2]$.

19. Give an example of two polynomials of degree 9 whose sum has degree 4.

20. Find a polynomial whose zeros are -3, 2, and 5.

21. Find a polynomial p such that $p(-1) = 0$, $p(4) = 0$, and $p(2) = 3$.

22. Explain why $x^7 + 9999x^6 - 88x^5 + 77x^4 - 6x^3 + 55$ is negative for negative values of x with very large absolute value.

23. Write
$$\frac{3x^{80} + 2}{x^6 - 5} + \frac{x^7 + 10}{x^2 + 9}$$
as a ratio, with the numerator and denominator each written as a sum of terms of the form cx^m.

24. Write
$$\frac{3x^{80} + 2}{x^6 - 5} \Big/ \frac{x^7 + 10}{x^2 + 9}$$
as a ratio, with the numerator and denominator each written as a sum of terms of the form cx^m.

25. Suppose
$$r(x) = \frac{300x^{80} + 299}{x^{76} - 101} \quad \text{and} \quad s(x) = \frac{x^7 + 1}{x^2 + 9}.$$
Which is larger, $r(10^{100})$ or $s(10^{100})$?

26. Write the domain of $\dfrac{x^5 + 2}{x^2 + 7x - 1}$ as a union of intervals.

27. Write
$$\frac{4x^5 - 2x^4 + 3x^2 + 1}{2x^2 - 1}$$
in the form $G(x) + \dfrac{R(x)}{2x^2 - 1}$, where G is a polynomial and R is a linear function.

28. Find the asymptotes of the graph of the function f defined by
$$f(x) = \frac{3x^2 + 5x + 1}{x^2 + 7x + 10}.$$

29. Give an example of a rational function whose asymptotes in the xy-plane are the lines $x = 2$ and $x = 5$.

30. Give an example of a rational function whose asymptotes in the xy-plane are the lines $x = 2$, $x = 5$, and $y = 3$.

31. Write
$$\frac{-2 + 5i}{4 + 3i}$$
in the form $a + bi$, where a and b are real numbers.

32. Verify that
$$\left(-\frac{1}{2} + \frac{\sqrt{3}}{2}i\right)^3 = 1.$$

33. Find all solutions to the following system of equations:
$$x + 2y + 3z = 4$$
$$4x + 5y + 6z = 7$$
$$7x + 8y - 9z = 1.$$

CHAPTER
3

Starry Night *was painted by Vincent Van Gogh in 1889. The brightness of a star as seen from Earth is measured using a logarithmic scale.*

Exponents and Logarithms

This chapter focuses on understanding exponents and logarithms, along with applications of these crucial concepts.

We will begin by using the algebraic properties of exponentiation by integers to define $x^{1/m}$ for m a positive integer. As we will see, the function that takes the mth root of a number is simply the inverse of the function that raises a number to the mth power. Once we have defined $x^{1/m}$, the algebraic properties of exponentiation force us to a natural definition of exponentiation by rational numbers. From there we finally reach the notion of exponentiation by an arbitrary real number.

Logarithms will be defined as inverse functions of exponentiation. We will see that the important algebraic properties of logarithms follow directly from the algebraic properties of exponentiation.

In the last two sections of this chapter we will use exponents to model population growth, compound interest, and radioactive decay. We will also see how logarithms are used to measure earthquakes, sound, and stars.

3.1   *Rational and Real Exponents*

SECTION OBJECTIVES

By the end of this section you should

- understand why $x^{1/m}$ is defined to equal the number whose m^{th} power equals x;
- understand why $x^{n/m}$ is defined to equal $(x^{1/m})^n$;
- be able to manipulate and simplify expressions involving exponents.

So far we have defined exponentiation by integers. In this section we will define exponentiation by arbitrary real numbers. We will begin by making sense of the expression $x^{1/m}$, where m is a positive integer. From there we will progress to exponentiation by rational numbers, and then finally to exponentiation by arbitrary real numbers.

Roots

Suppose x is a real number and m is a positive integer. How should we define $x^{1/m}$? To answer this question, we will let the algebraic properties of exponentiation force the definition upon us, as we did when we defined exponentiation by negative integers in Section 2.3.

Recall that if x is a real number and m and n are positive integers, then

$$(x^n)^m = x^{nm}.$$

We would like the equation above to hold even when m and n are not positive integers. In particular, if we take n equal to $1/m$, the equation above becomes

$$(x^{1/m})^m = x.$$

Thus we see that we should define $x^{1/m}$ to be a number that when raised to the mth power gives x.

How should $8^{1/3}$ be defined?

EXAMPLE 1

SOLUTION   Taking $x = 8$ and $m = 3$ in the equation above, we get

$$(8^{1/3})^3 = 8.$$

The expression x^3 is called the **cube** *of x.*

Thus $8^{1/3}$ should be defined to be a number that when cubed gives 8. The only such number is 2; thus we should define $8^{1/3}$ to equal 2.

Similarly, $(-8)^{1/3}$ should be defined to equal -2, because -2 is the only number that when cubed gives -8. The next example shows that special care must be used when defining $x^{1/m}$ if m is an even integer.

| EXAMPLE 2 | How should $9^{1/2}$ be defined? |

SOLUTION   In the equation $(x^{1/m})^m = x$, take $x = 9$ and $m = 2$ to get

$$(9^{1/2})^2 = 9.$$

Thus $9^{1/2}$ should be defined to be a number that when squared gives 9. Both 3 and -3 have a square equal to 9; thus we have a choice. When this happens, we will always choose the positive possibility. Thus $9^{1/2}$ is defined to equal 3.

The next example shows the problem that arises when trying to define $x^{1/m}$ if x is negative and m is an even integer.

| EXAMPLE 3 | How should $(-9)^{1/2}$ be defined? |

Complex numbers were invented so that meaning could be given to expressions such as $(-9)^{1/2}$, but we restrict our attention here to real numbers.

SOLUTION   In the equation $(x^{1/m})^m = x$, take $x = -9$ and $m = 2$ to get

$$((-9)^{1/2})^2 = -9.$$

Thus $(-9)^{1/2}$ should be defined to be a number that when squared gives -9. But no such real number exists, because the square of a real number cannot be negative. Hence we leave $(-9)^{1/2}$ undefined when working only with real numbers, just as we left $1/0$ and 0^0 undefined, because no possible definition could preserve the necessary algebraic properties.

With the experience of the previous examples, we are now ready to give the formal definition of $x^{1/m}$.

Roots

If m is a positive integer and x is a real number, then $x^{1/m}$ is defined to be the number satisfying the equation

$$(x^{1/m})^m = x,$$

with the following provisions:

- If $x < 0$ and m is an even integer, then $x^{1/m}$ is undefined.
- If $x > 0$ and m is an even integer, then $x^{1/m}$ is chosen to be the positive number satisfying the equation above.

The number $x^{1/m}$ is called the **m^{th} root** of x. Thus the mth root of x is the number that when raised to the mth power gives x, with the understanding that if m is even and x is positive, we choose the positive number with this property.

The number $x^{1/2}$ is called the **square root** of x, and $x^{1/3}$ is called the **cube root** of x. For example, the square root of $\frac{16}{9}$ equals $\frac{4}{3}$, and the cube root of 125 equals 5. The notation $\sqrt{x}$ denotes the square root of x, and the notation $\sqrt[3]{x}$ denotes the cube root of x. For example, $\sqrt{9} = 3$ and $\sqrt[3]{\frac{1}{8}} = \frac{1}{2}$. More generally, the notation $\sqrt[m]{x}$ denotes the mth root of x.

Notation for roots

$$\sqrt{x} = x^{1/2};$$

$$\sqrt[m]{x} = x^{1/m}.$$

The expression $\sqrt{2}$ cannot be simplified any further—there does not exist a rational number whose square equals 2 (see Section 0.1). Thus the expression $\sqrt{2}$ is usually left simply as $\sqrt{2}$, unless a numeric calculation is needed. The key property of $\sqrt{2}$ is that

$$\left(\sqrt{2}\right)^2 = 2.$$

The rational number 1.414 is a good approximation of $\sqrt{2}$.

Make sure that you understand why the equation above holds as a consequence of our definitions. The example below should help solidify this kind of understanding.

Show that $\sqrt{7 + 4\sqrt{3}} = 2 + \sqrt{3}$.

EXAMPLE 4

SOLUTION   No one knows a nice way to simplify an expression of the form $\sqrt{a + b\sqrt{c}}$. Thus we have no obvious way to work with the left side of the equation above. However, to say that the square root of $7 + 4\sqrt{3}$ equals $2 + \sqrt{3}$ means that the square of $2 + \sqrt{3}$ equals $7 + 4\sqrt{3}$. Thus to verify the equation above, we will square the right side and see if we get $7 + 4\sqrt{3}$. Here is the calculation:

$$\left(2 + \sqrt{3}\right)^2 = 2^2 + 2 \cdot 2 \cdot \sqrt{3} + \sqrt{3}^2$$

$$= 4 + 4\sqrt{3} + 3$$

$$= 7 + 4\sqrt{3}.$$

Thus $\sqrt{7 + 4\sqrt{3}} = 2 + \sqrt{3}$.

The key point to understand in the definition of $x^{1/m}$ is that the mth root function is simply the inverse function of the mth power function. Although we did not use this language when we defined m^{th} roots, we could have done so, because we defined $y^{1/m}$ as the number that makes the equation $\left(y^{1/m}\right)^m = y$ hold, exactly as done in the definition of an inverse function (see Section 1.5). Here is a restatement of mth roots in terms of inverse functions:

The inverse of an increasing function is increasing. Thus the function $x^{1/m}$ is increasing for every positive integer m.

Because the function $x^{1/m}$ is the inverse of the function x^m, we can obtain the graph of $x^{1/m}$ by reflection of the graph of x^m through the line $y = x$, as is the case with any one-to-one function and its inverse. For the case when $m = 2$, we already did this, obtaining the graph of $\sqrt{x}$ by reflecting the graph of x^2 through the line $y = x$; see Section 1.6. Here are the graphs of $x^{1/2}$ and $x^{1/3}$:

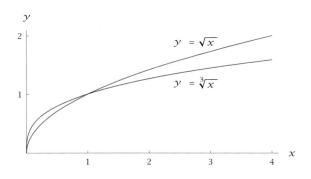

The graphs of $y = \sqrt{x}$ (blue) and $y = \sqrt[3]{x}$ (red) on the interval $[0, 4]$.

Rational Exponents

Having defined exponentiation by numbers of the form $1/m$, where m is a positive integer, we will now find it easy to define exponentiation by rational numbers.

Recall from Section 2.3 that if n and p are positive integers, then

$$x^{np} = (x^p)^n$$

for every real number x. If we assume that the equation above should hold even when p is not a positive integer, we are led to the definition of exponentiation by a rational number. Specifically, suppose m is a positive integer and we take $p = 1/m$ in the equation above, getting

$$x^{n/m} = (x^{1/m})^n.$$

The left side of the equation above does not yet make sense, because we have not yet defined exponentiation by a rational number. But the right side of the equation above does make sense, because we have defined $x^{1/m}$ and we have defined the nth power of every number. Thus we can use the right side of the equation above to define the left side, which we now do.

Exponentiation by a rational number

If n is an integer and m is a positive integer, then $x^{n/m}$ is defined by the equation

$$x^{n/m} = (x^{1/m})^n$$

whenever this makes sense.

The phrase "whenever this makes sense" in this definition is meant to exclude the case where m is even and $x < 0$ (because then $x^{1/m}$ is undefined) and the case where $n \leq 0$ and $x = 0$ (because then 0^n is undefined).

The definition above contains a subtlety that needs some comment, but before getting to that we should look at an example.

Evaluate $8^{4/3}$.

EXAMPLE 5

SOLUTION
$$8^{4/3} = (8^{1/3})^4 = 2^4 = 16$$

Because every rational number can be written in the form n/m, where n is an integer and m is a positive integer, the boxed definition of $x^{n/m}$ seems to give a definition of exponentiation by a rational number. However, the subtlety that needs our attention stems from the lack of uniqueness in representing a rational number, as shown by the next example.

(a) Evaluate $16^{3/2}$.

(b) Evaluate $16^{6/4}$.

EXAMPLE 6

SOLUTION

(a)
$$16^{3/2} = (16^{1/2})^3 = 4^3 = 64$$

(b)
$$16^{6/4} = (16^{1/4})^6 = 2^6 = 64$$

Of course we recognize that $\frac{6}{4}$ equals $\frac{3}{2}$, and thus part (b) of the example above could have been done by reducing $16^{6/4}$ to $16^{3/2}$ and using part (a). Instead, we applied the definition of exponentiation by a rational number directly to $16^{6/4}$. Fortunately our results in parts (a) and (b) above agree, or we would have a serious problem concerning the consistency of the definition.

The computation above showing that $16^{3/2}$ and $16^{6/4}$ are equal is no coincidence. The same thing would happen if 16 is replaced by an arbitrary positive number and if $\frac{6}{4}$ and $\frac{3}{2}$ are replaced by arbitrary fractions that are equal to each other. Some of the problems at the end of this section ask you to think about why this happens.

For $x > 0$, the definition of $x^{n/m}$ can be applied whether or not n/m is expressed in reduced form.

Real Exponents

At this stage we have defined exponentiation by rational numbers, but an expression such as $7^{\sqrt{2}}$ has not yet been defined. Nevertheless, the following example should make sense to you as the only reasonable way to think about exponentiation by an irrational number.

EXAMPLE 7

Find an approximation for $7^{\sqrt{2}}$.

SOLUTION   Because $\sqrt{2}$ is approximately 1.414, we expect that $7^{\sqrt{2}}$ should be approximately $7^{1.414}$ (which has been defined, because 1.414 is a rational number). A calculator shows that $7^{1.414} \approx 15.66638$.

If we use a better approximation of $\sqrt{2}$, then we should get a better approximation of $7^{\sqrt{2}}$. For example, 1.41421356 is a better rational approximation of $\sqrt{2}$ than 1.414. A calculator shows that

$$7^{1.41421356} \approx 15.67289,$$

which turns out to be correct for the first five digits after the decimal point in the decimal expansion of $7^{\sqrt{2}}$.

We could continue this process by taking rational approximations as close as we wish to $\sqrt{2}$, thus getting approximations as accurate as we wish to $7^{\sqrt{2}}$.

For convenience in dealing with quantities that cannot be expressed exactly in decimal notation, we use the symbol $\approx$, which means "approximately equal to". For example, $\sqrt{2} \approx 1.414$.

The example above gives the idea for defining exponentiation by an irrational number:

Exponentiation by an irrational number

Suppose $b > 0$ and x is an irrational number. Then b^x is the number that is approximated by numbers of the form b^r as r takes on rational values that approximate x.

The definition of b^x above does not have the level of rigor expected of a mathematical definition, but the idea should be clear from the example above. A rigorous approach to this question would take us beyond material appropriate for a precalculus course. Thus we will rely on our intuitive sense of the loose definition given above.

The graphical interpretation of this definition, to which we now turn, may help solidify this intuition. The figure above plots the points $(x, 2^x)$ as x varies from -1 to 1 in increments of 0.05.

Instead of taking x in increments of 0.05, we could have taken x in increments of 0.001 or some smaller number, getting more points on the partial graph. As the increments become smaller, the partial graph will appear increasingly like a smooth curve, and we can fill in the tiny gaps to get an actual smooth curve, as shown in the figure here.

We can think of obtaining the graph of 2^x on the interval $[-1, 1]$ by smoothly filling in the gaps, as has been done in the figure here. The graph

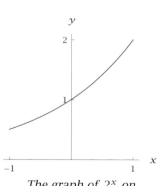

A partial graph of 2^x on the interval $[-1, 1]$.

The graph of 2^x on the interval $[-1, 1]$.

should then show all points of the form $(x, 2^x)$, including for irrational values of x (provided that $-1 \leq x \leq 1$), and we can think of the graph as defining the values of 2^x for irrational values of x. For example, we could read off an approximate value for $2^{1/\sqrt{2}}$ from the graph above. If we need a more accurate estimate, we could change the scale of the graph, concentrating only on a small interval containing $2^{1/\sqrt{2}}$.

Now that we have defined 2^x for all real numbers x, we can define a function f by $f(x) = 2^x$. The domain of this function is the set of real numbers; the range of this function is the set of positive numbers.

Be careful to distinguish the graphs of the functions 2^x and x^2. These graphs have different shapes. The function 2^x is increasing on the entire real line, but the function x^2 is decreasing on the interval $(-\infty, 0]$ and is increasing on the interval $[0, \infty)$.

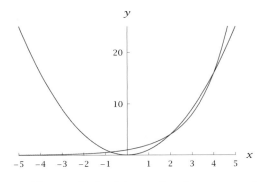

The graphs of 2^x (blue) and x^2 (red) on the interval $[-5, 5]$.

The graph of 2^x (blue) gets very close to the x-axis for negative values of x with large absolute value. The graph of x^2 (red) is a parabola with its vertex at the origin.

We conclude this section by summarizing the crucial algebraic properties of exponents. Recall that for exponentiation by positive integers, the key algebraic properties followed quickly from the definition of exponentiation as repeated multiplication. As we extended our definition of exponentiation to larger classes of numbers, the definitions were chosen so that the following algebraic properties are preserved:

Algebraic properties of exponents

Suppose a and b are positive numbers and x and y are real numbers. Then

$$b^x b^y = b^{x+y}, \qquad b^{-x} = \frac{1}{b^x},$$

$$(b^x)^y = b^{xy},$$

$$a^x b^x = (ab)^x, \qquad \frac{a^x}{a^y} = a^{x-y},$$

$$b^0 = 1, \qquad \frac{a^x}{b^x} = \left(\frac{a}{b}\right)^x.$$

As an example of using these properties, if we take $x = \frac{1}{2}$ in the third equation above then we obtain the following property:

Never, ever, make the mistake of thinking that $\sqrt{a} + \sqrt{b}$ equals $\sqrt{a + b}$.

$$\sqrt{a}\sqrt{b} = \sqrt{ab}.$$

Here is an example of how this identity can be used:

EXAMPLE 8

Simplify $\sqrt{2}\sqrt{6}$.

SOLUTION

$$\sqrt{2}\sqrt{6} = \sqrt{12} = \sqrt{4 \cdot 3} = \sqrt{4}\sqrt{3} = 2\sqrt{3}$$

EXERCISES

For Exercises 1–8, evaluate the indicated quantities. Do not use a calculator because otherwise you will not gain the understanding that these exercises should help you attain.

1. $25^{3/2}$ 3. $32^{3/5}$ 5. $32^{-4/5}$ 7. $(-8)^{7/3}$
2. $8^{5/3}$ 4. $81^{3/4}$ 6. $8^{-5/3}$ 8. $(-27)^{4/3}$

For Exercises 9–20, expand the indicated expression.

9. $(2 + \sqrt{3})^2$

10. $(3 + \sqrt{2})^2$

11. $(2 - 3\sqrt{5})^2$

12. $(3 - 5\sqrt{2})^2$

13. $(2 + \sqrt{3})^4$

14. $(3 + \sqrt{2})^4$

15. $(3 + \sqrt{x})^2$

16. $(5 + \sqrt{x})^2$

17. $(3 - \sqrt{2x})^2$

18. $(5 - \sqrt{3x})^2$

19. $(1 + 2\sqrt{3x})^2$

20. $(3 + 2\sqrt{5x})^2$

For Exercises 21–32, find a formula for the inverse function f^{-1} of the indicated function f.

21. $f(x) = x^9$

22. $f(x) = x^{12}$

23. $f(x) = x^{1/7}$

24. $f(x) = x^{1/11}$

25. $f(x) = x^{-2/5}$

26. $f(x) = x^{-17/7}$

27. $f(x) = \frac{x^4}{81}$

28. $f(x) = 32x^5$

29. $f(x) = 6 + x^3$

30. $f(x) = x^6 - 5$

31. $f(x) = 4x^{3/7} - 1$

32. $f(x) = 7 + 8x^{5/9}$

For Exercises 33–38, find a formula for $(f \circ g)(x)$ assuming that f and g are the indicated functions.

33. $f(x) = x^{1/2}$ and $g(x) = x^{3/7}$

34. $f(x) = x^{5/3}$ and $g(x) = x^{4/9}$

35. $f(x) = 3 + x^{5/4}$ and $g(x) = x^{2/7}$

36. $f(x) = x^{2/3} - 7$ and $g(x) = x^{9/16}$

37. $f(x) = 5x^{\sqrt{2}}$ and $g(x) = x^{\sqrt{8}}$

38. $f(x) = 7x^{\sqrt{12}}$ and $g(x) = x^{\sqrt{3}}$

For Exercises 39–46, find all real numbers x that satisfy the indicated equation.

39. $x - 5\sqrt{x} + 6 = 0$

40. $x - 7\sqrt{x} + 12 = 0$

41. $x - \sqrt{x} = 6$

42. $x - \sqrt{x} = 12$

43. $x^{2/3} - 6x^{1/3} = -8$

44. $x^{2/3} + 3x^{1/3} = 10$

45. $x^4 - 3x^2 = 10$

46. $x^4 - 8x^2 = -15$

47. Suppose x is a number such that $3^x = 4$. Evaluate 3^{-2x}.

48. Suppose x is a number such that $2^x = \frac{1}{3}$. Evaluate 2^{-4x}.

49. Suppose x is a number such that $2^x = 5$. Evaluate 8^x.

50. Suppose x is a number such that $3^x = 5$. Evaluate $\left(\frac{1}{9}\right)^x$.

For Exercises 51–56, evaluate the indicated quantities assuming that f and g are the functions defined by

$$f(x) = 2^x \quad and \quad g(x) = \frac{x + 1}{x + 2}.$$

51. $(f \circ g)(-1)$

52. $(g \circ f)(0)$

53. $(f \circ g)(0)$

54. $(g \circ f)(\frac{3}{2})$

55. $(f \circ f)(\frac{1}{2})$

56. $(f \circ f)(\frac{3}{5})$

57. Find an integer m such that

$$\left((3 + 2\sqrt{5})^2 - m\right)^2$$

is an integer.

58. Find an integer m such that

$$\left((5 - 2\sqrt{3})^2 - m\right)^2$$

is an integer.

PROBLEMS

Some problems require considerably more thought than the exercises.
Unlike exercises, problems usually have more than one correct answer.

59. Sketch the graph of the functions $\sqrt{x} + 1$ and $\sqrt{x+1}$ on the interval $[0, 4]$.

60. Sketch the graph of the functions $2x^{1/3}$ and $(2x)^{1/3}$ on the interval $[0, 8]$.

61. Sketch the graphs of the functions $x^{1/4}$ and $x^{1/5}$ on the interval $[0, 81]$.

62. Show that $\sqrt{2 + \sqrt{3}} = \sqrt{\frac{3}{2}} + \sqrt{\frac{1}{2}}$.

63. Show that $\sqrt{2 - \sqrt{3}} = \sqrt{\frac{3}{2}} - \sqrt{\frac{1}{2}}$.

64. Show that $\sqrt{9 - 4\sqrt{5}} = \sqrt{5} - 2$.

65. Show that $(23 - 8\sqrt{7})^{1/2} = 4 - \sqrt{7}$.

66. Make up a problem similar in form to the problem above, without duplicating anything in this book.

67. Show that $(99 + 70\sqrt{2})^{1/3} = 3 + 2\sqrt{2}$.

68. Show that $(-37 + 30\sqrt{3})^{1/3} = -1 + 2\sqrt{3}$.

69. Show that if x and y are positive numbers with $x \neq y$, then

$$\frac{x - y}{\sqrt{x} - \sqrt{y}} = \sqrt{x} + \sqrt{y}.$$

70. Explain why

$$10^{100}(\sqrt{10^{200} + 1} - 10^{100})$$

is approximately equal to $\frac{1}{2}$.

71. Explain why the equation $\sqrt{x^2} = x$ is not valid for all real numbers x and should be replaced by the equation $\sqrt{x^2} = |x|$.

72. Explain why the equation $\sqrt{x^8} = x^4$ is valid for all real numbers x, with no necessity for using absolute value.

73. Show that if x and y are positive numbers, then

$$\sqrt{x + y} < \sqrt{x} + \sqrt{y}.$$

[*In particular, if x and y are positive numbers, then $\sqrt{x + y} \neq \sqrt{x} + \sqrt{y}$.*]

74. Show that if $0 < x < y$, then

$$\sqrt{y} - \sqrt{x} < \sqrt{y - x}.$$

75. Explain why the spoken phrase "the square root of x plus one" could be interpreted in two different ways that would not give the same result.

76. One of the graphs in this section suggests that

$$\sqrt{x} < \sqrt[3]{x} \quad \text{if} \quad 0 < x < 1$$

and

$$\sqrt{x} > \sqrt[3]{x} \quad \text{if} \quad x > 1.$$

Explain why each of these inequalities holds.

77. What is the domain of the function $(3 + x)^{1/4}$?

78. What is the domain of the function $(1 + x^2)^{1/8}$?

79. Suppose x is a positive number. Using only the definitions of roots and integer powers, explain why

$$\left(x^{1/2}\right)^3 = \left(x^{1/4}\right)^6.$$

80. Suppose x is a positive number and n is a positive integer. Using only the definitions of roots and integer powers, explain why

$$\left(x^{1/2}\right)^n = \left(x^{1/4}\right)^{2n}.$$

81. Suppose x is a positive number and n and p are positive integers. Using only the definitions of roots and integer powers, explain why

$$\left(x^{1/2}\right)^n = \left(x^{1/(2p)}\right)^{np}.$$

82. Suppose x is a positive number and m, n, and p are positive integers. Using only the definitions of roots and integer powers, explain why

$$\left(x^{1/m}\right)^n = \left(x^{1/(mp)}\right)^{np}.$$

83. Using the result from the problem above, explain why the definition of exponentiation of a positive number by a positive rational number gives the same result even if the positive rational number is not expressed in reduced form.

84. Using the result that $\sqrt{2}$ is irrational (proved in Section 0.1), show that $2^{5/2}$ is irrational.

85. Using the result that $\sqrt{2}$ is irrational, explain why $2^{1/6}$ is irrational.

86. Suppose you have a calculator that can only compute square roots. Explain how you could use this calculator to compute $7^{1/8}$.

87. Suppose you have a calculator that can only compute square roots and can multiply. Explain how you could use this calculator to compute $7^{3/4}$.

88. Give an example of three irrational numbers x, y, and z such that

$$xyz$$

is a rational number.

89. Give an example of three irrational numbers x, y, and z such that

$$(x^y)^z$$

is a rational number.

90. Is the function f defined by $f(x) = 2^x$ for every real number x an even function, an odd function, or neither?

91. What is wrong with the following string of equalities, which seems to show that $-1 = 1$?

$$-1 = i \cdot i = \sqrt{-1}\sqrt{-1} = \sqrt{(-1)(-1)} = \sqrt{1} = 1$$

WORKED-OUT SOLUTIONS to Odd-numbered Exercises

Do not read these worked-out solutions before first struggling to do the exercises yourself. Otherwise you risk the danger of mimicking the techniques shown here without understanding the ideas.

Best way to learn: Carefully read the section of the textbook, then do all the odd-numbered exercises (even if they have not been assigned) and check your answers here. If you get stuck on an exercise, reread the section of the textbook—then try the exercise again. If you are still stuck, then look at the worked-out solution here.

For Exercises 1–8, evaluate the indicated quantities. Do not use a calculator because otherwise you will not gain the understanding that these exercises should help you attain.

1. $25^{3/2}$

   SOLUTION $25^{3/2} = (25^{1/2})^3 = 5^3 = 125$

3. $32^{3/5}$

   SOLUTION $32^{3/5} = (32^{1/5})^3 = 2^3 = 8$

5. $32^{-4/5}$

   SOLUTION $32^{-4/5} = (32^{1/5})^{-4} = 2^{-4} = \dfrac{1}{2^4} = \dfrac{1}{16}$

7. $(-8)^{7/3}$

   SOLUTION $(-8)^{7/3} = ((-8)^{1/3})^7$

   $$= (-2)^7$$

   $$= -128$$

For Exercises 9–20, expand the indicated expression.

9. $(2 + \sqrt{3})^2$

   SOLUTION

   $$(2 + \sqrt{3})^2 = 2^2 + 2 \cdot 2 \cdot \sqrt{3} + \sqrt{3}^2$$

   $$= 4 + 4\sqrt{3} + 3$$

   $$= 7 + 4\sqrt{3}$$

11. $(2 - 3\sqrt{5})^2$

SOLUTION

$$(2 - 3\sqrt{5})^2 = 2^2 - 2 \cdot 2 \cdot 3 \cdot \sqrt{5} + 3^2 \cdot \sqrt{5}^2$$
$$= 4 - 12\sqrt{5} + 9 \cdot 5$$
$$= 49 - 12\sqrt{5}$$

13. $(2 + \sqrt{3})^4$

SOLUTION Note that

$$(2 + \sqrt{3})^4 = \left((2 + \sqrt{3})^2\right)^2.$$

Thus first we need to compute $(2 + \sqrt{3})^2$. We already did that in Exercise 9, getting

$$(2 + \sqrt{3})^2 = 7 + 4\sqrt{3}.$$

Thus

$$(2 + \sqrt{3})^4 = \left((2 + \sqrt{3})^2\right)^2$$
$$= (7 + 4\sqrt{3})^2$$
$$= 7^2 + 2 \cdot 7 \cdot 4 \cdot \sqrt{3} + 4^2 \cdot \sqrt{3}^2$$
$$= 49 + 56\sqrt{3} + 16 \cdot 3$$
$$= 97 + 56\sqrt{3}.$$

15. $(3 + \sqrt{x})^2$

SOLUTION

$$(3 + \sqrt{x})^2 = 3^2 + 2 \cdot 3 \cdot \sqrt{x} + \sqrt{x}^2$$
$$= 9 + 6\sqrt{x} + x$$

17. $(3 - \sqrt{2x})^2$

SOLUTION

$$(3 - \sqrt{2x})^2 = 3^2 - 2 \cdot 3 \cdot \sqrt{2x} + \sqrt{2x}^2$$
$$= 9 - 6\sqrt{2x} + 2x$$

19. $(1 + 2\sqrt{3x})^2$

SOLUTION

$$(1 + 2\sqrt{3x})^2 = 1^2 + 2 \cdot 2 \cdot \sqrt{3x} + 2^2 \cdot \sqrt{3x}^2$$
$$= 1 + 4\sqrt{3x} + 4 \cdot 3x$$
$$= 1 + 4\sqrt{3x} + 12x$$

For Exercises 21–32, find a formula for the inverse function f^{-1} of the indicated function f.

21. $f(x) = x^9$

SOLUTION By the definition of roots, the inverse of f is the function f^{-1} defined by

$$f^{-1}(y) = y^{1/9}.$$

23. $f(x) = x^{1/7}$

SOLUTION By the definition of roots, $f = g^{-1}$, where g is the function defined by $g(y) = y^7$. Thus $f^{-1} = (g^{-1})^{-1} = g$. In other words,

$$f^{-1}(y) = y^7.$$

25. $f(x) = x^{-2/5}$

SOLUTION To find a formula for f^{-1}, we solve the equation $x^{-2/5} = y$ for x. Raising both sides of this equation to the power $-\frac{5}{2}$, we get $x = y^{-5/2}$. Hence

$$f^{-1}(y) = y^{-5/2}.$$

27. $f(x) = \frac{x^4}{81}$

SOLUTION To find a formula for f^{-1}, we solve the equation $\frac{x^4}{81} = y$ for x. Multiplying both sides by 81 and then raising both sides of this equation to the power $\frac{1}{4}$, we get $x = (81y)^{1/4} = 81^{1/4}y^{1/4} = 3y^{1/4}$. Hence

$$f^{-1}(y) = 3y^{1/4}.$$

29. $f(x) = 6 + x^3$

SOLUTION To find a formula for f^{-1}, we solve the equation $6 + x^3 = y$ for x. Subtracting 6 from both sides and then raising both sides of this equation to the power $\frac{1}{3}$, we get $x = (y - 6)^{1/3}$. Hence

$$f^{-1}(y) = (y - 6)^{1/3}.$$

31. $f(x) = 4x^{3/7} - 1$

SOLUTION To find a formula for f^{-1}, we solve the equation $4x^{3/7} - 1 = y$ for x. Adding 1 to both sides, then dividing both sides by 4, and then raising both sides of this equation to the power $\frac{7}{3}$, we get $x = \left(\frac{y+1}{4}\right)^{7/3}$. Hence

$$f^{-1}(y) = \left(\frac{y+1}{4}\right)^{7/3}.$$

For Exercises 33–38, find a formula for $(f \circ g)(x)$ assuming that f and g are the indicated functions.

33. $f(x) = x^{1/2}$ and $g(x) = x^{3/7}$

SOLUTION

$$(f \circ g)(x) = f(g(x)) = f(x^{3/7}) = \left(x^{3/7}\right)^{1/2}$$
$$= x^{3/14}$$

35. $f(x) = 3 + x^{5/4}$ and $g(x) = x^{2/7}$

SOLUTION

$$(f \circ g)(x) = f(g(x)) = f(x^{2/7}) = 3 + \left(x^{2/7}\right)^{5/4}$$
$$= 3 + x^{5/14}$$

37. $f(x) = 5x^{\sqrt{2}}$ and $g(x) = x^{\sqrt{8}}$

SOLUTION

$$(f \circ g)(x) = f(g(x)) = f(x^{\sqrt{8}})$$
$$= 5\left(x^{\sqrt{8}}\right)^{\sqrt{2}} = 5x^{\sqrt{16}} = 5x^4$$

For Exercises 39–46, find all real numbers x that satisfy the indicated equation.

39. $x - 5\sqrt{x} + 6 = 0$

SOLUTION This equation involves $\sqrt{x}$; thus we make the substitution $\sqrt{x} = y$. Squaring both sides of the equation $\sqrt{x} = y$ gives $x = y^2$. With these substitutions, the equation above becomes

$$y^2 - 5y + 6 = 0.$$

This new equation can now be solved either by factoring the left side or by using the quadratic

formula (see Section 2.2). Let's factor the left side, getting

$$(y - 2)(y - 3) = 0.$$

Thus $y = 2$ or $y = 3$ (the same result could have been obtained by using the quadratic formula).

Substituting $\sqrt{x}$ for y now shows that $\sqrt{x} = 2$ or $\sqrt{x} = 3$. Thus $x = 4$ or $x = 9$.

41. $x - \sqrt{x} = 6$

SOLUTION This equation involves $\sqrt{x}$; thus we make the substitution $\sqrt{x} = y$. Squaring both sides of the equation $\sqrt{x} = y$ gives $x = y^2$. Making these substitutions and subtracting 6 from both sides, we have

$$y^2 - y - 6 = 0.$$

This new equation can now be solved either by factoring the left side or by using the quadratic formula. Let's use the quadratic formula, getting

$$y = \frac{1 \pm \sqrt{1 + 24}}{2} = \frac{1 \pm 5}{2}.$$

Thus $y = 3$ or $y = -2$ (the same result could have been obtained by factoring).

Substituting $\sqrt{x}$ for y now shows that $\sqrt{x} = 3$ or $\sqrt{x} = -2$. The first possibility corresponds to the solution $x = 9$. There are no real numbers x such that $\sqrt{x} = -2$. Thus $x = 9$ is the only solution to this equation.

43. $x^{2/3} - 6x^{1/3} = -8$

SOLUTION This equation involves $x^{1/3}$ and $x^{2/3}$; thus we make the substitution $x^{1/3} = y$. Squaring both sides of the equation $x^{1/3} = y$ gives $x^{2/3} = y^2$. Making these substitutions and adding 8 to both sides, we have

$$y^2 - 6y + 8 = 0.$$

This new equation can now be solved either by factoring the left side or by using the quadratic formula. Let's factor the left side, getting

$$(y - 2)(y - 4) = 0.$$

Thus $y = 2$ or $y = 4$ (the same result could have been obtained by using the quadratic formula).

Substituting $x^{1/3}$ for y now shows that $x^{1/3} = 2$ or $x^{1/3} = 4$. Thus $x = 2^3$ or $x = 4^3$. In other words, $x = 8$ or $x = 64$.

45. $x^4 - 3x^2 = 10$

SOLUTION   This equation involves x^2 and x^4; thus we make the substitution $x^2 = y$. Squaring both sides of the equation $x^2 = y$ gives $x^4 = y^2$. Making these substitutions and subtracting 10 from both sides, we have

$$y^2 - 3y - 10 = 0.$$

This new equation can now be solved either by factoring the left side or by using the quadratic formula. Let's factor the left side, getting

$$(y - 5)(y + 2) = 0.$$

Thus $y = 5$ or $y = -2$ (the same result could have been obtained by using the quadratic formula).

Substituting x^2 for y now shows that $x^2 = 5$ or $x^2 = -2$. The first of these equations implies that $x = \sqrt{5}$ or $x = -\sqrt{5}$; the second equation is not satisfied by any real value of x. In other words, the original equation implies that $x = \sqrt{5}$ or $x = -\sqrt{5}$.

47. Suppose x is a number such that $3^x = 4$. Evaluate 3^{-2x}.

SOLUTION $\quad 3^{-2x} = (3^x)^{-2}$

$$= 4^{-2}$$

$$= \frac{1}{4^2}$$

$$= \frac{1}{16}$$

49. Suppose x is a number such that $2^x = 5$. Evaluate 8^x.

SOLUTION $\quad 8^x = (2^3)^x$

$$= 2^{3x}$$

$$= (2^x)^3$$

$$= 5^3$$

$$= 125$$

For Exercises 51–56, evaluate the indicated quantities assuming that f and g are the functions defined by

$$f(x) = 2^x \quad \text{and} \quad g(x) = \frac{x+1}{x+2}.$$

51. $(f \circ g)(-1)$

SOLUTION

$$(f \circ g)(-1) = f(g(-1)) = f(0) = 2^0 = 1$$

53. $(f \circ g)(0)$

SOLUTION

$$(f \circ g)(0) = f(g(0)) = f(\tfrac{1}{2}) = 2^{1/2} \approx 1.414$$

55. $(f \circ f)(\tfrac{1}{2})$

SOLUTION

$$(f \circ f)(\tfrac{1}{2}) = f(f(\tfrac{1}{2})) = f(2^{1/2})$$

$$\approx f(1.41421)$$

$$= 2^{1.41421}$$

$$\approx 2.66514$$

57. Find an integer m such that

$$\left((3 + 2\sqrt{5})^2 - m\right)^2$$

is an integer.

SOLUTION   First we evaluate $(3 + 2\sqrt{5})^2$:

$$(3 + 2\sqrt{5})^2 = 3^2 + 2 \cdot 3 \cdot 2 \cdot \sqrt{5} + 2^2 \cdot \sqrt{5}^2$$

$$= 9 + 12\sqrt{5} + 4 \cdot 5$$

$$= 29 + 12\sqrt{5}.$$

Thus

$$\left((3 + 2\sqrt{5})^2 - m\right)^2 = (29 + 12\sqrt{5} - m)^2.$$

If we choose $m = 29$, then we have

$$\left((3 + 2\sqrt{5})^2 - m\right)^2 = (12\sqrt{5})^2$$

$$= 12^2 \cdot \sqrt{5}^2$$

$$= 12^2 \cdot 5,$$

which is an integer. Any choice other than $m = 29$ will leave a term involving $\sqrt{5}$ when $(29 + 12\sqrt{5} - m)^2$ is expanded. Thus $m = 29$ is the only solution to this exercise.

3.2 | *Logarithms as Inverses of Exponentiation*

SECTION OBJECTIVES

By the end of this section you should

- understand the definition of the logarithm with an arbitrary base;
- understand the consequences of thinking of logarithms as inverse functions;
- be able to evaluate logarithms in simple cases;
- understand the relationship between logarithms with different bases.

Logarithms Base 2

x	2^x
-3	$\frac{1}{8}$
-2	$\frac{1}{4}$
-1	$\frac{1}{2}$
0	1
1	2
2	4
3	8

Consider the function f defined by $f(x) = 2^x$. The domain of this function is the set of real numbers, and the range of this function is the set of positive numbers. The table shown here gives the value of $f(x)$ for some choices of x. Each time x increases by 1, the value of $f(x)$ doubles; this happens because $2^{x+1} = 2 \cdot 2^x$.

The figure below shows part of the graph of f; for convenience, the scales on the two coordinate axes are not the same.

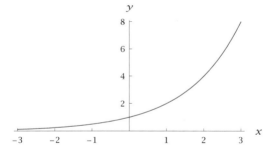

The graph of $y = 2^x$ on the interval $[-3, 3]$.

The graph of $y = 2^x$, as shown above, differs from the graph of $y = x^2$, which is a parabola. Recall that the square root function is the inverse of the function x^2 (with the domain of x^2 restricted to $[0, \infty)$ in order to obtain a one-to-one function). In this section we will define a new function, called the logarithm base 2, that is the inverse of the function 2^x.

y	$\log_2 y$
$\frac{1}{8}$	-3
$\frac{1}{4}$	-2
$\frac{1}{2}$	-1
1	0
2	1
4	2
8	3

Logarithm base 2

For each positive number y the **logarithm** base 2 of y, denoted $\log_2 y$, is defined to be the number x such that $2^x = y$.

For example, $\log_2 8$ equals 3 because $2^3 = 8$. Similarly, $\log_2 \frac{1}{32} = -5$ because $2^{-5} = \frac{1}{32}$. The table here gives the value of $\log_2 y$ for some choices of y. To help your understanding of logarithms, you should verify that each value of $\log_2 y$ given here is correct.

The definition of $\log_2 y$ as the number such that

$$2^{\log_2 y} = y$$

means that if f is the function defined by $f(x) = 2^x$, then the inverse function of f is given by the formula $f^{-1}(y) = \log_2 y$. Thus the table shown above giving values of $\log_2 y$ is obtained by interchanging the two columns of the earlier table giving the values of 2^x, as always happens with a function and its inverse.

Because a function and its inverse interchange domains and ranges, the domain of the function f^{-1} defined by $f^{-1}(y) = \log_2 y$ is the set of positive numbers, and the range of this function is the set of real numbers. An expression such as $\log_2 0$ makes no sense because there does not exist a number x such that $2^x = 0$.

The figure below shows part of the graph of $\log_2 x$. Because the function $\log_2 x$ is the inverse of the function 2^x, this graph is the reflection of the graph of 2^x through the line $y = x$.

"Algebra as far as the quadratic equation and the use of logarithms are often of value."

—Thomas Jefferson

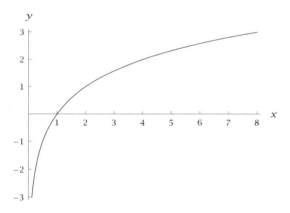

The graph of $\log_2 x$ *on the interval* $[\frac{1}{8}, 8]$.

The graph above shows that $\log_2 x$ is an increasing function. This behavior is expected, because 2^x is an increasing function and the inverse of an increasing function is increasing.

If x is a real number, then by definition of the logarithm the equation $\log_2 2^x = t$ means that $2^t = 2^x$, which implies that $t = x$. In other words,

$$\log_2 2^x = x.$$

If $f(x) = 2^x$, then $f^{-1}(y) = \log_2 y$ and the equation displayed above could be rewritten as $(f^{-1} \circ f)(x) = x$, which is an equation that always holds for a function and its inverse.

Logarithms with Arbitrary Base

We now take up the topic of defining logarithms with bases other than 2. No new ideas are needed for this more general situation—we will simply replace 2 by an arbitrary positive number $b \neq 1$. Here is the formal definition:

Logarithms

The base $b = 1$ is excluded because $1^x = 1$ for every real number x.

Suppose b and y are positive numbers, with $b \neq 1$.

- The **logarithm** base b of y, denoted $\log_b y$, is defined to be the number x such that $b^x = y$.

- Short version: $\log_b y = x$ means $b^x = y$.

EXAMPLE 1	Evaluate $\log_{10} 100 + \log_3 \frac{1}{81}$.

SOLUTION Note that $\log_{10} 100$ equals 2 because $10^2 = 100$. Also, $\log_3 \frac{1}{81}$ equals -4 because $3^{-4} = \frac{1}{81}$. Thus

$$\log_{10} 100 + \log_3 \frac{1}{81} = 2 + (-4) = -2.$$

Two important identities follow immediately from the definition:

The logarithm of 1 and the logarithm of the base

If b is a positive number with $b \neq 1$, then

- $\log_b 1 = 0$;

- $\log_b b = 1$.

The first of these identities holds because $b^0 = 1$; the second holds because $b^1 = b$.

The definition of $\log_b y$ as the number such that

$$b^{\log_b y} = y$$

means that if f is the function defined by $f(x) = b^x$ (here we have fixed a positive number $b \neq 1$), then the inverse function of f is given by the formula $f^{-1}(y) = \log_b y$. The equation displayed above could be written in the form $(f \circ f^{-1})(y) = y$, which is an equation that always holds for a function and its inverse. Because a function and its inverse interchange domains and *If $y \leq 0$, then $\log_b y$* ranges, the domain of the function f^{-1} defined by $f^{-1}(y) = \log_b y$ is the set *is not defined.* of positive numbers, and the range of this function is the set of real numbers.

Because the function $\log_b x$ is the inverse of the function b^x, the graph of $\log_b x$ is the reflection of the graph of b^x through the line $y = x$. For $b > 1$, the shape of the graph of $\log_b x$ is similar to the shape of the graph of $\log_2 x$ obtained earlier.

If $b > 1$, then $\log_b x$ is an increasing function; this occurs because b^x is an increasing function and the inverse of an increasing function is increasing.

If $b < 1$, then $\log_b x$ is an decreasing function because in that case b^x is a decreasing function.

Most applications of logarithms involve bases bigger than 1.

If x is a real number, then by definition of the logarithm the equation $\log_b b^x = t$ means that $b^t = b^x$, which implies that $t = x$. In other words,

$$\log_b b^x = x.$$

If $f(x) = b^x$, then $f^{-1}(y) = \log_b y$ and the equation displayed above could be rewritten as $(f^{-1} \circ f)(x) = x$, which is an equation that always holds for a function and its inverse.

Because the last two displayed equations are so crucial to working with logarithms, they are summarized below. Be sure that you are comfortable with these equations and understand why they hold.

Inverse properties of logarithms

If b and y are positive numbers, with $b \neq 1$, and x is a real number, then

$$b^{\log_b y} = y \quad \text{and} \quad \log_b b^x = x.$$

In applications of logarithms, the most commonly used values for the base are 10, 2, and the number e (which we will discuss in Chapter 4). The use of a logarithm with base 10 is so frequent that it gets a special name:

Common logarithm

- The logarithm base 10 is called the **common logarithm**.

- To simplify notation, sometimes logarithms base 10 are written without the base. If no base is displayed, then the base is assumed to be 10. In other words,

$$\log y = \log_{10} y.$$

John Napier, the Scottish mathematician who invented logarithms around 1614.

Thus, for example, $\log 1000 = 3$ (because $10^3 = 1000$) and $\log \frac{1}{100} = -2$ (because $10^{-2} = \frac{1}{100}$). If your calculator has a button labeled "log", then it will compute the logarithm base 10, which is often just called the logarithm.

Change of Base

If we want to use a calculator to evaluate something like $\log_2 73.9$, then we need a formula for converting logarithms from one base to another. Thus we now consider the relationship between logarithms with different bases.

To motivate the formula we will discover, first we look at an example. Note that $\log_2 64 = 6$ because $2^6 = 64$, and $\log_8 64 = 2$ because $8^2 = 64$. Thus

$$\log_2 64 = 3 \log_8 64.$$

The relationship above holds if 64 is replaced by an arbitrary positive number y. To see this, note that

$$y = 8^{\log_8 y}$$
$$= (2^3)^{\log_8 y}$$
$$= 2^{3\log_8 y},$$

which implies that

$$\log_2 y = 3\log_8 y.$$

In other words, the logarithm base 2 equals 3 times the logarithm base 8. Note that $3 = \log_2 8$.

The relationship derived above holds more generally. To see this, suppose a, b, and y are positive numbers, with $a \neq 1$ and $b \neq 1$. Then

$$y = b^{\log_b y}$$
$$= (a^{\log_a b})^{\log_b y}$$
$$= a^{(\log_a b)(\log_b y)}.$$

Your calculator can probably evaluate logarithms for only two bases. One of these is probably the logarithm base 10 (the common logarithm, probably labeled "log" on your calculator), and the other is probably the logarithm base e (this is the natural logarithm that we will discuss in the next chapter; it is probably labeled "ln" on your calculator).

The equation above implies that $\log_a y = (\log_a b)(\log_b y)$. Solving this equation for $\log_b y$ (so that both base a logarithms will be on the same side), we have the following formula for converting logarithms from one base to another:

Change of base for logarithms

If a, b, and y are positive numbers, with $a \neq 1$ and $b \neq 1$, then

$$\log_b y = \frac{\log_a y}{\log_a b}.$$

A special case of this formula, suitable for use with calculators, is to take $a = 10$, thus using common logarithms and getting the following formula:

Change of base with common logarithms

If b and y are positive numbers, with $b \neq 1$, then

$$\log_b y = \frac{\log y}{\log b}.$$

Evaluate $\log_2 73.9$.

EXAMPLE 2

SOLUTION   Use a calculator with $b = 2$ and $y = 73.9$ in the formula above, getting

$$\log_2 73.9 = \frac{\log 73.9}{\log 2} \approx 6.2075.$$

The change of base formula for logarithms implies that the graph of the logarithm using any base can be obtained from vertically stretching the graph of the logarithm using any other base, as shown in the following example.

Sketch the graphs of $\log_2 x$ and $\log x$ on the interval $[\frac{1}{8}, 8]$. What is the relationship between these two graphs?

EXAMPLE 3

SOLUTION   The change of base formula implies that $\log x = (\log 2)(\log_2 x)$. Because $\log 2 \approx 0.3$, this means that the graph of $\log x$ is obtained from the graph of $\log_2 x$ (sketched earlier) by stretching vertically by a factor of approximately 0.3.

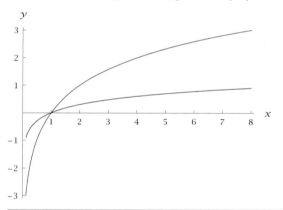

The graphs of $\log_2 x$ (blue) and $\log x$ (red) on the interval $[\frac{1}{8}, 8]$.

EXERCISES

For Exercises 1–16, evaluate the indicated expression. Do not use a calculator for these exercises.

1. $\log_2 64$
2. $\log_2 1024$
3. $\log_2 \frac{1}{128}$
4. $\log_2 \frac{1}{256}$
5. $\log_4 2$
6. $\log_8 2$
7. $\log_4 8$
8. $\log_8 128$

9. $\log 10000$
10. $\log \frac{1}{1000}$
11. $\log \sqrt{1000}$
12. $\log \frac{1}{\sqrt{10000}}$
13. $\log_2 8^{3.1}$
14. $\log_8 2^{6.3}$
15. $\log_{16} 32$
16. $\log_{27} 81$

17. Find a number y such that $\log_2 y = 7$.
18. Find a number t such that $\log_2 t = 8$.
19. Find a number y such that $\log_2 y = -5$.
20. Find a number t such that $\log_2 t = -9$.

For Exercises 21–28, find a number b such that the indicated equality holds.

21. $\log_b 64 = 1$
22. $\log_b 64 = 2$
23. $\log_b 64 = 3$
24. $\log_b 64 = 6$
25. $\log_b 64 = 12$
26. $\log_b 64 = 18$
27. $\log_b 64 = \frac{3}{2}$
28. $\log_b 64 = \frac{6}{5}$

29. Find a number x such that $\log_3(5x + 1) = 2$.
30. Find a number x such that $\log_4(3x + 1) = -2$.
31. ✐ Find a number x such that $13 = 10^{2x}$.
32. ✐ Find a number x such that $59 = 10^{3x}$.
33. ✐ Find a number t such that
$$\frac{10^t + 1}{10^t + 2} = 0.8.$$
34. ✐ Find a number t such that
$$\frac{10^t + 3.8}{10^t + 3} = 1.1.$$
35. ✐ Find a number x such that
$$10^{2x} + 10^x = 12.$$
36. ✐ Find a number x such that
$$10^{2x} - 3 \cdot 10^x = 18.$$

For Exercises 37-54, find a formula for the inverse function f^{-1} of the indicated function f.

37. $f(x) = 3^x$
38. $f(x) = 4.7^x$
39. $f(x) = 2^{x-5}$
40. $f(x) = 9^{x+6}$
41. $f(x) = 6^x + 7$
42. $f(x) = 5^x - 3$
43. $f(x) = 4 \cdot 5^x$
44. $f(x) = 8 \cdot 7^x$
45. $f(x) = 2 \cdot 9^x + 1$
46. $f(x) = 3 \cdot 4^x - 5$
47. $f(x) = \log_8 x$
48. $f(x) = \log_3 x$
49. $f(x) = \log_4(3x + 1)$
50. $f(x) = \log_7(2x - 9)$
51. $f(x) =$
    $5 + 3\log_6(2x + 1)$
52. $f(x) =$
    $8 + 9\log_2(4x - 7)$
53. $f(x) = \log_x 13$
54. $f(x) = \log_{5x} 6$

For Exercises 55-58, find a formula for $(f \circ g)(x)$ assuming that f and g are the indicated functions.

55. $f(x) = \log_6 x$ and $g(x) = 6^{3x}$
56. $f(x) = \log_5 x$ and $g(x) = 5^{3+2x}$
57. $f(x) = 6^{3x}$ and $g(x) = \log_6 x$
58. $f(x) = 5^{3+2x}$ and $g(x) = \log_5 x$
59. Find a number n such that $\log_3(\log_5 n) = 1$.
60. Find a number n such that $\log_3(\log_2 n) = 2$.
61. Find a number m such that $\log_7(\log_8 m) = 2$.
62. Find a number m such that $\log_5(\log_6 m) = 3$.

For Exercises 63-70, evaluate the indicated quantities. Your calculator is unlikely to be able to evaluate logarithms using any of the bases in these exercises, so you will need to use an appropriate change of base formula.

63. ✐ $\log_2 13$
64. ✐ $\log_4 27$
65. ✐ $\log_{13} 9.72$
66. ✐ $\log_{17} 12.31$
67. ✐ $\log_9 0.23$
68. ✐ $\log_7 0.58$
69. ✐ $\log_{4.38} 7.1$
70. ✐ $\log_{5.06} 99.2$

PROBLEMS

71. Explain why $\log_3 100$ is between 4 and 5.
72. Explain why $\log_{40} 3$ is between $\frac{1}{4}$ and $\frac{1}{3}$.
73. Show that $\log_2 3$ is an irrational number.
    [*Hint:* Use proof by contradiction: Assume that $\log_2 3$ is equal to a rational number $\frac{m}{n}$; write out what this means, and think about even and odd numbers.]
74. Show that $\log 2$ is irrational.
75. Explain why logarithms with base 0 are not defined.
76. Explain why logarithms with a negative base are not defined.
77. Explain why $\log_5 \sqrt{5} = \frac{1}{2}$.
78. Suppose a and b are positive numbers, with $a \neq 1$ and $b \neq 1$. Show that
$$\log_a b = \frac{1}{\log_b a}.$$
79. Suppose b and y are positive numbers, with $b \neq 1$ and $b \neq \frac{1}{2}$. Show that
$$\log_{2b} y = \frac{\log_b y}{1 + \log_b 2}.$$

WORKED-OUT SOLUTIONS *to Odd-numbered Exercises*

For Exercises 1–16, evaluate the indicated expression. Do not use a calculator for these exercises.

1. $\log_2 64$

   SOLUTION   If we let $x = \log_2 64$, then x is the number such that

   $$64 = 2^x.$$

   Because $64 = 2^6$, we see that $x = 6$. Thus $\log_2 64 = 6$.

3. $\log_2 \frac{1}{128}$

   SOLUTION   If we let $x = \log_2 \frac{1}{128}$, then x is the number such that

   $$\tfrac{1}{128} = 2^x.$$

   Because $\frac{1}{128} = \frac{1}{2^7} = 2^{-7}$, we see that $x = -7$. Thus $\log_2 \frac{1}{128} = -7$.

5. $\log_4 2$

   SOLUTION   Because $2 = 4^{1/2}$, we have $\log_4 2 = \frac{1}{2}$.

7. $\log_4 8$

   SOLUTION   Because $8 = 2 \cdot 4 = 4^{1/2} \cdot 4 = 4^{3/2}$, we have $\log_4 8 = \frac{3}{2}$.

9. $\log 10000$

   SOLUTION
   $$\log 10000 = \log 10^4$$
   $$= 4$$

11. $\log \sqrt{1000}$

   SOLUTION $\log \sqrt{1000} = \log 1000^{1/2}$
   $$= \log \left(10^3\right)^{1/2}$$
   $$= \log 10^{3/2}$$
   $$= \frac{3}{2}$$

13. $\log_2 8^{3.1}$

   SOLUTION $\log_2 8^{3.1} = \log_2 \left(2^3\right)^{3.1}$
   $$= \log_2 2^{9.3}$$
   $$= 9.3$$

15. $\log_{16} 32$

   SOLUTION $\log_{16} 32 = \log_{16} 2^5$
   $$= \log_{16} \left(2^4\right)^{5/4}$$
   $$= \log_{16} 16^{5/4}$$
   $$= \frac{5}{4}$$

17. Find a number y such that $\log_2 y = 7$.

   SOLUTION   The equation $\log_2 y = 7$ implies that
   $$y = 2^7 = 128.$$

19. Find a number y such that $\log_2 y = -5$.

   SOLUTION   The equation $\log_2 y = -5$ implies that
   $$y = 2^{-5} = \tfrac{1}{32}.$$

For Exercises 21–28, find a number b such that the indicated equality holds.

21. $\log_b 64 = 1$

   SOLUTION   The equation $\log_b 64 = 1$ implies that
   $$b^1 = 64.$$
   Thus $b = 64$.

23. $\log_b 64 = 3$

   SOLUTION   The equation $\log_b 64 = 3$ implies that
   $$b^3 = 64.$$
   Because $4^3 = 64$, this implies that $b = 4$.

25. $\log_b 64 = 12$

   SOLUTION   The equation $\log_b 64 = 12$ implies that
   $$b^{12} = 64.$$
   Thus

$$b = 64^{1/12}$$
$$= (2^6)^{1/12}$$
$$= 2^{6/12}$$
$$= 2^{1/2}$$
$$= \sqrt{2}.$$

27. $\log_b 64 = \frac{3}{2}$

SOLUTION The equation $\log_b 64 = \frac{3}{2}$ implies that

$$b^{3/2} = 64.$$

Raising both sides of this equation to the $2/3$ power, we get

$$b = 64^{2/3}$$
$$= (2^6)^{2/3}$$
$$= 2^4$$
$$= 16.$$

29. Find a number x such that $\log_3(5x + 1) = 2$.

SOLUTION The equation $\log_3(5x + 1) = 2$ implies that $5x + 1 = 3^2 = 9$. Thus $5x = 8$, which implies that $x = \frac{8}{5}$.

31. ✏ Find a number x such that $13 = 10^{2x}$.

SOLUTION The equation $13 = 10^{2x}$ implies that $2x = \log 13$. Thus $x = \frac{\log 13}{2}$, which is approximately equal to 0.557.

33. ✏ Find a number t such that

$$\frac{10^t + 1}{10^t + 2} = 0.8.$$

SOLUTION Multiplying both sides of the equation above by $10^t + 2$, we get

$$10^t + 1 = 0.8 \cdot 10^t + 1.6.$$

Solving this equation for 10^t gives $10^t = 3$, which means that $t = \log 3 \approx 0.477121$.

35. ✏ Find a number x such that

$$10^{2x} + 10^x = 12.$$

SOLUTION Note that $10^{2x} = (10^x)^2$. This suggests that we let $y = 10^x$. Then the equation above can be rewritten as

$$y^2 + y - 12 = 0.$$

The solutions to this equation (which can be found either by using the quadratic formula or by factoring) are $y = -4$ and $y = 3$. Thus $10^x = -4$ or $10^x = 3$. However, there is no real number x such that $10^x = -4$ (because 10^x is positive for every real number x), and thus we must have $10^x = 3$. Thus $x = \log 3 \approx 0.477121$.

For Exercises 37–54, find a formula for the inverse function f^{-1} of the indicated function f.

37. $f(x) = 3^x$

SOLUTION By definition of the logarithm, the inverse of f is the function f^{-1} defined by

$$f^{-1}(y) = \log_3 y.$$

39. $f(x) = 2^{x-5}$

SOLUTION To find a formula for $f^{-1}(y)$, we solve the equation $2^{x-5} = y$ for x. This equation means that $x - 5 = \log_2 y$. Thus $x = 5 + \log_2 y$. Hence

$$f^{-1}(y) = 5 + \log_2 y.$$

41. $f(x) = 6^x + 7$

SOLUTION To find a formula for $f^{-1}(y)$, we solve the equation $6^x + 7 = y$ for x. Subtract 7 from both sides, getting $6^x = y - 7$. This equation means that $x = \log_6(y - 7)$. Hence

$$f^{-1}(y) = \log_6(y - 7).$$

43. $f(x) = 4 \cdot 5^x$

SOLUTION To find a formula for $f^{-1}(y)$, we solve the equation $4 \cdot 5^x = y$ for x. Divide both sides by 4, getting $5^x = \frac{y}{4}$. This equation means that $x = \log_5 \frac{y}{4}$. Hence

$$f^{-1}(y) = \log_5 \frac{y}{4}.$$

45. $f(x) = 2 \cdot 9^x + 1$

SOLUTION To find a formula for $f^{-1}(y)$, we solve the equation $2 \cdot 9^x + 1 = y$ for x. Subtract 1 from both sides, then divide both sides by 2, getting $9^x = \frac{y-1}{2}$. This equation means that $x = \log_9 \frac{y-1}{2}$. Hence

$$f^{-1}(y) = \log_9 \frac{y-1}{2}.$$

47. $f(x) = \log_8 x$

SOLUTION By the definition of the logarithm, the inverse of f is the function f^{-1} defined by

$$f^{-1}(y) = 8^y.$$

49. $f(x) = \log_4(3x + 1)$

SOLUTION To find a formula for $f^{-1}(y)$, we solve the equation

$$\log_4(3x + 1) = y$$

for x. This equation means that $3x + 1 = 4^y$. Solving for x, we get $x = \frac{4^y - 1}{3}$. Hence

$$f^{-1}(y) = \frac{4^y - 1}{3}.$$

51. $f(x) = 5 + 3\log_6(2x + 1)$

SOLUTION To find a formula for $f^{-1}(y)$, we solve the equation

$$5 + 3\log_6(2x + 1) = y$$

for x. Subtracting 5 from both sides and then dividing by 3 gives

$$\log_6(2x + 1) = \frac{y - 5}{3}.$$

This equation means that $2x + 1 = 6^{(y-5)/3}$. Solving for x, we get $x = \frac{6^{(y-5)/3} - 1}{2}$. Hence

$$f^{-1}(y) = \frac{6^{(y-5)/3} - 1}{2}.$$

53. $f(x) = \log_x 13$

SOLUTION To find a formula for $f^{-1}(y)$, we solve the equation $\log_x 13 = y$ for x. This equation means that $x^y = 13$. Raising both sides to the power $\frac{1}{y}$, we get $x = 13^{1/y}$. Hence

$$f^{-1}(y) = 13^{1/y}.$$

For Exercises 55–58, find a formula for $(f \circ g)(x)$ assuming that f and g are the indicated functions.

55. $f(x) = \log_6 x$ and $g(x) = 6^{3x}$

SOLUTION

$$(f \circ g)(x) = f(g(x)) = f(6^{3x}) = \log_6 6^{3x} = 3x$$

57. $f(x) = 6^{3x}$ and $g(x) = \log_6 x$

SOLUTION

$$(f \circ g)(x) = f(g(x)) = f(\log_6 x)$$
$$= 6^{3\log_6 x} = \left(6^{\log_6 x}\right)^3 = x^3$$

59. Find a number n such that $\log_3(\log_5 n) = 1$.

SOLUTION The equation $\log_3(\log_5 n) = 1$ implies that $\log_5 n = 3$, which implies that $n = 5^3 = 125$.

61. Find a number m such that $\log_7(\log_8 m) = 2$.

SOLUTION The equation $\log_7(\log_8 m) = 2$ implies that

$$\log_8 m = 7^2 = 49.$$

The equation above now implies that

$$m = 8^{49}.$$

For Exercises 63–70, evaluate the indicated quantities. Your calculator is unlikely to be able to evaluate logarithms using any of the bases in these exercises, so you will need to use an appropriate change of base formula.

63. $\log_2 13$

SOLUTION $\log_2 13 = \dfrac{\log 13}{\log 2} \approx 3.70044$

65. $\log_{13} 9.72$

SOLUTION $\log_{13} 9.72 = \dfrac{\log 9.72}{\log 13} \approx 0.88664$

67. $\log_9 0.23$

SOLUTION $\log_9 0.23 = \dfrac{\log 0.23}{\log 9} \approx -0.668878$

69. $\log_{4.38} 7.1$

SOLUTION $\log_{4.38} 7.1 = \dfrac{\log 7.1}{\log 4.38} \approx 1.32703$

3.3 | *Algebraic Properties of Logarithms*

SECTION OBJECTIVES

By the end of this section you should

- be able to use the formula for the logarithm of a product;
- be able to use the formula for the logarithm of a quotient;
- understand the connection between how many digits a number has and the common logarithm of the number;
- be able to use the formula for the logarithm of a power.

Logarithm of a Product

To motivate the formula for the logarithm of a product, we note that

$$\log(10^2 10^3) = \log 10^5 = 5$$

and that

$$\log 10^2 = 2 \quad \text{and} \quad \log 10^3 = 3.$$

Putting these equations together, we see that

$$\log(10^2 10^3) = \log 10^2 + \log 10^3.$$

Never, ever, make the mistake of thinking that $\log_b(x + y)$ equals $\log_b x + \log_b y$. There is no nice formula for $\log_b(x + y)$.

More generally, logarithms convert products to sums, as we will now show. Suppose b, x, and y are positive numbers, with $b \neq 1$. Then

$$\log_b(xy) = \log_b(b^{\log_b x} b^{\log_b y})$$

$$= \log_b b^{\log_b x + \log_b y}$$

$$= \log_b x + \log_b y.$$

In other words, we have the following nice formula for the logarithm of a product:

Logarithm of a product

If b, x, and y are positive numbers, with $b \neq 1$, then

$$\log_b(xy) = \log_b x + \log_b y.$$

Never, ever, make the mistake of thinking that $\log_b(xy)$ equals the product $(\log_b x)(\log_b y)$.

Use the information that $\log 3 \approx 0.477$ to evaluate $\log 30000$.

EXAMPLE 1

SOLUTION

$$\log 30000 = \log(10^4 \cdot 3)$$
$$= \log(10^4) + \log 3$$
$$= 4 + \log 3$$
$$\approx 4.477.$$

Logarithm of a Quotient

As we have seen, the formula $\log_b(xy) = \log_b x + \log_b y$ arises naturally from the formula $b^s b^t = b^{s+t}$. Similarly, we will use the formula $b^s / b^t = b^{s-t}$ to derive a formula for the logarithm of a quotient. First we look at an example.

To motivate the formula for the logarithm of a quotient, we note that

$$\log \frac{10^8}{10^3} = \log 10^5 = 5$$

and that

$$\log 10^8 = 8 \quad \text{and} \quad \log 10^3 = 3.$$

Putting these equations together, we see that

$$\log \frac{10^8}{10^3} = \log 10^8 - \log 10^3.$$

More generally, logarithms convert quotients to differences, as we will now show.

Suppose b, x, and y are positive numbers, with $b \neq 1$. Then

$$\log_b \frac{x}{y} = \log_b \frac{b^{\log_b x}}{b^{\log_b y}}$$
$$= \log_b b^{\log_b x - \log_b y}$$
$$= \log_b x - \log_b y.$$

Never, ever, make the mistake of thinking that $\log_b(x - y)$ equals $\log_b x - \log_b y$. There is no nice formula for $\log_b(x - y)$.

In other words, we have the following formula for the logarithm of a quotient:

> ### Logarithm of a quotient
>
> If b, x, and y are positive numbers, with $b \neq 1$, then
>
> $$\log_b \frac{x}{y} = \log_b x - \log_b y.$$

Never, ever, make the mistake of thinking that $\log_b \frac{x}{y}$ equals $\dfrac{\log_b x}{\log_b y}$.

EXAMPLE 2   Use the information that $\log 7 \approx 0.845$ to evaluate $\log \frac{1000}{7}$.

SOLUTION
$$\log \frac{1000}{7} = \log 1000 - \log 7$$
$$= 3 - \log 7$$
$$\approx 2.155$$

As a special case of the formula for the logarithm of a quotient, take $x = 1$ in the formula above for the logarithm of a quotient, getting

$$\log_b \frac{1}{y} = \log_b 1 - \log_b y.$$

Recalling that $\log_b 1 = 0$, we get the following result:

Logarithm of a multiplicative inverse

If b and y are positive numbers, with $b \neq 1$, then

$$\log_b \frac{1}{y} = -\log_b y.$$

Common Logarithms and the Number of Digits

Note that 10^1 is a two-digit number, 10^2 is a three-digit number, 10^3 is a four-digit number, and so on. In general, 10^{n-1} is an n-digit number. Because 10^n, which consists of 1 followed by n zeros, is the smallest positive integer with $n + 1$ digits, we see that every integer in the interval $[10^{n-1}, 10^n)$ has n digits. Because $\log 10^{n-1} = n - 1$ and $\log 10^n = n$, this implies that an n-digit positive integer has a logarithm in the interval $[n - 1, n)$.

Digits and logarithms

The logarithm of an n-digit positive integer is in the interval $[n - 1, n)$.

Logs have many uses, and the word "log" has more than one meaning.

The conclusion above is often useful in making estimates. For example, without using a calculator we can see that the number 123456789, which has nine digits, has a logarithm between 8 and 9 (the actual value is about 8.09).

The next example shows how to use the conclusion above to determine the number of digits in a number from its logarithm.

Suppose M is a positive integer such that $\log M \approx 73.1$. How many digits does M have?

EXAMPLE 3

SOLUTION   Because 73.1 is in the interval $[73, 74)$, we can conclude that M is a 74-digit number.

Always round up the logarithm of a number to determine the number of digits. Here $\log M \approx 73.1$ is rounded up to show that M has 74 digits.

Logarithm of a Power

We will use the formula $(b^r)^t = b^{tr}$ to derive a formula for the logarithm of a power. First we look at an example.

To motivate the formula for the logarithm of a power, we note that

$$\log (10^3)^4 = \log 10^{12} = 12 \quad \text{and} \quad \log 10^3 = 3.$$

Putting these equations together, we see that

$$\log (10^3)^4 = 4 \log 10^3.$$

An expression such as $\log 10^{12}$ should be interpreted to mean $\log(10^{12})$, not $(\log 10)^{12}$.

More generally, logarithms convert exponentiation to multiplication, as we will now show.

Suppose b and y are positive numbers, with $b \neq 1$, and t is a real number. Then

$$\log_b y^t = \log_b (b^{\log_b y})^t$$

$$= \log_b b^{t \log_b y}$$

$$= t \log_b y.$$

In other words, we have the following formula for the logarithm of a power:

Logarithm of a power

If b and y are positive numbers, with $b \neq 1$, and t is a real number, then

$$\log_b y^t = t \log_b y.$$

The next example shows a nice application of the formula above.

How many digits does 3^{5000} have?

EXAMPLE 4

SOLUTION   We can answer this question by evaluating the common logarithm of 3^{5000}. Using the formula for the logarithm of a power and a calculator, we see that

$$\log 3^{5000} = 5000 \log 3 \approx 2385.61.$$

Thus 3^{5000} has 2386 digits.

Your calculator cannot evaluate 3^{5000}. Thus the formula for the logarithm of a power is needed even though a calculator is being used.

In the era before calculators and computers existed, books of common logarithm tables were frequently used to compute powers of numbers. As an example of how this worked, consider how these books of logarithms would have been used to evaluate $1.7^{3.7}$. The key to performing this calculation is the formula

$$\log 1.7^{3.7} = 3.7 \log 1.7.$$

With the advent of calculators and computers, books of logarithms have essentially disappeared. However, your calculator is using logarithms and the formula $\log_b y^t = t \log_b y$ *when you ask it to evaluate an expression such as* $1.7^{3.7}$.

Let's assume that we have a book that gives the logarithms of the numbers from 1 to 10 in increments of 0.001, meaning that the book gives the logarithms of 1.001, 1.002, 1.003, and so on.

The idea is first to compute the right side of the equation above. To do that, we would look in the book of logarithms, getting $\log 1.7 \approx 0.230449$. Multiplying the last number by 3.7, we would conclude that the right side of the equation above is approximately 0.852661. Thus, according to the equation above, we have

$$\log 1.7^{3.7} \approx 0.852661.$$

Hence we can evaluate $1.7^{3.7}$ by finding a number whose logarithm equals 0.852661. To do this, we would look through our book of logarithms and find that the closest match is provided by the entry showing that $\log 7.123 \approx 0.852663$. Thus $1.7^{3.7} \approx 7.123$.

Although nowadays logarithms rarely are used directly by humans for computations such as evaluating $1.7^{3.7}$, logarithms are used by your calculator for such computations. Logarithms also have important uses in calculus and several other branches of mathematics. Furthermore, logarithms have several practical uses—we will see some examples later in this chapter.

EXERCISES

1. For $x = 7$ and $y = 13$, evaluate each of the following:

    (a) $\log(x + y)$ (b) $\log x + \log y$

    [*This exercise and the next one emphasize that* $\log(x + y)$ *does not equal* $\log x + \log y$.]

2. For $x = 0.4$ and $y = 3.5$, evaluate each of the following:

    (a) $\log(x + y)$ (b) $\log x + \log y$

3. For $x = 3$ and $y = 8$, evaluate each of the following:

    (a) $\log(xy)$ (b) $(\log x)(\log y)$

    [*This exercise and the next one emphasize that* $\log(xy)$ *does not equal* $(\log x)(\log y)$.]

4. For $x = 1.1$ and $y = 5$, evaluate each of the following:

    (a) $\log(xy)$ (b) $(\log x)(\log y)$

5. For $x = 12$ and $y = 2$, evaluate each of the following:

    (a) $\log \frac{x}{y}$ (b) $\dfrac{\log x}{\log y}$

    [*This exercise and the next one emphasize that* $\log \frac{x}{y}$ *does not equal* $\frac{\log x}{\log y}$.]

6. For $x = 18$ and $y = 0.3$, evaluate each of the following:

    (a) $\log \frac{x}{y}$ (b) $\dfrac{\log x}{\log y}$

7. 📟 For $x = 5$ and $y = 2$, evaluate each of the following:

    (a) $\log x^y$ (b) $(\log x)^y$

    [*This exercise and the next one emphasize that* $\log x^y$ *does not equal* $(\log x)^y$.]

8. 📟 For $x = 2$ and $y = 3$, evaluate each of the following:

    (a) $\log x^y$ (b) $(\log x)^y$

9. Suppose N is a positive integer such that $\log N \approx 35.4$. How many digits does N have?

10. Suppose k is a positive integer such that $\log k \approx 83.2$. How many digits does k have?

11. Suppose m and n are positive integers such that $\log m \approx 32.1$ and $\log n \approx 7.3$. How many digits does mn have?

12. Suppose m and n are positive integers such that $\log m \approx 41.3$ and $\log n \approx 12.8$. How many digits does mn have?

13. Suppose m is a positive integer such that $\log m \approx 13.2$. How many digits does m^3 have?

14. Suppose M is a positive integer such that $\log M \approx 50.3$. How many digits does M^4 have?

15. Suppose $\log a = 118.7$ and $\log b = 119.7$. Evaluate $\frac{b}{a}$.

16. Suppose $\log a = 203.4$ and $\log b = 205.4$. Evaluate $\frac{b}{a}$.

17. Suppose y is such that $\log_2 y = 17.67$. Evaluate $\log_2 y^{100}$.

18. Suppose x is such that $\log_6 x = 23.41$. Evaluate $\log_6 x^{10}$.

For Exercises 19-32, evaluate the given quantities assuming that

$$\log_3 x = 5.3 \quad \textit{and} \quad \log_3 y = 2.1,$$

$$\log_4 u = 3.2 \quad \textit{and} \quad \log_4 v = 1.3.$$

19. $\log_3(9xy)$
20. $\log_4(2uv)$
21. $\log_3 \frac{x}{3y}$
22. $\log_4 \frac{u}{8v}$
23. $\log_3 \sqrt{x}$
24. $\log_4 \sqrt{u}$
25. $\log_3 \dfrac{1}{\sqrt{y}}$
26. $\log_4 \dfrac{1}{\sqrt{v}}$
27. $\log_3(x^2 y^3)$
28. $\log_4(u^3 v^4)$
29. $\log_3 \dfrac{x^3}{y^2}$
30. $\log_4 \dfrac{u^2}{v^3}$
31. $\log_9 x^{10}$
32. $\log_2 u^{100}$

For Exercises 33-40, find all numbers x that satisfy the given equation.

33. $\log_7(x + 5) - \log_7(x - 1) = 2$
34. $\log_4(x + 4) - \log_4(x - 2) = 3$
35. $\log_3(x + 5) + \log_3(x - 1) = 2$
36. $\log_5(x + 4) + \log_5(x + 2) = 2$
37. $\dfrac{\log_6(15x)}{\log_6(5x)} = 2$
38. $\dfrac{\log_9(13x)}{\log_9(4x)} = 2$
39. 📟 $(\log(3x)) \log x = 4$
40. 📟 $(\log(6x)) \log x = 5$

For Exercises 41-44, find the number of digits in the given number.

41. 📟 7^{4000} 43. 📟 $6^{700} \cdot 23^{1000}$
42. 📟 8^{4444} 44. 📟 $5^{999} \cdot 17^{2222}$

45. 📟 Find an integer k such that 18^k has 357 digits.

46. 📟 Find an integer n such that 22^n has 222 digits.

47. 📟 Find an integer m such that m^{1234} has 1991 digits.

48. 📟 Find an integer N such that N^{4321} has 6041 digits.

49. 📟 Find the smallest integer n such that $7^n > 10^{100}$.

50. 📟 Find the smallest integer k such that $9^k > 10^{1000}$.

51. 📟 Find the smallest integer M such that $5^{1/M} < 1.01$.

52. 📟 Find the smallest integer m such that $8^{1/m} < 1.001$.

53. 📟 Suppose $\log_8(\log_7 m) = 5$. How many digits does m have?

54. 📟 Suppose $\log_5(\log_9 m) = 6$. How many digits does m have?

55. 📟 At the end of 2004, the largest known prime number was $2^{24036583} - 1$. How many digits does this prime number have?
    [*A* **prime number** *is an integer greater than 1 that has no divisors other than itself and 1.*]

56. 📟 At the end of 2005, the largest known prime number was $2^{30402457} - 1$. How many digits does this prime number have?

PROBLEMS

57. Explain why
$$1 + \log x = \log(10x)$$
for every positive number x.

58. Explain why
$$2 - \log x = \log \frac{100}{x}$$
for every positive number x.

59. Explain why
$$(1 + \log x)^2 = \log(10x^2) + (\log x)^2$$
for every positive number x.

60. Explain why
$$\frac{1 + \log x}{2} = \log \sqrt{10x}$$
for every positive number x.

61. Pretend that you are living in the time before calculators and computers existed, and that you have a book showing the logarithms of 1.001, 1.002, 1.003, and so on, up to the logarithm of 9.999. Explain how you would find the logarithm of 457.2, which is beyond the range of your book.

62. Explain why books of logarithm tables, which were frequently used before the era of calculators and computers, gave logarithms only for numbers between 1 and 10.

63. 📱 Explain why there does not exist an integer m such that 67^m has 9236 digits.

64. Derive the formula for the logarithm of a quotient by applying the formula for the logarithm of a product to $\log_b (y \cdot \frac{x}{y})$.

[*Sometimes seeing an alternative derivation can help increase your understanding.*]

65. Derive the formula $\log_b \frac{1}{y} = -\log_b y$ directly from the formula $1/b^t = b^{-t}$.

66. Without doing any calculations, explain why the solutions to the equations in Exercises 37 and 38 are unchanged if we change the base for all the logarithms in those exercises to any positive number $b \neq 1$.

67. 📱 Do a web search to find the largest currently known prime number. Then calculate the number of digits in this number.
[*The discovery of a new largest known prime number usually gets some newspaper coverage, including a statement of the number of digits. Thus you can probably find on the web the number of digits in the largest currently known prime number; you are asked here to do the calculation to verify that the reported number of digits is correct.*]

68. Explain why expressing a large positive integer in binary notation (base 2) should take approximately 3.3 times as many digits as expressing the same positive integer in standard decimal notation (base 10).
[*For example, this problem predicts that 5×10^{12}, which requires 13 digits to express in decimal notation, should require approximately 13×3.3 digits (which equals 42.9 digits) to express in binary notation. Expressing 5×10^{12} in binary notation actually requires 43 digits.*]

WORKED-OUT SOLUTIONS *to Odd-numbered Exercises*

1. 📱 For $x = 7$ and $y = 13$, evaluate each of the following:

    (a) $\log(x + y)$ (b) $\log x + \log y$

    SOLUTION

    (a) $\log(7 + 13) = \log 20 \approx 1.30103$

    (b)
    $$\log 7 + \log 13 \approx 0.845098 + 1.113943$$
    $$= 1.959041$$

3. 📱 For $x = 3$ and $y = 8$, evaluate each of the following:

    (a) $\log(xy)$ (b) $(\log x)(\log y)$

SOLUTION

(a) $\log(3 \cdot 8) = \log 24 \approx 1.38021$

(b) $\qquad (\log 3)(\log 8) \approx (0.477121)(0.903090)$

$$\approx 0.430883$$

5. For $x = 12$ and $y = 2$, evaluate each of the following:

(a) $\log \frac{x}{y}$ (b) $\dfrac{\log x}{\log y}$

SOLUTION

(a) $\log \frac{12}{2} = \log 6 \approx 0.778151$

(b) $\dfrac{\log 12}{\log 2} \approx \dfrac{1.079181}{0.301030} \approx 3.58496$

7. For $x = 5$ and $y = 2$, evaluate each of the following:

(a) $\log x^y$ (b) $(\log x)^y$

SOLUTION

(a) $\log 5^2 = \log 25 \approx 1.39794$

(b) $(\log 5)^2 \approx (0.69897)^2 \approx 0.48856$

9. Suppose N is a positive integer such that $\log N \approx 35.4$. How many digits does N have?

SOLUTION   Because 35.4 is in the interval $[35, 36)$, we can conclude that N is a 36-digit number.

11. Suppose m and n are positive integers such that $\log m \approx 32.1$ and $\log n \approx 7.3$. How many digits does mn have?

SOLUTION   Note that

$$\log(mn) = \log m + \log n$$

$$\approx 32.1 + 7.3$$

$$= 39.4.$$

Thus mn has 40 digits.

13. Suppose m is a positive integer such that $\log m \approx 13.2$. How many digits does m^3 have?

SOLUTION   Note that

$$\log(m^3) = 3 \log m \approx 3 \times 13.2 = 39.6.$$

Because 39.6 is in the interval $[39, 40)$, we can conclude that m^3 is a 40-digit number.

15. Suppose $\log a = 118.7$ and $\log b = 119.7$. Evaluate $\frac{b}{a}$.

SOLUTION   Note that

$$\log \tfrac{b}{a} = \log b - \log a$$

$$= 119.7 - 118.7$$

$$= 1.$$

Thus $\frac{b}{a} = 10$.

17. Suppose y is such that $\log_2 y = 17.67$. Evaluate $\log_2 y^{100}$.

SOLUTION $\log_2 y^{100} = 100 \log_2 y$

$$= 100 \cdot 17.67$$

$$= 1767$$

For Exercises 19–32, evaluate the given quantities assuming that

$$\log_3 x = 5.3 \quad and \quad \log_3 y = 2.1,$$

$$\log_4 u = 3.2 \quad and \quad \log_4 v = 1.3.$$

19. $\log_3(9xy)$

SOLUTION

$$\log_3(9xy) = \log_3 9 + \log_3 x + \log_3 y$$

$$= 2 + 5.3 + 2.1$$

$$= 9.4$$

21. $\log_3 \frac{x}{3y}$

SOLUTION

$$\log_3 \tfrac{x}{3y} = \log_3 x - \log_3(3y)$$

$$= \log_3 x - \log_3 3 - \log_3 y$$

$$= 5.3 - 1 - 2.1$$

$$= 2.2$$

23. $\log_3 \sqrt{x}$

SOLUTION $\quad \log_3 \sqrt{x} = \log_3 x^{1/2}$

$$= \tfrac{1}{2} \log_3 x$$

$$= \tfrac{1}{2} \times 5.3$$

$$= 2.65$$

25. $\log_3 \dfrac{1}{\sqrt{y}}$

SOLUTION $\quad \log_3 \dfrac{1}{\sqrt{y}} = \log_3 y^{-1/2}$

$$= -\tfrac{1}{2} \log_3 y$$

$$= -\tfrac{1}{2} \times 2.1$$

$$= -1.05$$

27. $\log_3 (x^2 y^3)$

SOLUTION

$$\log_3 (x^2 y^3) = \log_3 x^2 + \log_3 y^3$$

$$= 2 \log_3 x + 3 \log_3 y$$

$$= 2 \cdot 5.3 + 3 \cdot 2.1$$

$$= 16.9$$

29. $\log_3 \dfrac{x^3}{y^2}$

SOLUTION

$$\log_3 \dfrac{x^3}{y^2} = \log_3 x^3 - \log_3 y^2$$

$$= 3 \log_3 x - 2 \log_3 y$$

$$= 3 \cdot 5.3 - 2 \cdot 2.1$$

$$= 11.7$$

31. $\log_9 x^{10}$

SOLUTION   Because $\log_3 x = 5.3$, we see that $3^{5.3} = x$. This equation can be rewritten as $\left(9^{1/2}\right)^{5.3} = x$, which can then be rewritten as $9^{2.65} = x$. In other words, $\log_9 x = 2.65$. Thus

$$\log_9 x^{10} = 10 \log_9 x = 26.5.$$

For Exercises 33–40, find all numbers x that satisfy the given equation.

33. $\log_7 (x + 5) - \log_7 (x - 1) = 2$

SOLUTION   Rewrite the equation as follows:

$$2 = \log_7 (x + 5) - \log_7 (x - 1)$$

$$= \log_7 \dfrac{x + 5}{x - 1}.$$

Thus

$$\dfrac{x + 5}{x - 1} = 7^2 = 49.$$

We can solve the equation above for x, getting $x = \tfrac{9}{8}$.

35. $\log_3 (x + 5) + \log_3 (x - 1) = 2$

SOLUTION   Rewrite the equation as follows:

$$2 = \log_3 (x + 5) + \log_3 (x - 1)$$

$$= \log_3 \big((x + 5)(x - 1)\big)$$

$$= \log_3 (x^2 + 4x - 5).$$

Thus

$$x^2 + 4x - 5 = 3^2 = 9,$$

which implies that

$$x^2 + 4x - 14 = 0.$$

We can solve the equation above using the quadratic formula, getting $x = 3\sqrt{2} - 2$ or $x = -3\sqrt{2} - 2$. However, both $x + 5$ and $x - 1$ are negative if $x = -3\sqrt{2} - 2$; because the logarithm of a negative number is undefined, we must discard this root of the equation above. We conclude that the only value of x satisfying the equation $\log_3 (x + 5) + \log_3 (x - 1) = 2$ is $x = 3\sqrt{2} - 2$.

37. $\dfrac{\log_6 (15x)}{\log_6 (5x)} = 2$

SOLUTION   Rewrite the equation as follows:

$$2 = \dfrac{\log_6 (15x)}{\log_6 (5x)}$$

$$= \dfrac{\log_6 15 + \log_6 x}{\log_6 5 + \log_6 x}.$$

Solving this equation for $\log_6 x$ (the first step in doing this is to multiply both sides by the denominator $\log_6 5 + \log_6 x$), we get

$$\log_6 x = \log_6 15 - 2\log_6 5$$
$$= \log_6 15 - \log_6 25$$
$$= \log_6 \tfrac{15}{25}$$
$$= \log_6 \tfrac{3}{5}.$$

Thus $x = \tfrac{3}{5}$.

39. ⬛ $(\log(3x))\log x = 4$

SOLUTION   Rewrite the equation as follows:

$$4 = (\log(3x))\log x$$
$$= (\log x + \log 3)\log x$$
$$= (\log x)^2 + (\log 3)(\log x).$$

Letting $y = \log x$, we can rewrite the equation above as
$$y^2 + (\log 3)y - 4 = 0.$$
Use the quadratic formula to solve the equation above for y, getting

$$y \approx -2.25274 \quad \text{or} \quad y \approx 1.77562.$$

Thus

$$\log x \approx -2.25274 \quad \text{or} \quad \log x \approx 1.77562,$$

which means that

$$x \approx 10^{-2.25274} \approx 0.00558807$$

or

$$x \approx 10^{1.77562} \approx 59.6509.$$

For Exercises 41–44, find the number of digits in the given number.

41. ⬛ 7^{4000}

SOLUTION   Using the formula for the logarithm of a power and a calculator, we have

$$\log 7^{4000} = 4000\log 7 \approx 3380.39.$$

Thus 7^{4000} has 3381 digits.

43. ⬛ $6^{700} \cdot 23^{1000}$

SOLUTION   Using the formulas for the logarithm of a product and the logarithm of a power, we have

$$\log(6^{700} \cdot 23^{1000}) = \log 6^{700} + \log 23^{1000}$$
$$= 700\log 6 + 1000\log 23$$
$$\approx 1906.43.$$

Thus $6^{700} \cdot 23^{1000}$ has 1907 digits.

45. ⬛ Find an integer k such that 18^k has 357 digits.

SOLUTION   We want to find an integer k such that
$$356 \le \log 18^k < 357.$$
Using the formula for the logarithm of a power, we can rewrite the inequalities above as
$$356 \le k\log 18 < 357.$$

Dividing by $\log 18$ gives
$$\tfrac{356}{\log 18} \le k < \tfrac{357}{\log 18}.$$
Using a calculator, we see that $\tfrac{356}{\log 18} \approx 283.6$ and $\tfrac{357}{\log 18} \approx 284.4$. Thus the only possible choice is to take $k = 284$.

Again using a calculator, we see that
$$\log 18^{284} = 284\log 18 \approx 356.5.$$

Thus 18^{284} indeed has 357 digits.

47. ⬛ Find an integer m such that m^{1234} has 1991 digits.

SOLUTION   We want to find an integer m such that
$$1990 \le \log m^{1234} < 1991.$$
Using the formula for the logarithm of a power, we can rewrite the inequalities above as
$$1990 \le 1234\log m < 1991.$$

Dividing by 1234 gives
$$\tfrac{1990}{1234} \le \log m < \tfrac{1991}{1234}.$$
Thus
$$10^{1990/1234} \le m < 10^{1991/1234}.$$

Using a calculator, we see that $10^{1990/1234} \approx 40.99$ and $10^{1991/1234} \approx 41.06$. Thus the only possible choice is to take $m = 41$.

Again using a calculator, we see that
$$\log 41^{1234} = 1234\log 41 \approx 1990.18.$$

Thus 41^{1234} indeed has 1991 digits.

49. $\blacklozenge$ Find the smallest integer n such that $7^n > 10^{100}$.

SOLUTION   Suppose $7^n > 10^{100}$. Taking the common logarithm of both sides, we have

$$\log 7^n > \log 10^{100},$$

which can be rewritten as

$$n \log 7 > 100.$$

This implies that

$$n > \frac{100}{\log 7} \approx 118.33.$$

The smallest integer that is bigger than 118.33 is 119. Thus we take $n = 119$.

51. $\blacklozenge$ Find the smallest integer M such that $5^{1/M} < 1.01$.

SOLUTION   Suppose $5^{1/M} < 1.01$. Taking the common logarithm of both sides, we have

$$\log 5^{1/M} < \log 1.01,$$

which can be rewritten as

$$\frac{\log 5}{M} < \log 1.01.$$

This implies that

$$M > \frac{\log 5}{\log 1.01} \approx 161.7.$$

The smallest integer that is bigger than 161.7 is 162. Thus we take $M = 162$.

53. $\blacklozenge$ Suppose $\log_8(\log_7 m) = 5$. How many digits does m have?

SOLUTION   The equation $\log_8(\log_7 m) = 5$ implies that

$$\log_7 m = 8^5 = 32768.$$

The equation above now implies that

$$m = 7^{32768}.$$

To compute the number of digits that m has, note that

$$\log m = \log 7^{32768} = 32768 \log 7 \approx 27692.2.$$

Thus m has 27693 digits.

55. $\blacklozenge$ At the end of 2004, the largest known prime number was $2^{24036583} - 1$. How many digits does this prime number have?

SOLUTION   To calculate the number of digits in $2^{24036583} - 1$, we need to evaluate $\log(2^{24036583} - 1)$. However, $2^{24036583} - 1$ is too large to evaluate directly on a calculator, and no formula exists for the logarithm of the difference of two numbers.

The trick here is to note that $2^{24036583}$ and $2^{24036583} - 1$ have the same number of digits, as we will now see. Although it is possible for a number and the number minus 1 to have a different number of digits (for example, 100 and 99 do not have the same number of digits), this happens only if the larger of the two numbers consists of 1 followed by a bunch of 0's and the smaller of the two numbers consists of all 9's. Here are three different ways to see that this situation does not apply to $2^{24036583}$ and $2^{24036583} - 1$ (pick whichever explanation seems easiest to you): (a) $2^{24036583}$ cannot end in a 0 because all positive integer powers of 2 end in either 2, 4, 6, or 8; (b) $2^{24036583}$ cannot end in a 0 because then it would be divisible by 5, but $2^{24036583}$ is divisible only by integer powers of 2; (c) $2^{24036583} - 1$ cannot consist of all 9's because then it would be divisible by 9, which is not possible for a prime number.

Now that we know that $2^{24036583}$ and $2^{24036583} - 1$ have the same number of digits, we can calculate the number of digits by taking the logarithm of $2^{24036583}$ and using the formula for the logarithm of a power. We have

$$\log 2^{24036583} = 24036583 \log 2 \approx 7235732.5.$$

Thus $2^{24036583}$ has 7235733 digits; hence $2^{24036583} - 1$ also has 7235733 digits.

3.4   *Exponential Growth*

We begin this section with a story.

A Doubling Fable

A mathematician in ancient India invented the game of chess. Filled with gratitude for the remarkable entertainment of this game, the King offered the mathematician anything he wanted. The King expected the mathematician to ask for rare jewels or a majestic palace.

But the mathematician asked only that he be given one grain of rice for the first square on a chessboard, plus two grains of rice for the next square, plus four grains for the next square, and so on, doubling the amount for each square, until the 64th square on an 8-by-8 chessboard had been reached. The King was pleasantly surprised that the mathematician had asked for such a modest reward.

A bag of rice was opened, and first 1 grain was set aside, then 2, then 4, then 8, and so on. As the eighth square (the end of the first row of the chessboard) was reached, 128 grains of rice were counted out, and the King was secretly delighted to be paying such a small reward and also wondering at the foolishness of the mathematician.

As the 16th square was reached, 32,768 grains of rice were counted out, but this was still a small part of a bag of rice. But the 21st square required a full bag of rice, and the 24th square required eight bags of rice. This was more than the King had expected, but it was a trivial amount because the royal granary contained about 200,000 bags of rice to feed the kingdom during the coming winter.

As the 31st square was reached, over a thousand bags of rice were required and were delivered from the royal granary. Now the King was worried. By the 37th square, the royal granary was two-thirds empty. The 38th square would have required more bags of rice than were left, but the King stopped the process and ordered that the mathematician's head be chopped off as a warning about the greed induced by exponential growth.

To understand why the mathematician's seemingly modest request turned out to be so extravagant, note that the nth square of the chessboard required 2^{n-1} grains of rice. These numbers start slowly but grow rapidly, as can be seen in the table below:

n	2^n	
10	1024	
20	1048576	
30	1073741824	*Powers of 2.*
40	1099511627776	
50	1125899906842624	
60	1152921504606846976	

The 64th square of the chessboard would have required 2^{63} grains of rice.

When estimating large powers of 2, approximating 2^{10} by 1000 often simplifies the calculation.

To get a rough estimate of the magnitude of this number, note that $2^{10} = 1024 \approx 10^3$. Thus

$$2^{63} = 2^3 \cdot 2^{60} = 8 \cdot (2^{10})^6 \approx 8 \cdot (10^3)^6 = 8 \cdot 10^{18} \approx 10^{19}.$$

As x gets large, 2^x increases much faster than x^2. For example, 2^{63} equals 9223372036854775808 but 63^2 equals only 3969.

If each large bag contains a million (which equals 10^6) grains of rice, then the approximately 10^{19} grains of rice needed for the 64th square would have required approximately $10^{19}/10^6$ bags of rice, or approximately 10^{13} bags of rice. If we assume that ancient India had a population of about ten million (which equals 10^7), then each resident would have had to produce about $10^{13}/10^7$ (which equals one million) bags of rice to satisfy the mathematician's request for the 64th square of the chessboard. Because it would have been impossible for each resident in India to produce a million bags of rice, the mathematician should not have been surprised at losing his head.

Functions with Exponential Growth

The function f defined by $f(x) = 2^x$ is an example of what is called a function with exponential growth. Other examples of functions of exponential growth are the functions g and h defined by $g(x) = 3 \cdot 5^x$ and $h(x) = 5 \cdot 7^{3x}$. More generally, we have the following definition:

Exponential growth

A function f is said to have **exponential growth** if f is of the form

$$f(x) = cb^{kx},$$

where c and k are positive constants and $b > 1$.

Functions with exponential growth increase rapidly. In fact, every function with exponential growth increases more rapidly than every polynomial, in the sense that if f is a function with exponential growth and p is any polynomial, then $f(x) > p(x)$ for all sufficiently large x. For example, $2^x > x^{1000}$ for all $x > 13747$.

Functions with exponential growth increase so rapidly that graphing them in the usual manner can display too little information. For example, consider the function 9^x on the interval $[0, 8]$:

The graph of 9^x on the interval $[0, 8]$.

In this graph, we cannot use the same scale on the x- and y-axes because 9^8 is larger than forty million. Due to the scale, the shape of the graph in the interval $[0, 5]$ gives little insight into the behavior of the function there. For example, this graph does not adequately distinguish between the values 9^2 (which equals 81) and 9^5 (which equals 59049).

Because the graphs of functions with exponential growth often do not provide sufficient visual information, data that is expected to have exponential growth is often plotted by taking the logarithm of the data. The advantage of this procedure is that if f is a function with exponential growth, then the logarithm of f is a linear function. For example, if $f(x) = 2^x$, then $\log f(x) = (\log 2)x$; thus the graph of $\log f$ is the line whose equation is $y = (\log 2)x$ (which is the line through the origin with slope $\log 2$).

More generally, if $f(x) = cb^{kx}$, then

$$\log f(x) = k(\log b)x + \log c.$$

Here k, $\log b$, and $\log c$ are all constants; thus the function $\log f$ is indeed linear.

For an example with real data, consider **Moore's Law**, which is the term used to describe the observation that computing power roughly doubles every 18 months. One standard measure of computing power is the number of transistors used per integrated circuit; the logarithm of this quantity is shown in the graph below for certain years between 1972 and 2000, with line segments connecting the available data points:

Here we are taking the logarithm base 10, but the conclusion about the linearity of the logarithm of f would hold regardless of the base used for the logarithm.

Moore's Law is named in honor of Gordon Moore, co-founder of Intel, who predicted in 1965 that computing power would follow a pattern of exponential growth.

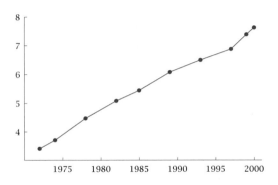

The logarithm of the number of transistors per integrated circuit. Moore's Law predicts exponential growth of computing power, which would make this graph a line.

The graph above of the logarithm of the number of transistors is roughly a line, as would be expected for a function with roughly exponential growth (the data used here about the number of transistors comes from Intel, the largest producer of integrated circuits used in computers).

Population Growth

Populations of various organisms, ranging from bacteria to humans, often exhibit exponential growth. To illustrate this behavior, we will begin by considering bacteria. Bacteria are single-celled creatures that reproduce by absorbing some nutrients, growing, and then dividing in half—one bacterium cell becomes two bacteria cells.

EXAMPLE 1

Suppose a colony of bacteria in a petri dish has 700 cells at 1 pm. These bacteria reproduce at a rate that leads to doubling every three hours. How many bacteria cells will be in the petri dish at 9 pm on the same day?

SOLUTION   Because the number of bacteria cells doubles every three hours, at 4 pm there will be 1400 cells, at 7 pm there will be 2800 cells, and so on. In other words, in three hours the number of cells increases by a factor of two, in six hours the number of cells increases by a factor of four, in nine hours the number of cells increases by a factor of eight, and so on. More generally, in t hours there are $t/3$ doubling periods. Hence in t hours the number of cells increases by a factor of $2^{t/3}$ and we should have $700 \cdot 2^{t/3}$ bacteria cells.

Thus at 9 pm, which is eight hours after 1 pm, our colony of bacteria should have $700 \cdot 2^{8/3}$ cells. However, this result should be thought of as an estimate rather than as an exact count. Actually, $700 \cdot 2^{8/3}$ is an irrational number (approximately equal to 4444.7), which makes no sense when counting bacteria cells. Thus we might predict that at 9 pm there would be about 4445 cells. Even better, because the real world rarely strictly adheres to formulas, we might expect between 4400 and 4500 cells at 9 pm.

Because functions with exponential growth increase so rapidly, they can be used to model real data for only limited time periods.

Although a function with exponential growth will often provide the best model for population growth for a certain time period, real population data cannot exhibit exponential growth for excessively long time periods. For example, the formula $700 \cdot 2^{t/3}$ derived above for our colony of bacteria predicts that after 10 days, which equals 240 hours, we would have about 10^{27} cells, which is far more than could fit in even a gigantic petri dish. The bacteria would have run out of space and nutrients long before reaching this population level.

Now we extend our example with bacteria to a more general situation. Suppose a population doubles every d time units (here the time units might be hours, days, years, or whatever unit is appropriate). Suppose also that at some specific time t_0 we know that the population is p_0. At time t there have been $t - t_0$ time units since time t_0. Thus at time t there have been $(t - t_0)/d$ doubling periods, and hence the population increases by a factor of $2^{(t-t_0)/d}$.

This factor must be multiplied by the population at the starting time t_0. In other words, at time t we could expect a population of $p_0 \cdot 2^{(t-t_0)/d}$.

We summarize the exponential growth population model as follows:

Exponential growth and doubling

If a population doubles every d time units, then the function p modeling this population growth is given by the formula

$$p(t) = p_0 \cdot 2^{(t-t_0)/d},$$

where p_0 is the population at time t_0.

Human population data often follow patterns of exponential growth for decades or centuries. The graph below shows the logarithm of the world population for each year from 1950 to 2000:

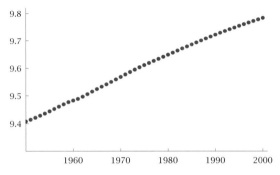

The logarithm of the world population each year from 1950 to 2000.

The data for this graph uses the mid-year world population as estimated by the U.S. Census Bureau.

The graph above comes close to fitting on a line, as expected for the logarithm of a function with exponential growth.

The world population in mid-year 1950 was about 2.56 billion. During the period 1950–2000, world population increased at a rate that doubled the population approximately every 40 years.

(a) Find a formula that estimates the mid-year world population for 1950-2000.

(b) Using the formula from part (a), estimate the world population in mid-year 1955.

EXAMPLE 2

World population is now increasing at a slower rate, doubling about every 69 years.

SOLUTION

(a) Using the formula and data above, we see that the mid-year world population in the year y, expressed in billions, was approximately

$$2.56 \cdot 2^{(y-1950)/40}.$$

Here we are using y rather than t as the time variable.

(b) Taking $y = 1955$ in the formula above gives the estimate that the mid-year world population in 1955 was $2.56 \cdot 2^{(1955-1950)/40}$ billion, which is approximately 2.79 billion. The actual value was about 2.78 billion; thus the formula has good accuracy in this case.

Compound Interest

The computation of compound interest involves functions with exponential growth. We begin with a simple example.

EXAMPLE 3

Suppose you deposit $8000 in a bank account that pays 5% annual interest rate. Assume that the bank pays interest once per year, at the end of each year, and that each year you place the interest in a cookie jar for safekeeping.

(a) How much will you have (original amount plus interest) at the end of one year?

(b) How much will you have (original amount plus interest) at the end of two years?

(c) How much will you have (original amount plus interest) at the end of three years?

(d) How much will you have (original amount plus interest) at the end of m years?

SOLUTION

(a) Because 5% of $8000 is $400, at the end of the first year you will receive $400 interest. Thus the total amount you will have at the end of one year is $8400.

(b) You receive $400 in interest at the end of the second year, bringing the amount in the cookie jar to $800 and the total amount to $8800.

(c) You receive $400 in interest at the end of the third year, bringing the amount in the cookie jar to $1200 and the total amount to $9200.

(d) Because you receive $400 interest each year, at the end of m years the cookie jar will contain $400m$ dollars. Thus the total amount you will have at the end of m years is $8000 + 400m$ dollars.

The situation in the example above, where interest is paid only on the original amount, is called **simple interest**. To generalize the example above, we can replace the $8000 used in the example above with an arbitrary initial amount P. Furthermore, we can replace the 5% annual interest rate with an arbitrary annual interest rate r, expressed as a number rather than as a percent (thus 5% interest would correspond to $r = 0.05$). Each year the interest received will be rP. Thus after m years the total interest received will be rPm. Hence the total amount after m years will be $P+rPm$. Factoring out P from this expression, we have the following result:

*The symbol P comes from **principal**, which is a fancy word for the initial amount.*

> ### *Simple interest*
>
> If interest is paid once per year at annual interest rate r, with no interest paid on the interest, then after m years an initial amount P grows to
>
> $$P(1 + rm).$$

The expression $P(1 + rm)$ that appears above is a linear function of m (assuming that the principal P and the interest rate r are constant). Thus when money grows with simple interest, linear functions arise naturally. We now turn to the more realistic situation of **compound interest**, meaning that interest is paid on the interest.

EXAMPLE 4

Suppose you deposit $8000 in a bank account that pays 5% annual interest rate. Assume that the bank pays interest once per year, at the end of each year, and that each year the interest is deposited in the bank account.

(a) How much will you have at the end of one year?

(b) How much will you have at the end of two years?

(c) How much will you have at the end of three years?

(d) How much will you have at the end of m years?

SOLUTION

(a) Because 5% of $8000 is $400, at the end of the first year you will receive $400 interest. Thus at the end of the first year the bank account will contain $8400.

(b) At the end of the second year you will receive as interest 5% of $8400, which equals $420, which when added to the bank account gives a total of $8820.

(c) At the end of the third year you will receive as interest 5% of $8820, which equals $441, which when added to the bank account gives a total of $9261.

(d) Note that each year the amount in the bank account increases by a factor of 1.05. At the end of the first year you will have

$$8000 \times 1.05$$

dollars (which equals $8400). At the end of two years, you will have the amount above multiplied by 1.05, which equals

$$8000 \times 1.05^2$$

dollars (which equals $8820). At the end of three years, you will have the amount above again multiplied by 1.05, which equals

$$8000 \times 1.05^3$$

dollars (which equals $9261). After m years, the original $8000 will have grown to

$$8000 \times 1.05^m$$

dollars.

The table below summarizes the data for the two methods of computing interest that we have considered in the last two examples.

year	simple interest		compound interest	
	interest	total	interest	total
initial amount		$8000		$8000
1	$400	$8400	$400	$8400
2	$400	$8800	$420	$8820
3	$400	$9200	$441	$9261

Simple and compound interest, once per year, on $8000 at 5%.

Note that after the first year in the table above, compound interest produces a higher total than simple interest. This happens because with compound interest, interest in paid on the interest.

The compound interest computation done in part (d) of the last example can be extended to more general situations. To generalize the example above, we can replace the $8000 used in the example above with an arbitrary initial amount P. Furthermore, we can replace the 5% annual interest rate with an arbitrary annual interest rate r, expressed as a number rather than as a percent. Each year the amount in the bank account increases by a factor of $1 + r$. Thus at the end of the first year the initial amount P will grow to $P(1 + r)$. At the end of two years, this will have grown to $P(1 + r)^2$. At the end of three years, this will have grown to $P(1 + r)^3$. More generally, we have the following result:

> ### Compound interest, once per year
>
> If interest is compounded once per year at annual interest rate r, then after m years an initial amount P grows to
>
> $$P(1 + r)^m.$$

The expression $P(1 + r)^m$ that appears above has exponential growth as a function of m (assuming that the principal P and the interest rate r are constant). Thus we see that when money grows with compound interest, functions with exponential growth arise naturally. Because functions with exponential growth increase rapidly, compound interest can lead to large amounts of money after long time periods.

EXAMPLE 5

Little historical evidence exists concerning the alleged sale of Manhattan. Most of the stories about this event should be considered legends.

Today Manhattan contains well-known New York City landmarks such as Times Square, the Empire State Building, Wall Street, United Nations headquarters, and Carrie Bradshaw's apartment.

In 1626 Dutch settlers supposedly purchased from Native Americans the island of Manhattan for $24. To determine whether or not this was a bargain, suppose $24 earned 7% per year (a reasonable rate for a real estate investment), compounded once per year since 1626. How much would this investment be worth by 2009?

SOLUTION
Because $2009 - 1626 = 383$, the formula above shows that an initial amount of $24 earning 7% per year compounded once per year would be worth

$$24(1.07)^{383}$$

dollars in 2009. A calculator shows that this is over four trillion dollars, which is more than the current assessed value of all land in Manhattan.

Interest is often compounded more than once per year. To see how this works, we now modify an earlier example. In our new example, interest will be paid and compounded twice per year rather than once per year. This means that instead of 5% interest being paid at the end of each year, the interest comes as two payments of 2.5% each year, with the 2.5% interest payments made at the end of every six months.

Suppose you deposit $8000 in a bank account that pays 5% annual interest rate, compounded twice per year. How much will you have at the end of one year?

EXAMPLE 6

SOLUTION   At the end of the first six months, interest of $200, which equals 2.5% of $8000, will be deposited into the bank account; the bank account will then have a total of $8200.

At the end of the second six months (in other words, at the end of the first year), 2.5% interest will be paid on the $8200 that was in the bank account for the previous six months. Because 2.5% of $8200 equals $205, the bank account will have $8405 at the end of the first year.

In the example above, the $8405 in the bank account at the end of the first year should be compared with the $8400 that would be in the bank account if interest had been paid only at the end of the year. The extra $5 arises because of the interest during the second six months on the interest earned at the end of the first six months.

As usual with compounding, the interest on the interest adds to the total.

Instead of compounding interest twice per year, as in the previous example, in the next example we will assume that interest will be compounded four times per year. At 5% annual interest, this would mean that 1.25% interest will be paid at the end of every three months.

Suppose you deposit $8000 in a bank account that pays 5% annual interest rate, compounded four times per year. How much will you have at the end of one year?

EXAMPLE 7

SOLUTION At the end of the first three months, interest of $100, which equals 1.25% of $8000, will be deposited into the bank account; the bank account will then have a total of $8100.

At the end of the second three months (in other words, at the end of six months), 1.25% interest will be paid on the $8100 that was in the bank account for the previous three months. Because 1.25% of $8100 equals $101.25, the bank account will have $8201.25 at the end of the first six months.

A similar calculation shows that the bank account will have $8303.77 at the end of the first nine months and $8407.56 at the end of the first year.

Compare the results of the last two examples. Note that the bank account will contain $8405 at the end of the first year if compounding twice per year but $8407.56 if compounding four times per year.

If interest is compounded 12 times per year (at the end of each month), then we can expect a higher total than when interest is compounded 4 times per year. The table below shows the growth of $8000 at 5% interest for three years, with compounding either 1, 2, 4, or 12 times per year.

More frequent compounding leads to higher total amounts because more frequent interest payments give more time for interest to earn on the interest. In Chapter 4 we will discuss what happens when interest is compounded a huge number of times per year.

	times compounded per year			
year	1	2	4	12
initial amount	$8000	$8000	$8000	$8000
1	$8400	$8405	$8408	$8409
2	$8820	$8831	$8836	$8840
3	$9261	$9278	$9286	$9292

The growth of $8000 at 5% interest, rounded to the nearest dollar.

To find a formula for how money grows when compounded more than once per year, consider a bank account with annual interest rate r, compounded twice per year. Thus every six months, the amount in the bank account increases by a factor of $1 + \frac{r}{2}$. After m years, this will happen $2m$ times. Thus an initial amount P will grow to $P(1 + \frac{r}{2})^{2m}$ in m years.

More generally, suppose now that an annual interest rate r is compounded n times per year. Then n times per year, the amount in the bank account increases by a factor of $1 + \frac{r}{n}$. After m years, this will happen nm times, leading to the following result:

Compound interest, n times per year

If interest is compounded n times per year at annual interest rate r, then after m years an initial amount P grows to

$$P\left(1 + \tfrac{r}{n}\right)^{nm}.$$

EXAMPLE 8

Suppose a bank account starting out with $8000 receives 5% annual interest, compounded twelve times per year. How much will be in the bank account after three years?

SOLUTION   Take $r = 0.05$, $n = 12$, $m = 3$, and $P = 8000$ in the formula above, which shows that after three years the amount in the bank account will be

$$8000\left(1 + \tfrac{0.05}{12}\right)^{12 \cdot 3}$$

dollars. A calculator shows that this amount is approximately $9292 (which is the last entry in the table above).

Advertisements from financial institutions often list the "APY" that you will earn on your money rather than the interest rate. The abbreviation "APY" denotes "annual percentage yield", which means the actual interest rate that you would receive at the end of one year after compounding. For example, if a bank is paying 5% annual interest, compounded once per month (as is fairly common), then the bank can legally advertise that it pays an APY of 5.116%. Here the APY equals 5.116% because

$$1.05116 = \left(1 + \frac{0.05}{12}\right)^{12}.$$

In other words, at 5% annual interest compounded twelve times per year, $1000 will grow to $1051.16. For a period of one year, this corresponds to simple annual interest of 5.116%.

EXERCISES

1. Without using a calculator or computer, give a rough estimate of 2^{83}.

2. Without using a calculator or computer, give a rough estimate of 2^{103}.

3. Without using a calculator or computer, determine which of the two numbers 2^{125} and $32 \cdot 10^{36}$ is larger.

4. Without using a calculator or computer, determine which of the two numbers 2^{400} and 17^{100} is larger.
   [*Hint:* Note that $2^4 = 16$.]

For Exercises 5–8, suppose you deposit into a savings account one cent on January 1, two cents on January 2, four cents on January 3, and so on, doubling the amount of your deposit each day (assume that you use an electronic bank that is open every day of the year).

5. How much will you deposit on January 7?

6. How much will you deposit on January 11?

7. What is the first day that your deposit will exceed $10,000?

8. What is the first day that your deposit will exceed $100,000?

For Exercises 9–12, suppose you deposit into your savings account one cent on January 1, three cents on January 2, nine cents on January 3, and so on, tripling the amount of your deposit each day.

9. How much will you deposit on January 7?

10. How much will you deposit on January 11?

11. What is the first day that your deposit will exceed $10,000?

12. What is the first day that your deposit will exceed $100,000?

13. Suppose $f(x) = 7 \cdot 2^{3x}$. Find a constant b such that the graph of $\log_b f$ has slope 1.

14. Suppose $f(x) = 4 \cdot 2^{5x}$. Find a constant b such that the graph of $\log_b f$ has slope 1.

15. A colony of bacteria is growing exponentially, doubling in size every 100 minutes. How many minutes will it take for the colony of bacteria to triple in size?

16. A colony of bacteria is growing exponentially, doubling in size every 140 minutes. How many minutes will it take for the colony of bacteria to become five times its current size?

17. At current growth rates, the Earth's population is doubling about every 69 years. If this growth rate were to continue, about how many years will it take for the Earth's population to increase 50% from the present level?

18. At current growth rates, the Earth's population is doubling about every 69 years. If this growth rate were to continue, about how many years will it take for the Earth's population to become one-fourth larger than the current level?

19. Suppose a colony of bacteria starts with 200 cells and triples in size every four hours.

    (a) Find a function that models the population growth of this colony of bacteria.

    (b) Approximately how many cells will be in the colony after six hours?

20. Suppose a colony of bacteria starts with 100 cells and triples in size every two hours.

    (a) Find a function that models the population growth of this colony of bacteria.

    (b) Approximately how many cells will be in the colony after one hour?

21. Suppose $700 is deposited in a bank account paying 6% interest per year, compounded 52 times per year. How much will be in the bank account at the end of 10 years?

22. Suppose $8000 is deposited in a bank account paying 7% interest per year, compounded 12 times per year. How much will be in the bank account at the end of 100 years?

23. Suppose a bank account paying 4% interest per year, compounded 12 times per year, contains $10,555 at the end of 10 years. What was the initial amount deposited in the bank account?

24. Suppose a bank account paying 6% interest per year, compounded four times per year, contains $27,707 at the end of 20 years. What was the initial amount deposited in the bank account?

25. Suppose a savings account pays 6% interest per year, compounded once per year. If the savings account starts with $500, how long would it take for the savings account to exceed $2000?

26. Suppose a savings account pays 5% interest per year, compounded four times per year. If the savings account starts with $600, how many years would it take for the savings account to exceed $1400?

27. Suppose a bank wants to advertise that $1000 deposited in its savings account will grow to $1040 in one year. This bank compounds interest 12 times per year. What annual interest rate must the bank pay?

28. Suppose a bank wants to advertise that $1000 deposited in its savings account will grow to $1050 in one year. This bank compounds interest 365 times per year. What annual interest rate must the bank pay?

29. An advertisement for real estate published in the 28 July 2004 electronic edition of the *New York Times* states:

> Did you know that the percent increase of the value of a home in Manhattan between the years 1950 and 2000 was 721%? Buy a home in Manhattan and invest in your future.

Suppose that instead of buying a home in Manhattan in 1950, someone had invested money in a bank account that compounds interest four times per year. What annual interest rate would the bank have to pay to equal the growth claimed in the ad?

30. Suppose that instead of buying a home in Manhattan in 1950, someone had invested money in a bank account that compounds interest once per month. What annual interest rate would the bank have to pay to equal the growth claimed in the ad from the previous exercise?

31. Suppose f is a function with exponential growth such that

$$f(1) = 3 \quad \text{and} \quad f(2) = 4.$$

Evaluate $f(3)$.

32. Suppose f is a function with exponential growth such that

$$f(3) = 2 \quad \text{and} \quad f(4) = 7.$$

Evaluate $f(5)$.

PROBLEMS

33. Explain how you would use a calculator to verify that

$$2^{13746} < 13746^{1000}$$

but

$$2^{13747} > 13747^{1000},$$

and then actually use a calculator to verify both these inequalities.

[*The numbers involved in these inequalities have over four thousand digits. Thus some cleverness in using your calculator is required.*]

34. Show that

$$2^{10n} = (1.024)^n 10^{3n}.$$

[*This equality leads to the approximation $2^{10n} \approx 10^{3n}$.*]

35. Show that if f is a function with exponential growth, then so is the square root of f. More precisely, show that if f is a function with exponential growth, then so is the function g defined by $g(x) = \sqrt{f(x)}$.

36. Explain why every function f with exponential growth can be represented by a formula of the form $f(x) = cb^x$ for appropriate choices of c and b.

37. Explain why every function f with exponential growth can be represented by a formula of the form $f(x) = c \cdot 2^{kx}$ for appropriate choices of c and k.

38. Find at least three newspaper articles that use the word "exponentially" (the easiest way to do this is to use the web site of a newspaper that allows searches of its articles). For each use of the word "exponentially" that you find in a newspaper article, discuss whether the word is used in its correct mathematical sense.

[*In a recent year the word "exponentially" appeared 87 times in the* New York Times.]

39. Suppose a bank pays annual interest rate r, compounded n times per year. Explain why the bank can advertise that its APY equals

$$\left(1 + \tfrac{r}{n}\right)^n - 1.$$

40. 🖉 Find an advertisement in a newspaper or web site that gives the interest rate (before compounding), the frequency of compounding, and the APY. Determine whether or not the APY has been computed correctly.

WORKED-OUT SOLUTIONS *to Odd-numbered Exercises*

1. Without using a calculator or computer, give a rough estimate of 2^{83}.

   SOLUTION

   $$2^{83} = 2^3 \cdot 2^{80} = 8 \cdot 2^{10 \cdot 8} = 8 \cdot (2^{10})^8$$

   $$\approx 8 \cdot (10^3)^8 = 8 \cdot 10^{24} \approx 10^{25}$$

3. Without using a calculator or computer, determine which of the two numbers 2^{125} and $32 \cdot 10^{36}$ is larger.

   SOLUTION Note that

   $$2^{125} = 2^5 \cdot 2^{120}$$

   $$= 32 \cdot (2^{10})^{12}$$

   $$> 32 \cdot (10^3)^{12}$$

   $$= 32 \cdot 10^{36}.$$

   Thus 2^{125} is larger than $32 \cdot 10^{36}$.

For Exercises 5–8, suppose you deposit into a savings account one cent on January 1, two cents on January 2, four cents on January 3, and so on, doubling the amount of your deposit each day (assume that you use an electronic bank that is open every day of the year).

5. How much will you deposit on January 7?

SOLUTION On the nth day, 2^{n-1} cents are deposited. Thus on January 7, the amount deposited is 2^6 cents. In other words, 0.64 will be deposited on January 7.

7. 🖉 What is the first day that your deposit will exceed $10,000?

SOLUTION On the nth day, 2^{n-1} cents are deposited. Because $10,000 equals 10^6 cents, we need to find the smallest integer n such that

$$2^{n-1} > 10^6.$$

We can do a quick estimate by noting that

$$10^6 = (10^3)^2 < (2^{10})^2 = 2^{20}.$$

Thus taking $n - 1 = 20$, which is equivalent to taking $n = 21$, should be close to the correct answer.

To be more precise, note that the inequality $2^{n-1} > 10^6$ is equivalent to the inequality

$$\log 2^{n-1} > \log 10^6,$$

which can be rewritten as

$$(n - 1) \log 2 > 6.$$

Dividing both sides by $\log 2$ and then adding 1 to both sides shows that this is equivalent to

$$n > 1 + \frac{6}{\log 2}.$$

A calculator shows that $1 + \frac{6}{\log 2} \approx 20.9$. Because 21 is the smallest integer bigger than 20.9, January 21 is the first day that the deposit will exceed $10,000.

For Exercises 9–12, suppose you deposit into your savings account one cent on January 1, three cents on January 2, nine cents on January 3, and so on, tripling the amount of your deposit each day.

9. How much will you deposit on January 7?

    SOLUTION On the nth day, 3^{n-1} cents are deposited. Thus on January 7, the amount deposited is 3^6 cents. Because $3^6 = 729$, we conclude that $7.29 will be deposited on January 7.

11. ✆ What is the first day that your deposit will exceed $10,000?

    SOLUTION On the nth day, 3^{n-1} cents are deposited. Because $10,000 equals 10^6 cents, we need to find the smallest integer n such that
    $$3^{n-1} > 10^6.$$
    This is equivalent to the inequality
    $$\log 3^{n-1} > \log 10^6,$$
    which can be rewritten as
    $$(n-1)\log 3 > 6.$$
    Dividing both sides by $\log 3$ and then adding 1 to both sides shows that this is equivalent to
    $$n > 1 + \frac{6}{\log 3}.$$
    A calculator shows that $1 + \frac{6}{\log 3} \approx 13.6$. Because 14 is the smallest integer bigger than 13.6, January 14 is the first day that the deposit will exceed $10,000.

13. Suppose $f(x) = 7 \cdot 2^{3x}$. Find a constant b such that the graph of $\log_b f$ has slope 1.

    SOLUTION Note that
    $$\log_b f(x) = \log_b 7 + \log_b 2^{3x}$$
    $$= \log_b 7 + 3(\log_b 2)x.$$
    Thus the slope of the graph of $\log_b f$ equals $3 \log_b 2$, which equals 1 when $\log_b 2 = \frac{1}{3}$. Thus $b^{1/3} = 2$, which means that $b = 2^3 = 8$.

15. ✆ A colony of bacteria is growing exponentially, doubling in size every 100 minutes. How many minutes will it take for the colony of bacteria to triple in size?

    SOLUTION Let $p(t)$ denote the number of cells in the colony of bacteria at time t, where t is measured in minutes. Then
    $$p(t) = p_0 2^{t/100},$$
    where p_0 is the number of cells at time 0. We need to find t such that $p(t) = 3p_0$. In other words, we need to find t such that
    $$p_0 2^{t/100} = 3p_0.$$
    Dividing both sides of the equation above by p_0 and then taking the logarithm of both sides gives
    $$\frac{t}{100}\log 2 = \log 3.$$
    Thus $t = 100\frac{\log 3}{\log 2}$, which is approximately 158.496. Thus the colony of bacteria will triple in size approximately every 158 minutes.

17. ✆ At current growth rates, the Earth's population is doubling about every 69 years. If this growth rate were to continue, about how many years will it take for the Earth's population to increase 50% from the present level?

    SOLUTION Let $p(t)$ denote the Earth's population at time t, where t is measured in years starting from the present. Then
    $$p(t) = p_0 2^{t/69},$$
    where p_0 is the present population of the Earth. We need to find t such that $p(t) = 1.5p_0$. In other words, we need to find t such that
    $$p_0 2^{t/69} = 1.5p_0.$$
    Dividing both sides of the equation above by p_0 and then taking the logarithm of both sides gives
    $$\frac{t}{69}\log 2 = \log 1.5.$$
    Thus $t = 69\frac{\log 1.5}{\log 2}$, which is approximately 40.4. Thus the Earth's population, at current growth rates, would increase by 50% in approximately 40.4 years.

19. 📱 Suppose a colony of bacteria starts with 200 cells and triples in size every four hours.

    (a) Find a function that models the population growth of this colony of bacteria.

    (b) Approximately how many cells will be in the colony after six hours?

    SOLUTION

(a) Let $p(t)$ denote the number of cells in the colony of bacteria at time t, where t is measured in hours. We know that $p(0) = 200$. In t hours, there are $t/4$ tripling periods; thus the number of cells increases by a factor of $3^{t/4}$. Hence
$$p(t) = 200 \cdot 3^{t/4}.$$

(b) After six hours, we could expect that there would be $p(6)$ cells of bacteria. Using the equation above, we have
$$p(6) = 200 \cdot 3^{6/4} = 200 \cdot 3^{3/2} \approx 1039.$$

21. 📱 Suppose $700 is deposited in a bank account paying 6% interest per year, compounded 52 times per year. How much will be in the bank account at the end of 10 years?

    SOLUTION With interest compounded 52 times per year at 6% per year, after 10 years $700 will grow to
    $$\$700\left(1 + \frac{0.06}{52}\right)^{52 \cdot 10} \approx \$1275.$$

23. 📱 Suppose a bank account paying 4% interest per year, compounded 12 times per year, contains $10,555 at the end of 10 years. What was the initial amount deposited in the bank account?

    SOLUTION Let P denote the initial amount deposited in the bank account. With interest compounded 12 times per year at 4% per year, after 10 years P dollars will grow to
    $$P\left(1 + \frac{0.04}{12}\right)^{12 \cdot 10}$$
    dollars, which we are told equals $10,555. Thus we need to solve the equation
    $$P\left(1 + \frac{0.04}{12}\right)^{120} = \$10,555.$$

The solution to this equation is
$$P = \$10,555 / \left(1 + \frac{0.04}{12}\right)^{120} \approx \$7080.$$

25. 📱 Suppose a savings account pays 6% interest per year, compounded once per year. If the savings account starts with $500, how long would it take for the savings account to exceed $2000?

    SOLUTION With 6% interest compounded once per year, a savings account starting with $500 would have
    $$500(1.06)^m$$
    dollars after m years. We want this amount to exceed $2000, which means that
    $$500(1.06)^m > 2000.$$

Dividing both sides by 500 and then taking the logarithm of both sides gives
$$m \log 1.06 > \log 4.$$

Thus
$$m > \frac{\log 4}{\log 1.06} \approx 23.8.$$
Because interest is compounded only once per year, m needs to be an integer. The smallest integer larger than 23.8 is 24. Thus it will take 24 years for the amount in the savings account to exceed $2000.

27. 📱 Suppose a bank wants to advertise that $1000 deposited in its savings account will grow to $1040 in one year. This bank compounds interest 12 times per year. What annual interest rate must the bank pay?

    SOLUTION Let r denote the annual interest rate to be paid by the bank. At that interest rate, compounded 12 times per year, in one year $1000 will grow to
    $$1000\left(1 + \frac{r}{12}\right)^{12}$$
    dollars. We want this to equal $1040, which means that we need to solve the equation
    $$1000\left(1 + \frac{r}{12}\right)^{12} = 1040.$$

To solve this equation, divide both sides by 1000 and then raise both sides to the power 1/12, getting
$$1 + \frac{r}{12} = 1.04^{1/12}.$$

Now subtract 1 from both sides and then multiply both sides by 12, getting

$$r = 12(1.04^{1/12} - 1) \approx 0.0393.$$

Thus the annual interest should be approximately 3.93%.

29. An advertisement for real estate published in the 28 July 2004 electronic edition of the *New York Times* states:

> Did you know that the percent increase of the value of a home in Manhattan between the years 1950 and 2000 was 721%? Buy a home in Manhattan and invest in your future.

Suppose that instead of buying a home in Manhattan in 1950, someone had invested money in a bank account that compounds interest four times per year. What annual interest rate would the bank have to pay to equal the growth claimed in the ad?

SOLUTION An increase of 721% means that the final value is 821% of the initial value. Let r denote the interest rate the bank would have to pay for the 50 years from 1950 to 2000 to grow to 821% of the initial value. At that interest rate, compounded four times per year, in 50 years an initial amount of P dollars grows to

$$P\left(1 + \tfrac{r}{4}\right)^{4 \times 50}$$

dollars. We want this to equal 8.21 times the initial amount, which means that we need to solve the equation

$$P\left(1 + \tfrac{r}{4}\right)^{200} = 8.21P.$$

To solve this equation, divide both sides by P and then raise both sides to the power $1/200$, getting

$$1 + \tfrac{r}{4} = 8.21^{1/200}.$$

Now subtract 1 from both sides and then multiply both sides by 4, getting

$$r = 4(8.21^{1/200} - 1) \approx 0.0423.$$

Thus the annual interest would need to be approximately 4.23% to equal the growth claimed in the ad.

[*Note that 4.23% is not a particularly high return for a long-term investment, contrary to the ad's implication.*]

31. Suppose f is a function with exponential growth such that

$$f(1) = 3 \quad \text{and} \quad f(2) = 4.$$

Evaluate $f(3)$.

SOLUTION Because f is a function with exponential growth, there exist constants c, b, and k such that

$$f(x) = cb^{kx}.$$

Taking $x = 1$ and then $x = 2$ in the equation above gives

$$cb^k = f(1) = 3 \quad \text{and} \quad cb^{2k} = f(2) = 4.$$

Dividing the second equation above by the first equation, we get

$$b^k = \tfrac{4}{3}.$$

Substituting this value for b^k into the equation $cb^k = 3$ and then solving for c shows that $c = \tfrac{9}{4}$. Thus

$$f(x) = cb^{kx} = c(b^k)^x = \tfrac{9}{4}\left(\tfrac{4}{3}\right)^x.$$

Now

$$f(3) = \tfrac{9}{4}\left(\tfrac{4}{3}\right)^3 = \tfrac{16}{3}.$$

Additional Applications of Exponents and Logarithms

Radioactive Decay and Half-Life

The graph of the function f defined by $f(x) = 2^{-x}$ shows that the values of 2^{-x} (which equals $1/2^x$) decrease rapidly as x increases:

The graph of 2^{-x} (which equals $1/2^x$) on the interval $[0, 7]$.

Extending this graph to the interval $[0, 10]$ would provide little information because the values of 2^{-x} on the interval $[7, 10]$ are so close to 0 that the graph there would appear to be in the x-axis.

More generally, a function f is said to have **exponential decay** if f is of the form

$$f(x) = cb^{-kx},$$

where c and k are positive constants and $b > 1$. For example, taking $c = 1$, $b = 2$, and $k = 1$, we have the function 2^{-x} discussed in the paragraph above.

Functions with exponential decay provide the appropriate models for radioactive decay. For example, consider radon, which decays into polonium. There is no known way to predict when a particular radon atom will decay into polonium.

However, scientists have observed that starting with a large sample of radon atoms, after 92 hours one-half of the radon atoms will decay into polonium. After another 92 hours, one-half of the remaining radon atoms will also decay into polonium. In other words, after 184 hours, only one-fourth of the original radon atoms will be left. After another 92 hours, one-half of

Even a milligram of radon will contain a huge number of atoms.

Pioneering work on radioactive decay was done by Marie Curie, the only person ever to win Nobel Prizes in both physics (1903) and chemistry (1911).

those remaining one-fourth of the original atoms will decay into polonium, leaving only one-eighth of the original radon atoms after 276 hours.

After t hours, the number of radon atoms will be reduced by half $t/92$ times. Thus after t hours, the number of radon atoms left will equal the original number of radon atoms divided by $2^{t/92}$. Here t need not be an integer multiple of 92. For example, our formula predicts that after five hours the original number of radon atoms will be divided by $2^{5/92}$. A calculator shows that $\frac{1}{2^{5/92}} \approx 0.963$. Indeed, observations verify that after five hours a sample of radon will contain 96.3% of the original number of radon atoms.

Because half of the atoms in any sample of radon will decay to polonium in 92 hours, we say that radon has a **half-life** of 92 hours. Some radon atoms exist for much less than 92 hours, and some radon atoms exist for much longer than 92 hours. As we have seen, the number of radon atoms left in an original sample after t hours is a function (of t) with exponential decay.

More generally, the half-life of a radioactive isotope is the length of time it takes for half the atoms in a large sample of the isotope to decay. The table below gives the approximate half-life for several radioactive isotopes (each isotope number shown in the table gives the total number of protons and neutrons in the variety of atom under consideration).

Some of the isotopes in this table are human creations that do not exist in nature. For example, the nitrogen on Earth is almost entirely nitrogen-14 (7 protons and 7 neutrons), which is not radioactive and does not decay. The nitrogen-13 listed here consists of 7 protons and 6 neutrons; it can be created in a laboratory, but it is radioactive and half of it will decay within 10 minutes.

isotope	half-life
neon-18	2 seconds
nitrogen-13	10 minutes
radon-222	92 hours
polonium-210	138 days
cesium-137	30 years
carbon-14	5730 years
plutonium-239	24,110 years
uranium-238	4.5 billion years

Half-life of some radioactive isotopes.

If a radioactive isotope has a half-life of h time units (here the time units might be seconds, minutes, hours, days, years, or whatever unit is appropriate), then after t time units the number of atoms of this isotope is reduced by half t/h times. Thus after t time units, the remaining number of atoms of the radioactive isotope will equal the original number of atoms divided by $2^{t/h}$. Because $\frac{1}{2^{t/h}} = 2^{-t/h}$, we have the following result:

Radioactive decay

If a radioactive isotope has half-life h, then the function modeling the number of atoms in a sample of this isotope is

$$a(t) = a_0 \cdot 2^{-t/h},$$

where a_0 is the number of atoms of the isotope in the sample at time 0.

The radioactive decay of carbon-14 leads to a clever way of determining the age of fossils, wood, and other remnants of plants and animals. Carbon-12, by far the most common form of carbon on Earth, is not radioactive and does not decay. Radioactive carbon-14 is produced regularly as cosmic rays hit the upper atmosphere. Radioactive carbon-14 then filters down to the lower atmosphere, where it is absorbed by all living organisms as part of the food or photosynthesis cycle. Carbon-14 accounts for about 10^{-10} percent of the carbon atoms in a living organism.

When an organism dies, it stops absorbing new carbon because it is no longer eating or engaging in photosynthesis. Thus no new carbon-14 is absorbed. The radioactive carbon-14 in the organism then decays, with half of it gone after 5730 years, as can be seen from the table above. By measuring the amount of carbon-14 as a percentage of the total amount of carbon in the remains of an organism, we can then determine how long ago it died.

The 1960 Nobel Prize in Chemistry was awarded to Willard Libby for his invention of this carbon-14 dating method.

EXAMPLE 1

Suppose a cat skeleton found in an old well has a ratio of carbon-14 to carbon-12 that is 61% of the corresponding ratio for living organisms. Approximately how long ago did the cat die?

SOLUTION   If we let t denote the number of years since the cat died, then we have

$$0.61 = 2^{-t/5730}.$$

To solve this equation for t, we take the logarithms of both sides, getting

$$\log 0.61 = -\frac{t}{5730} \log 2.$$

Solving this equation for t, we get

$$t = -5730 \frac{\log 0.61}{\log 2} \approx 4086.$$

Because there will be some errors in measuring the percentage of carbon-14 in the cat skeleton, we should not produce such a precise-looking estimate. Thus we might estimate that the skeleton is about 4100 years old. Or if we want to indicate even less precision, we might say that the cat died about four thousand years ago.

The author's cat.

Earthquakes and the Richter Scale

The intensity of an earthquake is measured by the size of the seismic waves generated by the earthquake. These numbers vary across such a huge scale that earthquakes are usually reported using the Richter magnitude scale, which is a logarithmic scale using common logarithms (base 10).

> ## Richter magnitude scale
>
> An earthquake with seismic waves of size S has **Richter magnitude**
>
> $$\log \frac{S}{S_0},$$
>
> where S_0 is the size of the seismic waves corresponding to what has been declared to be an earthquake with Richter magnitude 0.

The size of the seismic wave is roughly proportional to the amount of ground shaking.

A few points will help clarify this definition:

- The value of S_0 was set in 1935 by the American seismologist Charles Richter as approximately the size of the smallest seismic waves that could be measured at that time.

- The units used to measure S and S_0 do not matter (provided the same units are used for S and S_0) because any change in the scale of these units disappears in the ratio $\frac{S}{S_0}$.

- An increase of earthquake intensity by a factor of 10 corresponds to an increase of 1 in Richter magnitude, as can be seen from the equation

$$\log \frac{10S}{S_0} = \log 10 + \log \frac{S}{S_0} = 1 + \log \frac{S}{S_0}.$$

EXAMPLE 2

The world's most intense recorded earthquake struck Chile in 1960; it had Richter magnitude 9.5. The most intense recorded earthquake in the United States struck Alaska in 1964; it had Richter magnitude 9.2. Approximately how many times more intense was the 1960 earthquake in Chile than the 1964 earthquake in Alaska?

SOLUTION   Let S_C denote the size of the seismic waves from the 1960 earthquake in Chile and let S_A denote the size of the seismic waves from the 1964 earthquake in Alaska. Thus

$$9.5 = \log \frac{S_C}{S_0} \quad \text{and} \quad 9.2 = \log \frac{S_A}{S_0}.$$

Subtracting the second equation from the first equation, we get

$$0.3 = \log \frac{S_C}{S_0} - \log \frac{S_A}{S_0} = \log\left(\frac{S_C}{S_0} \Big/ \frac{S_A}{S_0}\right) = \log \frac{S_C}{S_A}.$$

As this example shows, even small differences in the Richter magnitude can correspond to large differences in intensity.

Thus

$$\frac{S_C}{S_A} = 10^{0.3} \approx 2.$$

In other words, the 1960 earthquake in Chile was approximately two times more intense than the 1964 earthquake in Alaska.

Sound Intensity and Decibels

The intensity of a sound is the amount of energy carried by the sound through each unit of area. The human ear can perceive sound over an enormous range of intensities. The ratio of the intensity of the sound level that causes pain to the intensity of the quietest sound that we can hear is over one trillion. Working with such large numbers can be inconvenient. Thus sound is usually measured in decibels, which is a logarithmic scale using common logarithms.

> ### Decibel scale for sound
>
> A sound with intensity E has
>
> $$10 \log \frac{E}{E_0}$$
>
> **decibels,** where E_0 is the intensity of an extremely quiet sound at the threshold of human hearing.

A few points will help clarify this definition:

The factor of 10 that appears in the definition of the decibel scale can be a minor nuisance. The "deci" part of the name "decibel" comes from this factor of 10.

- The value of E_0 is 10^{-12} watts per square meter.

- The intensity of sound is usually measured in watts per square meter, but the units used to measure E and E_0 do not matter (provided the same units are used for E and E_0) because any change in the scale of these units disappears in the ratio $\frac{E}{E_0}$.

- Multiplying sound intensity by a factor of 10 corresponds to adding 10 to the decibel measurement, as can be seen from the equation

$$10 \log \frac{10E}{E_0} = 10 \log 10 + 10 \log \frac{E}{E_0} = 10 + 10 \log \frac{E}{E_0}.$$

EXAMPLE 3

Because of worries about potential hearing damage, France passed a law limiting iPods and other MP3 players to a maximum possible volume of 100 decibels. Assuming that normal conversation has a sound level of 65 decibels, how many more times intense than normal conversation is the sound of an iPod operating at the French maximum of 100 decibels?

SOLUTION   Let E_F denote the sound intensity of 100 decibels allowed in France and let E_C denote the sound intensity of normal conversation. Thus

$$100 = 10 \log \frac{E_F}{E_0} \quad \text{and} \quad 65 = 10 \log \frac{E_C}{E_0}.$$

Subtracting the second equation from the first equation, we get

$$35 = 10 \log \frac{E_F}{E_0} - 10 \log \frac{E_C}{E_0}.$$

Thus

$$3.5 = \log \frac{E_F}{E_0} - \log \frac{E_C}{E_0} = \log\left(\frac{E_F}{E_0} \Big/ \frac{E_C}{E_0 0}\right) = \log \frac{E_F}{E_C}.$$

Thus

$$\frac{E_F}{E_C} = 10^{3.5} \approx 3162.$$

In other words, an iPod operating at the maximum legal French volume of 100 decibels produces sound about three thousand times more intense than normal conversation.

The increase in sound intensity by a factor of more than 3000 in the last example is not as drastic as it seems because of how we perceive loudness:

Loudness

The human ear perceives each increase in sound by 10 decibels to be a doubling of loudness (even though the sound intensity has actually increased by a factor of 10).

EXAMPLE 4

By what factor has the loudness increased in going from normal speech at 65 decibels to an iPod at 100 decibels?

SOLUTION   Here we have an increase of 35 decibels, so we have had an increase of 10 decibels 3.5 times. Thus the perceived loudness has doubled 3.5 times, which means that it has increased by a factor of $2^{3.5}$. Because $2^{3.5} \approx 11$, this means that an iPod operating at 100 decibels seems about 11 times louder than normal conversation.

Star Brightness and Apparent Magnitude

The ancient Greeks divided the visible stars into six groups based on their brightness. The brightest stars were called first magnitude stars. The next brightest group of stars were called second magnitude stars, and so on, until the sixth magnitude stars consisted of the barely visible stars.

About two thousand years later, astronomers made the ancient Greek star magnitude scale more precise. The typical first magnitude stars were about 100 times brighter than the typical sixth magnitude stars. Because there are five steps in going from the first magnitude to the sixth magnitude, this means that with each magnitude the brightness should decrease by a factor of $100^{1/5}$.

Because $100^{1/5} \approx 2.512$, each magnitude is approximately 2.512 times dimmer than the previous magnitude.

Originally the scale was defined so that Polaris, the North Star, had magnitude 2. If we let b_2 denote the brightness of Polaris, this would mean that a third magnitude star has brightness $b_2/100^{1/5}$, a fourth magnitude star has brightness $b_2/(100^{1/5})^2$, a fifth magnitude star has brightness $b_2/(100^{1/5})^3$, and so on. Thus the brightness b of a star with magnitude m should be given by the equation

$$b = \frac{b_2}{(100^{1/5})^{(m-2)}} = b_2 100^{(2-m)/5} = b_2 100^{2/5} 100^{-m/5} = b_0 100^{-m/5},$$

where $b_0 = b_2 100^{2/5}$. If we divide both sides of the equation above by b_0 and then take logarithms we get

$$\log \frac{b}{b_0} = \log 100^{-m/5} = -\frac{m}{5} \log 100 = -\frac{2m}{5}.$$

Solving this equation for m leads to the following definition:

> ## Apparent magnitude
>
> An object with brightness b has **apparent magnitude**
>
> $$\frac{5}{2} \log \frac{b_0}{b},$$
>
> where b_0 is the brightness of an object with magnitude 0.

A few points will help clarify this definition:

- The term "apparent magnitude" is more accurate than "magnitude" because we are measuring how bright a star appears from Earth. A glowing luminous star might appear dim from Earth because it is very far away.

- Although this apparent magnitude scale was originally set up for stars, it can be applied to other objects such as the full moon.

- Although the value of b_0 was originally set so that Polaris, the North Star, would have apparent magnitude 2, the definition has changed slightly. With the current definition of b_0, Polaris has magnitude close to 2 but not exactly equal to 2.

- The units used to measure brightness do not matter (provided the same units are used for b and b_0) because any change in the scale of these units disappears in the ratio $\frac{b_0}{b}$.

With good binoculars you can see stars with apparent magnitude 9. The Hubble telescope, which is in orbit around the Earth, can detect stars with apparent magnitude 30. How much better is the Hubble telescope than binoculars, measured in terms of the ratio of the brightness of stars that they can detect?

EXAMPLE 5

Because of the lack of atmospheric interference, the Hubble telescope can see dimmer stars than Earth-based telescopes of the same size.

SOLUTION   Let b_9 denote the brightness of a star with apparent magnitude 9 and let b_{30} denote the brightness of a star with apparent magnitude 30. Thus

$$9 = \frac{5}{2} \log \frac{b_0}{b_9} \quad \text{and} \quad 30 = \frac{5}{2} \log \frac{b_0}{b_{30}}.$$

Subtracting the first equation from the second equation, we get

$$21 = \frac{5}{2} \log \frac{b_0}{b_{30}} - \frac{5}{2} \log \frac{b_0}{b_9}.$$

Thus

$$\frac{42}{5} = \log \frac{b_0}{b_{30}} - \log \frac{b_0}{b_9} = \log\left(\frac{b_0}{b_{30}} \Big/ \frac{b_0}{b_9}\right) = \log \frac{b_9}{b_{30}}.$$

Thus

$$\frac{b_9}{b_{30}} = 10^{42/5} = 10^{8.4} \approx 250,000,000.$$

Thus the Hubble telescope can detect stars 250 million times dimmer than stars we can see with binoculars.

EXERCISES

1. About how many hours will it take for a sample of radon-222 to have only one-eighth as much radon-222 as the original sample?

2. About how many minutes will it take for a sample of nitrogen-13 to have only one sixty-fourth as much nitrogen-13 as the original sample?

3. About how many years will it take for a sample of cesium-137 to have only two-thirds as much cesium-137 as the original sample?

4. About how many years will it take for a sample of plutonium-239 to have only 1% as much plutonium-239 as the original sample?

5. Suppose a radioactive isotope is such that one-fifth of the atoms in a sample decay after three years. Find the half-life of this isotope.

6. Suppose a radioactive isotope is such that five-sixths of the atoms in a sample decay after four days. Find the half-life of this isotope.

7. Suppose the ratio of carbon-14 to carbon-12 in a mummified cat is 64% of the corresponding ratio for living organisms. About how long ago did the cat die?

8. Suppose the ratio of carbon-14 to carbon-12 in a fossilized wooden tool is 20% of the corresponding ratio for living organisms. About how old is the wooden tool?

9. How many more times intense is an earthquake with Richter magnitude 7 than an earthquake with Richter magnitude 5?

10. How many more times intense is an earthquake with Richter magnitude 6 than an earthquake with Richter magnitude 3?

11. The 1994 Northridge earthquake in Southern California, which killed several dozen people, had Richter magnitude 6.7. What would be the Richter magnitude of an earthquake that was 100 times more intense than the Northridge earthquake?

12. The 1995 earthquake in Kobe (Japan), which killed over 6000 people, had Richter magnitude 7.2. What would be the Richter magnitude of an earthquake that was 1000 times less intense than the Kobe earthquake?

13. The most intense recorded earthquake in the state of New York occurred in 1944; it had Richter magnitude 5.8. The most intense recorded earthquake in Minnesota occurred in 1975; it had Richter magnitude 5.0. Approximately how many times more intense was the 1944 earthquake in New York than the 1975 earthquake in Minnesota?

14. The most intense recorded earthquake in Wyoming occurred in 1959; it had Richter magnitude 6.5. The most intense recorded earthquake in Illinois occurred in 1968; it had Richter magnitude 5.3. Approximately how many times more intense was the 1959 earthquake in Wyoming than the 1968 earthquake in Illinois?

15. The most intense recorded earthquake in Texas occurred in 1931; it had Richter magnitude 5.8. If an earthquake were to strike Texas next year that was three times more intense than the current record in Texas, what would its Richter magnitude be?

16. The most intense recorded earthquake in Ohio occurred in 1937; it had Richter magnitude 5.4. If an earthquake were to strike Ohio next year that was 1.6 times more intense than the current record in Ohio, what would its Richter magnitude be?

17. Suppose you whisper at 20 decibels and normally speak at 60 decibels.

    (a) What is the ratio of the sound intensity of your normal speech to the sound intensity of your whisper?

    (b) How many times louder does your normal speech seem as compared to your whisper?

18. Suppose your vacuum cleaner makes a noise of 80 decibels and you normally speak at 60 decibels.

    (a) What is the ratio of the sound intensity of your vacuum cleaner to the sound intensity of your normal speech?

    (b) How many times louder does your vacuum cleaner seem as compared to your normal speech?

19. Suppose an airplane taking off makes a noise of 117 decibels and you normally speak at 63 decibels.

    (a) What is the ratio of the sound intensity of the airplane to the sound intensity of your normal speech?

    (b) How many times louder does the airplane seem than your normal speech?

20. Suppose your cell phone rings at a noise of 74 decibels and you normally speak at 61 decibels.

    (a) What is the ratio of the sound intensity of your cell phone ring to the sound intensity of your normal speech?

    (b) How many times louder does your cell phone ring seem than your normal speech?

21. Suppose a television is playing softly at a sound level of 50 decibels. What decibel level would make the television sound eight times as loud?

22. Suppose a radio is playing loudly at a sound level of 80 decibels. What decibel level would make the radio sound one-fourth as loud?

23. Suppose a motorcycle produces a sound level of 90 decibels. What decibel level would make the motorcycle sound one-third as loud?

24. Suppose a rock band is playing loudly at a sound level of 100 decibels. What decibel level would make the band sound three-fifths as loud?

25. How many times brighter is a star with apparent magnitude 2 than a star with apparent magnitude 17?

26. How many times brighter is a star with apparent magnitude 3 than a star with apparent magnitude 23?

27. Sirius, the brightest star that can be seen from Earth (not counting the sun), has an apparent magnitude of -1.4. Vega, which was the North Star about 12,000 years ago (slight changes in Earth's orbit lead to changing North Stars every several thousand years), has an apparent magnitude of 0.03. How many times brighter than Vega is Sirius?

28. The full moon has an apparent magnitude of approximately -12.6. How many times brighter than Sirius is the full moon?

29. Neptune has an apparent magnitude of about 7.8. What is the apparent magnitude of a star that is 20 times brighter than Neptune?

30. What is the apparent magnitude of a star that is eight times brighter than Neptune?

PROBLEMS

31. Suppose f is a function with exponential decay. Explain why the function g defined by $g(x) = \frac{1}{f(x)}$ is a function with exponential growth.

32. Show that an earthquake with Richter magnitude R has seismic waves of size $S_0 10^R$, where S_0 is the size of the seismic waves of an earthquake with Richter magnitude 0.

33. Do a web search to find the most intense earthquake in the United States in the last calendar year and the most intense earthquake in Japan in the last calendar year. Approximately how many times more intense was the larger of these two earthquakes than the smaller of the two?

34. Show that a sound with d decibels has intensity $E_0 10^{d/10}$, where E_0 is the intensity of a sound with 0 decibels.

35. Find at least three different web sites giving the apparent magnitude of Polaris (the North Star) accurate to at least two digits after the decimal point. If you find different values on different web sites (as the author did), then try to explain what could account for the discrepancy (and take this as a good lesson in the caution necessary when using the web as a source of scientific information).

36. Write a description of the logarithmic scale used for the pH scale, which measures acidity (this will probably require use of the library or the web).

WORKED-OUT SOLUTIONS *to Odd-numbered Exercises*

1. About how many hours will it take for a sample of radon-222 to have only one-eighth as much radon-222 as the original sample?

   SOLUTION The half-life of radon-222 is about 92 hours, as can be seen in the chart in this section. To reduce the number of radon-222 atoms to one-eighth the original number, we need 3 half-lives (because $2^3 = 8$). Thus it will take 276 hours (because $92 \times 3 = 276$) to have only one-eighth as much radon-222 as the original sample.

3. 📱 About how many years will it take for a sample of cesium-137 to have only two-thirds as much cesium-137 as the original sample?

   SOLUTION The half-life of cesium-137 is about 30 years, as can be seen in the chart in this section. Thus if we start with a atoms of cesium-137 at time 0, then after t years there will be
   $$a \cdot 2^{-t/30}$$
   atoms left. We want this to equal $\frac{2}{3}a$. Thus we must solve the equation
   $$a \cdot 2^{-t/30} = \tfrac{2}{3}a.$$
   To solve this equation for t, divide both sides by a and then take the logarithm of both sides, getting
   $$-\tfrac{t}{30} \log 2 = \log \tfrac{2}{3}.$$
   Now multiply both sides by -1, replace $-\log \frac{2}{3}$ by $\log \frac{3}{2}$, and then solve for t, getting

   $$t = 30 \frac{\log \frac{3}{2}}{\log 2} \approx 17.5.$$

   Thus two-thirds of the original sample will be left after approximately 17.5 years.

5. 📱 Suppose a radioactive isotope is such that one-fifth of the atoms in a sample decay after three years. Find the half-life of this isotope.

   SOLUTION Let h denote the half-life of this isotope, measured in years. If we start with a sample of a atoms of this isotope, then after 3 years there will be
   $$a \cdot 2^{-3/h}$$
   atoms left. We want this to equal $\frac{4}{5}a$. Thus we must solve the equation
   $$a \cdot 2^{-3/h} = \tfrac{4}{5}a.$$
   To solve this equation for h, divide both sides by a and then take the logarithm of both sides, getting
   $$-\tfrac{3}{h} \log 2 = \log \tfrac{4}{5}.$$
   Now multiply both sides by -1, replace $-\log \frac{4}{5}$ by $\log \frac{5}{4}$, and then solve for h, getting
   $$h = 3 \frac{\log 2}{\log \frac{5}{4}} \approx 9.3.$$
   Thus the half-life of this isotope is approximately 9.3 years.

7. 📱 Suppose the ratio of carbon-14 to carbon-12 in a mummified cat is 64% of the corresponding ratio for living organisms. About how long ago did the cat die?

SOLUTION The half-life of carbon-14 is 5730 years. If we start with a sample of a atoms of carbon-14, then after t years there will be

$$a \cdot 2^{-t/5730}$$

atoms left. We want to find t such that this equals $0.64a$. Thus we must solve the equation

$$a \cdot 2^{-t/5730} = 0.64a.$$

To solve this equation for t, divide both sides by a and then take the logarithm of both sides, getting

$$-\frac{t}{5730} \log 2 = \log 0.64.$$

Now solve for t, getting

$$t = -5730 \frac{\log 0.64}{\log 2} \approx 3689.$$

Thus the cat died about 3689 years ago. Carbon-14 cannot be measured with extreme accuracy. Thus it is better to estimate that the cat died about 3700 years ago (because a number such as 3689 conveys more accuracy than will be present in such measurements).

9. How many more times intense is an earthquake with Richter magnitude 7 than an earthquake with Richter magnitude 5?

SOLUTION Here is an informal but accurate solution: Each increase of 1 in the Richter magnitude corresponds to an increase in the size of the seismic wave by a factor of 10. Thus an increase of 2 in the Richter magnitude corresponds to an increase in the size of the seismic wave by a factor of 10^2. Hence an earthquake with Richter magnitude 7 is 100 times more intense than an earthquake with Richter magnitude 5.

Here is a more formal explanation using logarithms: Let S_7 denote the size of the seismic waves from an earthquake with Richter magnitude 7 and let S_5 denote the size of the seismic waves from an earthquake with Richter magnitude 5. Thus

$$7 = \log \frac{S_7}{S_0} \quad \text{and} \quad 5 = \log \frac{S_5}{S_0}.$$

Subtracting the second equation from the first equation, we get

$$2 = \log \frac{S_7}{S_0} - \log \frac{S_5}{S_0} = \log\left(\frac{S_7}{S_0} \Big/ \frac{S_5}{S_0}\right) = \log \frac{S_7}{S_5}.$$

Thus

$$\frac{S_7}{S_5} = 10^2 = 100.$$

Hence an earthquake with Richter magnitude 7 is 100 times more intense than an earthquake with Richter magnitude 5.

11. The 1994 Northridge earthquake in Southern California, which killed several dozen people, had Richter magnitude 6.7. What would be the Richter magnitude of an earthquake that was 100 times more intense than the Northridge earthquake?

SOLUTION Each increase of 1 in the Richter magnitude corresponds to an increase in the intensity of the earthquake by a factor of 10. Hence an increase in intensity by a factor of 100 (which equals 10^2) corresponds to an increase of 2 is the Richter magnitude. Thus an earthquake that was 100 times more intense than the Northridge earthquake would have Richter magnitude $6.7 + 2$, which equals 8.7.

13. ✐ The most intense recorded earthquake in the state of New York occurred in 1944; it had Richter magnitude 5.8. The most intense recorded earthquake in Minnesota occurred in 1975; it had Richter magnitude 5.0. Approximately how many times more intense was the 1944 earthquake in New York than the 1975 earthquake in Minnesota?

SOLUTION Let S_N denote the size of the seismic waves from the 1944 earthquake in New York and let S_M denote the size of the seismic waves from the 1975 earthquake in Minnesota. Thus

$$5.8 = \log \frac{S_N}{S_0} \quad \text{and} \quad 5.0 = \log \frac{S_M}{S_0}.$$

Subtracting the second equation from the first equation, we get

$$0.8 = \log \frac{S_N}{S_0} - \log \frac{S_M}{S_0} = \log\left(\frac{S_N}{S_0} \Big/ \frac{S_M}{S_0}\right) = \log \frac{S_N}{S_M}.$$

Thus

$$\frac{S_N}{S_M} = 10^{0.8} \approx 6.3.$$

In other words, the 1944 earthquake in New York was approximately 6.3 times more intense than the 1975 earthquake in Minnesota.

15. ✐ The most intense recorded earthquake in Texas occurred in 1931; it had Richter magnitude 5.8. If an earthquake were to strike Texas next year that was three times more intense than the current record in Texas, what would its Richter magnitude be?

SOLUTION   Let S_T denote the size of the seismic waves from the 1931 earthquake in Texas. Thus

$$5.8 = \log \frac{S_T}{S_0}.$$

An earthquake three times more intense would have Richter magnitude

$$\log \frac{3S_T}{S_0} = \log 3 + \log \frac{S_T}{S_0} \approx 0.477 + 5.8 = 6.277.$$

Because of the difficulty of obtaining accurate measurements, Richter magnitudes are usually reported with only one digit after the decimal place. Rounding off, we would thus say that an earthquake in Texas that was three times more intense than the current record would have Richter magnitude 6.3.

17. Suppose you whisper at 20 decibels and normally speak at 60 decibels.

   (a) What is the ratio of the sound intensity of your normal speech to the sound intensity of your whisper?

   (b) How many times louder does your normal speech seem as compared to your whisper?

   SOLUTION

(a) Each increase of 10 decibels corresponds to multiplying the sound intensity by a factor of 10. Going from a 20-decibel whisper to 60-decibel normal speech means that the sound intensity has been increased by a factor of 10 four times. Because $10^4 = 10,000$, this means that the ratio of the sound intensity of your normal speech to the sound intensity of your whisper is 10,000.

(b) Each increase of 10 decibels results in a doubling of loudness. Here we have an increase of 40 decibels, so we have had an increase of 10 decibels four times. Thus the perceived loudness has increased by a factor of 2^4. Because

$2^4 = 16$, this means that your normal conversation seems 16 times louder than your whisper.

19. ✐ Suppose an airplane taking off makes a noise of 117 decibels and you normally speak at 63 decibels.

   (a) What is the ratio of the sound intensity of the airplane to the sound intensity of your normal speech?

   (b) How many times louder does the airplane seem than your normal speech?

SOLUTION

(a) Let E_A denote the sound intensity of the airplane taking off and let E_S denote the sound intensity of your normal speech. Thus

$$117 = 10 \log \frac{E_A}{E_0} \quad \text{and} \quad 63 = 10 \log \frac{E_S}{E_0}.$$

Subtracting the second equation from the first equation, we get

$$54 = 10 \log \frac{E_A}{E_0} - 10 \log \frac{E_S}{E_0}.$$

Thus

$$5.4 = \log \frac{E_A}{E_0} - \log \frac{E_S}{E_0} = \log \left(\frac{E_A}{E_0} \Big/ \frac{E_S}{E_0} \right) = \log \frac{E_A}{E_S}.$$

Thus

$$\frac{E_A}{E_S} = 10^{5.4} \approx 251,189.$$

In other words, the airplane taking off produces sound about 250 thousand times more intense than your normal speech.

(b) Each increase of 10 decibels results in a doubling of loudness. Here we have an increase of 54 decibels, so we have had an increase of 10 decibels 5.4 times. Thus the perceived loudness has increased by a factor of $2^{5.4}$. Because $2^{5.4} \approx 42$, this means that the airplane seems about 42 times louder than your normal speech.

21. Suppose a television is playing softly at a sound level of 50 decibels. What decibel level would make the television sound eight times as loud?

   SOLUTION   Each increase of ten decibels makes the television sound twice as loud. Because

$8 = 2^3$, the sound level must double three times to make the television sound eight times as loud. Thus 30 decibels must be added to the sound level, raising it to 80 decibels.

23. Suppose a motorcycle produces a sound level of 90 decibels. What decibel level would make the motorcycle sound one-third as loud?

SOLUTION Each decrease of ten decibels makes the motorcycle sound half as loud. The sound level must be cut in half x times, where $\frac{1}{3} = \left(\frac{1}{2}\right)^x$, to make the motorcycle sound one-third as loud. This equation can be rewritten as $2^x = 3$. Taking common logarithms of both sides gives $x \log 2 = \log 3$, which implies that

$$x = \frac{\log 3}{\log 2} \approx 1.585.$$

Thus the sound level must be decreased by ten decibels 1.585 times, meaning that the sound level must be reduced by 15.85 decibels. Because $90 - 15.85 = 74.15$, a sound level of 74.15 decibels would make the motorcycle sound one-third as loud.

25. How many times brighter is a star with apparent magnitude 2 than a star with apparent magnitude 17?

SOLUTION Every five magnitudes correspond to a change in brightness by a factor of 100. Thus a change in 15 magnitudes corresponds to a change in brightness by a factor of 100^3 (because $15 = 5 \times 3$). Because $100^3 = (10^2)^3 = 10^6$, a star with apparent magnitude 2 is one million times brighter than a star with apparent magnitude 17.

27. Sirius, the brightest star that can be seen from Earth (not counting the sun), has an apparent magnitude of -1.4. Vega, which was the North Star about 12,000 years ago (slight changes in Earth's orbit lead to changing North Stars every several thousand years), has an apparent magnitude of 0.03. How many times brighter than Vega is Sirius?

SOLUTION Let b_V denote the brightness of Vega and let b_S denote the brightness of Sirius. Thus

$$0.03 = \frac{5}{2} \log \frac{b_0}{b_V} \quad \text{and} \quad -1.4 = \frac{5}{2} \log \frac{b_0}{b_S}.$$

Subtracting the second equation from the first equation, we get

$$1.43 = \frac{5}{2} \log \frac{b_0}{b_V} - \frac{5}{2} \log \frac{b_0}{b_S}.$$

Multiplying both sides by $\frac{2}{5}$, we get

$$0.572 = \log \frac{b_0}{b_V} - \log \frac{b_0}{b_S} = \log\left(\frac{b_0}{b_V} \Big/ \frac{b_0}{b_S}\right)$$

$$= \log \frac{b_S}{b_V}.$$

Thus

$$\frac{b_S}{b_V} = 10^{0.572} \approx 3.7.$$

Thus Sirius is approximately 3.7 times brighter than Vega.

29. Neptune has an apparent magnitude of about 7.8. What is the apparent magnitude of a star that is 20 times brighter than Neptune?

SOLUTION Each decrease of apparent magnitude by 1 corresponds to brightness increase by a factor of $100^{1/5}$. If we decrease the magnitude by x, then the brightness increases by a factor of $(100^{1/5})^x$. For this exercise, we want $20 = (100^{1/5})^x$. To solve this equation for x, take logarithms of both sides, getting

$$\log 20 = x \log 100^{1/5} = \frac{2x}{5}.$$

Thus

$$x = \frac{5}{2} \log 20 \approx 3.25.$$

Because $7.8 - 3.25 = 4.55$, we conclude that a star 20 times brighter than Neptune has apparent magnitude approximately 4.55.

CHAPTER SUMMARY

To check that you have mastered the most important concepts and skills covered in this chapter, make sure that you can do each item in the following list:

- Manipulate and simplify expressions involving exponents.
- Define logarithms.
- Use the change of base formula for logarithms.
- Use the formulas for the logarithm of a product, quotient, and power.

- Use common logarithms to determine how many digits a number has.
- Model population growth.
- Compute compound interest.
- Model radioactive decay using half-life.
- Use logarithmic scales for measuring earthquakes, sound, and stars.

To review a chapter, go through the list above to find items that you do not know how to do, then reread the material in the chapter about those items. Then try to answer the chapter review questions below without looking back at the chapter.

CHAPTER REVIEW QUESTIONS

1. Explain why $\sqrt{5}^2 = 5$.

2. Give an example of a number t such that $\sqrt{t^2} \neq t$.

3. Show that $(29 + 12\sqrt{5})^{1/2} = 3 + 2\sqrt{5}$.

4. Evaluate $32^{7/5}$.

5. Expand $(4 - 3\sqrt{5x})^2$.

6. What is the domain of the function f defined by $f(x) = x^{3/5}$?

7. What is the domain of the function f defined by $f(x) = (x - 5)^{3/4}$?

8. Find the inverse of the function f defined by
$$f(x) = 3 + 2x^{4/5}.$$

9. Find a formula for $(f \circ g)(x)$, where
$$f(x) = 3x^{\sqrt{32}} \quad \text{and} \quad g(x) = x^{\sqrt{2}}.$$

10. Explain how logarithms are defined.

11. What is the domain of the function f defined by $f(x) = \log_2 x$?

12. What is the range of the function f defined by $f(x) = \log_2 x$?

13. Explain why
$$3^{\log_3 7} = 7.$$

14. Explain why
$$\log_5 5^{444} = 444.$$

15. Without using a calculator or computer, estimate the number of digits in 2^{1000}.

16. Find all numbers x such that
$$\log x + \log(x + 2) = 1.$$

17. Evaluate $\log_5 \sqrt{125}$.

18. Find a number b such that $\log_b 9 = -2$.

19. 🖊 How many digits does 4^{7000} have?

20. 🖊 At the time this book was written, the largest known prime number not of the form $2^n - 1$ was $19249 \cdot 2^{13018586} + 1$. How many digits does this prime number have?

21. 🖊 Find the smallest integer m such that
$$8^m > 10^{500}.$$

22. Find the largest integer k such that
$$15^k < 11^{900}.$$

23. Which of the expressions
$$\log x + \log y \quad \text{and} \quad (\log x)(\log y)$$
can be rewritten using only one log?

24. Which of the expressions
$$\log x - \log y \quad \text{and} \quad \frac{\log x}{\log y}$$
can be rewritten using only one log?

25. Find a formula for the inverse of the function f defined by
$$f(x) = 4 + 5\log_3(7x + 2).$$

26. Find a formula for $(f \circ g)(x)$, where
$$f(x) = 7^{4x} \quad \text{and} \quad g(x) = \log_7 x.$$

27. Find a formula for $(f \circ g)(x)$, where
$$f(x) = \log_2 x \quad \text{and} \quad g(x) = 2^{5x-9}.$$

28. Evaluate $\log_{3.2} 456$.

29. Suppose $\log_6 t = 4.3$. Evaluate $\log_6 t^{200}$.

30. Suppose $\log_7 w = 3.1$ and $\log_7 z = 2.2$. Evaluate
$$\log_7 \frac{49w^2}{z^3}.$$

31. Suppose \$7000 is deposited in a bank account paying 4% interest per year, compounded 12 times per year. How much will be in the bank account at the end of 50 years?

32. Suppose \$5000 is deposited in a bank account that compounds interest four times per year. The bank account contains \$9900 after 13 years. What is the annual interest rate for this bank account?

33. A colony that initially contains 100 bacteria cells is growing exponentially, doubling in size every 75 minutes. Approximately how many bacteria cells will the colony have after 6 hours?

34. A colony of bacteria is growing exponentially, doubling in size every 50 minutes. How many minutes will it take for the colony to become six times its current size?

35. A colony of bacteria is growing exponentially, increasing in size from 200 to 500 cells in 100 minutes. How many minutes does it take the colony to double in size?

36. Explain why a population cannot have exponential growth indefinitely.

37. About how many years will it take for a sample of cesium-137, which has a half-life of 30 years, to have only 3% as much cesium-137 as the original sample?

38. How many more times intense is an earthquake with Richter magnitude 6.8 than an earthquake with Richter magnitude 6.1?

39. Explain why adding ten decibels to a sound multiplies the intensity of the sound by a factor of 10.

40. Most stars have an apparent magnitude that is a positive number. However, four stars (not counting the sun) have an apparent magnitude that is a negative number. Explain how a star can have a negative magnitude.

The St. Louis Gateway Arch, the tallest national monument in the United States. The shape of this arch comes directly from the exponential function involving e that we will learn about in this chapter.

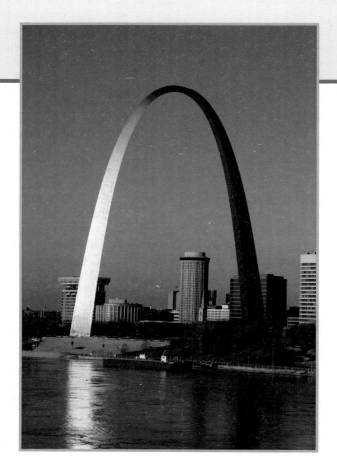

Area, e, and the Natural Logarithm

This chapter begins with a discussion of distance and length. Then we investigate area, finding methods for computing the area of triangles, trapezoids, circles, and ellipses.

We will next see how to estimate area using rectangles; this subject will be terrific preparation for integral calculus. These ideas lead us to the magical number e as well as to the natural logarithm and the exponential function. Our approach to e and the natural logarithm via area easily leads to several important properties and inequalities.

The chapter concludes by relooking at exponential growth through the lens of our new knowledge of e.

4.1   *Distance, Length, and Circles*

SECTION OBJECTIVES

By the end of this section you should

- be able to compute the distance between two points;
- be able to find the midpoint of a line segment;
- be able to find the closest point on a given line to a given point;
- understand the equation of a circle;
- understand that π is the ratio of the circumference and the diameter of any circle.

Distance between Two Points

We start gently with some concrete examples before getting to the formula for the distance between two points.

Find the distance between the point $(4, 3)$ and the origin.

SOLUTION   The distance between the point $(4, 3)$ and the origin is the length of the hypotenuse in the right triangle shown here. By the Pythagorean Theorem, this hypotenuse has length $\sqrt{4^2 + 3^2}$, which equals $\sqrt{25}$, which equals 5.

EXAMPLE 1

Here is another example, this time with neither of the points being the origin.

Find the distance between the points $(5, 6)$ and $(2, 1)$.

SOLUTION   The distance between the points $(5, 6)$ and $(2, 1)$ is the length of the hypotenuse in the right triangle shown here. The horizontal side of this triangle has length $5 - 2$, which equals 3, and the vertical side of this triangle has length $6 - 1$, which equals 5. By the Pythagorean Theorem, the hypotenuse has length $\sqrt{3^2 + 5^2}$, which equals $\sqrt{34}$.

EXAMPLE 2

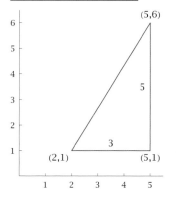

More generally, to find the formula for the distance between two points (x_1, y_1) and (x_2, y_2), consider the right triangle in the figure below:

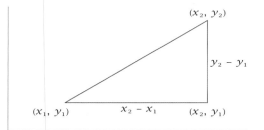

The length of the hypotenuse equals the distance between (x_1, y_1) and (x_2, y_2).

Starting with the points (x_1, y_1) and (x_2, y_2) in the figure above, make sure you understand why the third point in the triangle (the vertex at the right angle) has coordinates (x_2, y_1). Also, verify that the horizontal side of the triangle has length $x_2 - x_1$ and the vertical side of the triangle has length $y_2 - y_1$, as indicated in the figure above. The Pythagorean Theorem then gives the length of the hypotenuse, leading to the following formula:

As a special case of this formula, the distance between a point (x, y) and the origin is $\sqrt{x^2 + y^2}$.

Distance between two points

The distance between the points (x_1, y_1) and (x_2, y_2) is

$$\sqrt{(x_2 - x_1)^2 + (y_2 - y_1)^2}.$$

Using the formula above, we can now find the distance between two points without drawing a figure.

EXAMPLE 3   Find the distance between the points $(3, 1)$ and $(-4, -99)$.

SOLUTION   The distance between these two points is $\sqrt{\left(3 - (-4)\right)^2 + \left(1 - (-99)\right)^2}$, which equals $\sqrt{7^2 + 100^2}$, which equals $\sqrt{49 + 10000}$, which equals $\sqrt{10049}$.

Midpoints

This subsection begins with an intuitive definition of the midpoint of a line segment:

Midpoint

The **midpoint** of a line segment is the point on the line segment that lies halfway between the two endpoints.

As you might guess, the first coordinate of the midpoint of a line segment is the average of the first coordinates of the endpoints. Similarly, the second coordinate of the midpoint is the average of the second coordinates of the endpoints. Here is the formal statement of this formula:

Problems 45–47 at the end of this section will lead you to an explanation of why this formula for the midpoint is correct.

Midpoint

The midpoint of the line segment connecting (x_1, y_1) and (x_2, y_2) equals

$$\left(\frac{x_1 + x_2}{2}, \frac{y_1 + y_2}{2}\right).$$

The next example illustrates the use of the formula above.

(a) Find the midpoint of the line segment connecting $(1, 3)$ and $(5, 9)$.

EXAMPLE 4

(b) Verify that the distance between the midpoint found in (a) and the first endpoint $(1, 3)$ equals the distance between the midpoint found in (a) and the second endpoint $(5, 9)$.

(c) Verify that the midpoint found in (a) lies on the line connecting $(1, 3)$ and $(5, 9)$.

SOLUTION

(a) Using the formula above, we see that the midpoint of the line segment connecting $(1, 3)$ and $(5, 9)$ equals

$$\left(\frac{1 + 5}{2}, \frac{3 + 9}{2}\right),$$

which equals $(3, 6)$.

(b) First we compute the distance between the midpoint and the endpoint $(1, 3)$:

$$\text{distance between } (3, 6) \text{ and } (1, 3) = \sqrt{(3 - 1)^2 + (6 - 3)^2} = \sqrt{2^2 + 3^2}$$
$$= \sqrt{13}.$$

Next we compute the distance between the midpoint and the endpoint $(5, 9)$:

$$\text{distance between } (3, 6) \text{ and } (5, 9) = \sqrt{(3 - 5)^2 + (6 - 9)^2} = \sqrt{(-2)^2 + (-3)^2}$$
$$= \sqrt{13}.$$

As expected, these two distances are equal; the distance between the midpoint and either endpoint is $\sqrt{13}$.

(c) First we compute the slope of the line containing the midpoint and the endpoint $(1, 3)$:

$$\text{slope of line containing } (3, 6) \text{ and } (1, 3) = \frac{6 - 3}{3 - 1} = \frac{3}{2}.$$

Next we compute the slope of the line containing the midpoint and the endpoint $(5, 9)$:

$$\text{slope of line containing } (3, 6) \text{ and } (5, 9) = \frac{6 - 9}{3 - 5} = \frac{-3}{-2} = \frac{3}{2}.$$

As expected, these two slopes are equal. Thus the midpoint $(3, 6)$ and the endpoints $(1, 3)$ and $(5, 9)$ all lie on the same line.

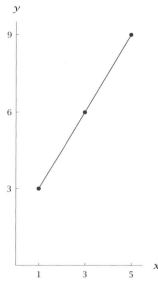

The point $(3, 6)$ is the midpoint of the line segment connecting $(1, 3)$ and $(5, 9)$.

Distance between a Point and a Line

The distance between a point and a line is defined to be the distance between the point and the closest point to it on the line. To find this closest point, use the formula for the distance between the given point and a typical point on the given line, and then complete the square to find where this distance is as small as possible. The following example illustrates this procedure:

EXAMPLE 5

Find the point on the line $y = 2x - 1$ in the xy-plane that is closest to the point $(2, 1)$. Then find the distance between the line $y = 2x - 1$ and the point $(2, 1)$.

SOLUTION A typical point on the line $y = 2x - 1$ has coordinates $(x, 2x - 1)$. The distance between this point and $(2, 1)$ equals

$$\sqrt{(x - 2)^2 + (2x - 1 - 1)^2},$$

which with a bit of algebra (do it!) can be rewritten as

$$\sqrt{5x^2 - 12x + 8}.$$

We want to make the quantity above as small as possible, which means that we need to make $5x^2 - 12x$ as small as possible. We have encountered this type of problem earlier; we can solve it by completing the square:

$$5x^2 - 12x = 5[x^2 - \tfrac{12}{5}x]$$

$$= 5[(x - \tfrac{6}{5})^2 - \tfrac{36}{25}].$$

The last quantity will be as small as possible when $x = \tfrac{6}{5}$. Plugging $x = \tfrac{6}{5}$ into the equation $y = 2x - 1$ gives $y = \tfrac{7}{5}$.

Thus $(\tfrac{6}{5}, \tfrac{7}{5})$ is the point on the line $y = 2x - 1$ that is closest to the point $(2, 1)$. The distance between $(\tfrac{6}{5}, \tfrac{7}{5})$ and $(2, 1)$ is $\sqrt{(\tfrac{6}{5} - 2)^2 + (\tfrac{7}{5} - 1)^2}$, which equals $\tfrac{2\sqrt{5}}{5}$. Thus the distance between the line $y = 2x - 1$ and $(2, 1)$ is $\tfrac{2\sqrt{5}}{5}$.

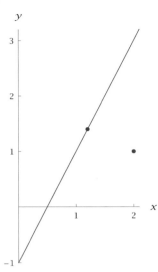

The line $y = 2x - 1$, the point $(2, 1)$, and the point on the line closest to $(2, 1)$.

Circles

The set of points that have distance 3 from the origin is the circle with radius 3 centered at the origin. To find the equation describing this circle in the xy-plane, note that a point (x, y) has distance 3 from the origin if and only if

$$\sqrt{x^2 + y^2} = 3.$$

Squaring both sides, we get

$$x^2 + y^2 = 9.$$

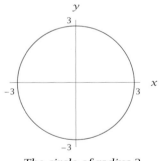

The circle of radius 3 centered at the origin.

More generally, suppose r is a positive number. The set of points that have distance r from the origin is the circle with radius r centered at the origin. A point (x, y) has distance r from the origin if and only if

$$\sqrt{x^2 + y^2} = r.$$

Squaring both sides, we get

$$x^2 + y^2 = r^2,$$

which is the usual form for the equation of the circle with radius r centered at the origin in the xy-plane.

We can also consider circles centered at points other than the origin.

Find the equation of the circle in the xy-plane centered at $(2, 1)$ with radius 5.

EXAMPLE 6

SOLUTION   This circle is the set of points whose distance from $(2, 1)$ equals 5. In other words, the circle centered at $(2, 1)$ with radius 5 is the set of points (x, y) satisfying the equation

$$\sqrt{(x - 2)^2 + (y - 1)^2} = 5.$$

Squaring both sides, we can more conveniently describe this circle as the set of points (x, y) such that

$$(x - 2)^2 + (y - 1)^2 = 25.$$

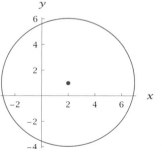

The circle centered at $(2, 1)$ with radius 5.

More generally, we could consider the circle centered at a point (h, k) with radius r. To find the equation describing this circle in the xy-plane, note that a point (x, y) has distance r from (h, k) if and only if

$$\sqrt{(x - h)^2 + (y - k)^2} = r.$$

Squaring both sides, we get the following result:

Equation of a circle

The circle with center (h, k) and radius r is the set of points (x, y) satisfying the equation

$$(x - h)^2 + (y - k)^2 = r^2.$$

For example, the equation $(x - 3)^2 + (y + 5)^2 = 7$ describes the circle in the xy-plane with radius $\sqrt{7}$ centered at $(3, -5)$.

Sometimes the equation of a circle may be in a form in which the radius and center are not obvious. You may then need to complete the square to find the radius and center. The following example illustrates this procedure:

Find the radius and center of the circle in the xy-plane described by

$$x^2 + 4x + y^2 - 6y = 12.$$

EXAMPLE 7

SOLUTION   Completing the square, we have

$$12 = x^2 + 4x + y^2 - 6y$$
$$= (x + 2)^2 - 4 + (y - 3)^2 - 9$$
$$= (x + 2)^2 + (y - 3)^2 - 13.$$

Adding 13 to the first and last sides of the equation above shows that

$$(x + 2)^2 + (y - 3)^2 = 25.$$

Thus we have a circle with radius 5 centered at $(-2, 3)$.

Length

The **length** of a line segment is the distance between the two endpoints. For example, the length of the line segment connecting the points $(-1, 4)$ and $(2, 6)$ equals

$$\sqrt{(2 - (-1))^2 + (6 - 4)^2},$$

which equals $\sqrt{13}$.

Defining the length of a path or curve in the coordinate plane is more complicated. A rigorous definition requires calculus, so we use the following intuitive definition:

> ### Length
>
> The **length** of a path or curve can be determined by placing a string on the path or curve and then measuring the length of the string when it is straightened into a line segment.

EXAMPLE 8

If a path consists of line segments, then the length of the path is the sum of the lengths of the line segments.

Find the length of the path shown here consisting of the line segment connecting $(-2, 2)$ with $(5, 3)$ followed by the line segment connecting $(5, 3)$ with $(2, 1)$.

SOLUTION   The first line segment has length

$$\sqrt{(5 - (-2))^2 + (3 - 2)^2},$$

which equals $\sqrt{50}$. The second line segment has length

$$\sqrt{(2 - 5)^2 + (1 - 3)^2},$$

which equals $\sqrt{13}$. Thus this path has length $\sqrt{50} + \sqrt{13}$.

You are probably already familiar with two other words that are used to denote the lengths of certain paths that begin and end at the same point. One word probably would have been enough, but the two following words are commonly used:

> ### Perimeter and circumference
>
> - The **perimeter** of a polygon is the length of the path that surrounds the polygon.
>
> - The **circumference** of a region is the length of the curve that surrounds the region.

For example, an equilateral triangle with sides of length ℓ has perimeter 3ℓ, and a square with sides of length ℓ has a perimeter 4ℓ. A rectangle with width w and height h has perimeter $2w + 2h$.

Just as the perimeter of a square is proportional to the length of one of its sides (with a constant of proportionality equal to 4), it is reasonable to believe that the circumference of a circle is proportional to its diameter.

Physical experiments confirm this belief. For example, suppose you have a very accurate ruler that can measure lengths with an accuracy of up to one-hundredth of an inch. If you place a string on top of a circle with diameter 1 inch, then straighten the string to a line segment, you will find that the string has length about 3.14 inches. Similarly, if you place a string on top of a circle with diameter 2 inches, then straighten the string to a line segment, you will find that the string has length about 6.28 inches. Thus the circumference of a circle with diameter two inches is twice the circumference of a circle with diameter 1 inch.

The circle on the left has been straightened into the line segment on the right. A measurement shows that this line segment is approximately 3.14 *times as long as the diameter of the circle, which is shown above in red.*

Similarly, you will find that for any circle that you measure, the ratio of the circumference to the diameter is approximately 3.14. The exact value of this ratio is so important that it gets its own symbol:

π

The ratio of the circumference to the diameter of a circle is called π.

It turns out that π is an irrational number (see Problem 46 in Section 5.4). For most practical purposes, 3.14 is a good approximation of π—the error is about 0.05%. If more accurate computations are needed, then 3.1416 is an even better approximation—the error is about 0.0002%.

A fraction that approximates π well is $\frac{22}{7}$ (notice how page 22 is numbered in this book)—the error is about 0.04%. A fraction that approximates π even better is $\frac{355}{113}$—the error is about 0.000008%.

Keep in mind that π is not equal to 3.14 or 3.1416 or $\frac{22}{7}$ or $\frac{355}{113}$. All of these are useful approximations, but π is an irrational number that cannot be represented exactly as a decimal number or as a fraction.

We have defined π to be the number such that a circle with diameter d has circumference πd. Because the diameter of a circle is equal to twice the radius, we have the following formula:

Circumference of a circle

A circle with radius r has circumference $2\pi r$.

Just for fun, here are the first 504 digits of π:

3.14159265358979323
846264338327950288
419716939937510582
097494459230781640
628620899862803482
534211706798214808
651328230664709384
460955058223172535
940812848111745028
410270193852110555
964462294895493038
196442881097566593
344612847564823378
678316527120190914
564856692346034861
045432664821339360
726024914127372458
700660631558817488
152092096282925409
171536436789259036
001133053054882046
652138414695194151
160943305727036575
959195309218611738
193261179310511854
807446237996274956
735188575272489122
793818301194912983

Does the decimal expansion of π contain one thousand consecutive 4's? No one knows, but mathematicians suspect that the answer is "yes".

EXERCISES

1. Find the distance between the points $(3, -2)$ and $(-1, 4)$.

2. Find the distance between the points $(-4, -7)$ and $(-8, -5)$.

3. Find two choices for t such that the distance between $(2, -1)$ and $(t, 3)$ equals 7.

4. Find two choices for t such that the distance between $(3, -2)$ and $(1, t)$ equals 5.

5. Find two points on the horizontal axis whose distance from $(3, 2)$ equals 7.

6. Find two points on the horizontal axis whose distance from $(1, 4)$ equals 6.

7. Find two points on the vertical axis whose distance from $(5, -1)$ equals 8.

8. Find two points on the vertical axis whose distance from $(2, -4)$ equals 5.

9. Find the midpoint of the line segment connecting $(-3, 4)$ and $(5, 7)$.

10. Find the midpoint of the line segment connecting $(6, -5)$ and $(-3, -8)$.

11. Find numbers x and y such that $(-2, 5)$ is the midpoint of the line segment connecting $(3, 1)$ and (x, y).

12. Find numbers x and y such that $(3, -4)$ is the midpoint of the line segment connecting $(-2, 5)$ and (x, y).

13. Find a number t such that the distance between $(2, 3)$ and $(t, 2t)$ is as small as possible.

14. Find a number t such that the distance between $(-2, 1)$ and $(3t, 2t)$ is as small as possible.

15. A ship sails north for 2 miles and then west for 5 miles. How far is the ship from its starting point?

16. A ship sails east for 7 miles and then south for 3 miles. How far is the ship from its starting point?

17. Find the point on the line $y = 3x + 1$ in the xy-plane that is closest to the point $(2, 4)$.

18. Find the point on the line $y = 2x - 3$ in the xy-plane that is closest to the point $(5, 1)$.

19. Find the equation of the circle in the xy-plane centered at $(3, -2)$ with radius 7.

20. Find the equation of the circle in the xy-plane centered at $(-4, 5)$ with radius 6.

21. Find two choices for b such that $(5, b)$ is on the circle with radius 4 centered at $(3, 6)$.

22. Find two choices for b such that $(b, 4)$ is on the circle with radius 3 centered at $(-1, 6)$.

23. Find the intersection of the line containing the points $(2, 3)$ and $(4, 7)$ and the circle with radius $\sqrt{15}$ centered at $(3, -3)$.

24. Find the intersection of the line containing the points $(3, 4)$ and $(1, 8)$ and the circle with radius $\sqrt{3}$ centered at $(2, 9)$.

25. Find the perimeter of the triangle that has vertices at $(1, 2)$, $(5, -3)$, and $(-4, -1)$.

26. Find the perimeter of the triangle that has vertices at $(-3, 1)$, $(4, -2)$, and $(5, -1)$.

27. Find the radius of a circle that has circumference 12.

28. Find the radius of a circle that has circumference 20.

29. Find the radius of a circle that has circumference 8 more than its diameter.

30. Find the radius of a circle that has circumference 12 more than its diameter.

For Exercises 31 and 32, find the following information about the circles in the xy-plane described by the given equation:

  (a) *center*   **(c)** *diameter*

  (b) *radius*   **(d)** *circumference*

31. $x^2 - 8x + y^2 + 2y = -14$

32. $x^2 + 5x + y^2 - 6y = 3$

33. Find the equation of the circle centered at the origin in the xy-plane that has circumference 9.

34. Find the equation of the circle in the xy-plane centered at $(3, 7)$ that has circumference 5.

35. Find the equation of the circle centered at the origin in the uv-plane that has twice the circumference of the circle whose equation equals

$$u^2 + v^2 = 10.$$

36. Find the equation of the circle centered at the origin in the tw-plane that has three times the circumference of the circle whose equation equals
$$t^2 + w^2 = 5.$$

37. Suppose a rope is just long enough to cover the equator of the Earth. About how much longer would the rope need to be so that it could be suspended seven feet above the entire equator?

38. Suppose a satellite is in orbit one hundred miles above the equator of the Earth. About how much further does the satellite travel in one orbit than would a person traveling once around the equator on the surface of the Earth?

39. Find the length of the graph of the function f defined by
$$f(x) = \sqrt{9 - x^2}$$
on the interval $[-3, 3]$.

40. Find the length of the graph of the function f defined by
$$f(x) = \sqrt{25 - x^2}$$
on the interval $[0, 5]$.

41. Find the two points where the circle of radius 2 centered at the origin intersects the circle of radius 3 centered at $(3, 0)$.

42. Find the two points where the circle of radius 3 centered at the origin intersects the circle of radius 4 centered at $(5, 0)$.

PROBLEMS

Some problems require considerably more thought than the exercises.
Unlike exercises, problems usually have more than one correct answer.

43. Find two points, one on the horizontal axis and one on the vertical axis, such that the distance between these two points equals 15.

44. Explain why there does not exist a point on the horizontal axis whose distance from $(5, 4)$ equals 3.

45. Suppose (x_1, y_1) and (x_2, y_2) are the endpoints of a line segment.

    (a) Show that the distance between the point $\left(\frac{x_1+x_2}{2}, \frac{y_1+y_2}{2}\right)$ and the endpoint (x_1, y_1) equals half the length of the line segment.

    (b) Show that the distance between the point $\left(\frac{x_1+x_2}{2}, \frac{y_1+y_2}{2}\right)$ and the endpoint (x_2, y_2) equals half the length of the line segment.

46. Suppose (x_1, y_1) and (x_2, y_2) are the endpoints of a line segment.

    (a) Show that the line containing the point $\left(\frac{x_1+x_2}{2}, \frac{y_1+y_2}{2}\right)$ and the endpoint (x_1, y_1) has slope $\frac{y_2-y_1}{x_2-x_1}$.

    (b) Show that the line containing the point $\left(\frac{x_1+x_2}{2}, \frac{y_1+y_2}{2}\right)$ and the endpoint (x_2, y_2) has slope $\frac{y_2-y_1}{x_2-x_1}$.

    (c) Explain why parts (a) and (b) of this problem imply that the point $\left(\frac{x_1+x_2}{2}, \frac{y_1+y_2}{2}\right)$ lies on the line containing the endpoints (x_1, y_1) and (x_2, y_2).

47. Explain why the two previous problems imply that $\left(\frac{x_1+x_2}{2}, \frac{y_1+y_2}{2}\right)$ is the midpoint of the line segment with endpoints (x_1, y_1) and (x_2, y_2).

48. (a) Find a function f such that the distance between the points $(1, 3)$ and $(x, f(x))$ equals the distance between $(5, 9)$ and $(x, f(x))$ for every real number x.

    (b) Find a linear function f such that the graph of f contains the point $(3, 6)$ and is perpendicular to the line containing $(1, 3)$ and $(5, 9)$.

    (c) Explain why the solutions to parts (a) and (b) of this problem are the same. Draw an appropriate figure to help illustrate your explanation.

49. Find six distinct points on the circle with center $(2, 3)$ and radius 5.

50. ✏ Find six distinct points on the circle with center $(4, 1)$ and circumference 3.

51. Show that a square whose diagonal has length d has perimeter $2\sqrt{2}d$.

WORKED-OUT SOLUTIONS *to Odd-numbered Exercises*

Do not read these worked-out solutions before first struggling to do the exercises yourself. Otherwise you risk the danger of mimicking the techniques shown here without understanding the ideas.

Best way to learn: Carefully read the section of the textbook, then do all the odd-numbered exercises (even if they have not been assigned) and check your answers here. If you get stuck on an exercise, reread the section of the textbook—then try the exercise again. If you are still stuck, then look at the worked-out solution here.

1. Find the distance between the points $(3, -2)$ and $(-1, 4)$.

   SOLUTION The distance between the points $(3, -2)$ and $(-1, 4)$ equals

   $$\sqrt{(-1-3)^2 + (4-(-2))^2},$$

   which equals $\sqrt{(-4)^2 + 6^2}$, which equals $\sqrt{16 + 36}$, which equals $\sqrt{52}$, which can be simplified as follows:

   $$\sqrt{52} = \sqrt{4 \cdot 13} = \sqrt{4} \cdot \sqrt{13} = 2\sqrt{13}.$$

   Thus the distance between the points $(3, -2)$ and $(-1, 4)$ equals $2\sqrt{13}$.

3. Find two choices for t such that the distance between $(2, -1)$ and $(t, 3)$ equals 7.

   SOLUTION The distance between $(2, -1)$ and $(t, 3)$ equals

   $$\sqrt{(t-2)^2 + 16}.$$

   We want this to equal 7, which means that we must have

   $$(t-2)^2 + 16 = 49.$$

   Subtracting 16 from both sides of the equation above gives

   $$(t-2)^2 = 33,$$

   which implies that $t - 2 = \pm\sqrt{33}$. Thus $t = 2 + \sqrt{33}$ or $t = 2 - \sqrt{33}$.

5. Find two points on the horizontal axis whose distance from $(3, 2)$ equals 7.

   SOLUTION A typical point on the horizontal axis has coordinates $(x, 0)$. The distance from this point to $(3, 2)$ is $\sqrt{(x-3)^2 + (0-2)^2}$. Thus we need to solve the equation

   $$\sqrt{(x-3)^2 + 4} = 7.$$

Squaring both sides of the equation above, and then subtracting 4 from both sides gives

$$(x-3)^2 = 45.$$

Thus $x - 3 = \pm\sqrt{45} = \pm 3\sqrt{5}$. Thus $x = 3 \pm 3\sqrt{5}$. Hence the two points on the horizontal axis whose distance from $(3, 2)$ equals 7 are $(3 + 3\sqrt{5}, 0)$ and $(3 - 3\sqrt{5}, 0)$.

7. Find two points on the vertical axis whose distance from $(5, -1)$ equals 8.

   SOLUTION A typical point on the vertical axis has coordinates $(0, y)$. The distance from this point to $(5, -1)$ is $\sqrt{(0-5)^2 + (y-(-1))^2}$. Thus we need to solve the equation

   $$\sqrt{25 + (y+1)^2} = 8.$$

   Squaring both sides of the equation above, and then subtracting 25 from both sides gives

   $$(y+1)^2 = 39.$$

   Thus $y + 1 = \pm\sqrt{39}$. Thus $y = -1 \pm \sqrt{39}$. Hence the two points on the vertical axis whose distance from $(5, -1)$ equals 8 are $(0, -1 + \sqrt{39})$ and $(0, -1 - \sqrt{39})$.

9. Find the midpoint of the line segment connecting $(-3, 4)$ and $(5, 7)$.

   SOLUTION The midpoint of the line segment connecting $(-3, 4)$ and $(5, 7)$ is

   $$\left(\frac{-3+5}{2}, \frac{4+7}{2}\right),$$

   which equals $(1, \frac{11}{2})$.

11. Find numbers x and y such that $(-2, 5)$ is the midpoint of the line segment connecting $(3, 1)$ and (x, y).

SOLUTION   The midpoint of the line segment connecting $(3, 1)$ and (x, y) is

$$\left(\frac{3+x}{2}, \frac{1+y}{2}\right).$$

We want this to equal $(-2, 5)$. Thus we must solve the equations

$$\frac{3+x}{2} = -2 \quad \text{and} \quad \frac{1+y}{2} = 5.$$

Solving these equations gives $x = -7$ and $y = 9$.

13. Find a number t such that the distance between $(2, 3)$ and $(t, 2t)$ is as small as possible.

SOLUTION   The distance between $(2, 3)$ and $(t, 2t)$ equals

$$\sqrt{(t-2)^2 + (2t-3)^2}.$$

We want to make this as small as possible, which happens when

$$(t-2)^2 + (2t-3)^2$$

is as small as possible. Note that

$$(t-2)^2 + (2t-3)^2 = 5t^2 - 16t + 13.$$

This will be as small as possible when $5t^2 - 16t$ is as small as possible. To find when that happens, we complete the square:

$$5t^2 - 16t = 5\left[t^2 - \frac{16}{5}t\right]$$

$$= 5\left[\left(t - \frac{8}{5}\right)^2 - \frac{64}{25}\right].$$

This quantity is made smallest when $t = \frac{8}{5}$.

15. A ship sails north for 2 miles and then west for 5 miles. How far is the ship from its starting point?

SOLUTION   The figure below shows the path of the ship. The length of the red line is the distance of the ship from its starting point. By the Pythagorean Theorem, this distance is $\sqrt{2^2 + 5^2}$ miles, which equals $\sqrt{29}$ miles.

We have assumed that the surface of the Earth is part of a plane rather than part of a sphere. For distances of less than a few hundred miles, this is a good approximation.

17. Find the point on the line $y = 3x + 1$ in the xy-plane that is closest to the point $(2, 4)$.

SOLUTION   A typical point on the line $y = 3x + 1$ in the xy-plane has coordinates $(x, 3x + 1)$. The distance between this point and $(2, 4)$ equals

$$\sqrt{(x-2)^2 + (3x + 1 - 4)^2},$$

which with a bit of algebra can be rewritten as

$$\sqrt{10x^2 - 22x + 13}.$$

We want to make the quantity above as small as possible, which means that we need to make $10x^2 - 22x$ as small as possible. This can be done by completing the square:

$$10x^2 - 22x = 10\left[x^2 - \frac{11}{5}x\right]$$

$$= 10\left[\left(x - \frac{11}{10}\right)^2 - \frac{121}{100}\right].$$

The last quantity will be as small as possible when $x = \frac{11}{10}$. Plugging $x = \frac{11}{10}$ into the equation $y = 3x + 1$ gives $y = \frac{43}{10}$. Thus $\left(\frac{11}{10}, \frac{43}{10}\right)$ is the point on the line $y = 3x + 1$ that is closest to the point $(2, 4)$.

19. Find the equation of the circle in the xy-plane centered at $(3, -2)$ with radius 7.

SOLUTION   The equation of this circle is

$$(x - 3)^2 + (y + 2)^2 = 49.$$

21. Find two choices for b such that $(5, b)$ is on the circle with radius 4 centered at $(3, 6)$.

SOLUTION   The equation of the circle with radius 4 centered at $(3, 6)$ is

$$(x - 3)^2 + (y - 6)^2 = 16.$$

The point $(5, b)$ is on this circle if and only if

$$(5 - 3)^2 + (b - 6)^2 = 16,$$

which is equivalent to the equation $(b - 6)^2 = 12$. Thus

$$b - 6 = \pm\sqrt{12} = \pm\sqrt{4 \cdot 3} = \pm\sqrt{4}\sqrt{3} = \pm 2\sqrt{3}.$$

Thus $b = 6 + 2\sqrt{3}$ or $b = 6 - 2\sqrt{3}$.

23. Find the intersection of the line containing the points $(2, 3)$ and $(4, 7)$ and the circle with radius $\sqrt{15}$ centered at $(3, -3)$.

    SOLUTION First we find the equation of the line containing the points $(2, 3)$ and $(4, 7)$. This line will have slope $\frac{7-3}{4-2}$, which equals 2. Thus the equation of this line will have the form $y = 2x + b$. Because $(2, 3)$ is on this line, we can substitute $x = 2$ and $y = 3$ into the last equation and then solve for b, getting $b = -1$. Thus the equation of the line containing the points $(2, 3)$ and $(4, 7)$ is

    $$y = 2x - 1.$$

    The equation of the circle with radius $\sqrt{15}$ centered at $(3, -3)$ is

    $$(x - 3)^2 + (y + 3)^2 = 15.$$

    To find the intersection of the circle and the line, we replace y by $2x - 1$ in the equation above, getting

    $$(x - 3)^2 + (2x + 2)^2 = 15.$$

    Expanding the terms in the equation above and then collecting terms gives the equation

    $$5x^2 + 2x - 2 = 0.$$

    Using the quadratic formula, we then find that

    $$x = \frac{-1 + \sqrt{11}}{5} \quad \text{or} \quad x = \frac{-1 - \sqrt{11}}{5}.$$

    Substituting these values of x into the equation $y = 2x - 1$ shows that the line intersects the circle in the points

    $$\left(\frac{-1 + \sqrt{11}}{5}, \frac{-7 + 2\sqrt{11}}{5}\right)$$

    and

    $$\left(\frac{-1 - \sqrt{11}}{5}, \frac{-7 - 2\sqrt{11}}{5}\right).$$

25. Find the perimeter of the triangle that has vertices at $(1, 2)$, $(5, -3)$, and $(-4, -1)$.

    SOLUTION The perimeter of the triangle equals the sum of the lengths of the three sides of the triangle. Thus we find the lengths of those three sides.

The side of the triangle connecting the vertices $(1, 2)$ and $(5, -3)$ has length

$$\sqrt{(5 - 1)^2 + (-3 - 2)^2} = \sqrt{41}.$$

The side of the triangle connecting the vertices $(5, -3)$ and $(-4, -1)$ has length

$$\sqrt{(-4 - 5)^2 + (-1 - (-3))^2} = \sqrt{85}.$$

The side of the triangle connecting the vertices $(-4, -1)$ and $(1, 2)$ has length

$$\sqrt{(1 - (-4))^2 + (2 - (-1))^2} = \sqrt{34}.$$

Thus the perimeter of the triangle equals $\sqrt{41} + \sqrt{85} + \sqrt{34}$.

27. Find the radius of a circle that has circumference 12.

    SOLUTION Let r denote the radius of this circle. Thus $2\pi r = 12$, which implies that $r = \frac{6}{\pi}$.

29. Find the radius of a circle that has circumference 8 more than its diameter.

    SOLUTION Let r denote the radius of this circle. Thus the circle has circumference $2\pi r$ and has diameter $2r$. Because the circumference is 8 more than diameter, we have $2\pi r = 2r + 8$. Thus $(2\pi - 2)r = 8$, which implies that $r = \frac{4}{\pi - 1}$.

For Exercises 31 and 32, find the following information about the circles in the xy-plane described by the given equation:
(a) *center*   **(c)** *diameter*
(b) *radius*   **(d)** *circumference*

31. $x^2 - 8x + y^2 + 2y = -14$

    SOLUTION Completing the square, we can rewrite the left side of this equation as follows:

    $$x^2 - 8x + y^2 + 2y = (x - 4)^2 - 16 + (y + 1)^2 - 1$$
    $$= (x - 4)^2 + (y + 1)^2 - 17.$$

    Substituting this expression into the left side of the original equation and then adding 17 to both sides shows that the original equation is equivalent to the equation

    $$(x - 4)^2 + (y + 1)^2 = 3.$$

    (a) The equation above shows that this circle has center $(4, -1)$.

(b) The equation above shows that this circle has radius $\sqrt{3}$.

(c) Because the diameter is twice the radius, this circle has diameter $2\sqrt{3}$.

(d) Because the circumference is 2π times the radius, this circle has circumference $2\pi\sqrt{3}$.

33. Find the equation of the circle centered at the origin in the xy-plane that has circumference 9.

SOLUTION   Let r denote the radius of this circle. Then $2\pi r = 9$, which implies that $r = \frac{9}{2\pi}$. Thus the equation of the circle is

$$x^2 + y^2 = \frac{81}{4\pi^2}.$$

35. Find the equation of the circle centered at the origin in the uv-plane that has twice the circumference of the circle whose equation equals

$$u^2 + v^2 = 10.$$

SOLUTION   The equation given above describes a circle centered at the origin whose radius equals $\sqrt{10}$. Because the circumference is proportional to the radius, if we want a circle with twice the circumference then we need to double the radius. Thus the circle we seek has radius $2\sqrt{10}$. Because $(2\sqrt{10})^2 = 2^2 \cdot \sqrt{10}^2 = 40$, the equation we seek is

$$u^2 + v^2 = 40.$$

37. Suppose a rope is just long enough to cover the equator of the Earth. About how much longer would the rope need to be so that it could be suspended seven feet above the entire equator?

SOLUTION   Assume that the equator of the Earth is a circle. This assumption is close enough to being correct to answer a question that requires only an approximation.

Assume that the radius of the Earth is r, measured in feet (note that we do not need to know the value of r for this exercise). For a rope to

cover the equator, it needs to have length $2\pi r$ feet. For a rope to be suspended seven feet above the equator, it would need to have length $2\pi(r + 7)$ feet, which equals $(2\pi r + 14\pi)$ feet. In other words, to be suspended seven feet above the equator, the rope would need to be only 14π feet longer than a rope covering the equator. Because $14\pi \approx 14 \cdot \frac{22}{7} = 44$, the rope would need to be about 44 feet longer than a rope covering the equator.

39. Find the length of the graph of the function f defined by

$$f(x) = \sqrt{9 - x^2}$$

on the interval $[-3, 3]$.

SOLUTION   The graph of f is the curve $y = \sqrt{9 - x^2}$, with x ranging from -3 to 3. Squaring both sides of this equation and then adding x^2 to both sides gives the equation $x^2 + y^2 = 9$, which is the equation of the circle of radius 3 centered at the origin. However, the equation $y = \sqrt{9 - x^2}$ implies that $y \geq 0$, and thus we have only the top half of the circle.

The entire circle of radius 3 has circumference 6π. Thus the graph of f, which is half of the circle, has length 3π.

41. Find the two points where the circle of radius 2 centered at the origin intersects the circle of radius 3 centered at $(3, 0)$.

SOLUTION   The equations of these two circles are

$$x^2 + y^2 = 4 \quad \text{and} \quad (x - 3)^2 + y^2 = 9.$$

Subtracting the first equation from the second equation, we get

$$(x - 3)^2 - x^2 = 5,$$

which simplifies to the equation $-6x + 9 = 5$, whose solution is $x = \frac{2}{3}$. Plugging this value of x into either of the equations above and solving for y gives $y = \pm\frac{4\sqrt{2}}{3}$. Thus the two circles intersect at the points $\left(\frac{2}{3}, \frac{4\sqrt{2}}{3}\right)$ and $\left(\frac{2}{3}, -\frac{4\sqrt{2}}{3}\right)$.

4.2 Areas of Simple Regions

SECTION OBJECTIVES

By the end of this section you should

- understand the formulas for the areas of squares, rectangles, parallelograms, triangles, and trapezoids;
- understand how area changes when the coordinate axes are stretched;
- understand why the area inside a circle is π times the radius squared;
- be able to compute the area inside an ellipse.

You probably already have a good intuitive notion of area. In this section we will try to strengthen this intuition and build a good understanding of the formulas for the area of the simplest regions.

Squares

A 1-by-1 square.

The most primitive notion of area is that a 1-by-1 square has area 1. If we can decompose a region into 1-by-1 squares, then the area of that region is the number of 1-by-1 squares into which it can be decomposed, as shown in the figure below:

A 3-by-3 square can be decomposed into nine 1-by-1 squares. Thus a 3-by-3 square has area 9.

The expression m^2 is called "m squared" because a square whose sides have length m has area m^2.

If m is a positive integer, then an m-by-m square can be decomposed into m^2 squares of size 1-by-1. Thus it is no surprise that the area of an m-by-m square equals m^2.

The same formula holds for squares whose side length is not necessarily an integer, as shown below:

Four $\frac{1}{2}$-by-$\frac{1}{2}$ squares fill up a 1-by-1 square. Thus each $\frac{1}{2}$-by-$\frac{1}{2}$ square has area $\frac{1}{4}$.

More generally, we have the following formula:

Area of a square

A square whose sides have length ℓ has area ℓ^2.

Rectangles

Consider a rectangle with base 3 and height 2, as shown here. This 3-by-2 rectangle can be decomposed into six 1-by-1 squares. Thus this rectangle has area 6.

Similarly, if b and h are positive integers, then a rectangle with base b and height h can be composed into bh squares of size 1-by-1, showing that the rectangle has area bh. More generally, the same formula is valid even if the base and height are not integers.

> ### Area of a rectangle
>
> A rectangle with base b and height h has area bh.

The unit of measurement for area is the square of the unit used for length. For example, if the length of the side of a square is 5 inches, then the area of the square is 25 square inches.

In the special case where the base equals the height, the formula for the area of a rectangle becomes the formula for the area of a square.

Parallelograms

A **parallelogram** is a quadrilateral (a four-sided polygon) in which both pairs of opposite sides are parallel, as shown here.

To find the area of a parallelogram, select one of the sides and call its length the **base**. The opposite side of the parallelogram will have the same length. The **height** of the parallelogram is then defined to be the length of a line segment that connects these two sides and is perpendicular to both of them. Thus in the figure shown here, the parallelogram has base b and both vertical line segments have length equal to the height h.

The two small triangles in the figure above have the same size and thus the same area. The rectangle in the figure above could be obtained from the parallelogram by moving the triangle on the right to the position of the triangle on the left. This shows that the parallelogram and the rectangle above have the same area. Because the area of the rectangle equals bh, we thus have the following formula for the area of a parallelogram:

The yellow region is a parallelogram with base b and height h. The area of the parallelogram is the same as the area of the rectangle (outlined in red) with base b and height h.

> ### Area of a parallelogram
>
> A parallelogram with base b and height h has area bh.

Triangles

To find the area of a triangle, select one of the sides and call its length the **base**. The **height** of the triangle is then defined to be the length of the perpendicular line segment that connects the opposite vertex to the side determining the base.

To derive the formula for the area of a triangle with base b and height h, draw two line segments, each parallel to and the same length as one of the sides of the triangle, to form a parallelogram as in the figure below:

A triangle with base b and height h.

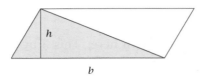

The triangle has been extended to a parallelogram by adjoining a second triangle with the same area as the original triangle.

The parallelogram above has base b and height h and hence has area bh. The original triangle has area equal to half the area of the parallelogram. Thus we obtain the following formula:

Area of a triangle

A triangle with base b and height h has area $\frac{1}{2}bh$.

| EXAMPLE 1 |

Find the area of the triangle whose vertices are $(1, 0)$, $(9, 0)$, and $(7, 3)$.

SOLUTION   Choose the side connecting $(1, 0)$ and $(9, 0)$ as the base of this triangle. Thus this triangle has base $9 - 1$, which equals 8.

The height of this triangle is the length of the red line shown here; this height equals the second coordinate of the vertex $(7, 3)$. In other words, this triangle has height 3.

Thus this triangle has area $\frac{1}{2} \cdot 8 \cdot 3$, which equals 12.

A right triangle with area $\frac{1}{2}ab$.

Consider the special case where our triangle happens to be a right triangle, with the right angle between sides of length a and b. Choosing b to be the base of the triangle, we see that the height of this triangle equals a. Thus in this case the area of the triangle equals $\frac{1}{2}ab$.

Trapezoids

A **trapezoid** is a quadrilateral that has at least one pair of parallel sides, as for example shown here. The lengths of a pair of opposite parallel sides are called the **bases**, which are denoted below by b_1 and b_2. The **height** of the trapezoid, denoted h below, is then defined to be the length of a line segment that connects these two sides and that is perpendicular to both of them.

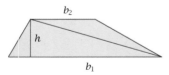

A trapezoid with bases b_1 and b_2 and height h.

The diagonal in the figure here divides the trapezoid into two triangles. The lower triangle has base b_1 and height h; thus the lower triangle has area $\frac{1}{2}b_1h$. The upper triangle has base b_2 and height h; thus the upper triangle has area $\frac{1}{2}b_2h$. The area of the trapezoid is the sum of the areas of these two triangles. Thus the area of the trapezoid equals $\frac{1}{2}b_1h + \frac{1}{2}b_2h$. Factoring out the $\frac{1}{2}$ and the h in this expression gives the following formula:

Area of a trapezoid

A trapezoid with bases b_1, b_2 and height h has area $\frac{1}{2}(b_1 + b_2)h$.

Note that $\frac{1}{2}(b_1 + b_2)$ is just the average of the two bases of the trapezoid. In the special case where the trapezoid is a parallelogram, the two bases are equal and we are back to the familiar formula that the area of a parallelogram equals the base times the height.

Find the area of the region in the xy-plane under the line $y = 2x$, above the x-axis, and between the lines $x = 2$ and $x = 5$.

EXAMPLE 2

SOLUTION

The line $x = 2$ intersects the line $y = 2x$ at the point $(2, 4)$. The line $x = 5$ intersects the line $y = 2x$ at the point $(5, 10)$.

Thus the region in question is the trapezoid shown above. The parallel sides of this trapezoid (the two vertical sides) have lengths 4 and 10, and thus this trapezoid has bases 4 and 10. As can be seen from the figure above, this trapezoid has height 3 (note that in this trapezoid, the height is the length of the horizontal side). Thus the area of this trapezoid is $\frac{1}{2} \cdot (4 + 10) \cdot 3$, which equals 21.

Stretching

Suppose a square whose sides have length 1 has its sides tripled in length, resulting in a square whose sides have length 3, as shown here. You can think of this transformation as stretching both vertically and horizontally by a factor of 3. This transformation increases the area of the square by a factor of 9.

Consider now the transformation that stretches horizontally by a factor of 3 and stretches vertically by a factor of 2. This transformation changes a square whose sides have length 1 into a rectangle with base 3 and height 2, as shown here. Thus the area has been increased by a factor of 6.

More generally, suppose c, d are positive numbers, and consider the transformation that stretches horizontally by a factor of c and stretches vertically by a factor of d. This transformation changes a square whose sides have length 1 into a rectangle with base c and height d, as shown here. Thus the area has been increased by a factor of cd.

We need not restrict our attention to squares. The transformation that stretches horizontally by a factor of c and stretches vertically by a factor of d will change any region into a new region whose area has been changed by a factor of cd. This result follows from the result for squares, because any region can be approximated by a union of squares, as shown here for a triangle. Here is the formal statement of this result:

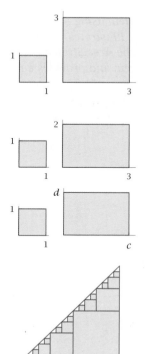

> ### Area Stretch Theorem
>
> Suppose R is a region in the coordinate plane and c, d are positive numbers. Let R' be the region obtained from R by stretching horizontally by a factor of c and stretching vertically by a factor of d. Then
>
> the area of R' equals cd times the area of R.

EXAMPLE 3

Find the ratio of the area of the region below on the right to the area of the region below on the left.

    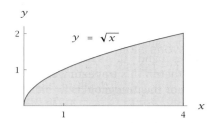

We solve this problem using a trick that illustrates the use of the Area Stretch Theorem and provides a review of two important function transformations from Section 1.3.

SOLUTION   Let f be the function with domain $[0, 1]$ defined by $f(x) = \sqrt{x}$. Thus the region above on the left is the region in the xy-plane under the graph of f, above the x-axis, and between the y-axis and the line $x = 1$.

Define a function g by

$$g(x) = 2f\left(\frac{x}{4}\right) = 2\sqrt{\frac{x}{4}} = \sqrt{x}.$$

Our results on function transformations (see Section 1.3) show that the graph of g is obtained from the graph of f by stretching horizontally by a factor of 4 and stretching vertically by a factor of 2. The Area Stretch Theorem now implies that these transformations increase the area by a factor of $4 \cdot 2$, which equals 8. Thus the area of the region on the right is 8 times the area of the region on the left.

Circles

Consider the region inside a circle of radius 1 centered at the origin. If we stretch both horizontally and vertically by a factor of r, this region becomes the region inside the circle of radius r centered at the origin. This result is fairly obvious geometrically, but we can also verify it algebraically. To do this, consider a typical point (x, y) inside the circle of radius 1 centered at the origin. Thus

$$x^2 + y^2 < 1.$$

When stretching both horizontally and vertically by a factor of r, the point (x, y) becomes the point (rx, ry). This point satisfies the inequality

$$(rx)^2 + (ry)^2 < r^2.$$

Thus the transformed point (rx, ry) is inside the circle of radius r, as we expected.

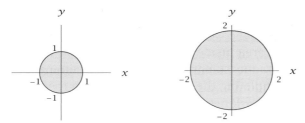

Stretching both horizontally and vertically by a factor of 2 transforms a circle of radius 1 into a circle of radius 2.

An equilateral triangle with sides of length r has area $\frac{\sqrt{3}}{4}r^2$, and a square with sides of length r has area r^2. Thus we should not be surprised that the area inside a circle of radius r equals a constant times r^2.

The Area Stretch Theorem now implies that the area inside a circle of radius r equals r^2 times the area inside a circle of radius 1. For convenience, let p denote the area inside a circle of radius 1. We have shown that the area inside a circle of radius r equals $r^2 p$, which we will write in the more familiar form pr^2. We need to find the value of p.

To find p, consider a circle of radius 1 surrounded by a slightly larger circle with the same center and with radius r, as shown here. Cut out the region between the two circles, then cut a slit in it and unwind it into the shape of a trapezoid (this requires a tiny bit of distortion) as shown below. The trapezoid will have height $r - 1$, which is the distance between the two original circles. The trapezoid will have bases 2π and $2\pi r$, corresponding to the circumferences of the two circles. Thus the trapezoid will have area

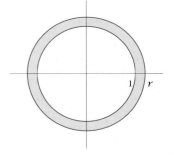

$$\tfrac{1}{2}(2\pi r + 2\pi)(r - 1),$$

which equals $\pi(r + 1)(r - 1)$, which equals $\pi(r^2 - 1)$.

One base of the trapezoid is the circumference of the circle of radius 1; the other base is the circumference of the circle of radius r.

The area inside the larger circle equals the area inside the circle of radius 1 plus the area of the region between the two circles. In other words, the area inside the larger circle equals $p + \pi(r^2 - 1)$. The area inside the larger circle also equals pr^2, because the larger circle has radius r. Thus we have

Our derivation of the formula for the area inside a circle shows the intimate connection between the area and the circumference of a circle.

$$pr^2 = p + \pi(r^2 - 1).$$

Subtracting p from both sides, we get

$$p(r^2 - 1) = \pi(r^2 - 1).$$

Pie and π: The area of this pie with radius 4 inches is 16π square inches.

Thus $p = \pi$. In other words, the area inside a circle of radius r equals πr^2. Hence we have derived the following formula:

> ### Area inside a circle
>
> The area inside a circle of radius r is πr^2.

Thus to find the area inside a circle, we must first find the radius of the circle. Finding the radius sometimes requires a preliminary algebraic manipulation such as completing the square, as shown in the following example.

EXAMPLE 4

Consider the circle described by the equation

$$x^2 - 8x + y^2 + 6y = 4.$$

(a) Find the center of this circle.

(b) Find the radius of this circle.

(c) Find the circumference of this circle.

(d) Find the area inside this circle.

"The universe cannot be read until we have learnt the language and become familiar with the characters in which it is written. It is written in mathematical language, and the letters are triangles, circles and other geometrical figures, without which means it is humanly impossible to comprehend a single word."
—Galileo

SOLUTION To obtain the desired information about the circle, we will put its equation in a standard form. This can be done by completing the square:

$$4 = x^2 - 8x + y^2 + 6y$$
$$= (x - 4)^2 - 16 + (y + 3)^2 - 9$$
$$= (x - 4)^2 + (y + 3)^2 - 25.$$

Adding 25 to the first and last sides above shows that the circle is described by the equation

$$(x - 4)^2 + (y + 3)^2 = 29.$$

(a) The equation above shows that the center of the circle is $(4, -3)$.

Do not make the mistake of thinking that this circle has radius 29.

(b) The equation above shows that the radius of the circle is $\sqrt{29}$.

(c) Because the circle has radius $\sqrt{29}$, its circumference is $2\sqrt{29}\pi$.

(d) Because the circle has radius $\sqrt{29}$, its area is 29π.

Ellipses

Suppose the circle of radius 1 centered at the origin is stretched horizontally by a factor of 5 and stretched vertically by a factor of 2. This transformation changes the circle shown below on the left into the ellipse shown below on the right:

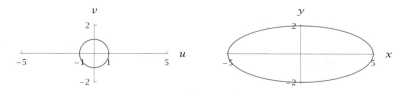

Stretching horizontally by a factor of 5 and stretching vertically by a factor of 2 transforms the circle on the left into the ellipse on the right.

To find the equation of this ellipse, consider a typical point (u, v) on the circle of radius 1 centered at the origin (the circle above is drawn in the uv-plane; the ellipse above is drawn in the xy-plane). Thus

$$u^2 + v^2 = 1.$$

When stretching horizontally by a factor of 5 and stretching vertically by a factor of 2, the point (u, v) transforms to the point $(5u, 2v)$. Rewriting the equation above in terms of this new point, we have

$$\frac{(5u)^2}{25} + \frac{(2v)^2}{4} = 1.$$

Writing the transformed point $(5u, 2v)$ as (x, y), thus setting $x = 5u$ and $y = 2v$, the equation above can be rewritten as

$$\frac{x^2}{25} + \frac{y^2}{4} = 1,$$

which is the equation of the ellipse shown above on the right.

The region inside the ellipse above is obtained from the region inside the circle of radius 1 by stretching horizontally by a factor of 5 and stretching vertically by a factor of 2. Because $5 \cdot 2 = 10$, the Area Stretch Theorem tells us that the area inside this ellipse equals 10 times the area inside the circle of radius 1. Because the area inside a circle of radius 1 is π, we conclude that the area inside this ellipse is 10π.

More generally, suppose a and b are positive numbers. Suppose the circle of radius 1 centered at the origin is stretched horizontally by a factor of a and stretched vertically by a factor of b. Using the same reasoning as above (just replace 5 by a and replace 2 by b), we see that the equation of the resulting ellipse in the xy-plane is

$$\frac{x^2}{a^2} + \frac{y^2}{b^2} = 1.$$

The Area Stretch Theorem now gives us the following formula:

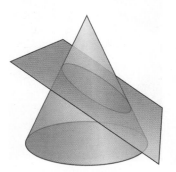

The ancient Greeks discovered that the intersection of a cone and an appropriately positioned plane is an ellipse.

If a and b both equal r, then our ellipse is a circle with radius r. This formula then asserts that the area inside a circle of radius r equals πr^2, which agrees with our previous formula.

Area inside an ellipse

Suppose a and b are positive numbers. Then the area inside the ellipse

$$\frac{x^2}{a^2} + \frac{y^2}{b^2} = 1$$

is πab.

EXAMPLE 5

Find the area inside the ellipse

$$4x^2 + 5y^2 = 3.$$

SOLUTION   To put the equation of this ellipse in the form given by the area formula, begin by dividing both sides by 3, and then force the equation into the desired form, as follows:

$$1 = \tfrac{4}{3}x^2 + \tfrac{5}{3}y^2$$

$$= \frac{x^2}{\frac{3}{4}} + \frac{y^2}{\frac{3}{5}}$$

$$= \frac{x^2}{\left(\frac{\sqrt{3}}{2}\right)^2} + \frac{y^2}{\sqrt{\frac{3}{5}}^2}.$$

Thus the area inside the ellipse is $\pi \cdot \frac{\sqrt{3}}{2} \cdot \sqrt{\frac{3}{5}}$, which equals $\frac{3\sqrt{5}}{10}\pi$.

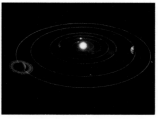

The German mathematician Johannes Kepler, who in 1609 published his discovery that the orbits of the planets are ellipses, not circles or combinations of circles as had been previously thought.

Kepler also discovered that a line joining a planet to the sun sweeps out equal areas in equal times.

Ellipses need not be centered at the origin. For example, the equation

$$\frac{(x-5)^2}{9} + \frac{(y-7)^2}{16} = 1$$

represents an ellipse centered at a point $(5, 7)$. This ellipse is obtained by shifting the ellipse whose equation is $\frac{x^2}{9} + \frac{y^2}{16} = 1$ right 5 units and up 7 units. The formula above tells us that the area inside the ellipse $\frac{x^2}{9} + \frac{y^2}{16} = 1$ is 12π, and thus the area inside the ellipse $\frac{(x-5)^2}{9} + \frac{(y-7)^2}{16} = 1$ is also 12π.

More generally, if a and b are positive numbers, then the equation

$$\frac{(x-h)^2}{a^2} + \frac{(y-k)^2}{b^2} = 1$$

represents an ellipse centered at a point (h, k). This ellipse is obtained by shifting the ellipse whose equation is $\frac{x^2}{a^2} + \frac{y^2}{b^2} = 1$. Thus the area inside the ellipse $\frac{(x-h)^2}{a^2} + \frac{(y-k)^2}{b^2} = 1$ is πab.

EXERCISES

1. Find the area of a triangle that has two sides of length 6 and one side of length 10.

2. Find the area of a triangle that has two sides of length 6 and one side of length 4.

3. (a) Find the distance from the point $(2, 3)$ to the line containing the points $(-2, -1)$ and $(5, 4)$.

   (b) Use the information from part (a) to find the area of the triangle whose vertices are $(2, 3)$, $(-2, -1)$, and $(5, 4)$.

4. (a) Find the distance from the point $(3, 4)$ to the line containing the points $(1, 5)$ and $(-2, 2)$.

   (b) Use the information from part (a) to find the area of the triangle whose vertices are $(3, 4)$, $(1, 5)$, and $(-2, 2)$.

5. Find the area of the triangle whose vertices are $(2, 0)$, $(9, 0)$, and $(4, 5)$.

6. Find the area of the triangle whose vertices are $(-3, 0)$, $(2, 0)$, and $(4, 3)$.

7. Suppose $(2, 3)$, $(1, 1)$, and $(7, 1)$ are three vertices of a parallelogram, two of whose sides are shown here.

   (a) Find the fourth vertex of this parallelogram.

   (b) Find the area of this parallelogram.

8. Suppose $(3, 4)$, $(2, 1)$, and $(6, 1)$ are three vertices of a parallelogram, two of whose sides are shown here.

   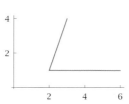

   (a) Find the fourth vertex of this parallelogram.

   (b) Find the area of this parallelogram.

9. Find the area of this trapezoid, whose vertices are $(1, 1)$, $(7, 1)$, $(5, 3)$, and $(2, 3)$.

10. Find the area of this trapezoid, whose vertices are $(2, 1)$, $(6, 1)$, $(8, 4)$, and $(1, 4)$.

11. Find the area of the region in the xy-plane under the line $y = \frac{x}{2}$, above the x-axis, and between the lines $x = 2$ and $x = 6$.

12. Find the area of the region in the xy-plane under the line $y = 3x + 1$, above the x-axis, and between the lines $x = 1$ and $x = 5$.

13. Let $f(x) = |x|$. Find the area of the region in the xy-plane under the graph of f, above the x-axis, and between the lines $x = -2$ and $x = 5$.

14. Let $f(x) = |2x|$. Find the area of the region in the xy-plane under the graph of f, above the x-axis, and between the lines $x = -3$ and $x = 4$.

15. Find the area of the region in the xy-plane under the curve $y = \sqrt{4 - x^2}$ (with $-2 \le x \le 2$) and above the x-axis.

16. Find the area of the region in the xy-plane under the curve $y = \sqrt{9 - x^2}$ (with $-3 \le x \le 3$) and above the x-axis.

17. Using the answer from Exercise 15, find the area of the region in the xy-plane under the curve $y = 3\sqrt{4 - x^2}$ (with $-2 \le x \le 2$) and above the x-axis.

18. Using the answer from Exercise 16, find the area of the region in the xy-plane under the curve $y = 5\sqrt{9 - x^2}$ (with $-3 \le x \le 3$) and above the x-axis.

19. Using the answer from Exercise 15, find the area of the region in the xy-plane under the curve $y = \sqrt{4 - \frac{x^2}{9}}$ (with $-6 \le x \le 6$) and above the x-axis.

20. Using the answer from Exercise 16, find the area of the region in the xy-plane under the curve $y = \sqrt{9 - \frac{x^2}{16}}$ (with $-12 \le x \le 12$) and above the x-axis.

21. Find the area of the region in the xy-plane under the curve

$$y = 1 + \sqrt{4 - x^2},$$

above the x-axis, and between the lines $x = -2$ and $x = 2$.

22. Find the area of the region in the xy-plane under the curve

$$y = 2 + \sqrt{9 - x^2},$$

above the x-axis, and between the lines $x = -3$ and $x = 3$.

Use the following figure for the next two exercises.

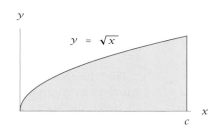

23. Suppose $c = 9$. Find the ratio between the area of the region above to the area of the region on the left in Example 3.

24. Suppose $c = 13$. Find the ratio between the area of the region above to the area of the region on the left in Example 3.

25. Find the area inside a circle with diameter 7.

26. Find the area inside a circle with diameter 9.

27. Find the area inside a circle with circumference 5.

28. Find the area inside a circle with circumference 7.

29. Find the area inside the circle whose equation is

$$x^2 - 6x + y^2 + 10y = 1.$$

30. Find the area inside the circle whose equation is

$$x^2 + 5x + y^2 - 3y = 1.$$

31. Find a number t such that the area inside the circle

$$3x^2 + 3y^2 = t$$

is 8.

32. Find a number t such that the area inside the circle

$$5x^2 + 5y^2 = t$$

is 2.

In Exercises 33–40, find the area inside the ellipse in the xy-plane determined by the given equation.

33. $\dfrac{x^2}{7} + \dfrac{y^2}{16} = 1$

34. $\dfrac{x^2}{9} + \dfrac{y^2}{5} = 1$

35. $2x^2 + 3y^2 = 1$

36. $10x^2 + 7y^2 = 1$

37. $3x^2 + 2y^2 = 7$

38. $5x^2 + 9y^2 = 3$

39. $3x^2 + 4x + 2y^2 + 3y = 2$

40. $4x^2 + 2x + 5y^2 + y = 2$

41. Find a positive number c such that the area inside the ellipse

$$2x^2 + cy^2 = 5$$

is 3.

42. Find a positive number c such that the area inside the ellipse

$$cx^2 + 7y^2 = 3$$

is 2.

43. Find numbers a and b such that $a > b$, $a + b = 15$, and the area inside the ellipse

$$\frac{x^2}{a^2} + \frac{y^2}{b^2} = 1$$

is 36π.

44. Find numbers a and b such that $a > b$, $a + b = 5$, and the area inside the ellipse

$$\frac{x^2}{a^2} + \frac{y^2}{b^2} = 1$$

is 3π.

PROBLEMS

45. Explain why a square yard contains 9 square feet.

46. Explain why a square foot contains 144 square inches.

47. Find a formula that gives the area of a square in terms of the length of the diagonal of the square.

48. Find a formula that gives the area of a square in terms of the perimeter.

49. Suppose a and b are positive numbers. Draw a figure of a square whose sides have length $a + b$. Partition this square into a square whose sides have length a, a square whose sides have length b, and two rectangles in a way that illustrates the identity

$$(a + b)^2 = a^2 + 2ab + b^2.$$

50. Find an example of a parallelogram whose area equals 10 and whose perimeter equals 16 (give the coordinates for all four vertices of your parallelogram).

51. Show that an equilateral triangle with sides of length r has area $\frac{\sqrt{3}}{4}r^2$.

52. Show that an equilateral triangle with area A has sides of length $\frac{2\sqrt{A}}{3^{1/4}}$.

53. Suppose $0 < a < b$. Show that the area of the region under the line $y = x$, above the x-axis, and between the lines $x = a$ and $x = b$ is $\frac{b^2 - a^2}{2}$.

54. Show that the area inside a circle with circumference c is $\frac{c^2}{4\pi}$.

55. Find a formula that gives the area inside a circle in terms of the diameter of the circle.

56. In ancient China and Babylonia, the area inside a circle was said to be one-half the radius times the circumference. Show that this formula agrees with our formula for the area inside a circle.

57. Suppose a, b, and c are positive numbers. Show that the area inside the ellipse

$$ax^2 + by^2 = c$$

is $\pi \frac{c}{\sqrt{ab}}$.

WORKED-OUT SOLUTIONS *to Odd-numbered Exercises*

1. Find the area of a triangle that has two sides of length 6 and one side of length 10.

   SOLUTION   By the Pythagorean Theorem (see figure below), the height of this triangle equals $\sqrt{6^2 - 5^2}$, which equals $\sqrt{11}$.

   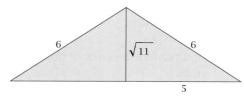

   A triangle that has two sides of length 6 and one side of length 10.

   Thus the area of this triangle equals $5\sqrt{11}$.

3. (a) Find the distance from the point $(2, 3)$ to the line containing the points $(-2, -1)$ and $(5, 4)$.

   (b) Use the information from part (a) to find the area of the triangle whose vertices are $(2, 3)$, $(-2, -1)$, and $(5, 4)$.

   SOLUTION

   (a) To find the distance from the point $(2, 3)$ to the line containing the points $(-2, -1)$ and $(5, 4)$, we first find the equation of the line containing the points $(-2, -1)$ and $(5, 4)$. The slope of this line equals

   $$\frac{4 - (-1)}{5 - (-2)},$$

   which equals $\frac{5}{7}$. Thus the equation of the line containing the points $(-2, -1)$ and $(5, 4)$ is

   $$\frac{y - 4}{x - 5} = \frac{5}{7},$$

which can be rewritten as

$$y = \tfrac{5}{7}x + \tfrac{3}{7}.$$

To find the distance from the point $(2, 3)$ to the line containing the points $(-2, -1)$ and $(5, 4)$, we want to find the equation of the line containing the point $(2, 3)$ that is perpendicular to the line containing the points $(-2, -1)$ and $(5, 4)$. The equation of this line is

$$\frac{y - 3}{x - 2} = -\frac{7}{5},$$

which can be rewritten as

$$y = -\tfrac{7}{5}x + \tfrac{29}{5}.$$

To find where this line intersects the line containing the points $(-2, -1)$ and $(5, 4)$, we need to solve the equation

$$\tfrac{5}{7}x + \tfrac{3}{7} = -\tfrac{7}{5}x + \tfrac{29}{5}.$$

Simple algebra shows that the solution to this equation is $x = \tfrac{94}{37}$. Plugging this value of x into the equation of either line shows that $y = \tfrac{83}{37}$. Thus the two lines intersect at the point $\left(\tfrac{94}{37}, \tfrac{83}{37}\right)$.

Thus the distance from the point $(2, 3)$ to the line containing the points $(-2, -1)$ and $(5, 4)$ is the distance from the point $(2, 3)$ to the point $\left(\tfrac{94}{37}, \tfrac{83}{37}\right)$. This distance equals

$$\sqrt{\left(2 - \tfrac{94}{37}\right)^2 + \left(3 - \tfrac{83}{37}\right)^2},$$

which equals $\sqrt{\tfrac{32}{37}}$, which equals $4\sqrt{\tfrac{2}{37}}$.

(b) We will consider the line segment connecting the points $(-2, -1)$, and $(5, 4)$ to be the base of this triangle. In part (a), we found that the height of this triangle equals $4\sqrt{\tfrac{2}{37}}$.

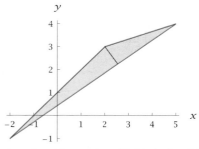

The triangle with vertices $(2, 3)$, $(-2, -1)$, *and* $(5, 4)$, *with a line segment showing its height.*

The base of the triangle is the distance between the points $(-2, -1)$ and $(5, 4)$. This distance equals $\sqrt{74}$. Thus the area of the triangle (one-half the base times the height) equals

$$\tfrac{1}{2}\sqrt{74}\left(4\sqrt{\tfrac{2}{37}}\right),$$

which equals 4.

[There are easier ways to find the area of this triangle, but the technique used here gives you practice with several important concepts.]

5. Find the area of the triangle whose vertices are $(2, 0)$, $(9, 0)$, and $(4, 5)$.

SOLUTION Choose the side connecting $(2, 0)$ and $(9, 0)$ as the base of this triangle. Thus the triangle below has base $9 - 2$, which equals 7.

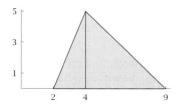

The height of this triangle is the length of the red line shown here; this height equals the second coordinate of the vertex $(4, 5)$. In other words, this triangle has height 5.

Thus this triangle has area $\tfrac{1}{2} \cdot 7 \cdot 5$, which equals $\tfrac{35}{2}$.

7. Suppose $(2, 3)$, $(1, 1)$, and $(7, 1)$ are three vertices of a parallelogram, two of whose sides are shown here.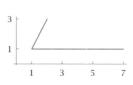

(a) Find the fourth vertex of this parallelogram.

(b) Find the area of this parallelogram.

SOLUTION

(a) Consider the horizontal side of the parallelogram connecting the points $(1, 1)$ and $(7, 1)$. This side has length 6. Thus the opposite side, which connects the point $(2, 3)$ and the fourth vertex, must also be horizontal and have length

6. Thus the second coordinate of the fourth vertex is the same as the second coordinate of $(2, 3)$, and the first coordinate of the fourth vertex is obtained by adding 6 to the first coordinate of $(2, 3)$. Hence the fourth vertex equals $(8, 3)$.

(b) The base of this parallelogram is the length of the side connecting the points $(1, 1)$ and $(7, 1)$, which equals 6. The height of this parallelogram is the length of a vertical line segment connecting the two horizontal sides. Because one of the horizontal sides lies on the line $y = 1$ and the other horizontal side lies on the line $y = 3$, a vertical line segment connecting these two sides will have length 2. Thus the parallelogram has height 2. Because this parallelogram has base 6 and height 2, it has area 12.

9. Find the area of this trapezoid, whose vertices are $(1, 1)$, $(7, 1)$, $(5, 3)$, and $(2, 3)$.

SOLUTION One base of this trapezoid is the length of the side connecting the points $(1, 1)$ and $(7, 1)$, which equals 6. The other base of this trapezoid is the length of the side connecting the points $(5, 3)$ and $(2, 3)$, which equals 3.

The height of this trapezoid is the length of a vertical line segment connecting the two horizontal sides. Because one of the horizontal sides lies on the line $y = 1$ and the other horizontal side lies on the line $y = 3$, a vertical line segment connecting these two sides will have length 2. Thus the trapezoid has height 2.

Because this trapezoid has bases 6 and 3 and has height 2, it has area $\frac{1}{2}(6 + 3) \cdot 2$, which equals 9.

11. Find the area of the region in the xy-plane under the line $y = \frac{x}{2}$, above the x-axis, and between the lines $x = 2$ and $x = 6$.

SOLUTION The line $x = 2$ intersects the line $y = \frac{x}{2}$ at the point $(2, 1)$. The line $x = 6$ intersects the line $y = \frac{x}{2}$ at the point $(6, 3)$.

Thus the region in question is the trapezoid shown above. The parallel sides of this trapezoid (the two vertical sides) have lengths 1 and 3, and thus this trapezoid has bases 1 and 3. As can be seen from the figure above, this trapezoid has height 4. Thus the area of this trapezoid is $\frac{1}{2} \cdot (1 + 3) \cdot 4$, which equals 8.

13. Let $f(x) = |x|$. Find the area of the region in the xy-plane under the graph of f, above the x-axis, and between the lines $x = -2$ and $x = 5$.

SOLUTION

The region under consideration is the union of two triangles, as shown here.

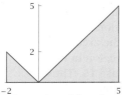

One of the triangles has base 2 and height 2 and thus has area 2. The other triangle has base 5 and height 5 and thus has area $\frac{25}{2}$. Thus the area of the region under consideration equals $2 + \frac{25}{2}$, which equals $\frac{29}{2}$.

15. Find the area of the region in the xy-plane under the curve $y = \sqrt{4 - x^2}$ (with $-2 \leq x \leq 2$) and above the x-axis.

SOLUTION

Square both sides of the equation $y = \sqrt{4 - x^2}$ and then add x^2 to both sides.

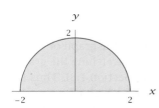

This gives the equation $x^2 + y^2 = 4$, which is the equation of a circle of radius 2 centered at the origin. However, the equation $y = \sqrt{4 - x^2}$ forces y to be nonnegative, and thus we have only the top half of the circle. Thus the region in question, which is shown above, has half the area inside a circle of radius 2. Hence the area of this region is $\frac{1}{2}\pi \cdot 2^2$, which equals 2π.

17. Using the answer from Exercise 15, find the area of the region in the xy-plane under the curve $y = 3\sqrt{4 - x^2}$ (with $-2 \le x \le 2$) and above the x-axis.

SOLUTION

The region in this exercise is obtained from the region in Exercise 15 by stretching vertically by a factor of 3. Thus by the Area Stretch Theorem, the area of this region is 3 times the area of the region in Exercise 15. Thus this region has area 6π.

19. Using the answer from Exercise 15, find the area of the region in the xy-plane under the curve $y = \sqrt{4 - \frac{x^2}{9}}$ (with $-6 \le x \le 6$) and above the x-axis.

SOLUTION Define a function f with domain the interval $[-2, 2]$ by $f(x) = \sqrt{4 - x^2}$. Define a function h with domain the interval $[-6, 6]$ by $h(x) = f(\frac{x}{3})$. Thus

$$h(x) = f(\tfrac{x}{3}) = \sqrt{4 - (\tfrac{x}{3})^2} = \sqrt{4 - \tfrac{x^2}{9}}.$$

Hence the graph of h is obtained by horizontally stretching the graph of f by a factor of 3 (see Section 1.3). Thus the region in this exercise is obtained from the region in Exercise 15 by stretching horizontally by a factor of 3.

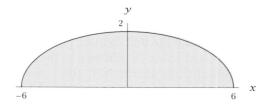

Thus by the Area Stretch Theorem, this region has area 6π.

21. Find the area of the region in the xy-plane under the curve

$$y = 1 + \sqrt{4 - x^2},$$

above the x-axis, and between the lines $x = -2$ and $x = 2$.

SOLUTION The curve $y = 1 + \sqrt{4 - x^2}$ is obtained by shifting the curve $y = \sqrt{4 - x^2}$ up 1 unit.

Thus we have the region above, which should be compared to the region shown in the solution to Exercise 15:

To find the area of this region, we break it into two parts. One part consists of the rectangle shown above that has base 4 and height 1 (and thus has area 4); the other part is obtained by shifting the region in Exercise 15 up 1 unit (and thus has area 2π, which is the area of the region in Exercise 15). Adding together the areas of these two parts, we conclude that the region shown above has area $4 + 2\pi$.

Use the following figure for the next two exercises.

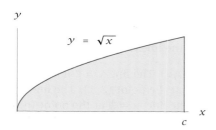

23. Suppose $c = 9$. Find the ratio between the area of the region above to the area of the region on the left in Example 3.

SOLUTION Let f be the function with domain $[0, 1]$ defined by $f(x) = \sqrt{x}$. Define a function g by

$$g(x) = 3f\left(\frac{x}{9}\right) = 3\sqrt{\frac{x}{9}} = \sqrt{x}.$$

Our results on function transformations (see Section 1.3) show that the graph of g is obtained from the graph of f by stretching horizontally by a factor of 9 and stretching vertically by a factor of 3. The Area Stretch Theorem now implies that these transformations increase the area by a factor of $9 \cdot 3$, which equals 27. Thus the area of the region above is 27 times the area of the region on the left in Example 3.

25. Find the area inside a circle with diameter 7.

SOLUTION A circle with diameter 7 has radius $\frac{7}{2}$. Thus the area inside this circle is $\pi\left(\frac{7}{2}\right)^2$, which equals $\frac{49\pi}{4}$.

27. Find the area inside a circle with circumference 5.

SOLUTION Let r denote the radius of this circle. Thus $2\pi r = 5$, which implies that $r = \frac{5}{2\pi}$. Thus the area inside this circle is $\pi\left(\frac{5}{2\pi}\right)^2$, which equals $\frac{25}{4\pi}$.

29. Find the area inside the circle whose equation is
$$x^2 - 6x + y^2 + 10y = 1.$$

SOLUTION To find the radius of the circle given by the equation above, we complete the square, as follows:

$$1 = x^2 - 6x + y^2 + 10y$$
$$= (x - 3)^2 - 9 + (y + 5)^2 - 25$$
$$= (x - 3)^2 + (y + 5)^2 - 34.$$

Adding 34 to both sides of this equation gives

$$(x - 3)^2 + (y + 5)^2 = 35.$$

Thus we see that this circle is centered at $(3, -5)$ (which is irrelevant for this exercise)

and that it has radius $\sqrt{35}$. Thus the area inside this circle equals $\pi\sqrt{35}^2$, which equals 35π.

31. Find a number t such that the area inside the circle
$$3x^2 + 3y^2 = t$$
is 8.

SOLUTION Rewriting the equation above as

$$x^2 + y^2 = \left(\sqrt{\tfrac{t}{3}}\right)^2,$$

we see that this circle has radius $\sqrt{\frac{t}{3}}$. Thus the area inside this circle is $\pi\left(\sqrt{\tfrac{t}{3}}\right)^2$, which equals $\frac{\pi t}{3}$. We want this area to equal 8, which means we need to solve the equation $\frac{\pi t}{3} = 8$. Thus $t = \frac{24}{\pi}$.

In Exercises 33–40, find the area inside the ellipse in the xy-plane determined by the given equation.

33. $\dfrac{x^2}{7} + \dfrac{y^2}{16} = 1$

SOLUTION Rewrite the equation of this ellipse as

$$\frac{x^2}{\sqrt{7}^2} + \frac{y^2}{4^2} = 1.$$

Thus the area inside this ellipse is $4\sqrt{7}\pi$.

35. $2x^2 + 3y^2 = 1$

SOLUTION Rewrite the equation of this ellipse in the form given by the area formula, as follows:

$$1 = 2x^2 + 3y^2$$
$$= \frac{x^2}{\frac{1}{2}} + \frac{y^2}{\frac{1}{3}}$$
$$= \frac{x^2}{\sqrt{\frac{1}{2}}^2} + \frac{y^2}{\sqrt{\frac{1}{3}}^2}.$$

Thus the area inside the ellipse is $\pi \cdot \sqrt{\frac{1}{2}} \cdot \sqrt{\frac{1}{3}}$, which equals $\frac{\pi}{\sqrt{6}}$. Multiplying numerator and denominator by $\sqrt{6}$, we see that we could also express this area as $\frac{\sqrt{6}\pi}{6}$.

37. $3x^2 + 2y^2 = 7$

SOLUTION   To put the equation of the ellipse in the form given by the area formula, begin by dividing both sides by 7, and then force the equation into the desired form, as follows:

$$1 = \tfrac{3}{7}x^2 + \tfrac{2}{7}y^2$$

$$= \frac{x^2}{\frac{7}{3}} + \frac{y^2}{\frac{7}{2}}$$

$$= \frac{x^2}{\sqrt{\frac{7}{3}}^2} + \frac{y^2}{\sqrt{\frac{7}{2}}^2}.$$

Thus the area inside the ellipse is $\pi \cdot \sqrt{\frac{7}{3}} \cdot \sqrt{\frac{7}{2}}$, which equals $\frac{7\pi}{\sqrt{6}}$. Multiplying numerator and denominator by $\sqrt{6}$, we see that we could also express this area as $\frac{7\sqrt{6}\pi}{6}$.

39. $3x^2 + 4x + 2y^2 + 3y = 2$

SOLUTION   To put the equation of this ellipse in a standard form, we complete the square, as follows:

$$2 = 3x^2 + 4x + 2y^2 + 3y$$

$$= 3[x^2 + \tfrac{4}{3}x] + 2[y^2 + \tfrac{3}{2}y]$$

$$= 3\big[(x + \tfrac{2}{3})^2 - \tfrac{4}{9}\big] + 2\big[(y + \tfrac{3}{4})^2 - \tfrac{9}{16}\big]$$

$$= 3(x + \tfrac{2}{3})^2 - \tfrac{4}{3} + 2(y + \tfrac{3}{4})^2 - \tfrac{9}{8}$$

$$= 3(x + \tfrac{2}{3})^2 + 2(y + \tfrac{3}{4})^2 - \tfrac{59}{24}$$

Adding $\frac{59}{24}$ to both sides of this equation gives

$$3(x + \tfrac{2}{3})^2 + 2(y + \tfrac{3}{4})^2 = \tfrac{107}{24}.$$

Now multiplying both sides of this equation by $\frac{24}{107}$ gives

$$\tfrac{72}{107}(x + \tfrac{2}{3})^2 + \tfrac{48}{107}(y + \tfrac{3}{4})^2 = 1.$$

We rewrite this equation in the form

$$\frac{\left(x + \frac{2}{3}\right)^2}{\left(\frac{\sqrt{107}}{\sqrt{72}}\right)^2} + \frac{\left(y + \frac{3}{4}\right)^2}{\left(\frac{\sqrt{107}}{\sqrt{48}}\right)^2} = 1$$

Thus the area inside this ellipse is

$$\pi \frac{\sqrt{107}}{\sqrt{72}}\frac{\sqrt{107}}{\sqrt{48}}$$

Because $\sqrt{72}\sqrt{48} = \sqrt{36 \cdot 2}\sqrt{16 \cdot 3} = 6\sqrt{2} \cdot 4\sqrt{3}$, this equals

$$\pi \frac{107}{24\sqrt{6}}.$$

Multiplying numerator and denominator by $\sqrt{6}$ also allows us to express this area as

$$\pi \frac{107\sqrt{6}}{144}.$$

41. Find a positive number c such that the area inside the ellipse

$$2x^2 + cy^2 = 5$$

is 3.

SOLUTION   To put the equation of the ellipse in the form given by the area formula, begin by dividing both sides by 5, and then force the equation into the desired form, as follows:

$$1 = \tfrac{2}{5}x^2 + \tfrac{c}{5}y^2$$

$$= \frac{x^2}{\frac{5}{2}} + \frac{y^2}{\frac{5}{c}}$$

$$= \frac{x^2}{\sqrt{\frac{5}{2}}^2} + \frac{y^2}{\sqrt{\frac{5}{c}}^2}.$$

Thus the area inside the ellipse is $\pi \cdot \sqrt{\frac{5}{2}} \cdot \sqrt{\frac{5}{c}}$, which equals $\frac{5\pi}{\sqrt{2c}}$. We want this area to equal 3, so we must solve the equation $\frac{5\pi}{\sqrt{2c}} = 3$. Squaring both sides and then solving for c gives $c = \frac{25\pi^2}{18}$.

43. Find numbers a and b such that $a > b$, $a + b = 15$, and the area inside the ellipse

$$\frac{x^2}{a^2} + \frac{y^2}{b^2} = 1$$

is 36π.

SOLUTION   The area inside the ellipse is πab. Thus we need to solve the simultaneous equations

$$a + b = 15 \quad \text{and} \quad ab = 36.$$

The first equation can be rewritten as $b = 15 - a$, and this value for b can then be substituted into the second equation, giving the equation

$$a(15 - a) = 36.$$

This is equivalent to the equation $a^2 - 15a + 36 = 0$, whose solutions (which can be found either through factoring or the quadratic formula) are $a = 3$ and $a = 12$. Choosing $a = 3$ gives $b = 15 - a = 12$, which violates the condition that $a > b$. Choosing $a = 12$ gives $b = 15 - 12 = 3$. Thus the only solution to this exercise is $a = 12$, $b = 3$.

4.3 | *e and the Natural Logarithm*

SECTION OBJECTIVES

By the end of this section you should

- understand how to use rectangles to approximate the area under a curve;
- understand the definition of *e*;
- understand the definition of the natural logarithm and its connection with area;
- be able to work comfortably with the exponential and natural logarithm functions.

We will focus on the area under the special curve $y = \frac{1}{x}$. This section will help prepare you for dealing with some of the crucial ideas in calculus, without the burden of the notation needed for calculus.

Estimating Area Using Rectangles

Our investigation of the area under parts of the curve $y = \frac{1}{x}$ will lead us to *e*, one of the most useful numbers in mathematics, and to the natural logarithm.

We begin by considering the yellow region shown here, whose area is denoted by area$(\frac{1}{x}, 1, 2)$. In other words, area$(\frac{1}{x}, 1, 2)$ equals the area of the region in the *xy*-plane under the curve $y = \frac{1}{x}$, above the *x*-axis, and between the lines $x = 1$ and $x = 2$.

The basic idea for calculating areas in calculus is to approximate the area of the region in question by rectangles whose area we can compute. The next example illustrates this procedure in the crudest possible fashion by using only one rectangle.

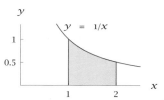

The area of this yellow region is denoted by area$(\frac{1}{x}, 1, 2)$.

Show that
$$\text{area}(\tfrac{1}{x}, 1, 2) < 1$$
by enclosing the corresponding region in a single rectangle.

EXAMPLE 1

SOLUTION   The smallest rectangle (with sides parallel to the coordinate axes) that contains the region under consideration is the 1-by-1 square shown here.

Because the region under consideration lies inside the 1-by-1 square, the figure here allows us to conclude that the area of the region under consideration is less than 1. In other words,
$$\text{area}(\tfrac{1}{x}, 1, 2) < 1.$$

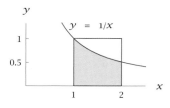

Now consider the yellow region shown below:

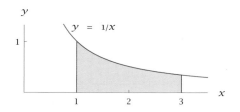

The area of this yellow region is denoted by area$(\frac{1}{x}, 1, 3)$.

The area of the yellow region above is denoted by area$(\frac{1}{x}, 1, 3)$. In other words, area$(\frac{1}{x}, 1, 3)$ equals the area of the region in the xy-plane under the curve $y = \frac{1}{x}$, above the x-axis, and between the lines $x = 1$ and $x = 3$.

The next example illustrates the procedure for approximating the area of a region by placing rectangles inside the region.

EXAMPLE 2

Show that area$(\frac{1}{x}, 1, 3) > 1$ by placing eight rectangles, each with the same size base, inside the corresponding region.

Unlike the previous crude example, this time we use eight rectangles to get a more accurate estimate.

SOLUTION   Place eight rectangles under the curve, as shown in the figure below:

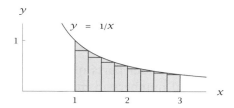

Because these eight rectangles lie inside the region under consideration, the area of the region is larger than the sum of the areas of the rectangles.

To compute the sum of the areas of the eight rectangles, first note that we have divided the interval $[1, 3]$, which has length 2, into eight intervals of equal size. Thus the base of each rectangle has length $\frac{1}{4}$.

Consider the first rectangle, whose base is the interval $[1, \frac{5}{4}]$. The figure above shows that the height of this first rectangle is $1/\frac{5}{4}$, which equals $\frac{4}{5}$. Because the first rectangle has base $\frac{1}{4}$ and height $\frac{4}{5}$, the area of the first rectangle equals $\frac{1}{4} \cdot \frac{4}{5}$, which equals $\frac{1}{5}$.

Similarly, the base of the second rectangle is the interval $[\frac{5}{4}, \frac{3}{2}]$. The figure above shows that the height of this second rectangle is $1/\frac{3}{2}$, which equals $\frac{2}{3}$. Because the second rectangle has base $\frac{1}{4}$ and height $\frac{2}{3}$, the area of the second rectangle equals $\frac{1}{4} \cdot \frac{2}{3}$, which equals $\frac{1}{6}$.

The area of the third rectangle is computed in the same fashion. Specifically, the third rectangle has base $\frac{1}{4}$ and height $1/\frac{7}{4}$, which equals $\frac{4}{7}$. Thus the area of the third rectangle equals $\frac{1}{4} \cdot \frac{4}{7}$, which equals $\frac{1}{7}$.

The first three rectangles have area $\frac{1}{5}$, $\frac{1}{6}$, and $\frac{1}{7}$, as we have now computed. From this data, you might guess that the eight rectangles have area $\frac{1}{5}, \frac{1}{6}, \frac{1}{7}, \frac{1}{8}, \frac{1}{9}, \frac{1}{10}, \frac{1}{11}$, and $\frac{1}{12}$. This guess is correct, as you should verify using the same procedure as used above to compute the area of the first three rectangles.

The inequality here goes in the opposite direction from the inequality in the previous example because now we are placing the rectangles under the curve rather than above it.

Thus the sum of the areas of all eight rectangles is

$$\tfrac{1}{5} + \tfrac{1}{6} + \tfrac{1}{7} + \tfrac{1}{8} + \tfrac{1}{9} + \tfrac{1}{10} + \tfrac{1}{11} + \tfrac{1}{12},$$

which equals $\frac{28271}{27720}$. Hence

$$\text{area}(\tfrac{1}{x}, 1, 3) > \tfrac{28271}{27720}.$$

The fraction on the right has a larger numerator than denominator; thus this fraction is larger than 1. Hence without further computation the inequality above shows that

$$\text{area}(\tfrac{1}{x}, 1, 3) > 1.$$

In the example above, $\frac{28271}{27720}$, which is approximately 1.0199, gives us an estimate for area$(\frac{1}{x}, 1, 3)$. If we want a more accurate estimate, we could divide the interval $[1, 3]$ into more intervals of equal size, and then use each of those smaller intervals as the base for a rectangle that lies under the curve $y = \frac{1}{x}$. The table below shows the sum of the areas of the rectangles for several different choices of the number of intervals into which $[1, 3]$ is divided (the sums have been rounded off to five digits):

number of rectangles	sum of area of rectangles
8	1.0199
10	1.0349
100	1.0920
1000	1.0979
10000	1.0985
100000	1.0986

Estimates of area$(\frac{1}{x}, 1, 3)$.

The sum of the areas of these rectangles was calculated with the aid of a computer.

The actual value of area$(\frac{1}{x}, 1, 3)$ is an irrational number whose first five digits are 1.0986. The table above shows that we can get an accurate estimate of the area of the region under study by dividing the interval $[1, 3]$ into many small intervals and then computing the sum of the corresponding rectangles that lie under the curve $y = \frac{1}{x}$.

Defining *e*

The area under portions of the curve $y = \frac{1}{x}$ has some remarkable properties. To discuss these properties, we introduce the following notation, which we have already used for $c = 2$ and $c = 3$:

area$(\frac{1}{x}, 1, c)$

For $c > 1$, let area$(\frac{1}{x}, 1, c)$ denote the area of the yellow region below:

In other words, area$(\frac{1}{x}, 1, c)$ is the area of the region under the curve $y = \frac{1}{x}$, above the x-axis, and between the lines $x = 1$ and $x = c$.

To get a feeling for how area$(\frac{1}{x}, 1, c)$ depends on c, consider the following table:

c	$\operatorname{area}(\frac{1}{x}, 1, c)$
2	0.693147
3	1.098612
4	1.386294
5	1.609438
6	1.791759
7	1.945910
8	2.079442
9	2.197225

Here values of
$\operatorname{area}(\frac{1}{x}, 1, c)$ are
rounded off to six
digits after the
decimal point.

The table above agrees with the inequalities that we derived earlier in this section: $\operatorname{area}(\frac{1}{x}, 1, 2) < 1$ and $\operatorname{area}(\frac{1}{x}, 1, 3) > 1$.

Before reading the next paragraph, pause for a moment to see if you can discover a relationship between entries in the table above.

If you look for a relationship between entries in the table above, most likely the first thing you will notice is that $\operatorname{area}(\frac{1}{x}, 1, 4) = 2\operatorname{area}(\frac{1}{x}, 1, 2)$. To see if any other such relationships lurk in the table, we now add a third column showing the ratio of $\operatorname{area}(\frac{1}{x}, 1, c)$ with $\operatorname{area}(\frac{1}{x}, 1, 2)$ and a fourth column showing the ratio of $\operatorname{area}(\frac{1}{x}, 1, c)$ with $\operatorname{area}(\frac{1}{x}, 1, 3)$ (both new columns rounded off to five digits after the decimal point):

c	$\operatorname{area}(\frac{1}{x}, 1, c)$	$\dfrac{\operatorname{area}(\frac{1}{x}, 1, c)}{\operatorname{area}(\frac{1}{x}, 1, 2)}$	$\dfrac{\operatorname{area}(\frac{1}{x}, 1, c)}{\operatorname{area}(\frac{1}{x}, 1, 3)}$
2	0.693147	1.00000	0.63093
3	1.098612	1.58496	1.00000
4	1.386294	2.00000	1.26186
5	1.609438	2.32193	1.46497
6	1.791759	2.58496	1.63093
7	1.945910	2.80735	1.77124
8	2.079442	3.00000	1.89279
9	2.197225	3.16993	2.00000

The integer entries in the last two columns stand out. We already noted that $\operatorname{area}(\frac{1}{x}, 1, 4) = 2\operatorname{area}(\frac{1}{x}, 1, 2)$; the table above now shows the nice relationships $\operatorname{area}(\frac{1}{x}, 1, 8) = 3\operatorname{area}(\frac{1}{x}, 1, 2)$ and $\operatorname{area}(\frac{1}{x}, 1, 9) = 2\operatorname{area}(\frac{1}{x}, 1, 3)$. Because $4 = 2^2$ and $8 = 2^3$ and $9 = 3^2$, we write these equations more suggestively as

$$\operatorname{area}(\tfrac{1}{x}, 1, 2^2) = 2\operatorname{area}(\tfrac{1}{x}, 1, 2);$$

$$\operatorname{area}(\tfrac{1}{x}, 1, 2^3) = 3\operatorname{area}(\tfrac{1}{x}, 1, 2);$$

$$\operatorname{area}(\tfrac{1}{x}, 1, 3^2) = 2\operatorname{area}(\tfrac{1}{x}, 1, 3).$$

The equations above suggest the following remarkable formula:

An area formula

$$\text{area}(\tfrac{1}{x}, 1, c^t) = t \, \text{area}(\tfrac{1}{x}, 1, c)$$

for every $c > 1$ and every $t > 0$.

We have already seen that the formula above holds in three special cases. The formula above will be derived more generally in the next section. For now, assume temporarily that this has been done.

The right side of the equation above would be simplified if c is such that $\text{area}(\tfrac{1}{x}, 1, c) = 1$. Thus we make the following definition:

Definition of *e*

e is the number such that

$$\text{area}(\tfrac{1}{x}, 1, e) = 1.$$

Earlier in this chapter we showed that $\text{area}(\tfrac{1}{x}, 1, 2)$ is less than 1 and that $\text{area}(\tfrac{1}{x}, 1, 3)$ is greater than 1. Thus for some number between 2 and 3, the area of the region we are considering must equal 1, and that number is called *e*.

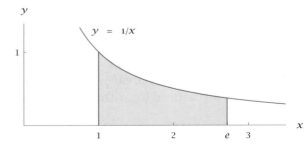

This region under the curve $y = \frac{1}{x}$ has area 1.

The number *e* is given a special name because it is so useful. We will see some applications of *e* later in this chapter, and you will see even more applications of *e* in your calculus course.

It turns out that *e* is an irrational number. Here is a 40-digit approximation of *e*:

$$e \approx 2.7182818284590452353602874713526624977757$$

For many practical purposes, 2.718 is a good approximation of e—the error is about 0.01%.

The fraction $\frac{19}{7}$ approximates *e* fairly well—the error is about 0.1%. The fraction $\frac{2721}{1001}$ approximates *e* even better—the error is about 0.000004%.

Keep in mind that *e* is not equal to 2.718 or $\frac{19}{7}$ or $\frac{2721}{1001}$. All of these are useful approximations, but *e* is an irrational number that cannot be represented exactly as a decimal number or as a fraction.

As part of a puzzle aimed at attracting mathematically skilled employees, Google once put up billboards around the country asking for the first 10-digit prime number found in consecutive digits of e. The solution, found with the aid of a computer, is 7427466391, which starts in the 99th digit after the decimal point in the decimal representation of e.

Defining the Natural Logarithm

The formula

$$\text{area}(\tfrac{1}{x}, 1, c^t) = t \, \text{area}(\tfrac{1}{x}, 1, c)$$

was introduced above. This formula should remind you of the behavior of logarithms with respect to powers. We will now see that the area under the curve $y = \frac{1}{x}$ is indeed intimately connected with a logarithm.

In the formula above, set c equal to e and use the equation $\text{area}(\tfrac{1}{x}, 1, e) = 1$ to see that

$$\text{area}(\tfrac{1}{x}, 1, e^t) = t$$

for every positive number t.

Now consider an arbitrary number $c > 1$. We can write c as a power of e in the usual fashion: $c = e^{\log_e c}$. Thus

$$\text{area}(\tfrac{1}{x}, 1, c) = \text{area}(\tfrac{1}{x}, 1, e^{\log_e c}) = \log_e c,$$

where the last equality comes from setting $t = \log_e c$ in the equation from the previous paragraph.

The logarithm with base e, which appeared above, is so useful that it gets a special name and special notation.

Natural logarithm

For $c > 0$ the **natural logarithm** of c, denoted $\ln c$, is defined by

$$\ln c = \log_e c.$$

As an indication of the usefulness of e and the natural logarithm, take a look at your calculator. It probably has buttons for e^x and $\ln x$.

With this new notation, we can rewrite the equality $\text{area}(\tfrac{1}{x}, 1, c) = \log_e c$, which was derived just before we defined the natural logarithm, as follows:

Natural logarithms as areas

For $c > 1$, the natural logarithm of c is the area of the region below:

In other words,

$$\ln c = \text{area}(\tfrac{1}{x}, 1, c),$$

which means that $\ln c$ equals the area of the region under the curve $y = \frac{1}{x}$, above the x-axis, and between the lines $x = 1$ and $x = c$.

Properties of the Exponential Function and ln

The function whose value at a number x equals e^x is so important that it also gets a special name.

> ### The exponential function
>
> The **exponential function** is the function f defined by
>
> $$f(x) = e^x$$
>
> for every real number x.

The graph of the exponential function e^x looks similar to the graphs of the functions 2^x or 3^x or any other function with exponential growth. Specifically, e^x grows rapidly as x gets large, and e^x is close to 0 for negative values of x with large absolute value.

The domain of the exponential function is the set of real numbers, and the range of the exponential function is the set of positive numbers. Furthermore, the exponential function is an increasing function, as is every function of the form b^x for $b > 1$.

Powers of e have the same algebraic properties as powers of any number. Thus the identities listed below should already be familiar to you. They are included here as a review of key algebraic properties in the specific case of powers of e.

> ### Properties of powers of e
>
> $$e^0 = 1$$
>
> $$e^1 = e$$
>
> $$e^x e^y = e^{x+y}$$
>
> $$e^{-x} = \frac{1}{e^x}$$
>
> $$\frac{e^x}{e^y} = e^{x-y}$$
>
> $$(e^x)^y = e^{xy}$$

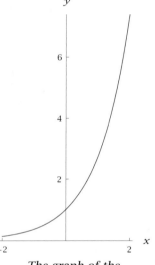

The graph of the exponential function e^x on $[-2, 2]$. The same scale is used on both axes to show the rapid growth and decay of e^x.

The natural logarithm of a positive number x, denoted $\ln x$, equals $\log_e x$. Thus the graph of the natural logarithm looks similar to the graphs of the functions $\log_2 x$ or $\log x$ or $\log_b x$ for any number $b > 1$. Specifically, $\ln x$ grows slowly as x gets large. Furthermore, if x is a small positive number, then $\ln x$ is a negative number with large absolute value, as shown in the following figure:

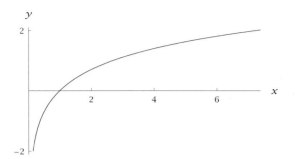

The graph of $\ln x$ *on the interval* $[e^{-2}, e^2]$. *The same scale is used on both axes to show the slow growth of* $\ln x$ *and the rapid descent near 0 toward negative numbers with large absolute value.*

The domain of $\ln x$ is the set of positive numbers, and the range of $\ln x$ is the set of real numbers. Furthermore, $\ln x$ is an increasing function because it is the inverse of the increasing function e^x.

Recall that in this book, as in most precalculus books, $\log x$ means $\log_{10} x$. However, the natural logarithm is so important that many mathematicians use $\log x$ to denote the natural logarithm rather than the logarithm with base 10.

Because the natural logarithm is the logarithm with base e, it has all the properties we saw earlier for logarithms with an arbitrary base. For review, we summarize the key properties here. In the box below, we assume that x and y are positive numbers.

Properties of the natural logarithm

$$\ln 1 = 0$$

$$\ln e = 1$$

$$\ln(xy) = \ln x + \ln y$$

$$\ln \tfrac{1}{x} = -\ln x$$

$$\ln \tfrac{x}{y} = \ln x - \ln y$$

$$\ln x^t = t \ln x$$

The exponential function e^x and the natural logarithm $\ln x$ (which equals $\log_e x$) are the inverse functions for each other, just as the functions 2^x and $\log_2 x$ are the inverse functions for each other (in this statement, we could replace 2 by any positive number $b \neq 1$). Thus the exponential function and the natural logarithm exhibit the same behavior as any two functions that are the inverse functions for each other. For review, we summarize here the key properties connecting the exponential function and the natural logarithm:

Connections between the exponential function and the natural logarithm

- $\ln y = x$ means $e^x = y$.

- $\ln e^x = x$ for every real number x.

- $e^{\ln y} = y$ for every positive number y.

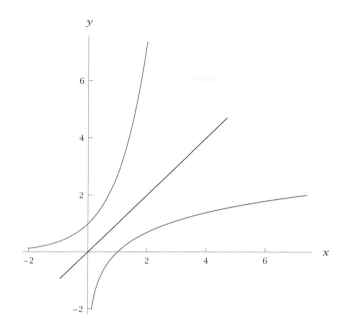

The figure here shows the graphs of e^x (blue) on $[-2, 2]$ and $\ln x$ (red) on $[e^{-2}, e^2]$. Each graph is the reflection of the other through the line $y = x$ (black).

As usual for a function and its inverse, the graphs of the exponential function and the natural logarithm are symmetric to each other with respect to the line $y = x$.

EXERCISES

1. 📱 For $x = 7$ and $y = 13$, evaluate each of the following:

   (a) $\ln(x + y)$ (b) $\ln x + \ln y$

   [*This exercise and the next one emphasize that $\ln(x + y)$ does not equal $\ln x + \ln y$.*]

2. 📱 For $x = 0.4$ and $y = 3.5$, evaluate each of the following:

   (a) $\ln(x + y)$ (b) $\ln x + \ln y$

3. 📱 For $x = 3$ and $y = 8$, evaluate each of the following:

   (a) $\ln(xy)$ (b) $(\ln x)(\ln y)$

   [*This exercise and the next one emphasize that $\ln(xy)$ does not equal $(\ln x)(\ln y)$.*]

4. 📱 For $x = 1.1$ and $y = 5$, evaluate each of the following:

   (a) $\ln(xy)$ (b) $(\ln x)(\ln y)$

5. 📱 For $x = 12$ and $y = 2$, evaluate each of the following:

   (a) $\ln \frac{x}{y}$ (b) $\frac{\ln x}{\ln y}$

   [*This exercise and the next one emphasize that $\ln \frac{x}{y}$ does not equal $\frac{\ln x}{\ln y}$.*]

6. 📱 For $x = 18$ and $y = 0.3$, evaluate each of the following:

   (a) $\ln \frac{x}{y}$ (b) $\frac{\ln x}{\ln y}$

7. Find a number y such that $\ln y = 4$.

8. Find a number c such that $\ln c = 5$.

9. Find a number x such that $\ln x = -2$.

10. Find a number x such that $\ln x = -3$.

11. Find a number t such that $\ln(2t + 1) = -4$.

12. Find a number w such that $\ln(3w - 2) = 5$.

13. Find all numbers y such that $\ln(y^2 + 1) = 3$.

14. Find all numbers r such that $\ln(2r^2 - 3) = -1$.

15. Find a number x such that $e^{3x-1} = 2$.

16. Find a number y such that $e^{4y-3} = 5$.

For Exercises 17–24, find all numbers x that satisfy the given equation.

17. $\ln(x + 5) - \ln(x - 1) = 2$

18. $\ln(x + 4) - \ln(x - 2) = 3$

19. $\ln(x + 5) + \ln(x - 1) = 2$

20. $\ln(x + 4) + \ln(x + 2) = 2$

21. $\dfrac{\ln(12x)}{\ln(5x)} = 2$

22. $\dfrac{\ln(11x)}{\ln(4x)} = 2$

23. $(\ln(3x)) \ln x = 4$

24. $(\ln(6x)) \ln x = 5$

25. Find the number c such that $\text{area}(\frac{1}{x}, 1, c) = 2$.

26. Find the number c such that $\text{area}(\frac{1}{x}, 1, c) = 3$.

27. Find the number t that makes e^{t^2+6t} as small as possible.
    [Here e^{t^2+6t} means $e^{(t^2+6t)}$.]

28. Find the number t that makes e^{t^2+8t+3} as small as possible.

29. Find a number x such that
$$e^{2x} + e^x = 6.$$

30. Find a number x such that
$$e^{2x} - 4e^x = 12.$$

31. Find a number y such that
$$\frac{1 + \ln y}{2 + \ln y} = 0.9.$$

32. Find a number w such that
$$\frac{4 - \ln w}{3 - 5 \ln w} = 3.6.$$

For Exercises 33–36, find a formula for $(f \circ g)(x)$ assuming that f and g are the indicated functions.

33. $f(x) = \ln x$ and $g(x) = e^{5x}$

34. $f(x) = \ln x$ and $g(x) = e^{4-7x}$

35. $f(x) = e^{2x}$ and $g(x) = \ln x$

36. $f(x) = e^{8-5x}$ and $g(x) = \ln x$

For each of the functions f given in Exercises 37–46:

  (a) *Find the domain of f.*

  (b) *Find the range of f.*

  (c) *Find a formula for f^{-1}.*

  (d) *Find the domain of f^{-1}.*

  (e) *Find the range of f^{-1}.*

You can check your solutions to part (c) by verifying that $f^{-1} \circ f = I$ and $f \circ f^{-1} = I$. (Recall that I is the function defined by $I(x) = x$.)

37. $f(x) = 2 + \ln x$ 42. $f(x) = 5e^{9x}$

38. $f(x) = 3 - \ln x$ 43. $f(x) = 4 + \ln(x - 2)$

39. $f(x) = 4 - 5 \ln x$ 44. $f(x) = 3 + \ln(x + 5)$

40. $f(x) = -6 + 7 \ln x$ 45. $f(x) = 5 + 6e^{7x}$

41. $f(x) = 3e^{2x}$ 46. $f(x) = 4 - 2e^{8x}$

PROBLEMS

47. Verify that the last five rectangles in the figure in Example 2 have area $\frac{1}{8}$, $\frac{1}{9}$, $\frac{1}{10}$, $\frac{1}{11}$, and $\frac{1}{12}$.

48. Consider this figure:

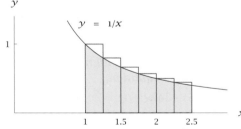

The region under the curve $y = \frac{1}{x}$, above the x-axis, and between the lines $x = 1$ and $x = 2.5$.

  (a) Calculate the sum of the areas of all six rectangles shown in the figure above.

  (b) Explain why the calculation you did in part (a) shows that
$$\text{area}(\tfrac{1}{x}, 1, 2.5) < 1.$$

  (c) Explain why the inequality above shows that $e > 2.5$.

49. Explain why
$$\ln x \approx 2.302585 \log x$$
for every positive number x.

50. Explain why the solution to part (b) of Exercise 5 in this section is the same as the solution to part (b) of Exercise 5 in Section 3.3.

51. Suppose c is a number such that $\text{area}(\frac{1}{x}, 1, c) > 1000$. Explain why $c > 2^{1000}$.

The functions cosh and sinh are defined by

$$\cosh x = \frac{e^x + e^{-x}}{2} \quad and \quad \sinh x = \frac{e^x - e^{-x}}{2}$$

for every real number x. For reasons that do not concern us here, these functions are called the hyperbolic cosine and hyperbolic sine; they are useful in engineering.

52. Show that cosh is an even function.

53. Show that sinh is an odd function.

54. Show that

$$(\cosh x)^2 - (\sinh x)^2 = 1$$

for every real number x.

55. Show that $\cosh x \geq 1$ for every real number x.

56. Show that

$$\cosh(x + y) = \cosh x \cosh y + \sinh x \sinh y$$

for all real numbers x and y.

57. Show that

$$\sinh(x + y) = \sinh x \cosh y + \cosh x \sinh y$$

for all real numbers x and y.

58. Show that

$$(\cosh x + \sinh x)^t = \cosh(tx) + \sinh(tx)$$

for all real numbers x and t.

59. Show that if x is very large, then

$$\cosh x \approx \sinh h \approx \frac{e^x}{2}.$$

60. Show that the range of sinh is the set of real numbers.

61. Show that sinh is a one-to-one function and that its inverse is given by the formula

$$(\sinh)^{-1}(y) = \ln(y + \sqrt{y^2 + 1})$$

for every real number y.

62. Show that the range of cosh is the interval $[1, \infty)$.

63. Suppose f is the function defined by

$$f(x) = \cosh x$$

for every $x \geq 0$. In other words, f is defined by the same formula as cosh, but the domain of f is the interval $[0, \infty)$ and the domain of cosh is the set of real numbers. Show that f is a one-to-one function and that its inverse is given by the formula

$$f^{-1}(y) = \ln(y + \sqrt{y^2 - 1})$$

for every $y \geq 1$.

64. Write a description of how the shape of the St. Louis Gateway Arch, whose picture appears on the opening page of this chapter, is related to the graph of $\cosh x$.

    [*You should be able to find the necessary information using an appropriate web search.*]

WORKED-OUT SOLUTIONS *to Odd-numbered Exercises*

1. For $x = 7$ and $y = 13$, evaluate each of the following:

   (a) $\ln(x + y)$ (b) $\ln x + \ln y$

   SOLUTION

   (a) $\ln(7 + 13) = \ln 20 \approx 2.99573$

   (b) $\qquad \ln 7 + \ln 13 \approx 1.94591 + 2.56495$

   $$= 4.51086$$

3. For $x = 3$ and $y = 8$, evaluate each of the following:

   (a) $\ln(xy)$ (b) $(\ln x)(\ln y)$

   SOLUTION

   (a) $\ln(3 \cdot 8) = \ln 24 \approx 3.17805$

   (b) $\qquad (\ln 3)(\ln 8) \approx (1.09861)(2.07944)$

   $$\approx 2.2845$$

5. For $x = 12$ and $y = 2$, evaluate each of the following:

   (a) $\ln \frac{x}{y}$ (b) $\frac{\ln x}{\ln y}$

SOLUTION

(a) $\ln \frac{12}{2} = \ln 6 \approx 1.79176$

(b) $\dfrac{\ln 12}{\ln 2} \approx \dfrac{2.48491}{0.693147} \approx 3.58496$

7. Find a number y such that $\ln y = 4$.

SOLUTION Recall that $\ln y$ is simply shorthand for $\log_e y$. Thus the equation $\ln y = 4$ can be rewritten as $\log_e y = 4$. The definition of a logarithm now implies that $y = e^4$.

9. Find a number x such that $\ln x = -2$.

SOLUTION Recall that $\ln x$ is simply shorthand for $\log_e x$. Thus the equation $\ln x = -2$ can be rewritten as $\log_e x = -2$. The definition of a logarithm now implies that $x = e^{-2}$.

11. Find a number t such that $\ln(2t + 1) = -4$.

SOLUTION The equation $\ln(2t + 1) = -4$ implies that
$$e^{-4} = 2t + 1.$$
Solving this equation for t, we get
$$t = \frac{e^{-4} - 1}{2}.$$

13. Find all numbers y such that $\ln(y^2 + 1) = 3$.

SOLUTION The equation $\ln(y^2 + 1) = 3$ implies that
$$e^3 = y^2 + 1.$$
Thus $y^2 = e^3 - 1$, which means that $y = \sqrt{e^3 - 1}$ or $y = -\sqrt{e^3 - 1}$.

15. Find a number x such that $e^{3x-1} = 2$.

SOLUTION The equation $e^{3x-1} = 2$ implies that
$$3x - 1 = \ln 2.$$
Solving this equation for x, we get
$$x = \frac{1 + \ln 2}{3}.$$

For Exercises 17–24, find all numbers x that satisfy the given equation.

17. $\ln(x + 5) - \ln(x - 1) = 2$

SOLUTION Our equation can be rewritten as follows:
$$2 = \ln(x + 5) - \ln(x - 1)$$
$$= \ln \frac{x + 5}{x - 1}.$$
Thus
$$\frac{x + 5}{x - 1} = e^2.$$
We can solve the equation above for x, getting
$$x = \frac{e^2 + 5}{e^2 - 1}.$$

19. $\ln(x + 5) + \ln(x - 1) = 2$

SOLUTION Our equation can be rewritten as follows:
$$2 = \ln(x + 5) + \ln(x - 1)$$
$$= \ln((x + 5)(x - 1))$$
$$= \ln(x^2 + 4x - 5).$$
Thus
$$x^2 + 4x - 5 = e^2,$$
which implies that
$$x^2 + 4x - (e^2 + 5) = 0.$$
We can solve the equation above using the quadratic formula, getting $x = -2 + \sqrt{9 + e^2}$ or $x = -2 - \sqrt{9 + e^2}$. However, both $x + 5$ and $x - 1$ are negative if $x = -2 - \sqrt{9 + e^2}$; because the logarithm of a negative number is undefined, we must discard this root of the equation above. We conclude that the only value of x satisfying the equation $\ln(x + 5) + \ln(x - 1) = 2$ is $x = -2 + \sqrt{9 + e^2}$.

21. $\dfrac{\ln(12x)}{\ln(5x)} = 2$

SOLUTION Our equation can be rewritten as follows:
$$2 = \frac{\ln(12x)}{\ln(5x)}$$
$$= \frac{\ln 12 + \ln x}{\ln 5 + \ln x}.$$
Solving this equation for $\ln x$ (the first step in doing this is to multiply both sides by the denominator $\ln 5 + \ln x$), we get

$\ln x = \ln 12 - 2\ln 5$

$= \ln 12 - \ln 25$

$= \ln \frac{12}{25}.$

Thus $x = \frac{12}{25}.$

23. (ln(3x)) ln x = 4

SOLUTION   Our equation can be rewritten as follows:

$4 = (\ln(3x))\ln x$

$= (\ln x + \ln 3)\ln x$

$= (\ln x)^2 + (\ln 3)(\ln x).$

Letting $y = \ln x$, we can rewrite the equation above as

$$y^2 + (\ln 3)y - 4 = 0.$$

Use the quadratic formula to solve the equation above for y, getting

$$y \approx -2.62337 \quad \text{or} \quad y \approx 1.52476.$$

Thus

$$\ln x \approx -2.62337 \quad \text{or} \quad \ln x \approx 1.52476,$$

which means that

$$x \approx e^{-2.62337} \approx 0.072558$$

or

$$x \approx e^{1.52476} \approx 4.59403.$$

25. Find the number c such that area$(\frac{1}{x}, 1, c) = 2.$

SOLUTION   Because $2 = \text{area}(\frac{1}{x}, 1, c) = \ln c$, we see that $c = e^2.$

27. Find the number t that makes e^{t^2+6t} as small as possible.

SOLUTION   Because e^x is an increasing function of x, the number e^{t^2+6t} will be as small as possible when $t^2 + 6t$ is as small as possible. To find when $t^2 + 6t$ is as small as possible, we complete the square:

$$t^2 + 6t = (t+3)^2 - 9.$$

The equation above shows that $t^2 + 6t$ is as small as possible when $t = -3.$

29. Find a number x such that

$$e^{2x} + e^x = 6.$$

SOLUTION   Note that $e^{2x} = (e^x)^2$. This suggests that we let $t = e^x$. Then the equation above can be rewritten as

$$t^2 + t - 6 = 0.$$

The solutions to this equation (which can be found either by using the quadratic formula or by factoring) are $t = -3$ and $t = 2$. Thus $e^x = -3$ or $e^x = 2$. However, there is no real number x such that $e^x = -3$ (because e^x is positive for every real number x), and thus we must have $e^x = 2$. Thus $x = \ln 2 \approx 0.693147.$

31. Find a number y such that

$$\frac{1 + \ln y}{2 + \ln y} = 0.9.$$

SOLUTION   Multiplying both sides of the equation above by $2 + \ln y$ and then solving for $\ln y$ gives $\ln y = 8$. Thus $y = e^8 \approx 2980.96.$

For Exercises 33–36, find a formula for $(f \circ g)(x)$ assuming that f and g are the indicated functions.

33. $f(x) = \ln x$ and $g(x) = e^{5x}$

SOLUTION

$$(f \circ g)(x) = f(g(x)) = f(e^{5x}) = \ln e^{5x} = 5x$$

35. $f(x) = e^{2x}$ and $g(x) = \ln x$

SOLUTION

$$(f \circ g)(x) = f(g(x)) = f(\ln x)$$
$$= e^{2\ln x} = (e^{\ln x})^2 = x^2$$

For each of the functions f given in Exercises 37–46:

(a) *Find the domain of f.*

(b) *Find the range of f.*

(c) *Find a formula for f^{-1}.*

(d) *Find the domain of f^{-1}.*

(e) *Find the range of f^{-1}.*

You can check your solutions to part (c) by verifying that $f^{-1} \circ f = I$ and $f \circ f^{-1} = I$. (Recall that I is the function defined by $I(x) = x$.)

37. $f(x) = 2 + \ln x$

SOLUTION

(a) The expression $2 + \ln x$ makes sense for all positive numbers x. Thus the domain of f is the set of positive numbers.

(b) To find the range of f, we need to find the numbers y such that

$$y = 2 + \ln x$$

for some x in the domain of f. In other words, we need to find the values of y such that the equation above can be solved for a positive number x. To solve this equation for x, subtract 2 from both sides, getting $y - 2 = \ln x$, which implies that

$$x = e^{y-2}.$$

The expression above on the right makes sense for every real number y and produces a positive number x (because e raised to any power is positive). Thus the range of f is the set of real numbers.

(c) The expression above shows that f^{-1} is given by the expression

$$f^{-1}(y) = e^{y-2}.$$

(d) The domain of f^{-1} equals the range of f. Thus the domain of f^{-1} is the set of real numbers.

(e) The range of f^{-1} equals the domain of f. Thus the range of f^{-1} is the set of positive numbers.

39. $f(x) = 4 - 5 \ln x$

SOLUTION

(a) The expression $4 - 5 \ln x$ makes sense for all positive numbers x. Thus the domain of f is the set of positive numbers.

(b) To find the range of f, we need to find the numbers y such that

$$y = 4 - 5 \ln x$$

for some x in the domain of f. In other words, we need to find the values of y such that the equation above can be solved for a positive number x. To solve this equation for x, subtract 4 from both sides, then divide both sides by -5, getting $\frac{4-y}{5} = \ln x$, which implies that

$$x = e^{(4-y)/5}.$$

The expression above on the right makes sense for every real number y and produces a positive number x (because e raised to any power is positive). Thus the range of f is the set of real numbers.

(c) The expression above shows that f^{-1} is given by the expression

$$f^{-1}(y) = e^{(4-y)/5}.$$

(d) The domain of f^{-1} equals the range of f. Thus the domain of f^{-1} is the set of real numbers.

(e) The range of f^{-1} equals the domain of f. Thus the range of f^{-1} is the set of positive numbers.

41. $f(x) = 3e^{2x}$

SOLUTION

(a) The expression $3e^{2x}$ makes sense for all real numbers x. Thus the domain of f is the set of real numbers.

(b) To find the range of f, we need to find the numbers y such that

$$y = 3e^{2x}$$

for some x in the domain of f. In other words, we need to find the values of y such that the equation above can be solved for a real number x. To solve this equation for x, divide both sides by 3, getting $\frac{y}{3} = e^{2x}$, which implies that $2x = \ln \frac{y}{3}$. Thus

$$x = \frac{\ln \frac{y}{3}}{2}.$$

The expression above on the right makes sense for every positive number y and produces a real number x. Thus the range of f is the set of positive numbers.

(c) The expression above shows that f^{-1} is given by the expression

$$f^{-1}(y) = \frac{\ln \frac{y}{3}}{2}.$$

(d) The domain of f^{-1} equals the range of f. Thus the domain of f^{-1} is the set of positive numbers.

(e) The range of f^{-1} equals the domain of f. Thus the range of f^{-1} is the set of real numbers.

43. $f(x) = 4 + \ln(x - 2)$

SOLUTION

(a) The expression $4 + \ln(x - 2)$ makes sense when $x > 2$. Thus the domain of f is the interval $(2, \infty)$.

(b) To find the range of f, we need to find the numbers y such that

$$y = 4 + \ln(x - 2)$$

for some x in the domain of f. In other words, we need to find the values of y such that the equation above can be solved for a number $x > 2$. To solve this equation for x, subtract 4 from both sides, getting $y - 4 = \ln(x - 2)$, which implies that $x - 2 = e^{y-4}$. Thus

$$x = 2 + e^{y-4}.$$

The expression above on the right makes sense for every real number y and produces a number $x > 2$ (because e raised to any power is positive). Thus the range of f is the set of real numbers.

(c) The expression above shows that f^{-1} is given by the expression

$$f^{-1}(y) = 2 + e^{y-4}.$$

(d) The domain of f^{-1} equals the range of f. Thus the domain of f^{-1} is the set of real numbers.

(e) The range of f^{-1} equals the domain of f. Thus the range of f^{-1} is the interval $(2, \infty)$.

45. $f(x) = 5 + 6e^{7x}$

SOLUTION

(a) The expression $5 + 6e^{7x}$ makes sense for all real numbers x. Thus the domain of f is the set of real numbers.

(b) To find the range of f, we need to find the numbers y such that

$$y = 5 + 6e^{7x}$$

for some x in the domain of f. In other words, we need to find the values of y such that the equation above can be solved for a real number x. To solve this equation for x, subtract 5 from both sides, then divide both sides by 6, getting $\frac{y-5}{6} = e^{7x}$, which implies that $7x = \ln \frac{y-5}{6}$. Thus

$$x = \frac{\ln \frac{y-5}{6}}{7}.$$

The expression above on the right makes sense for every $y > 5$ and produces a real number x. Thus the range of f is the interval $(5, \infty)$.

(c) The expression above shows that f^{-1} is given by the expression

$$f^{-1}(y) = \frac{\ln \frac{y-5}{6}}{7}.$$

(d) The domain of f^{-1} equals the range of f. Thus the domain of f^{-1} is the interval $(5, \infty)$.

(e) The range of f^{-1} equals the domain of f. Thus the range of f^{-1} is the set of real numbers.

4.4 | *Approximations with e and* ln

SECTION OBJECTIVES

By the end of this section you should

- be able to approximate $\ln(1 + t)$ for small values of t;
- be able to approximate e^t for small values of t;
- be able to approximate $(1 + \frac{r}{x})^x$ when x is much larger than r;
- understand the area formula that led to e and the natural logarithm.

Approximation of the Natural Logarithm

The table below shows the value of the natural logarithm of $1 + t$, rounded off to show six significant digits, for some small values of t:

t	$\ln(1 + t)$
0.05	0.0487902
0.005	0.00498754
0.0005	0.000499875
0.00005	0.0000499988
0.000005	0.00000499999

Values of $\ln(1 + t)$, *rounded off to six significant digits.*

The word "small" in this context does not have a rigorous meaning, but think of numbers t such as those shown in the table above. For purposes of visibility, t as shown in the figure is larger than what we have in mind.

This table leads us to guess that if t is a small positive number, then $\ln(1 + t)$ is approximately equal to t, with the approximation becoming more accurate as t becomes smaller. This guess is correct, as we will now see.

Suppose that $t > 0$. Recall from the previous section that $\ln(1 + t) = \text{area}(\frac{1}{x}, 1, 1 + t)$. In other words, $\ln(1+t)$ equals the area of the region shown below on the left. If t is a small positive number, then the area of this region is approximately equal to the area of the rectangle shown below on the right. This rectangle has base t and height 1; thus the rectangle has area t. We conclude that $\ln(1 + t) \approx t$.

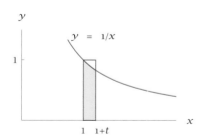

The area of the region on the left equals $\ln(1 + t)$.
The rectangle on the right has area t.
Thus $\ln(1 + t) \approx t$.

We derived the approximation $\ln(1 + t) \approx t$ under the assumption that t is a small positive number. However, the same result also holds if t is a negative number with small absolute value, as illustrated by the following table:

t	$\ln(1 + t)$
-0.05	-0.0512933
-0.005	-0.00501254
-0.0005	-0.000500125
-0.00005	-0.0000500013
-0.000005	-0.00000500001

Values of $\ln(1 + t)$, *rounded off to six significant digits.*

The following summary of our observations is meant to apply to both positive and negative values of t. The phrase "close to 0" does not have a rigorous meaning, but think of numbers t such as those shown in the two tables above.

If you have difficulty remembering whether $\ln(1 + t)$ *or* $\ln t$ *is approximately* t *for* t *close to 0, then take* $t = 0$ *and recall that* $\ln 1 = 0$; *this should point you toward the correct approximation* $\ln(1 + t) \approx t$.

Approximation of the natural logarithm

If t is close to 0, then $\ln(1 + t) \approx t$.

The approximation formula above demonstrates again why the natural logarithm deserves the title "natural". No base for logarithms other than e produces such a nice approximation formula.

Inequalities with the Natural Logarithm

Consider now the figure here, where we assume that t is positive but not necessarily small. In this figure, $\ln(1 + t)$ equals the area of the yellow region under the curve. This region contains the lower rectangle; thus the lower rectangle has a smaller area. The lower rectangle has base t and height $\frac{1}{1+t}$ and hence has area $\frac{t}{1+t}$. Thus

$$\frac{t}{1 + t} < \ln(1 + t).$$

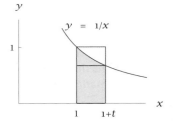

The large rectangle in the figure above has base t and height 1 and thus has area t. The yellow region under the curve is contained in the large rectangle; thus the large rectangle has a bigger area. In other words,

$$\ln(1 + t) < t.$$

The area of the yellow region under the curve is greater than the area of the lower rectangle and is less than the area of the large rectangle.

Putting together the inequalities from the previous two paragraphs, we have the result below. This result is valid for all positive numbers t, regardless of whether t is small or large.

Inequalities with the natural logarithm

If $t > 0$, then $\dfrac{t}{1 + t} < \ln(1 + t) < t$.

If t is small, then $\frac{t}{1+t}$ and t are close to each other, showing that either one is a good estimate for $\ln(1 + t)$. For small t, the estimate $\ln(1 + t) \approx t$ is usually easier to use than the estimate $\ln(1 + t) \approx \frac{t}{1+t}$. However, if we need an estimate that is either slightly too large or slightly too small, then the result above shows which one to use.

Approximations with the Exponential Function

The table below shows the value of e^t, rounded off to show three nonzero digits, for some small values of t:

t	e^t
0.05	1.051
0.005	1.00501
0.0005	1.0005001
0.00005	1.000050001
0.000005	1.00000500001

Values of e^t, rounded off to three nonzero digits.

This table leads us to guess that if t is close to 0, then e^t is approximately equal to $1 + t$, with the approximation becoming more accurate as t becomes smaller. This guess is correct, as we will now see.

Suppose t is close to 0. Then, as we have already seen, $t \approx \ln(1 + t)$. Thus

$$e^t \approx e^{\ln(1+t)} = 1 + t.$$

If you have difficulty remembering whether e^t is approximately $1 + t$ or is approximately t for t close to 0, then take $t = 0$ and recall that $e^0 = 1$; this should point you toward the correct approximation $e^t \approx 1 + t$.

Hence we have the following result:

Approximation of the exponential function

If t is close to 0, then $e^t \approx 1 + t$.

Another useful approximation gives good estimates for e^r even when r is not close to 0. As an example, consider the following table of values of $(1 + \frac{1}{x})^x$ for large values of x:

x	$(1 + \frac{1}{x})^x$
100	2.70481
1000	2.71692
10000	2.71815
100000	2.71827
1000000	2.71828

Values of $(1 + \frac{1}{x})^x$, rounded off to six digits.

You may recognize the last entry in the table above as the value of e, rounded off to six digits. In other words, it appears that $(1 + \frac{1}{x})^x \approx e$ for large values of x. We will now see that an even more general approximation is valid.

Let r be any number, and suppose x is a number whose absolute value is so large that $\frac{r}{x}$ is close to 0. Then, as we already know, $e^{r/x} \approx 1 + \frac{r}{x}$. Thus

$$e^r = (e^{r/x})^x \approx (1 + \tfrac{r}{x})^x.$$

Hence we have the following result:

Approximation of the exponential function

If the absolute value of x is much larger than the absolute value of r, then

$$(1 + \tfrac{r}{x})^x \approx e^r.$$

For example, taking $r = 1$, this approximation shows that

$$\left(1 + \frac{1}{x}\right)^x \approx e$$

for large values of x, confirming the results indicated by the table above.

Notice how e appears naturally in formulas that seem to have nothing to do with e. For example, $(1 + \frac{1}{1000000})^{1000000}$ is approximately equal to e. If we had not discovered e through other means, we probably would have discovered it by investigating $(1 + \frac{1}{x})^x$ for large values of x.

An Area Formula

In the previous section, the area formula

$$\operatorname{area}(\tfrac{1}{x}, 1, c^t) = t\operatorname{area}(\tfrac{1}{x}, 1, c)$$

played a crucial role, leading to the definitions of e and the natural logarithm. Although we motivated and stated this formula in the previous section, we deferred its derivation. The remainder of this section derives this formula.

We start by introducing some slightly more general notation than was used in the previous section.

$\operatorname{area}(\frac{1}{x}, b, c)$

For positive numbers b and c with $b < c$, let $\operatorname{area}(\frac{1}{x}, b, c)$ denote the area of the yellow region below:

In other words, $\operatorname{area}(\frac{1}{x}, b, c)$ is the area of the region under the curve $y = \frac{1}{x}$, above the x-axis, and between the lines $x = b$ and $x = c$.

The solution to the next example contains the key idea that will help us derive the area formula. In this example and the other results in the remainder of this section, we cannot use the equation area$(\frac{1}{x}, 1, c) = \ln c$. Using that equation would be circular reasoning because we are now trying to show that area$(\frac{1}{x}, 1, c^t) = t$ area$(\frac{1}{x}, 1, c)$, which was used to show that area$(\frac{1}{x}, 1, c) = \ln c$.

EXAMPLE 1

Explain why area$(\frac{1}{x}, 1, 2) = $ area$(\frac{1}{x}, 2, 4) = $ area$(\frac{1}{x}, 4, 8)$.

SOLUTION We need to explain why the three regions below have the same area.

  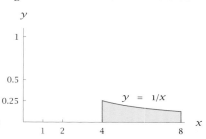

The region in the center is obtained from the region on the left by stretching horizontally by a factor of 2 and stretching vertically by a factor of $\frac{1}{2}$. Thus the Area Stretch Theorem implies that these two regions have the same area.

Similarly, the region on the right is obtained from the region on the left by stretching horizontally by a factor of 4 and stretching vertically by a factor of $\frac{1}{4}$. Thus the Area Stretch Theorem implies that these two regions have the same area.

Define a function f with domain $[1, 2]$ by

$$f(x) = \frac{1}{x}$$

and define a function g by

$$g(x) = \tfrac{1}{2}f(\tfrac{x}{2}) = \frac{1}{2}\frac{1}{\frac{x}{2}} = \frac{1}{x}.$$

Our results on function transformations (see Section 1.3) show that the graph of g is obtained from the graph of f by stretching horizontally by a factor of 2 and stretching vertically by a factor of $\frac{1}{2}$. In other words, the region above in the center is obtained from the region above on the left by stretching horizontally by a factor of 2 and stretching vertically by a factor of $\frac{1}{2}$. The Area Stretch Theorem (see Section 4.2) now implies that the area of the region in the center is $2 \cdot \frac{1}{2}$ times the area of the region on the left. Because $2 \cdot \frac{1}{2} = 1$, this implies that the two regions have the same area.

To show that the region above on the right has the same area as the region above on the left, follow the same procedure, but now define a function h by

$$h(x) = \tfrac{1}{4}f(\tfrac{x}{4}) = \frac{1}{4}\frac{1}{\frac{x}{4}} = \frac{1}{x}.$$

The graph of h is obtained from the graph of f by stretching horizontally by a factor of 4 and stretching vertically by a factor of $\frac{1}{4}$. Thus the region above on the right is obtained from the region above on the left by stretching horizontally by a factor of 4 and stretching vertically by a factor of $\frac{1}{4}$. The Area Stretch Theorem now implies that these two regions have the same area.

By inspecting a table of numbers in the previous section, we noticed that area$(\frac{1}{x}, 1, 2^3)$ = 3 area$(\frac{1}{x}, 1, 2)$. The next result explains why this is true.

Explain why area$(\frac{1}{x}, 1, 2^3)$ = 3 area$(\frac{1}{x}, 1, 2)$.

EXAMPLE 2

SOLUTION The idea here is to partition the region under the curve $y = \frac{1}{x}$, above the x-axis, and between the lines $x = 1$ and $x = 8$ into three regions, as shown below:

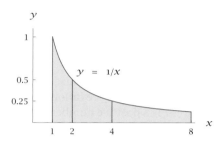

The previous example shows that each of these three regions has the same area. Thus area$(\frac{1}{x}, 1, 2^3)$ = 3 area$(\frac{1}{x}, 1, 2)$.

In the example above, there is nothing special about the number 2. We can replace 2 by an arbitrary number $c > 1$, and using the same reasoning as in the two previous examples we can conclude that

$$\text{area}(\tfrac{1}{x}, 1, c^3) = 3\,\text{area}(\tfrac{1}{x}, 1, c).$$

Furthermore, there is nothing special here about the number 3 in the equation above. Replacing 3 by an arbitrary number positive integer t, we can use the same reasoning to show that

$$\text{area}(\tfrac{1}{x}, 1, c^t) = t\,\text{area}(\tfrac{1}{x}, 1, c)$$

whenever $c > 1$ and t is a positive integer.

At this point, we have derived the desired area formula with the restriction that t must be a positive integer. If you have understood everything up to this point, this is an excellent achievement and a reasonable stopping place. If you want to understand the full area formula, then work through the following example, which removes the restriction that t be an integer.

Explain why

$$\text{area}(\tfrac{1}{x}, 1, c^t) = t\,\text{area}(\tfrac{1}{x}, 1, c)$$

for every $c > 1$ and every $t > 0$.

EXAMPLE 3

SOLUTION First we will verify the desired equation when t is a positive rational number. So suppose $t = \frac{m}{n}$, where m and n are positive integers. Using the restricted area formula that we have already derived, but replacing c by $c^{n/m}$ and replacing t by m, we have

$$\text{area}(\tfrac{1}{x}, 1, (c^{n/m})^m) = m\,\text{area}(\tfrac{1}{x}, 1, c^{n/m}).$$

Because $(c^{n/m})^m = c^n$, we can rewrite the equation above as

$$\text{area}(\tfrac{1}{x}, 1, c^n) = m\,\text{area}(\tfrac{1}{x}, 1, c^{n/m}).$$

By the restricted area formula that we have already derived, the left side of the equation above equals $n\,\text{area}(\tfrac{1}{x}, 1, c)$. Thus $n\,\text{area}(\tfrac{1}{x}, 1, c) = m\,\text{area}(\tfrac{1}{x}, 1, c^{n/m})$, which implies that

$$\text{area}(\tfrac{1}{x}, 1, c^{n/m}) = \frac{n}{m}\,\text{area}(\tfrac{1}{x}, 1, c).$$

In other words, we have now shown that

$$\text{area}(\tfrac{1}{x}, 1, c^t) = t\,\text{area}(\tfrac{1}{x}, 1, c)$$

whenever t is a positive rational number. Because every positive number can be approximated as closely as we like by a positive rational number, this implies that the equation above holds whenever t is a positive number. This completes the derivation of our area formula.

EXERCISES

For Exercises 1-14, estimate the indicated value without using a calculator.

1. $\ln 1.003$

2. $\ln 1.0007$

3. $\ln 0.993$

4. $\ln 0.9996$

5. $\ln 3.0012 - \ln 3$

6. $\ln 4.001 - \ln 4$

7. $e^{0.0013}$

8. $e^{0.00092}$

9. $e^{-0.0083}$

10. $e^{-0.00046}$

11. $\dfrac{e^9}{e^{8.997}}$

12. $\dfrac{e^5}{e^{4.984}}$

13. $\left(\dfrac{e^{7.001}}{e^7}\right)^2$

14. $\left(\dfrac{e^{8.0002}}{e^8}\right)^3$

15. Estimate the value of
$$\left(1 + \frac{3}{10^{100}}\right)^{(10^{100})}.$$

[*Your calculator will be unable to evaluate directly the expressions in this exercise and the next five exercises. Thus you will need to do more than button pushing for these exercises.*]

16. Estimate the value of
$$\left(1 + \frac{5}{10^{90}}\right)^{(10^{90})}.$$

17. Estimate the value of
$$\left(1 - \frac{4}{9^{80}}\right)^{(9^{80})}.$$

18. Estimate the value of
$$\left(1 - \frac{2}{8^{99}}\right)^{(8^{99})}.$$

19. Estimate the value of
$$(1 + 10^{-1000})^{2 \cdot 10^{1000}}.$$

20. Estimate the value of
$$(1 + 10^{-100})^{3 \cdot 10^{100}}.$$

21. Estimate the slope of the line containing the points
$$(5, \ln 5) \quad \text{and} \quad (5 + 10^{-100}, \ln(5 + 10^{-100})).$$

22. Estimate the slope of the line containing the points
$$(4, \ln 4) \quad \text{and} \quad (4 + 10^{-1000}, \ln(4 + 10^{-1000})).$$

23. Suppose t is a small positive number. Estimate the slope of the line containing the points $(4, e^4)$ and $(4 + t, e^{4+t})$.

24. Suppose r is a small positive number. Estimate the slope of the line containing the points $(7, e^7)$ and $(7 + r, e^{7+r})$.

25. Suppose r is a small positive number. Estimate the slope of the line containing the points $(e^2, 6)$ and $(e^{2+r}, 6 + r)$.

26. Suppose b is a small positive number. Estimate the slope of the line containing the points $(e^3, 5 + b)$ and $(e^{3+b}, 5)$.

27. Find a number r such that
$$\left(1 + \frac{r}{10^{90}}\right)^{(10^{90})} \approx 5.$$

28. Find a number r such that
$$\left(1 + \frac{r}{10^{75}}\right)^{(10^{75})} \approx 4.$$

29. Find the number c such that
$$\text{area}(\tfrac{1}{x}, 2, c) = 3.$$

30. Find the number c such that
$$\text{area}(\tfrac{1}{x}, 5, c) = 4.$$

PROBLEMS

31. Show that
$$\frac{1}{10^{20} + 1} < \ln(1 + 10^{-20}) < \frac{1}{10^{20}}.$$

32. (a) Using a calculator, verify that
$$\log(1 + t) \approx 0.434294t$$
for some small numbers t (for example, try $t = 0.001$ and then smaller values of t).

   (b) Explain why the approximation above follows from the approximation $\ln(1 + t) \approx t$.

33. (a) Using a calculator or computer, verify that
$$2^t - 1 \approx 0.693147t$$
for some small numbers t (for example, try $t = 0.001$ and then smaller values of t).

   (b) Explain why $2^t = e^{t \ln 2}$ for every number t.

   (c) Explain why the approximation in part (a) follows from the approximation $e^t \approx 1 + t$.

34. Suppose x is a positive number.

   (a) Explain why $x^t = e^{t \ln x}$ for every number t.

   (b) Explain why
$$\frac{x^t - 1}{t} \approx \ln x$$
if t is close to 0.

   [*Part (b) of this problem gives another illustration of why the natural logarithm deserves the title "natural".*]

35. (a) Using a calculator or computer, verify that
$$\left(1 + \tfrac{\ln 10}{x}\right)^x \approx 10$$
for large values of x (for example, try $x = 1000$ and then larger values of x).

   (b) Explain why the approximation above follows from the approximation $(1 + \frac{r}{x})^x \approx e^r$.

36. Using a calculator, discover a formula for a good approximation for
$$\ln(2 + t) - \ln 2$$
for small values of t (for example, try $t = 0.04$, $t = 0.02$, $t = 0.01$, and then smaller values of t). Then explain why your formula is indeed a good approximation.

37. Show that for every positive number c, we have
$$\ln(c + t) - \ln c \approx \tfrac{t}{c}$$
for small values of t.

38. Show that for every number c, we have
$$e^{c+t} - e^c \approx t e^c$$
for small values of t.

39. Show that if $t > 0$, then $1 + t < e^t$.
   [*This problem and the next problem combine to show that*
$$1 + t < e^t < (1 + t)^{1+t}$$
if $t > 0$.]

40. Show that if $t > 0$, then $e^t < (1 + t)^{1+t}$.

41. Show that if $x > 0$, then $(1 + \tfrac{1}{x})^x < e$.

[*This problem and the next problem combine to show that*

$$\left(1 + \tfrac{1}{x}\right)^x < e < \left(1 + \tfrac{1}{x}\right)^{x+1}$$

if $x > 0$.]

42. Show that if $x > 0$, then $e < \left(1 + \tfrac{1}{x}\right)^{x+1}$.

43. (a) Show that
$$1.01^{100} < e < 1.01^{101}.$$

 (b) Explain why
$$\frac{1.01^{100} + 1.01^{101}}{2}$$
 is a reasonable estimate of e.

44. Show that
$$\text{area}(\tfrac{1}{x}, \tfrac{1}{b}, 1) = \text{area}(\tfrac{1}{x}, 1, b)$$
 for every number $b > 1$.

45. Show that if $0 < a < 1$, then
$$\text{area}(\tfrac{1}{x}, a, 1) = -\ln a.$$

46. Show that
$$\text{area}(\tfrac{1}{x}, a, b) = \text{area}(\tfrac{1}{x}, 1, \tfrac{b}{a})$$
 whenever $0 < a < b$.

47. Show that
$$\text{area}(\tfrac{1}{x}, a, b) = \ln \frac{b}{a}$$
 whenever $0 < a < b$.

48. Show that $\sinh x \approx x$ if x is close to 0. [*The definition of $\sinh$ was given before Exercise 52 in Section 4.3.*]

WORKED-OUT SOLUTIONS *to Odd-numbered Exercises*

For Exercises 1–14, estimate the indicated value without using a calculator.

1. $\ln 1.003$

 SOLUTION
$$\ln 1.003 = \ln(1 + 0.003) \approx 0.003$$

3. $\ln 0.993$

 SOLUTION
$$\ln 0.993 = \ln(1 + (-0.007)) \approx -0.007$$

5. $\ln 3.0012 - \ln 3$

 SOLUTION
$$\ln 3.0012 - \ln 3 = \ln \frac{3.0012}{3} = \ln 1.0004$$
$$= \ln(1 + 0.0004)$$
$$\approx 0.0004$$

7. $e^{0.0013}$

 SOLUTION
$$e^{0.0013} \approx 1 + 0.0013 = 1.0013$$

9. $e^{-0.0083}$

SOLUTION
$$e^{-0.0083} \approx 1 + (-0.0083) = 0.9917$$

11. $\dfrac{e^9}{e^{8.997}}$

 SOLUTION
$$\frac{e^9}{e^{8.997}} = e^{9-8.997} = e^{0.003} \approx 1 + 0.003 = 1.003$$

13. $\left(\dfrac{e^{7.001}}{e^7}\right)^2$

 SOLUTION
$$\left(\frac{e^{7.001}}{e^7}\right)^2 = (e^{7.001-7})^2 = (e^{0.001})^2$$
$$= e^{0.002}$$
$$\approx 1 + 0.002 = 1.002$$

15. Estimate the value of
$$\left(1 + \frac{3}{10^{100}}\right)^{(10^{100})}.$$

 SOLUTION $\left(1 + \dfrac{3}{10^{100}}\right)^{(10^{100})} \approx e^3 \approx 20.09$

17. Estimate the value of
$$\left(1 - \frac{4}{9^{80}}\right)^{(9^{80})}.$$

SOLUTION $\left(1 - \dfrac{4}{980}\right)^{(980)} \approx e^{-4} \approx 0.01832$

19. 📱 Estimate the value of
$$(1 + 10^{-1000})^{2 \cdot 10^{1000}}.$$

SOLUTION

$$(1 + 10^{-1000})^{2 \cdot 10^{1000}} = \left((1 + 10^{-1000})^{10^{1000}}\right)^2$$

$$= \left((1 + \dfrac{1}{10^{1000}})^{10^{1000}}\right)^2$$

$$\approx e^2$$

$$\approx 7.389$$

21. Estimate the slope of the line containing the points
$$(5, \ln 5) \quad \text{and} \quad (5 + 10^{-100}, \ln(5 + 10^{-100})).$$

SOLUTION The slope of the line containing the points
$$(5, \ln 5) \quad \text{and} \quad (5 + 10^{-100}, \ln(5 + 10^{-100}))$$
is obtained in the usual way by taking the ratio of the difference of the second coordinates with the difference of the first coordinates:

$$\dfrac{\ln(5 + 10^{-100}) - \ln 5}{5 + 10^{-100} - 5} = \dfrac{\ln(1 + \frac{1}{5} \cdot 10^{-100})}{10^{-100}}$$

$$\approx \dfrac{\frac{1}{5} \cdot 10^{-100}}{10^{-100}}$$

$$= \dfrac{1}{5}.$$

Thus the slope of the line in question is approximately $\frac{1}{5}$.

23. 📱 Suppose t is a small positive number. Estimate the slope of the line containing the points $(4, e^4)$ and $(4 + t, e^{4+t})$.

SOLUTION The slope of the line containing $(4, e^4)$ and $(4 + t, e^{4+t})$ is obtained in the usual way by taking the ratio of the difference of the second coordinates with the difference of the first coordinates:

$$\dfrac{e^{4+t} - e^4}{4 + t - 4} = \dfrac{e^4(e^t - 1)}{t}$$

$$\approx \dfrac{e^4(1 + t - 1)}{t}$$

$$= e^4$$

$$\approx 54.598$$

Thus the slope of the line in question is approximately 54.598.

25. 📱 Suppose r is a small positive number. Estimate the slope of the line containing the points $(e^2, 6)$ and $(e^{2+r}, 6 + r)$.

SOLUTION The slope of the line containing $(e^2, 6)$ and $(e^{2+r}, 6 + r)$ is obtained in the usual way by taking the ratio of the difference of the second coordinates with the difference of the first coordinates:

$$\dfrac{6 + r - 6}{e^{2+r} - e^2} = \dfrac{r}{e^2(e^r - 1)}$$

$$\approx \dfrac{r}{e^2(1 + r - 1)}$$

$$= \dfrac{1}{e^2}$$

$$\approx 0.135$$

Thus the slope of the line in question is approximately 0.135.

27. 📱 Find a number r such that
$$\left(1 + \dfrac{r}{10^{90}}\right)^{(10^{90})} \approx 5.$$

SOLUTION If r is not a huge number, then
$$\left(1 + \dfrac{r}{10^{90}}\right)^{(10^{90})} \approx e^r.$$

Thus we need to find a number r such that $e^r \approx 5$. This implies that $r \approx \ln 5 \approx 1.60944$.

29. 📱 Find the number c such that
$$\text{area}(\tfrac{1}{x}, 2, c) = 3.$$

SOLUTION We have

$$3 = \text{area}(\tfrac{1}{x}, 2, c)$$

$$= \text{area}(\tfrac{1}{x}, 1, c) - \text{area}(\tfrac{1}{x}, 1, 2)$$

$$= \ln c - \ln 2$$

$$= \ln \tfrac{c}{2}.$$

Thus $\frac{c}{2} = e^3$, which implies that $c = 2e^3 \approx 40.171$.

4.5 | *Exponential Growth Revisited*

SECTION OBJECTIVES

By the end of this section you should

- understand the connection between continuous compounding and e;
- be able to make computations concerning continuous compounding;
- be able to estimate doubling time under continuous compounding.

Continuously Compounded Interest

Recall that if interest is compounded n times per year at annual interest rate r, then after t years an initial amount P grows to

$$P\left(1 + \tfrac{r}{n}\right)^{nt};$$

see Section 3.4 to review the derivation of this formula. More frequent compounding leads to a larger amount, because interest is earned on the interest more frequently. We could imagine compounding interest once per month ($n = 12$), or once per day ($n = 365$), or once per hour ($n = 365 \times 24 = 8760$), or once per minute ($n = 365 \times 24 \times 60 = 525600$), or once per second ($n = 365 \times 24 \times 60 \times 60 = 31536000$), or even more frequently.

To see what happens when interest is compounded very frequently, we need to consider what happens to the formula above when n is very large. Recall from the last section that if the interest rate r is fixed while n becomes very large, then $\left(1 + \tfrac{r}{n}\right)^n \approx e^r$. Thus

$$P\left(1 + \tfrac{r}{n}\right)^{nt} = P\left(\left(1 + \tfrac{r}{n}\right)^n\right)^t$$

$$\approx P\left(e^r\right)^t$$

$$= Pe^{rt}.$$

In other words, if interest is compounded many times per year at annual interest rate r, then after t years an initial amount P grows to approximately Pe^{rt}. We can think of Pe^{rt} as the amount that we would have if interest were compounded continuously. This formula is actually shorter and cleaner than the formula involving compounding n times per year.

Many banks and other financial institutions use continuous compounding rather than compounding a specific number of times per year. Thus they use the formula derived above involving e, which we now restate as follows:

This bank has been paying continuously compounded interest for many years.

Continuous compounding

If interest is compounded continuously at annual interest rate r, then after t years an initial amount P grows to

$$Pe^{rt}.$$

This formula for continuous compounding gives another example of how e arises naturally.

Continuous compounding always produces a larger amount than compounding any specific number of times per year. However, for moderate initial amounts, moderate interest rates, and moderate time periods, the difference is not large, as shown in the following example.

Suppose $10,000 is placed in a bank account that pays 5% annual interest.

(a) If interest is compounded continuously, how much will be in the bank account after 10 years?

(b) If interest is compounded four times per year, how much will be in the bank account after 10 years?

SOLUTION

(a) The continuous compounding formula shows that $10,000 compounded continuously for 10 years at 5% annual interest grows to become

$$\$10,000e^{0.05\times10} \approx \$16,487.$$

(b) The compound interest formula shows that $10,000 compounded four times per year for 10 years at 5% annual interest grows to become

$$\$10,000\left(1 + \tfrac{0.05}{4}\right)^{4\times10} \approx \$16,436.$$

EXAMPLE 1

Continuous compounding indeed yields more in this example, as expected, but the difference is only about $51 after 10 years.

See Exercise 25 for an example of the dramatic difference continuous compounding can make over a very long time period.

Continuous Growth Rates

The model presented above of continuous compounding of interest can be applied to any situation with continuous growth at a fixed percentage. The units of time do not necessarily need to be years, but as usual the same time units must be used in all aspects of the model. Similarly, the quantity being measured need not be dollars; for example, this model works well for population growth over time intervals that are not too large.

Because continuous growth at a fixed percentage behaves the same as continuous compounding with money, the formulas are the same. Instead of referring to an annual interest rate that is compounded continuously, we use the term **continuous growth rate**. In other words, the continuous growth rate operates like an interest rate that is continuously compounded.

The continuous growth rate gives a good way to measure how fast something is growing. Again, the magic number e plays a special role. Our result above about continuous compounding can be restated to apply to more general situations, as follows:

> ### Continuous growth rates
>
> If a quantity has a continuous growth rate of r per unit time, then after t time units an initial amount P grows to
>
> $$Pe^{rt}.$$

EXAMPLE 2	Suppose a colony of bacteria has a continuous growth rate of 10% per hour. By what percent will the colony have grown after five hours?

A continuous growth rate of 10% per hour does not imply that the colony increases by 10% after one hour. In one hour the colony increases in size by a factor of $e^{0.1}$, which is approximately 1.105. In other words, with a continuous growth rate of 10% per hour, the colony increases by approximately 10.5% after one hour.

SOLUTION   A continuous growth rate of 10% per hour means that we should set $r = 0.1$. If the colony starts at size P at time 0, then at time t (measured in hours) its size will be $Pe^{0.1t}$.

Thus after five hours the size of the colony will be $Pe^{0.5}$, which is an increase by a factor of $e^{0.5}$ over the initial size P. Because $e^{0.5} \approx 1.65$, this means that the colony will grow by about 65% after five hours.

Doubling Your Money

The following example shows how to compute how long it takes to double your money with continuous compounding.

EXAMPLE 3	How many years does it take for money to double at 5% annual interest compounded continuously?

SOLUTION   After t years an initial amount P compounded continuously at 5% annual interest grows to $Pe^{0.05t}$. We want this to equal twice the initial amount. Thus we must solve the equation

$$Pe^{0.05t} = 2P,$$

which is equivalent to the equation $e^{0.05t} = 2$, which implies that $0.05t = \ln 2$. Thus

$$t = \frac{\ln 2}{0.05} \approx \frac{0.693}{0.05} = \frac{69.3}{5} \approx 13.9.$$

Hence the initial amount of money will double in about 13.9 years.

Suppose we want to know how long it takes money to double at 4% annual interest compounded continuously instead of 5%. Repeating the calculation above, but with 0.04 replacing 0.05, we see that money doubles in about $\frac{69.3}{4}$ years at 4% annual interest compounded continuously. More generally, money doubles in about $\frac{69.3}{R}$ years at R percent interest compounded continuously. Here R is expressed as a percent, rather than as a number. In other words, 5% interest corresponds to $R = 5$.

For quick estimates, usually it is best to round up the 69.3 appearing in the expression $\frac{69.3}{R}$ to 70. Using 70 instead of 69 is easier because 70 is evenly divisible by more numbers than 69 (for a similar reason, some people even use 72 instead of 70). Thus we have the following useful approximation formula:

Doubling time

At R percent annual interest compounded continuously, money doubles in approximately

$$\frac{70}{R}$$

years.

This approximation formula illustrates again the usefulness of the natural logarithm. The number 70 appearing in this formula is really an approximation for 69.3, which is an approximation for $100 \ln 2$.

For example, this formula shows that at 5% annual interest compounded continuously, money doubles in about $\frac{70}{5}$ years, which equals 14 years. This is close enough to the more precise estimate of 13.9 years that we obtained above. Furthermore, the computation using the $\frac{70}{R}$ estimate is easy enough to do without a calculator.

Instead of focusing on how long it takes money to double at a specified interest rate, we could ask what interest rate is required to make money double in a specified time period. Here is an example:

What annual interest rate is needed so that money will double in seven years when compounded continuously?

EXAMPLE 4

SOLUTION After seven years an initial amount P compounded continuously at $R\%$ annual interest grows to $Pe^{7R/100}$. We want this to equal twice the initial amount. Thus we must solve the equation

$$Pe^{7R/100} = 2P,$$

which is equivalent to the equation $e^{7R/100} = 2$, which implies that $\frac{7R}{100} = \ln 2$. Thus

$$R = \frac{100 \ln 2}{7} \approx \frac{69.3}{7} \approx 9.9.$$

Hence about 9.9% annual interest will make money double in seven years.

Suppose we want to know what annual interest rate is needed to double money in 11 years when compounded continuously. Repeating the calculation above, but with 11 replacing 7, we see that about $\frac{69.3}{11}\%$ annual interest would be needed. More generally, we see that to double money in t years, $\frac{69.3}{t}$ percent interest is needed.

For quick estimates, usually it is best to round up the 69.3 appearing in the expression $\frac{69.3}{t}$ to 70. Thus we have the following useful approximation formula:

> ### *Doubling rate*
>
> The annual interest rate needed for money to double in t years with continuous compounding is approximately
>
> $$\frac{70}{t}$$
>
> percent.

For example, this formula shows that for money to double in seven years when compounded continuously requires about $\frac{70}{7}$% annual interest, which equals 10%. This is close enough to the more precise estimate of 9.9% that we obtained above.

EXERCISES

1. How much would an initial amount of $2000, compounded continuously at 6% annual interest, become after 25 years?

2. How much would an initial amount of $3000, compounded continuously at 7% annual interest, become after 15 years?

3. How much would you need to deposit in a bank account paying 4% annual interest compounded continuously so that at the end of 10 years you would have $10,000?

4. How much would you need to deposit in a bank account paying 5% annual interest compounded continuously so that at the end of 15 years you would have $20,000?

5. Suppose a bank account that compounds interest continuously grows from $100 to $110 in two years. What annual interest rate is the bank paying?

6. Suppose a bank account that compounds interest continuously grows from $200 to $224 in three years. What annual interest rate is the bank paying?

7. Suppose a colony of bacteria has a continuous growth rate of 15% per hour. By what percent will the colony have grown after eight hours?

8. Suppose a colony of bacteria has a continuous growth rate of 20% per hour. By what percent will the colony have grown after seven hours?

9. Suppose a country's population increases by a total of 3% over a two-year period. What is the continuous growth rate for this country?

10. Suppose a country's population increases by a total of 6% over a three-year period. What is the continuous growth rate for this country?

11. Suppose the amount of the world's computer hard disk storage increases by a total of 200% over a four-year period. What is the continuous growth rate for the amount of the world's hard disk storage?

12. Suppose the number of cell phones in the world increases by a total of 150% over a five-year period. What is the continuous growth rate for the number of cell phones in the world?

13. Suppose a colony of bacteria has a continuous growth rate of 30% per hour. If the colony contains 8000 cells now, how many did it contain five hours ago?

14. Suppose a colony of bacteria has a continuous growth rate of 40% per hour. If the colony contains 7500 cells now, how many did it contain three hours ago?

15. Suppose a colony of bacteria has a continuous growth rate of 35% per hour. How long does it take the colony to triple in size?

16. Suppose a colony of bacteria has a continuous growth rate of 70% per hour. How long does it take the colony to quadruple in size?

17. About how many years does it take for money to double when compounded continuously at 2% per year?

18. About how many years does it take for money to double when compounded continuously at 10% per year?

19. About how many years does it take for $200 to become $800 when compounded continuously at 2% per year?

20. About how many years does it take for $300 to become $2,400 when compounded continuously at 5% per year?

21. How long does it take for money to triple when compounded continuously at 5% per year?

22. How long does it take for money to increase by a factor of five when compounded continuously at 7% per year?

23. Find a formula for estimating how long money takes to triple at R percent annual interest rate compounded continuously.

24. Find a formula for estimating how long money takes to increase by a factor of ten at R percent annual interest compounded continuously.

25. Suppose one bank account pays 5% annual interest compounded once per year, and a second bank account pays 5% annual interest compounded continuously. If both bank accounts start with the same initial amount, how long will it take for the second bank account to contain twice the amount of the first bank account?

26. Suppose one bank account pays 3% annual interest compounded once per year, and a second bank account pays 4% annual interest compounded continuously. If both bank accounts start with the same initial amount, how long will it take for the second bank account to contain 50% more than the first bank account?

27. Suppose a colony of 100 bacteria cells has a continuous growth rate of 30% per hour. Suppose a second colony of 200 bacteria cells has a continuous growth rate of 20% per hour. How long does it take for the two colonies to have the same number of bacteria cells?

28. Suppose a colony of 50 bacteria cells has a continuous growth rate of 35% per hour. Suppose a second colony of 300 bacteria cells has a continuous growth rate of 15% per hour. How long does it take for the two colonies to have the same number of bacteria cells?

29. Suppose a colony of bacteria has doubled in five hours. What is the approximate continuous growth rate of this colony of bacteria?

30. Suppose a colony of bacteria has doubled in two hours. What is the approximate continuous growth rate of this colony of bacteria?

31. Suppose a colony of bacteria has tripled in five hours. What is the continuous growth rate of this colony of bacteria?

32. Suppose a colony of bacteria has tripled in two hours. What is the continuous growth rate of this colony of bacteria?

PROBLEMS

33. Using compound interest, explain why

$$\left(1 + \frac{0.05}{n}\right)^n < e^{0.05}$$

for every positive integer n.

34. Suppose that in Exercise 9 we had simply divided the 3% increase over two years by 2, getting 1.5% per year. Explain why this number is close to the more accurate answer of approximately 1.48% per year.

35. Suppose that in Exercise 11 we had simply divided the 200% increase over four years by 4, getting 50% per year. Explain why we should not be surprised that this number is not close to the more accurate answer of approximately 27.5% per year.

36. In Section 3.4 we saw that if a population doubles every d time units, then the function p modeling this population growth is given by the formula
$$p(t) = p_0 \cdot 2^{t/d},$$
where p_0 is the population at time 0. Some books do not use the formula above but instead use the formula
$$p(t) = p_0 e^{(t \ln 2)/d}.$$
Show that the two formulas above are really the same.

[*Which of the two formulas in this problem do you think is cleaner and easier to understand?*]

37. In Section 3.5 we saw that if a radioactive isotope has half-life h, then the function modeling the number of atoms in a sample of this isotope is
$$a(t) = a_0 \cdot 2^{-t/h},$$
where a_0 is the number of atoms of the isotope in the sample at time 0. Many books do not use the formula above but instead use the formula
$$a(t) = a_0 e^{-(t \ln 2)/h}.$$
Show that the two formulas above are really the same.

[*Which of the two formulas in this problem do you think is cleaner and easier to understand?*]

38. Explain why every function f with exponential growth (see Section 3.4 for the definition) can be written in the form
$$f(x) = ce^{kx},$$
where c and k are positive constants.

WORKED-OUT SOLUTIONS *to Odd-numbered Exercises*

1. How much would an initial amount of $2000, compounded continuously at 6% annual interest, become after 25 years?

SOLUTION After 25 years, $2000 compounded continuously at 6% annual interest would grow to $2000e^{0.06 \times 25}$ dollars, which equals $2000e^{1.5}$ dollars, which is approximately $8963.

3. How much would you need to deposit in a bank account paying 4% annual interest compounded continuously so that at the end of 10 years you would have $10,000?

SOLUTION We need to find P such that
$$10000 = Pe^{0.04 \times 10} = Pe^{0.4}.$$
Thus
$$P = \frac{10000}{e^{0.4}} \approx 6703.$$
In other words, the initial amount in the bank account should be $\frac{10000}{e^{0.4}}$ dollars, which is approximately $6703.

5. Suppose a bank account that compounds interest continuously grows from $100 to $110 in two years. What annual interest rate is the bank paying?

SOLUTION Let r denote the annual interest rate paid by the bank. Then
$$110 = 100e^{2r}.$$
Dividing both sides of this equation by 100 gives $1.1 = e^{2r}$, which implies that $2r = \ln 1.1$, which is equivalent to
$$r = \frac{\ln 1.1}{2} \approx 0.0477.$$
Thus the annual interest is approximately 4.77%.

7. Suppose a colony of bacteria has a continuous growth rate of 15% per hour. By what percent will the colony have grown after eight hours?

SOLUTION A continuous growth rate of 15% per hour means that we should set $r = 0.15$. If the colony starts at size P at time 0, then at time t (measured in hours) its size will be $Pe^{0.15t}$.

Because $0.15 \times 8 = 1.2$, after eight hours the size of the colony will be $Pe^{1.2}$, which is an increase by a factor of $e^{1.2}$ over the initial size P. Because $e^{1.2} \approx 3.32$, this means that the colony will be about 332% of its original size after eight hours. Thus the colony will have grown by about 232% after eight hours.

9. ✏️ Suppose a country's population increases by a total of 3% over a two-year period. What is the continuous growth rate for this country?

   SOLUTION   A 3% increase means that we have 1.03 times as much as the initial amount. Thus $1.03P = Pe^{2r}$, where P is the country's population at the beginning of the measurement period and r is the country's continuous growth rate. Thus $e^{2r} = 1.03$, which means that $2r = \ln 1.03$. Thus $r = \frac{\ln 1.03}{2} \approx 0.0148$. Thus the country's continuous growth rate is approximately 1.48% per year.

11. ✏️ Suppose the amount of the world's computer hard disk storage increases by a total of 200% over a four-year period. What is the continuous growth rate for the amount of the world's hard disk storage?

   SOLUTION   A 200% increase means that we have three times as much as the initial amount. Thus $3P = Pe^{4r}$, where P is amount of the world's hard disk storage at the beginning of the measurement period and r is the continuous growth rate. Thus $e^{4r} = 3$, which means that $4r = \ln 3$. Thus $r = \frac{\ln 3}{4} \approx 0.275$. Thus the continuous growth rate is approximately 27.5%.

13. ✏️ Suppose a colony of bacteria has a continuous growth rate of 30% per hour. If the colony contains 8000 cells now, how many did it contain five hours ago?

   SOLUTION   Let P denote the number of cells at the initial time five hours ago. Thus we have $8000 = Pe^{0.3 \times 5}$, or $8000 = Pe^{1.5}$. Thus

   $$P = 8000/e^{1.5} \approx 1785.$$

15. ✏️ Suppose a colony of bacteria has a continuous growth rate of 35% per hour. How long does it take the colony to triple in size?

   SOLUTION   Let P denote the initial size of the colony, and let t denote the time that it takes the colony to triple in size. Then $3P = Pe^{0.35t}$, which means that $e^{0.35t} = 3$. Thus $0.35t = \ln 3$, which implies that $t = \frac{\ln 3}{0.35} \approx 3.14$. Thus the colony triples in size in approximately 3.14 hours.

17. About how many years does it take for money to double when compounded continuously at 2% per year?

   SOLUTION   At 2% per year compounded continuously, money will double in approximately $\frac{70}{2}$ years, which equals 35 years.

19. About how many years does it take for $200 to become $800 when compounded continuously at 2% per year?

   SOLUTION   At 2% per year, money doubles in approximately 35 years. For $200 to become $800, it must double twice. Thus this will take about 70 years.

21. ✏️ How long does it take for money to triple when compounded continuously at 5% per year?

   SOLUTION   To triple an initial amount P in t years at 5% annual interest compounded continuously, the following equation must hold:

   $$Pe^{0.05t} = 3P.$$

   Dividing both sides by P and then taking the natural logarithm of both sides gives $0.05t = \ln 3$. Thus $t = \frac{\ln 3}{0.05}$. Thus it would take $\frac{\ln 3}{0.05}$ years, which is about 22 years.

23. ✏️ Find a formula for estimating how long money takes to triple at R percent annual interest rate compounded continuously.

   SOLUTION   To triple an initial amount P in t years at R percent annual interest compounded continuously, the following equation must hold:

   $$Pe^{Rt/100} = 3P.$$

   Dividing both sides by P and then taking the natural logarithm of both sides gives $Rt/100 = \ln 3$. Thus $t = \frac{100 \ln 3}{R}$. Because $\ln 3 \approx 1.10$, this shows that money triples in about $\frac{110}{R}$ years.

25. Suppose one bank account pays 5% annual interest compounded once per year, and a second bank account pays 5% annual interest compounded continuously. If both bank accounts start with the same initial amount, how long will it take for the second bank account to contain twice the amount of the first bank account?

SOLUTION Suppose both bank accounts start with P dollars. After t years, the first bank account will contain $P(1.05)^t$ dollars and the second bank account will contain $Pe^{0.05t}$ dollars. Thus we need to solve the equation

$$\frac{Pe^{0.05t}}{P(1.05)^t} = 2.$$

The initial amount P drops out of this equation (as expected), and we can rewrite this equation as follows:

$$2 = \frac{e^{0.05t}}{1.05^t} = \frac{(e^{0.05})^t}{1.05^t} = \left(\frac{e^{0.05}}{1.05}\right)^t.$$

Taking the natural logarithm of the first and last terms above gives

$$\ln 2 = t \ln \frac{e^{0.05}}{1.05} = t(\ln e^{0.05} - \ln 1.05)$$

$$= t(0.05 - \ln 1.05),$$

which we can then solve for t, getting

$$t = \frac{\ln 2}{0.05 - \ln 1.05}.$$

Using a calculator to evaluate the expression above, we see that t is approximately 573 years.

27. Suppose a colony of 100 bacteria cells has a continuous growth rate of 30% per hour. Suppose a second colony of 200 bacteria cells has a continuous growth rate of 20% per hour. How long does it take for the two colonies to have the same number of bacteria cells?

SOLUTION After t hours, the first colony contains $100e^{0.3t}$ bacteria cells and the second colony contains $200e^{0.2t}$ bacteria cells. Thus we need to solve the equation

$$100e^{0.3t} = 200e^{0.2t}.$$

Dividing both sides by 100 and then dividing both sides by $e^{0.2t}$ gives the equation

$$e^{0.1t} = 2.$$

Thus $0.1t = \ln 2$, which implies that

$$t = \frac{\ln 2}{0.1} \approx 6.93.$$

Thus the two colonies have the same number of bacteria cells in a bit less than 7 hours.

29. Suppose a colony of bacteria has doubled in five hours. What is the approximate continuous growth rate of this colony of bacteria?

SOLUTION The approximate formula for doubling the number of bacteria is the same as for doubling money. Thus if a colony of bacteria doubles in five hours, then it has a continuous growth rate of approximately 70/5% per hour. In other words, this colony of bacteria has a continuous growth rate of approximately 14% per hour.

31. Suppose a colony of bacteria has tripled in five hours. What is the continuous growth rate of this colony of bacteria?

SOLUTION Let r denote the continuous growth rate of this colony of bacteria. If the colony initially contains P bacteria cells, then after five hours it will contain Pe^{5r} bacteria cells. Thus we need to solve the equation

$$Pe^{5r} = 3P.$$

Dividing both sides by P gives the equation $e^{5r} = 3$, which implies that $5r = \ln 3$. Thus

$$r = \frac{\ln 3}{5} \approx 0.2197.$$

Thus the continuous growth rate of this colony of bacteria is approximately 22% per hour.

CHAPTER SUMMARY

To check that you have mastered the most important concepts and skills covered in this chapter, make sure that you can do each item in the following list:

- Compute the distance between two points.
- Find the midpoint of a line segment.
- Find the equation of a circle, given its center and radius.
- Compute the area of triangles and trapezoids.
- Compute the area inside a circle or ellipse.
- Explain how area changes when stretching either horizontally or vertically or both.
- Approximate the area under a curve using rectangles.

- Explain the definition of e.
- Explain the definition of the natural logarithm.
- Give at least one explanation of why the natural logarithm deserves to be called "natural".
- Approximate e^h and $\ln(1 + h)$ for h close to 0.
- Compute continuously compounded interest.
- Estimate how long it takes to double money at a given interest rate.

To review a chapter, go through the list above to find items that you do not know how to do, then reread the material in the chapter about those items. Then try to answer the chapter review questions below without looking back at the chapter.

CHAPTER REVIEW QUESTIONS

1. Find the distance between the points $(5, -6)$ and $(-2, -4)$.

2. Find two points, one on the horizontal axis and one on the vertical axis, such that the distance between these two points equals 21.

3. Find the equation of the circle in the xy-plane centered at $(-4, 3)$ that has radius 6.

4. Find the center, radius, and circumference of the circle in the xy-plane described by

$$x^2 - 8x + y^2 + 10y = 2.$$

   Also, find the area inside this circle.

5. Find the area of a triangle that has two sides of length 8 and one side of length 3.

6. Find the perimeter of the parallelogram whose vertices are $(2, 1)$, $(7, 1)$, $(10, 3)$, and $(5, 3)$.

7. Find the perimeter of the triangle whose vertices are $(1, 2)$, $(6, 2)$, and $(7, 5)$.

8. Find the perimeter of the trapezoid whose vertices are $(2, 3)$, $(8, 3)$, $(9, 5)$, and $(-1, 5)$.

9. Find the area of the parallelogram whose vertices are $(2, 1)$, $(7, 1)$, $(10, 3)$, and $(5, 3)$.

10. Find the area of the triangle whose vertices are $(1, 2)$, $(6, 2)$, and $(7, 5)$.

11. Find the area of the trapezoid whose vertices are $(2, 3)$, $(8, 3)$, $(9, 5)$, and $(-1, 5)$.

12. Find the area inside the ellipse

$$3x^2 + 2y^2 = 5.$$

13. What is the definition of e?

14. What are the domain and range of the function f defined by $f(x) = e^x$?

15. What is the definition of the natural logarithm?

16. What are the domain and range of the function g defined by $g(y) = \ln y$?

17. Find a number t such that $\ln(4t + 3) = 5$.

18. Find a number t that makes $(e^{t+8})^t$ as small as possible.

19. Find a number w such that $e^{2w-7} = 6$.

20. Find a formula for the inverse of the function g defined by $g(x) = 8 - 3e^{5x}$.

21. Find a formula for the inverse of the function h defined by $h(x) = 1 - 5\ln(x + 4)$.

22. Find the area of the region under the curve $y = \frac{1}{x}$, above the x-axis, and between the lines $x = 1$ and $x = e^2$.

23. Find a number c such that the area of the region under the curve $y = \frac{1}{x}$, above the x-axis, and between the lines $x = 1$ and $x = c$ is 45.

24. What is the area of the region under the curve $y = \frac{1}{x}$, above the x-axis, and between the lines $x = 3$ and $x = 5$?

25. Draw an appropriate figure and use it to explain why
$$\ln(1.0001) \approx 0.0001.$$

26. Estimate the slope of the line containing the points $(2, \ln(6 + 10^{-500}))$ and $(6, \ln 6)$.

27. Estimate the value of $\dfrac{e^{1000.002}}{e^{1000}}$.

28. Estimate the slope of the line containing the points $(6, e^{0.0002})$ and $(2, 1)$.

29. Estimate the value of
$$\left(1 - \frac{6}{788}\right)^{(788)}.$$

30. How much would an initial amount of $12,000, compounded continuously at 6% annual interest, become after 20 years?

31. How much would you need to deposit in a bank account paying 6% annual interest compounded continuously so that at the end of 25 years you would have $100,000?

32. Suppose a bank account that compounds interest continuously grows from $2000 to $2878.15 in seven years. What annual interest rate is the bank paying?

33. Approximately how many years does it take for money to double when compounded continuously at 5% per year?

34. Suppose a colony of bacteria has doubled in 10 hours. What is the approximate continuous growth rate of this colony of bacteria?

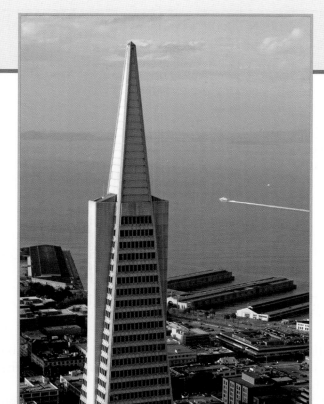

The Transamerica Pyramid in San Francisco. Architects used trigonometry to design the unusual triangular faces of this building.

Trigonometric Functions

This chapter introduces the trigonometric functions. These remarkably useful functions appear in many parts of mathematics.

Trigonometric functions live most comfortably in the context of the unit circle. Thus this chapter begins with a careful examination of the unit circle, including a discussion of negative angles and angles greater than 360°.

Many formulas become simpler if angles are measured in radians rather than degrees. Hence we will become familiar with radians before defining the basic trigonometric functions—the cosine, sine, and tangent.

After defining the trigonometric functions in the context of the unit circle, we will see how these functions allow us to compute the measurements of right triangles. We will also dip into the vast sea of trigonometric identities.

The last part of this chapter deals with inverse trigonometric functions, building on our previous work with inverse functions.

5.1 | *The Unit Circle*

SECTION OBJECTIVES

By the end of this section you should

- understand the angle corresponding to a radius of the unit circle;
- understand negative angles;
- understand angles greater than 360°;
- be able to compute the length of a circular arc;
- be able to find the coordinates of the endpoint of the radius of the unit circle corresponding to any multiple of 30° or 45°.

The Equation of the Unit Circle

Trigonometry takes place most conveniently in the context of the unit circle. Thus we begin this chapter by acquainting ourselves with this crucial object.

The unit circle

The **unit circle** is the circle of radius 1 centered at the origin.

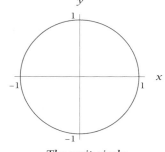

The unit circle.

As can be seen in the figure here, the unit circle intersects the horizontal axis at the points $(1, 0)$ and $(-1, 0)$, and it intersects the vertical axis at the points $(0, 1)$ and $(0, -1)$.

The unit circle in the xy-plane is described by the equation below. You should become thoroughly familiar with this equation.

Equation of the unit circle

The unit circle in the xy-plane is the set of points (x, y) such that

$$x^2 + y^2 = 1.$$

EXAMPLE 1

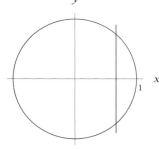

The unit circle and the line $x = \frac{2}{3}$.

Find the points on the unit circle whose first coordinate equals $\frac{2}{3}$.

SOLUTION We need to find the intersection of the unit circle and the line in the xy-plane whose equation is $x = \frac{2}{3}$, as shown here. To find this intersection, set x equal to $\frac{2}{3}$ in the equation of the unit circle ($x^2 + y^2 = 1$) and then solve for y. In other words, we need to solve the equation

$$\left(\tfrac{2}{3}\right)^2 + y^2 = 1.$$

This simplifies to the equation $y^2 = \frac{5}{9}$, which implies that $y = \frac{\sqrt{5}}{3}$ or $y = -\frac{\sqrt{5}}{3}$. Thus the points on the unit circle whose first coordinate equals $\frac{2}{3}$ are $\left(\frac{2}{3}, \frac{\sqrt{5}}{3}\right)$ and $\left(\frac{2}{3}, -\frac{\sqrt{5}}{3}\right)$.

The next example shows how to find the coordinates of the points where the unit circle intersects the line through the origin with slope 1 (which in the xy-plane is described by the equation $y = x$).

Find the points on the unit circle whose two coordinates are equal.

EXAMPLE 2

SOLUTION We need to find the intersection of the unit circle and the line in the xy-plane whose equation is $y = x$. To find this intersection, set y equal to x in the equation of the unit circle ($x^2 + y^2 = 1$) and then solve for x. In other words, we need to solve the equation

$$x^2 + x^2 = 1.$$

This simplifies to the equation $2x^2 = 1$, which implies that $x = \frac{\sqrt{2}}{2}$ or $x = -\frac{\sqrt{2}}{2}$. Thus the points on the unit circle whose coordinates are equal are $(\frac{\sqrt{2}}{2}, \frac{\sqrt{2}}{2})$ and $(-\frac{\sqrt{2}}{2}, -\frac{\sqrt{2}}{2})$.

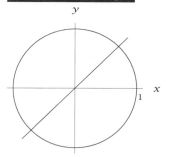

The unit circle and the line $y = x$.

Angles in the Unit Circle

The **positive horizontal axis**, which plays a special role in trigonometry, is the set of points on the horizontal axis that lie to the right of the origin. When we want to call attention to the positive horizontal axis, sometimes we draw it thicker than normal, as shown here.

We will also occasionally refer to the negative horizontal axis, the positive vertical axis, and the negative vertical axis. These terms are sufficiently descriptive so that definitions are almost unneeded, but here are the formal definitions:

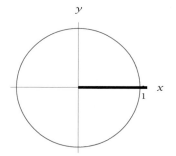

The unit circle with a thickened positive horizontal axis.

Positive and negative horizontal and vertical axes

- The **positive horizontal axis** is the set of points in the coordinate plane of the form $(x, 0)$, where $x > 0$.

- The **negative horizontal axis** is the set of points in the coordinate plane of the form $(x, 0)$, where $x < 0$.

- The **positive vertical axis** is the set of points in the coordinate plane of the form $(0, y)$, where $y > 0$.

- The **negative vertical axis** is the set of points in the coordinate plane of the form $(0, y)$, where $y < 0$.

Trigonometry focuses on the angle between a radius of the unit circle and the positive horizontal axis, measured counterclockwise from the positive horizontal axis to the radius. **Counterclockwise** refers to the opposite direction from the motion of a clock's hands. For example, the figure here shows the radius of the unit circle whose endpoint is $(\frac{\sqrt{2}}{2}, \frac{\sqrt{2}}{2})$. This radius has a $45°$ angle with the positive horizontal axis.

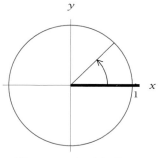

The arrow in this figure indicates the counterclockwise direction.

The radius ending at $(0, 1)$ on the positive vertical axis has a 90° angle with the positive horizontal axis. Similarly, the radius ending at $(-1, 0)$ on the negative horizontal axis has a 180° angle with the positive horizontal axis.

Going all the way around the circle corresponds to a 360° angle, getting us back to where we started with the radius ending at $(1, 0)$ on the positive horizontal axis. The figure below illustrates these key angles:

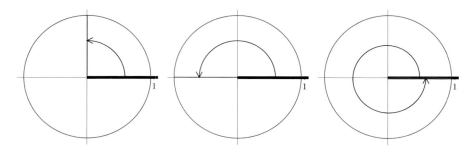

Angles of 90° *(left),* 180° *(center), and* 360° *(right)*
with the positive horizontal axis.

As a test that you clearly understand the concept of measuring the angle a radius makes with the positive horizontal axis, be sure that the caption for the figure below seems right to you.

The raised small circle denotes degrees. Thus "20°" is pronounced "twenty degrees".

Note that the radius below making a 20° angle with the positive horizontal axis lies somewhat above the positive horizontal axis. Furthermore, the radius making a 100° angle with the positive horizontal axis lies slightly to the left of the positive vertical axis (because 100° is slightly bigger than 90°). Finally, the radius making a 200° angle with the positive horizontal axis lies somewhat below the negative horizontal axis (because 200° is somewhat bigger than 180°).

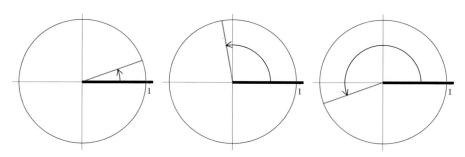

Angles of 20° *(left),* 100° *(center), and* 200° *(right)*
with the positive x-axis.

Negative Angles

Calculus requires the use of negative angles as well as positive angles. The angle between a radius of the unit circle and the positive horizontal axis is declared to be negative when measured clockwise from the positive horizontal axis. For example, the figure below shows three negative angles:

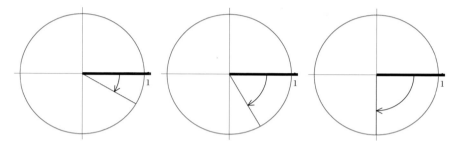

Angles of $-30°$ (left), $-60°$ (center), and $-90°$ (right) with the positive horizontal axis.

Clockwise *refers to the direction in which a clock's hands move, as shown by the arrows here.*

If no indication is given of whether an angle measurement is to be made by moving counterclockwise or by moving clockwise, then we cannot determine whether the angle is positive or negative.

For example, consider the radius shown below on the left. Measuring clockwise from the positive horizontal axis, this radius makes angle of $-60°$ with the positive horizontal axis. Or measuring counterclockwise from the positive horizontal axis, this radius makes an angle of $300°$ with the positive horizontal axis. Depending on the context, either of these interpretations could be correct. As we will see later, for some applications either interpretation works fine.

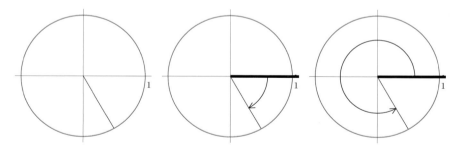

Does the radius on the left correspond to an angle of $-60°$ (as in the center) or to an angle of $300°$ (as on the right)?

In summary, the angle determined by a radius on the unit circle is measured as follows:

> *Positive and negative angles*
>
> - Angle measurements for a radius on the unit circle are made from the positive horizontal axis.
>
> - Positive angles correspond to moving counterclockwise from the positive horizontal axis.
>
> - Negative angles correspond to moving clockwise from the positive horizontal axis.

Angles Greater Than 360°

Just as calculus sometimes requires the use of negative angles, calculus also sometimes requires the use of angles whose absolute value is greater than 360°. To see how to obtain such angles, consider the 40° angle shown below on the left. Starting from the positive horizontal axis and moving counterclockwise, we could end up at the same radius by going completely around the circle (360°) and then continuing for another 40°, for a total of 400° as shown in the center below. Or we could go completely around the circle twice (720°) and then continue counterclockwise for another 40° for a total of 760°, as shown below on the right:

We could continue to add multiples of 360°, showing that the same radius corresponds to an angle of 40 + 360n degrees for every positive integer n.

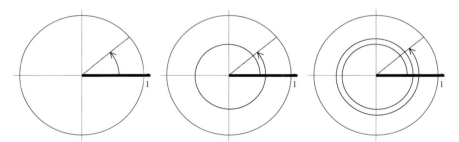

The same radius corresponds to a 40° angle (left),
a 400° angle (center), a 760° angle (right), and so on.

We can get another set of angles for the same radius by measuring clockwise from the positive horizontal axis. The figure below in the center shows that our radius with an angle of 40° with the positive horizontal axis also can be considered to correspond to an angle of −320°. Or we could go completely around the circle in the clockwise direction (−360°) and then continue clockwise to the radius (another −320°) for a total of −680°, as shown below on the right:

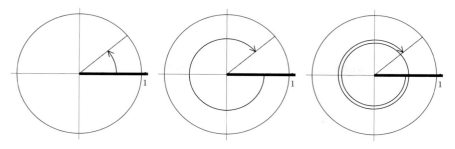

The same radius corresponds to a 40° angle (left),
a −320° angle (center), a −680° angle (right), and so on.

*We could continue
to subtract multiples
of* 360° *here, show-
ing that the same ra-
dius corresponds to
an angle of* 40 + 360n
*degrees for every neg-
ative integer n.*

Starting with an arbitrary angle of θ degrees instead of 40°, the results above become the following result:

Multiple choices for the angle corresponding to a radius

A radius of the unit circle corresponding to an angle of θ degrees also corresponds to an angle of $\theta + 360n$ degrees for every integer n.

Length of a Circular Arc

The circular arc on the unit circle corresponding to a 90° angle is shown here as the thickened part of the unit circle. If we place a string to cover this circular arc and then straighten out the string, its length will be what we call the length of the circular arc.

To find the length of this circular arc, recall that the length (circumference) of the entire unit circle equals 2π. The circular arc here is one-fourth of the unit circle. Thus its length equals $\frac{2\pi}{4}$, which equals $\frac{\pi}{2}$.

More generally, suppose $0 < \theta \leq 360$ and consider a circular arc on the unit circle corresponding to an angle of θ degrees, as shown in the thickened part of the unit circle below. The length of this circular arc equals the fraction of the entire circle taken up by this circular arc times the circumference of the entire circle. In other words, the length of this circular arc equals $\frac{\theta}{360} \cdot 2\pi$, which equals $\frac{\theta\pi}{180}$.

In the following summary of the result that we derived above, we assume that $0 < \theta \leq 360$:

Length of a circular arc

A circular arc on the unit circle corresponding to an angle of θ degrees has length $\frac{\theta\pi}{180}$.

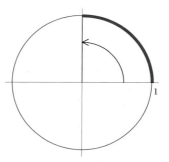

*The circular arc
corresponding to 90°
has length $\frac{\pi}{2}$.*

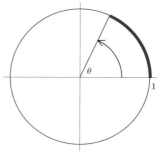

*The circular arc
corresponding to θ
degrees has length $\frac{\theta\pi}{180}$.*

Special Points on the Unit Circle

We have already seen that the radius of the unit circle that makes a 45° angle with the positive horizontal axis has its endpoint at $(\frac{\sqrt{2}}{2}, \frac{\sqrt{2}}{2})$. The coordinates of the endpoint can also be explicitly found for the radius corresponding to 30° and for the radius corresponding to 60°. To do this, we first need to examine the dimensions of a right triangle with those angles.

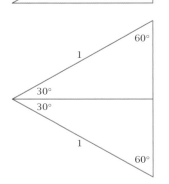

Consider a right triangle, one of whose angles is 30°. Because the angles of a triangle add up to 180°, the other angle of the triangle is 60°. Suppose this triangle has a hypotenuse of length 1, as shown in the figure here. Our goal is to find the lengths of the other two sides of the triangle.

Reflect the triangle through the base adjacent to the 30° angle, creating the figure shown here. Notice that all three angles in the large triangle are 60°. Thus the large triangle is an equilateral triangle. We already knew that two sides of this large triangle have length 1, as labeled here; now we know that the third side also has length 1.

Looking at the two smaller triangles here, we see that each side opposite the 30° angle has half the length of the vertical side of the large triangle. Thus the vertical side in the top triangle has length $\frac{1}{2}$. The Pythagorean Theorem then implies that the horizontal side has length $\frac{\sqrt{3}}{2}$ (you should verify this). Thus the dimensions of this triangle are as in the figure shown below:

Because the large triangle is an equilateral triangle, the unlabeled vertical side of the large triangle has length 1. Thus in the top triangle, the vertical side has length $\frac{1}{2}$.

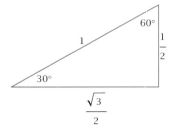

In a triangle with angles of 30°, 60°, and 90°, the side opposite the 30° angle has half the length of the hypotenuse.

In summary, we have shown the following:

Dimensions of a triangle with angles of 30°, 60°, and 90°

In a triangle with angles of 30°, 60°, and 90° and hypotenuse of length 1,

- the side opposite the 30° angle has length $\frac{1}{2}$;

- the side opposite the 60° angle has length $\frac{\sqrt{3}}{2}$.

Because of its origin in Latin, the plural of "radius" is "radii".

Now we turn to the question of finding the endpoints of the radii of the unit circle that make a 30° angle and a 60° angle with the positive horizontal axis. Those radii are shown in the figure below. If we drop a perpendicular line segment from the endpoint of each radius to the horizontal axis, as shown below, we get a pair of 30°-60°-90° triangles. The hypotenuse of each of these triangles is a radius of the unit circle and hence has length 1.

Thus the other sides of each triangle have length $\frac{1}{2}$ and $\frac{\sqrt{3}}{2}$, with the side opposite the 30° angle having length $\frac{1}{2}$. Hence the radius corresponding to 30° has its endpoint at $(\frac{\sqrt{3}}{2}, \frac{1}{2})$ and the radius corresponding to 60° has its endpoint at $(\frac{1}{2}, \frac{\sqrt{3}}{2})$.

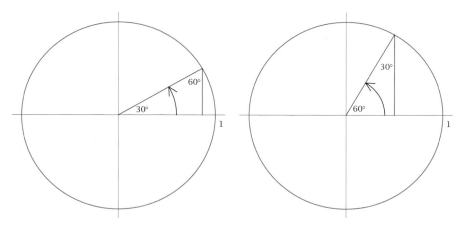

This radius has endpoint $(\frac{\sqrt{3}}{2}, \frac{1}{2})$.   *This radius has endpoint $(\frac{1}{2}, \frac{\sqrt{3}}{2})$.*

The table here shows the endpoint of the radius of the unit circle corresponding to some special angles (as usual, angles are measured counterclockwise from the positive horizontal axis). As we will see soon, the trigonometric functions were invented to extend this table to arbitrary angles.

angle	endpoint of radius
0°	$(1, 0)$
30°	$(\frac{\sqrt{3}}{2}, \frac{1}{2})$
45°	$(\frac{\sqrt{2}}{2}, \frac{\sqrt{2}}{2})$
60°	$(\frac{1}{2}, \frac{\sqrt{3}}{2})$
90°	$(0, 1)$
180°	$(-1, 0)$

EXERCISES

1. Find all numbers t such that $(\frac{1}{3}, t)$ is a point on the unit circle.

2. Find all numbers t such that $(\frac{3}{5}, t)$ is a point on the unit circle.

3. Find all numbers t such that $(t, -\frac{2}{5})$ is a point on the unit circle.

4. Find all numbers t such that $(t, -\frac{3}{7})$ is a point on the unit circle.

5. Find the points where the line through the origin with slope 3 intersects the unit circle.

6. Find the points where the line through the origin with slope 4 intersects the unit circle.

7. Suppose an ant walks counterclockwise on the unit circle from the point $(1, 0)$ to the endpoint of the radius that forms an angle of 70° with the positive horizontal axis. How far has the ant walked?

8. Suppose an ant walks counterclockwise on the unit circle from the point $(1, 0)$ to the endpoint of the radius that forms an angle of 130° with the positive horizontal axis. How far has the ant walked?

9. What angle corresponds to a circular arc on the unit circle with length $\frac{\pi}{5}$?

10. What angle corresponds to a circular arc on the unit circle with length $\frac{\pi}{6}$?

11. 📱 What angle corresponds to a circular arc on the unit circle with length $\frac{5}{2}$?

12. 📱 What angle corresponds to a circular arc on the unit circle with length 1?

13. Find the lengths of both circular arcs on the unit circle connecting the points $(1, 0)$ and $(\frac{\sqrt{2}}{2}, \frac{\sqrt{2}}{2})$.

14. Find the lengths of both circular arcs on the unit circle connecting the points $(1, 0)$ and $(-\frac{\sqrt{2}}{2}, \frac{\sqrt{2}}{2})$.

For each of the angles in Exercises 15–20, find the endpoint of the radius of the unit circle that makes the given angle with the positive horizontal axis.

15. $120°$ 17. $-30°$ 19. $390°$

16. $240°$ 18. $-150°$ 20. $510°$

For Exercises 21–26, find the angle the radius of the unit circle ending at the given point makes with the positive horizontal axis. Among the infinitely many possible correct solutions, choose the one with the smallest absolute value.

21. $(-\frac{1}{2}, \frac{\sqrt{3}}{2})$ 24. $(\frac{1}{2}, -\frac{\sqrt{3}}{2})$

22. $(-\frac{\sqrt{3}}{2}, \frac{1}{2})$ 25. $(-\frac{\sqrt{2}}{2}, -\frac{\sqrt{2}}{2})$

23. $(\frac{\sqrt{2}}{2}, -\frac{\sqrt{2}}{2})$ 26. $(-\frac{1}{2}, -\frac{\sqrt{3}}{2})$

27. Find the lengths of both circular arcs on the unit circle connecting the point $(\frac{1}{2}, \frac{\sqrt{3}}{2})$ and the point that makes an angle of $130°$ with the positive horizontal axis.

28. Find the lengths of both circular arcs on the unit circle connecting the point $(\frac{\sqrt{3}}{2}, -\frac{1}{2})$ and the point that makes an angle of $50°$ with the positive horizontal axis.

29. Find the lengths of both circular arcs on the unit circle connecting the point $(-\frac{\sqrt{2}}{2}, -\frac{\sqrt{2}}{2})$ and the point that makes an angle of $125°$ with the positive horizontal axis.

30. Find the lengths of both circular arcs on the unit circle connecting the point $(-\frac{\sqrt{3}}{2}, -\frac{1}{2})$ and the point that makes an angle of $20°$ with the positive horizontal axis.

31. What is the slope of the radius of the unit circle that has a $30°$ angle with the positive horizontal axis?

32. What is the slope of the radius of the unit circle that has a $60°$ angle with the positive horizontal axis?

PROBLEMS

Some problems require considerably more thought than the exercises. Unlike exercises, problems usually have more than one correct answer.

For each of the angles listed in Problems 33–40, sketch the unit circle and the radius that makes the indicated angle with the positive horizontal axis. Be sure to include an arrow to show the direction in which the angle is measured from the positive horizontal axis.

33. $20°$ 36. $330°$ 39. $-75°$

34. $80°$ 37. $460°$ 40. $-170°$

35. $160°$ 38. $-10°$

41. Find the formula for the length of a circular arc corresponding to an angle of θ degrees on a circle of radius r.

WORKED-OUT SOLUTIONS *to Odd-numbered Exercises*

Do not read these worked-out solutions before first struggling to do the exercises yourself. Otherwise you risk the danger of mimicking the techniques shown here without understanding the ideas.

Best way to learn: Carefully read the section of the textbook, then do all the odd-numbered exercises (even if they have not been assigned) and check your answers here. If you get stuck on an exercise, reread the section of the textbook—then try the exercise again. If you are still stuck, then look at the worked-out solution here.

1. Find all numbers t such that $(\frac{1}{3}, t)$ is a point on the unit circle.

    SOLUTION   For $(\frac{1}{3}, t)$ to be a point on the unit circle means that the sum of the squares of the coordinates equals 1. In other words,

    $$\left(\tfrac{1}{3}\right)^2 + t^2 = 1.$$

    This simplifies to the equation $t^2 = \frac{8}{9}$, which implies that $t = \frac{\sqrt{8}}{3}$ or $t = -\frac{\sqrt{8}}{3}$. Because $\sqrt{8} = \sqrt{4 \cdot 2} = \sqrt{4} \cdot \sqrt{2} = 2\sqrt{2}$, we can rewrite this as $t = \frac{2\sqrt{2}}{3}$ or $t = -\frac{2\sqrt{2}}{3}$.

3. Find all numbers t such that $(t, -\frac{2}{5})$ is a point on the unit circle.

    SOLUTION   For $(t, -\frac{2}{5})$ to be a point on the unit circle means that the sum of the squares of the coordinates equals 1. In other words,

    $$t^2 + \left(-\tfrac{2}{5}\right)^2 = 1.$$

    This simplifies to the equation $t^2 = \frac{21}{25}$, which implies that $t = \frac{\sqrt{21}}{5}$ or $t = -\frac{\sqrt{21}}{5}$.

5. Find the points where the line through the origin with slope 3 intersects the unit circle.

    SOLUTION   The line through the origin with slope 3 is characterized by the equation $y = 3x$. Substituting this value for y into the equation for the unit circle ($x^2 + y^2 = 1$) gives

    $$x^2 + (3x)^2 = 1,$$

    which simplifies to the equation $10x^2 = 1$. Thus $x = \frac{\sqrt{10}}{10}$ or $x = -\frac{\sqrt{10}}{10}$. Using each of these values of x along with the equation $y = 3x$ gives the points $\left(\frac{\sqrt{10}}{10}, \frac{3\sqrt{10}}{10}\right)$ and $\left(-\frac{\sqrt{10}}{10}, -\frac{3\sqrt{10}}{10}\right)$ as the points of intersection of the line $y = 3x$ and the unit circle.

7. Suppose an ant walks counterclockwise on the unit circle from the point $(1, 0)$ to the endpoint of the radius that forms an angle of 70° with the positive horizontal axis. How far has the ant walked?

    SOLUTION   We need to find the length of the circular arc on the unit circle corresponding to a 70° angle. This length equals $\frac{70\pi}{180}$, which equals $\frac{7\pi}{18}$.

9. What angle corresponds to a circular arc on the unit circle with length $\frac{\pi}{5}$?

    SOLUTION   Let θ be such that the angle of θ degrees corresponds to an arc on the unit circle with length $\frac{\pi}{5}$. Thus $\frac{\theta\pi}{180} = \frac{\pi}{5}$. Solving this equation for θ, we get $\theta = 36$. Thus the angle in question is 36°.

11. 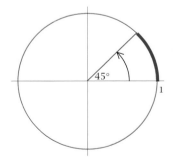 What angle corresponds to a circular arc on the unit circle with length $\frac{5}{2}$?

    SOLUTION   Let θ be such that the angle of θ degrees corresponds to an arc on the unit circle with length $\frac{5}{2}$. Thus $\frac{\theta\pi}{180} = \frac{5}{2}$. Solving this equation for θ, we get $\theta = \frac{450}{\pi}$. Thus the angle in question is $\frac{450}{\pi}°$, which is approximately equal to 143.2°.

13. Find the lengths of both circular arcs on the unit circle connecting the points $(1, 0)$ and $\left(\frac{\sqrt{2}}{2}, \frac{\sqrt{2}}{2}\right)$.

    SOLUTION   The radius of the unit circle ending at the point $\left(\frac{\sqrt{2}}{2}, \frac{\sqrt{2}}{2}\right)$ makes an angle of 45° with the positive horizontal axis. One of the circular arcs connecting $(1, 0)$ and $\left(\frac{\sqrt{2}}{2}, \frac{\sqrt{2}}{2}\right)$ is shown below as the thickened circular arc; the other circular arc connecting $(1, 0)$ and $\left(\frac{\sqrt{2}}{2}, \frac{\sqrt{2}}{2}\right)$ is the unthickened part of the unit circle below.

    The length of the thickened arc below is $\frac{45\pi}{180}$, which equals $\frac{\pi}{4}$. The entire unit circle has length 2π. Thus the length of the other circular arc below is $2\pi - \frac{\pi}{4}$, which equals $\frac{7\pi}{4}$.

The thickened circular arc has length $\frac{\pi}{4}$. The other circular arc has length $\frac{7\pi}{4}$.

For each of the angles in Exercises 15–20, find the endpoint of the radius of the unit circle that makes the given angle with the positive horizontal axis.

15. 120°

SOLUTION The radius making a 120° angle with the positive horizontal axis is shown below. The angle from this radius to the negative horizontal axis equals 180° − 120°, which equals 60° as shown in the figure below. Drop a perpendicular line segment from the endpoint of the radius to the horizontal axis, forming a right triangle as shown below. We already know that one angle of this right triangle is 60°; thus the other angle must be 30°, as labeled below:

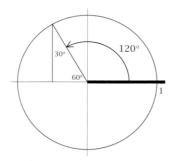

The side of the right triangle opposite the 30° angle has length $\frac{1}{2}$; the side of the right triangle opposite the 60° angle has length $\frac{\sqrt{3}}{2}$. Looking at the figure above, we see that the first coordinate of the endpoint of the radius is the negative of the length of the side opposite the 30° angle, and the second coordinate of the endpoint of the radius is the length of the side opposite the 60° angle. Thus the endpoint of the radius is $\left(-\frac{1}{2}, \frac{\sqrt{3}}{2}\right)$.

17. −30°

SOLUTION The radius making a −30° angle with the positive horizontal axis is shown below. Draw a perpendicular line segment from the endpoint of the radius to the horizontal axis, forming a right triangle as shown below. We already know that one angle of this right triangle is 30°; thus the other angle must be 60°, as labeled below.

The side of the right triangle opposite the 30° angle has length $\frac{1}{2}$; the side of the right triangle opposite the 60° angle has length $\frac{\sqrt{3}}{2}$. Looking at the figure below, we see that the first coordinate of the endpoint of the radius is the length

of the side opposite the 60° angle, and the second coordinate of the endpoint of the radius is the negative of the length of the side opposite the 30° angle. Thus the endpoint of the radius is $\left(\frac{\sqrt{3}}{2}, -\frac{1}{2}\right)$.

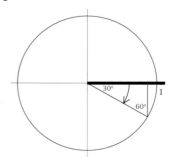

19. 390°

SOLUTION The radius making a 390° angle with the positive horizontal axis is obtained by starting at the horizontal axis, making one complete counterclockwise rotation, and then continuing for another 30°. The resulting radius is shown below. Drop a perpendicular line segment from the endpoint of the radius to the horizontal axis, forming a right triangle as shown below. We already know that one angle of this right triangle is 30°; thus the other angle must be 60°, as labeled below.

The side of the right triangle opposite the 30° angle has length $\frac{1}{2}$; the side opposite the 60° angle has length $\frac{\sqrt{3}}{2}$. Looking at the figure below, we see that the first coordinate of the endpoint of the radius is the length of the side opposite the 60° angle, and the second coordinate of the endpoint of the radius is the length of the side opposite the 30° angle. Thus the endpoint of the radius is $\left(\frac{\sqrt{3}}{2}, \frac{1}{2}\right)$.

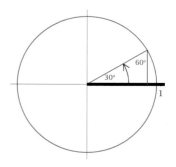

For Exercises 21–26, find the angle the radius of the unit circle ending at the given point makes with the positive horizontal axis. Among the infinitely many possible correct solutions, choose the one with the smallest absolute value.

21. $\left(-\frac{1}{2}, \frac{\sqrt{3}}{2}\right)$

SOLUTION   Draw the radius whose endpoint is $\left(-\frac{1}{2}, \frac{\sqrt{3}}{2}\right)$. Drop a perpendicular line segment from the endpoint of the radius to the horizontal axis, forming a right triangle. The hypotenuse of this right triangle is a radius of the unit circle and thus has length 1. The horizontal side has length $\frac{1}{2}$ and the vertical side of this triangle has length $\frac{\sqrt{3}}{2}$ because the endpoint of the radius is $\left(-\frac{1}{2}, \frac{\sqrt{3}}{2}\right)$.

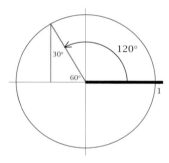

Thus we have a 30°-60°-90° triangle, with the 30° angle opposite the horizontal side of length $\frac{1}{2}$, as labeled above. Because $180 - 60 = 120$, the radius makes a 120° angle with the positive horizontal axis, as shown above.

In addition to making a 120° angle with the positive horizontal axis, this radius also makes with the positive horizontal axis angles of 480°, 840°, and so on. This radius also makes with the positive horizontal axis angles of $-240°$, $-600°$, and so on. But of all the possible choices for this angle, the one with the smallest absolute value is 120°.

23. $\left(\frac{\sqrt{2}}{2}, -\frac{\sqrt{2}}{2}\right)$

SOLUTION   Draw the radius whose endpoint is $\left(\frac{\sqrt{2}}{2}, -\frac{\sqrt{2}}{2}\right)$. Draw a perpendicular line segment from the endpoint of the radius to the horizontal axis, forming a right triangle. The hypotenuse of this right triangle is a radius of

the unit circle and thus has length 1. The horizontal side has length $\frac{\sqrt{2}}{2}$ and the vertical side of this triangle also has length $\frac{\sqrt{2}}{2}$ because the endpoint of the radius is $\left(\frac{\sqrt{2}}{2}, -\frac{\sqrt{2}}{2}\right)$.

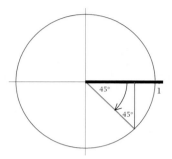

Thus we have here an isosceles right triangle, with two angles of 45° as labeled above.

In addition to making a $-45°$ angle with the positive horizontal axis, this radius also makes with the positive horizontal axis angles of 315°, 675°, and so on. This radius also makes with the positive horizontal axis angles of $-405°$, $-765°$, and so on. But of all the possible choices for this angle, the one with the smallest absolute value is $-45°$.

25. $\left(-\frac{\sqrt{2}}{2}, -\frac{\sqrt{2}}{2}\right)$

SOLUTION   Draw the radius whose endpoint is $\left(-\frac{\sqrt{2}}{2}, -\frac{\sqrt{2}}{2}\right)$. Draw a perpendicular line segment from the endpoint of the radius to the horizontal axis, forming a right triangle. The hypotenuse of this right triangle is a radius of the unit circle and thus has length 1. The horizontal side has length $\frac{\sqrt{2}}{2}$ and the vertical side of this triangle also has length $\frac{\sqrt{2}}{2}$ because the endpoint of the radius is $\left(-\frac{\sqrt{2}}{2}, -\frac{\sqrt{2}}{2}\right)$.

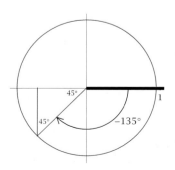

Thus we have here an isosceles right triangle, with two angles of 45° as labeled above. Because the radius makes a 45° angle with the negative horizontal axis, it makes a $-135°$ angle with the positive horizontal axis, as shown below (because $135° = 180° - 45°$).

In addition to making a $-135°$ angle with the positive horizontal axis, this radius also makes with the positive horizontal axis angles of 225°, 585°, and so on. This radius also makes with the positive horizontal axis angles of $-495°$, $-855°$, and so on. But of all the possible choices for this angle, the one with the smallest absolute value is $-135°$.

27. Find the lengths of both circular arcs on the unit circle connecting the point $(\frac{1}{2}, \frac{\sqrt{3}}{2})$ and the point that makes an angle of 130° with the positive horizontal axis.

    SOLUTION   The radius of the unit circle ending at the point $(\frac{1}{2}, \frac{\sqrt{3}}{2})$ makes an angle of 60° with the positive horizontal axis. One of the circular arcs connecting $(\frac{1}{2}, \frac{\sqrt{3}}{2})$ and the point that makes an angle of 130° with the positive horizontal axis is shown below as the thickened circular arc; the other circular arc connecting these two points is the unthickened part of the unit circle below.

    The thickened arc below corresponds to an angle of 70° (because $70° = 130° - 60°$). Thus the length of the thickened arc below is $\frac{70\pi}{180}$, which equals $\frac{7\pi}{18}$. The entire unit circle has length 2π. Thus the length of the other circular arc below is $2\pi - \frac{7\pi}{18}$, which equals $\frac{29\pi}{18}$.

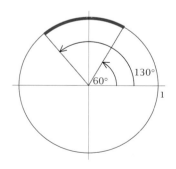

The thickened circular arc has length $\frac{7\pi}{18}$. The other circular arc has length $\frac{29\pi}{18}$.

29. Find the lengths of both circular arcs on the unit circle connecting the point $(-\frac{\sqrt{2}}{2}, -\frac{\sqrt{2}}{2})$ and the point that makes an angle of 125° with the positive horizontal axis.

    SOLUTION   The radius of the unit circle ending at $(-\frac{\sqrt{2}}{2}, -\frac{\sqrt{2}}{2})$ makes an angle of 225° with the positive horizontal axis (because $225° = 180° + 45°$). One of the circular arcs connecting $(-\frac{\sqrt{2}}{2}, -\frac{\sqrt{2}}{2})$ and the point that makes an angle of 125° with the positive horizontal axis is shown below as the thickened circular arc; the other circular arc connecting these two points is the unthickened part of the unit circle below.

    The thickened arc below corresponds to an angle of 100° (because $100° = 225° - 125°$). Thus the length of the thickened arc below is $\frac{100\pi}{180}$, which equals $\frac{5\pi}{9}$. The entire unit circle has length 2π. Thus the length of the other circular arc below is $2\pi - \frac{5\pi}{9}$, which equals $\frac{13\pi}{9}$.

The thickened circular arc has length $\frac{5\pi}{9}$. The other circular arc has length $\frac{13\pi}{9}$.

31. What is the slope of the radius of the unit circle that has a 30° angle with the positive horizontal axis?

    SOLUTION   The radius of the unit circle that has a 30° angle with the positive horizontal axis has its initial point at $(0, 0)$ and its endpoint at $(\frac{\sqrt{3}}{2}, \frac{1}{2})$. Thus the slope of this radius is

    $$\frac{\frac{1}{2} - 0}{\frac{\sqrt{3}}{2} - 0},$$

    which equals $\frac{1}{\sqrt{3}}$, which equals $\frac{\sqrt{3}}{3}$.

5.2 *Radians*

A Natural Unit of Measurement for Angles

We have been measuring angles in degrees, with $360°$ corresponding to a rotation through the entire circle. Hence $180°$ corresponds to a rotation through one-half the circle (thus generating a line), and $90°$ corresponds to a rotation through one-fourth the circle (thus generating a right angle).

There is nothing natural about the choice of 360 as the number of degrees in a complete circle. Mathematicians have introduced another unit of measurement for angles, called **radians**. Radians are used in calculus rather than degrees because the use of radians leads to much nicer formulas than would be obtained by using degrees.

The unit circle has circumference 2π. In other words, an ant walking around the unit circle once would have walked a total distance of 2π. Because going around the circle once corresponds to traveling a distance of 2π, the following definition is a natural choice for a unit of measurement for angles. As we will see, this definition makes angles as measured in radians correspond to arc length on the unit circle.

The use of $360°$ to denote a complete rotation around the circle is a historical artifact that probably arose from trying to make one day's rotation of the Earth around the sun (or the sun around the Earth) correspond to $1°$, as would be the case if the year had 360 days instead of 365 days.

Radians

Radians are a unit of measurement for angles such that 2π radians correspond to a rotation through an entire circle.

Radians and degrees are two different units for measuring angles. To translate between radians and degrees, note that a rotation through an entire circle equals 2π radians and also equals $360°$. Thus

$$2\pi \text{ radians} = 360°.$$

Rotation through half a circle equals π radians (because rotation through an entire circle equals 2π radians). Rotation through half a circle also equals $180°$. Thus

$$\pi \text{ radians} = 180°.$$

Because rotation through an entire circle equals 2π radians, a right angle (which amounts to one-fourth of a circle) equals $\frac{\pi}{2}$ radians. A right angle also equals 90°. Thus

$$\tfrac{\pi}{2} \text{ radians} = 90°.$$

Try to think of the geometry of the key angles directly in terms of radians instead of translating to degrees:

- *One complete rotation around a circle is 2π radians.*

- *The angles of a triangle add up to π radians.*

- *A right angle is $\frac{\pi}{2}$ radians.*

- *Each angle of an equilateral triangle is $\frac{\pi}{3}$ radians.*

- *The line $y = x$ in the xy-plane makes an angle of $\frac{\pi}{4}$ radians with the positive x-axis.*

- *In a right triangle with a hypotenuse of length 1 and another side with length $\frac{1}{2}$, the angle opposite the side with length $\frac{1}{2}$ is $\frac{\pi}{6}$ radians.*

The last three equations displayed above give translations between radians and degrees for three commonly used angles. Rather than memorize these equations, think in radians instead of always translating back to degrees (just as the best way to internalize a foreign language is to think in it instead of in your native language). Thus you should think that a right angle is $\frac{\pi}{2}$ radians (rather than 90°), that a line corresponds to π radians (rather than 180°), and that a complete counterclockwise rotation once around the whole unit circle equals 2π radians (rather than 360°). To help you begin this process, the following figure shows the three angles we discussed above, with the caption giving the angle measurements only in radians:

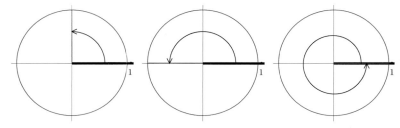

Angles of $\frac{\pi}{2}$ radians (left), π radians (center), and 2π radians (right)
with the positive horizontal axis.

If both sides of the equation $\frac{\pi}{2}$ radians = 90° are divided by 2, we get

$$\tfrac{\pi}{4} \text{ radians} = 45°.$$

Similarly, if both sides of the equation π radians = 180° are divided by 3 and also divided by 6, we get the equations

$$\tfrac{\pi}{3} \text{ radians} = 60° \quad \text{and} \quad \tfrac{\pi}{6} \text{ radians} = 30°.$$

These last three angles are displayed below, again with the caption giving angle measurements only in radians to help you think in those units:

Angles of $\frac{\pi}{6}$ radians (left), $\frac{\pi}{4}$ radians (center), and $\frac{\pi}{3}$ radians (right)
with the positive horizontal axis.

The table below summarizes the translations between degrees and radians for the most commonly used angles. As you work more with radians, you will need to refer to this table less frequently because these translations will become part of your automatic vocabulary:

degrees	radians
30°	$\frac{\pi}{6}$ radians
45°	$\frac{\pi}{4}$ radians
60°	$\frac{\pi}{3}$ radians
90°	$\frac{\pi}{2}$ radians
180°	π radians
360°	2π radians

Translation between degrees and radians for commonly used angles.

If we start with the equation 2π radians $= 360°$ and divide both sides by 2π, we see that

$$1 \text{ radian} = \left(\frac{180}{\pi}\right)^\circ.$$

Because $\frac{180}{\pi} \approx 57.3$, one radian equals approximately 57.3°.

Multiplying both sides of the equation above by an arbitrary number θ, we get the formula for converting radians to degrees:

Converting from radians to degrees

$$\theta \text{ radians} = \left(\frac{180\theta}{\pi}\right)^\circ$$

To convert in the other direction (from degrees to radians), start with the equation $360° = 2\pi$ radians and divide both sides by 360, getting

$$1° = \frac{\pi}{180} \text{ radians.}$$

Multiplying both sides of the equation above by an arbitrary number θ, we get the formula for converting degrees to radians:

Converting from degrees to radians

$$\theta° = \frac{\theta\pi}{180} \text{ radians}$$

You should not need to memorize the two boxed formulas above for converting between radians and degrees. You need to remember only the defining equation 2π radians $= 360°$, from which you can derive the other formulas as needed. The following two examples illustrate this procedure (without using the two boxed formulas above). We begin with an example converting from radians to degrees.

EXAMPLE 1

Convert $\frac{7\pi}{90}$ radians to degrees.

SOLUTION   Start with the equation

$$2\pi \text{ radians} = 360°.$$

Divide both sides by 2 to obtain

$$\pi \text{ radians} = 180°.$$

Now multiply both sides by $\frac{7}{90}$, obtaining

$$\frac{7\pi}{90} \text{ radians} = \frac{7}{90} \cdot 180° = 14°.$$

The next example illustrates the procedure for converting from degrees to radians.

EXAMPLE 2

Convert 10° to radians.

SOLUTION   Start with the equation

$$360° = 2\pi \text{ radians}.$$

Divide both sides by 360 to obtain

Because $\frac{\pi}{18} \approx$ 0.1745, this example shows that 10° is approximately 0.1745 radians.

$$1° = \frac{\pi}{180} \text{ radians}.$$

Now multiply both sides by 10, obtaining

$$10° = \frac{10\pi}{180} \text{ radians} = \frac{\pi}{18} \text{ radians}.$$

Negative Angles

In the last section we introduced negative angles, which are measured clockwise from the positive horizontal axis. We can now think of such angles as being measured in radians instead of degrees. The figure below shows some examples of commonly used negative angles:

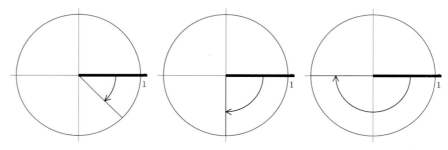

Angles of $-\frac{\pi}{4}$ radians (left), $-\frac{\pi}{2}$ radians (center), and $-\pi$ radians (right), as measured from the positive horizontal axis.

Angles Greater Than 2π

In the last section we saw that we could obtain angles larger than 360° by starting at the positive horizontal axis and moving counterclockwise around the circle for more than a complete rotation. The same principle applies when working with radians, except that a complete counterclockwise rotation around the circle is measured as 2π radians rather than 360°.

For example, consider the angle of π radians shown below on the left. We could end up at the same radius by moving counterclockwise completely around the circle (2π radians) and then continuing for another π radians, for a total of 3π radians as shown in the center below. Or we could go completely around the circle twice (4π radians) and then continue counterclockwise for another π radians for a total of 5π radians, as shown below on the right.

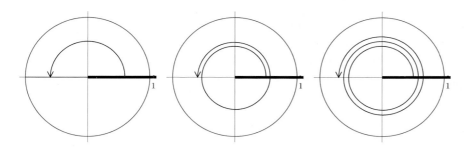

The same radius corresponds to π radians (left), 3π radians (center), 5π radians, and so on.

In the figure above, we could continue to add multiples of 2π, showing that the same radius corresponds to an angle of $\pi + 2\pi n$ radians for every positive integer n.

Just as we did when working in degrees, we can get another set of angles for the same radius by measuring clockwise from the positive horizontal axis. The figure below in the center shows that our radius with an angle of π radians can also be considered to correspond to an angle of $-\pi$ radians. Or we could go completely around the circle in the clockwise direction (-2π radians) and then continue clockwise to the radius (another $-\pi$ radians) for a total of -3π radians, as shown below on the right.

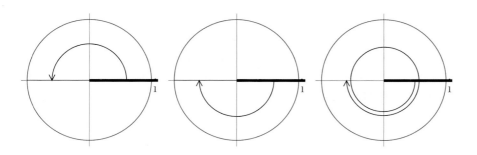

The same radius corresponds to π radians (left), $-\pi$ radians (center), -3π radians, and so on.

In the figure above, we could continue to subtract multiples of 2π radians, showing that the same radius corresponds to an angle of $\pi + 2\pi n$ radians for every integer n, positive or negative. If we had started with an arbitrary angle of θ radians instead of π radians, we would obtain the following result:

> ### Multiple choices for the angle corresponding to a radius
>
> A radius of the unit circle corresponding to an angle of θ radians also corresponds to an angle of $\theta + 2\pi n$ radians for every integer n.

Length of a Circular Arc

In the last section, we found a formula for the length of a circular arc corresponding to an angle measured in degrees. We will now derive the formula that should be used when measuring angles in radians.

We begin by considering a circular arc on the unit circle corresponding to one radian (which is a bit more than $57°$), as shown here. The entire circle corresponds to an angle of 2π radians; thus the fraction of the circle contained in this circular arc is $\frac{1}{2\pi}$. Thus the length of this circular arc equals $\frac{1}{2\pi}$ times the circumference of the entire unit circle. In other words, the length of this circular arc equals $\frac{1}{2\pi} \cdot 2\pi$, which equals 1.

Similarly, suppose $0 < \theta \leq 2\pi$. The fraction of the circle contained in a circular arc corresponding to an angle of θ radians is $\frac{\theta}{2\pi}$. Thus the length of a circular arc on the unit circle corresponding to an angle of θ radians is $\frac{\theta}{2\pi} \cdot 2\pi$. Hence we have the following result:

The circular arc on the unit circle corresponding to 1 radian has length 1.

> ### Length of a circular arc
>
> If $0 < \theta \leq 2\pi$, then a circular arc on the unit circle corresponding to an angle of θ radians has length θ.

The formula above using radians is much cleaner than the corresponding formula using degrees (see Section 5.1). The formula above should not be a surprise, because we defined radians so that 2π radians equals the whole circle, which has length 2π for the unit circle. In fact the definition of radians was chosen precisely to make this formula come out so nicely.

Some textbooks make the box above the definition of radians, rather than the approach taken here of defining the whole circle to measure 2π radians and then getting the box above as a consequence. Either way is fine; the key point is that you should be comfortable with thinking about radians as measuring arc length.

Area of a Slice

The following example will help us find a formula for the area of a slice inside a circle.

If a 14-inch pizza is cut into six slices of equal size, what is the area of one slice? (Pizza sizes are measured in terms of the diameter of the pizza.)

EXAMPLE 3

SOLUTION   The diameter of the pizza is 14 inches; thus the radius of the pizza is 7 inches. Hence the entire pizza has area 49π square inches. One slice is one-sixth of the entire pizza. Thus a slice of this pizza has area $\frac{49\pi}{6}$ square inches.

To find the general formula for the area of a slice inside a circle, consider a circle with radius r. The area inside this circle is πr^2. The area of a slice with angle θ radians equals the fraction of the entire circle taken up by the slice times πr^2. The whole circle corresponds to 2π radians, and thus the fraction taken up by a slice with angle θ is $\frac{\theta}{2\pi}$. Putting all this together, we see that the area of the slice with angle θ radians is $(\frac{\theta}{2\pi})(\pi r^2)$, which equals $\frac{1}{2}\theta r^2$. Thus we have the following formula:

> ### Area of a slice
>
> A slice with angle θ radians inside a circle of radius r has area $\frac{1}{2}\theta r^2$.

This clean formula would not be as nice if the angle θ were measured in degrees instead of radians.

To test that the formula above is correct, we can let θ equal 2π radians, which means that the slice is the entire circle. The formula above tells us that the area should equal $\frac{1}{2}(2\pi)r^2$, which equals πr^2, which is indeed the area inside a circle of radius r.

Special Points on the Unit Circle

The table below shows the endpoint of the radius of the unit circle corresponding to some special angles (measured from the positive horizontal axis, as usual). This is the same as the table in Section 5.1, except now we use radians rather than degrees.

angle	endpoint of radius
0 radians	$(1, 0)$
$\frac{\pi}{6}$ radians	$(\frac{\sqrt{3}}{2}, \frac{1}{2})$
$\frac{\pi}{4}$ radians	$(\frac{\sqrt{2}}{2}, \frac{\sqrt{2}}{2})$
$\frac{\pi}{3}$ radians	$(\frac{1}{2}, \frac{\sqrt{3}}{2})$
$\frac{\pi}{2}$ radians	$(0, 1)$
π radians	$(-1, 0)$

Coordinates of the endpoint of the radius of the unit circle corresponding to some special angles.

The example below shows how to find the endpoints of the radius of the unit circle associated with additional special angles.

| EXAMPLE 4 |

Find the coordinates of the endpoint of the radius of the unit circle that corresponds to the angle of $\frac{14\pi}{3}$ radians.

SOLUTION   Recall that integer multiples of 2π radians do not matter when locating the radius corresponding to an angle. Thus we write

$$\frac{14\pi}{3} = \frac{12\pi + 2\pi}{3} = 4\pi + \frac{2\pi}{3},$$

and we will use $\frac{2\pi}{3}$ radians instead of $\frac{14\pi}{3}$ radians in this problem.

At this point you may be more comfortable switching to degrees. Note that $\frac{2\pi}{3}$ radians equals 120°. Thus now we need to solve the problem of finding the coordinates of the endpoint of the radius of the unit circle that corresponds to 120°. This problem is solved in the worked-out solution to Exercise 15 in Section 5.1, where we see that the radius in question has its endpoint at $\left(-\frac{1}{2}, \frac{\sqrt{3}}{2}\right)$.

EXERCISES

In Exercises 1–8, convert each angle to radians.

1. 15°
2. 40°
3. −45°
4. −60°
5. 270°
6. 240°
7. 1080°
8. 1440°

In Exercises 9–16, convert each angle to degrees.

9. 4π radians
10. 6π radians
11. $\frac{\pi}{9}$ radians
12. $\frac{\pi}{10}$ radians
13. 3 radians
14. 5 radians
15. $-\frac{2\pi}{3}$ radians
16. $-\frac{3\pi}{4}$ radians

17. Suppose an ant walks counterclockwise on the unit circle from the point $(0, 1)$ to the endpoint of the radius that forms an angle of $\frac{5\pi}{4}$ radians with the positive horizontal axis. How far has the ant walked?

18. Suppose an ant walks counterclockwise on the unit circle from the point $(-1, 0)$ to the endpoint of the radius that forms an angle of 6 radians with the positive horizontal axis. How far has the ant walked?

19. ✐ Find the lengths of both circular arcs of the unit circle connecting the point $(1, 0)$ and the endpoint of the radius that makes an angle of 3 radians with the positive horizontal axis.

20. ✐ Find the lengths of both circular arcs of the unit circle connecting the point $(1, 0)$ and the endpoint of the radius that makes an angle of 4 radians with the positive horizontal axis.

21. ✐ Find the lengths of both circular arcs of the unit circle connecting the point $\left(\frac{\sqrt{2}}{2}, -\frac{\sqrt{2}}{2}\right)$ and the point whose radius makes an angle of 1 radian with the positive horizontal axis.

22. ✐ Find the lengths of both circular arcs of the unit circle connecting the point $\left(-\frac{\sqrt{2}}{2}, \frac{\sqrt{2}}{2}\right)$ and the point whose radius makes an angle of 2 radians with the positive horizontal axis.

23. For a 16-inch pizza, find the area of a slice with angle $\frac{3}{4}$ radians.

24. For a 14-inch pizza, find the area of a slice with angle $\frac{4}{5}$ radians.

25. Suppose a slice of a 12-inch pizza has an area of 20 square inches. What is the angle of this slice?

26. Suppose a slice of a 10-inch pizza has an area of 15 square inches. What is the angle of this slice?

27. Suppose a slice of pizza with an angle of $\frac{5}{6}$ radians has an area of 21 square inches. What is the diameter of this pizza?

28. Suppose a slice of pizza with an angle of 1.1 radians has an area of 25 square inches. What is the diameter of this pizza?

For each of the angles in Exercises 29–34, find the endpoint of the radius of the unit circle that makes the given angle with the positive horizontal axis.

29. $\frac{5\pi}{6}$ radians   32. $-\frac{3\pi}{4}$ radians

30. $\frac{7\pi}{6}$ radians   33. $\frac{5\pi}{2}$ radians

31. $-\frac{\pi}{4}$ radians   34. $\frac{11\pi}{2}$ radians

PROBLEMS

For each of the angles listed in Problems 35–42, sketch the unit circle and the radius that makes the indicated angle with the positive horizontal axis. Be sure to include an arrow to show the direction in which the angle is measured from the positive horizontal axis.

35. $\frac{5\pi}{18}$ radians   39. $\frac{11\pi}{5}$ radians

36. $\frac{1}{2}$ radian   40. $-\frac{\pi}{12}$ radians

37. 2 radians   41. -1 radian

38. 5 radians   42. $-\frac{8\pi}{9}$ radians

43. Find the formula for the length of a circular arc corresponding to an angle of θ radians on a circle of radius r.

44. Most dictionaries define acute angles and obtuse angles in terms of degrees. Restate these definitions in terms of radians.

45. Find a formula (in terms of θ) for the area of the region bounded by the thickened radii and the thickened circular arc shown below.

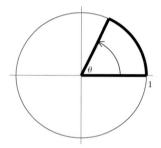

Here $0 < \theta < 2\pi$ and the radius shown above makes an angle of θ radians with the positive horizontal axis.

46. Suppose the region bounded by the thickened radii and circular arc shown above is removed. Find a formula (in terms of θ) for the perimeter of the remaining region inside the unit circle.

WORKED-OUT SOLUTIONS *to Odd-numbered Exercises*

In Exercises 1–8, convert each angle to radians.

1. $15°$

    SOLUTION   Start with the equation

    $$360° = 2\pi \text{ radians}.$$

    Divide both sides by 360 to obtain

    $$1° = \frac{\pi}{180} \text{ radians}.$$

    Now multiply both sides by 15, obtaining

    $$15° = \frac{15\pi}{180} \text{ radians} = \frac{\pi}{12} \text{ radians}.$$

3. $-45°$

    SOLUTION   Start with the equation

    $$360° = 2\pi \text{ radians}.$$

    Divide both sides by 360 to obtain

    $$1° = \frac{\pi}{180} \text{ radians}.$$

    Now multiply both sides by -45, obtaining

    $$-45° = -\frac{45\pi}{180} \text{ radians} = -\frac{\pi}{4} \text{ radians}.$$

5. $270°$

    SOLUTION   Start with the equation

    $$360° = 2\pi \text{ radians}.$$

    Divide both sides by 360 to obtain

$$1° = \frac{\pi}{180} \text{ radians.}$$

Now multiply both sides by 270, obtaining

$$270° = \frac{270\pi}{180} \text{ radians} = \frac{3\pi}{2} \text{ radians.}$$

7. 1080°

SOLUTION   Start with the equation

$$360° = 2\pi \text{ radians.}$$

Divide both sides by 360 to obtain

$$1° = \frac{\pi}{180} \text{ radians.}$$

Now multiply both sides by 1080, obtaining

$$1080° = \frac{1080\pi}{180} \text{ radians} = 6\pi \text{ radians.}$$

In Exercises 9–16, convert each angle to degrees.

9. 4π radians

SOLUTION   Start with the equation

$$2\pi \text{ radians} = 360°.$$

Multiply both sides by 2, obtaining

$$4\pi \text{ radians} = 2 \cdot 360° = 720°.$$

11. $\frac{\pi}{9}$ radians

SOLUTION   Start with the equation

$$2\pi \text{ radians} = 360°.$$

Divide both sides by 2 to obtain

$$\pi \text{ radians} = 180°.$$

Now divide both sides by 9, obtaining

$$\frac{\pi}{9} \text{ radians} = \frac{180°}{9} = 20°.$$

13. 3 radians

SOLUTION   Start with the equation

$$2\pi \text{ radians} = 360°.$$

Divide both sides by 2π to obtain

$$1 \text{ radian} = \frac{180°}{\pi}.$$

Now multiply both sides by 3, obtaining

$$3 \text{ radians} = 3 \cdot \frac{180°}{\pi} = \frac{540°}{\pi}.$$

15. $-\frac{2\pi}{3}$ radians

SOLUTION   Start with the equation

$$2\pi \text{ radians} = 360°.$$

Divide both sides by 2 to obtain

$$\pi \text{ radians} = 180°.$$

Now multiply both sides by $-\frac{2}{3}$, obtaining

$$-\frac{2\pi}{3} \text{ radians} = -\frac{2}{3} \cdot 180° = -120°.$$

17. Suppose an ant walks counterclockwise on the unit circle from the point $(0, 1)$ to the endpoint of the radius that forms an angle of $\frac{5\pi}{4}$ radians with the positive horizontal axis. How far has the ant walked?

SOLUTION   The radius whose endpoint equals $(0, 1)$ makes an angle of $\frac{\pi}{2}$ radians with the positive horizontal axis. This radius corresponds to the smaller angle shown below.

Because $\frac{5\pi}{4} = \pi + \frac{\pi}{4}$, the radius that forms an angle of $\frac{5\pi}{4}$ radians with the positive horizontal axis lies $\frac{\pi}{4}$ radians beyond the negative horizontal axis (half-way between the negative horizontal axis and the negative vertical axis). Thus the ant ends its walk at the endpoint of the radius corresponding to the larger angle shown below:

The ant walks along the thickened circular arc shown above. This circular arc corresponds to an angle of $\frac{5\pi}{4} - \frac{\pi}{2}$ radians, which equals $\frac{3\pi}{4}$ radians. Thus the distance walked by the ant is $\frac{3\pi}{4}$.

19. Find the lengths of both circular arcs of the unit circle connecting the point $(1,0)$ and the endpoint of the radius that makes an angle of 3 radians with the positive horizontal axis.

    SOLUTION   Because 3 is a bit less than π, the radius that makes an angle of 3 radians with the positive horizontal axis lies a bit above the negative horizontal axis, as shown below. The thickened circular arc corresponds to an angle of 3 radians and thus has length 3. The entire unit circle has length 2π. Thus the length of the other circular arc is $2\pi - 3$, which is approximately 3.28.

21. Find the lengths of both circular arcs of the unit circle connecting the point $(\frac{\sqrt{2}}{2}, -\frac{\sqrt{2}}{2})$ and the point whose radius makes an angle of 1 radian with the positive horizontal axis.

    SOLUTION   The radius of the unit circle whose endpoint equals $(\frac{\sqrt{2}}{2}, -\frac{\sqrt{2}}{2})$ makes an angle of $-\frac{\pi}{4}$ radians with the positive horizontal axis, as shown with the clockwise arrow below. The radius that makes an angle of 1 radian with the positive horizontal axis is shown with a counterclockwise arrow.

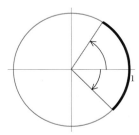

Thus the thickened circular arc above corresponds to an angle of $1 + \frac{\pi}{4}$ and thus has length $1 + \frac{\pi}{4}$, which is approximately 1.79. The entire unit circle has length 2π. Thus the length of the other circular arc below is $2\pi - (1 + \frac{\pi}{4})$, which equals $\frac{7\pi}{4} - 1$, which is approximately 4.50.

23. For a 16-inch pizza, find the area of a slice with angle $\frac{3}{4}$ radians.

    SOLUTION   Pizzas are measured by their diameters; thus this pizza has a radius of 8 inches. Thus the area of the slice is $\frac{1}{2} \cdot \frac{3}{4} \cdot 8^2$, which equals 24 square inches.

25. Suppose a slice of a 12-inch pizza has an area of 20 square inches. What is the angle of this slice?

   SOLUTION   This pizza has a radius of 6 inches. Let θ denote the angle of this slice, measured in radians. Then
   $$20 = \tfrac{1}{2}\theta \cdot 6^2.$$
   Solving this equation for θ, we get $\theta = \frac{10}{9}$ radians.

27. Suppose a slice of pizza with an angle of $\frac{5}{6}$ radians has an area of 21 square inches. What is the diameter of this pizza?

    SOLUTION   Let r denote the radius of this pizza. Thus
    $$21 = \tfrac{1}{2} \cdot \tfrac{5}{6}r^2.$$
    Solving this equation for r, we get $r = \sqrt{\frac{252}{5}} \approx 7.1$. Thus the diameter of the pizza is approximately 14.2 inches.

For each of the angles in Exercises 29–34, find the endpoint of the radius of the unit circle that makes the given angle with the positive horizontal axis.

29. $\frac{5\pi}{6}$ radians

SOLUTION For this exercise it may be easier to convert to degrees. Thus we translate $\frac{5\pi}{6}$ radians to 150°.

The radius making a 150° angle with the positive horizontal axis is shown below. The angle from this radius to the negative horizontal axis equals 180° − 150°, which equals 30° as shown in the figure below. Drop a perpendicular line segment from the endpoint of the radius to the horizontal axis, forming a right triangle as shown below. We already know that one angle of this right triangle is 30°; thus the other angle must be 60°, as labeled below.

The side of the right triangle opposite the 30° angle has length $\frac{1}{2}$; the side of the right triangle opposite the 60° angle has length $\frac{\sqrt{3}}{2}$. Looking at the figure below, we see that the first coordinate of the endpoint of the radius is the negative of the length of the side opposite the 60° angle, and the second coordinate of the endpoint of the radius is the length of the side opposite the 30° angle. Thus the endpoint of the radius is $\left(-\frac{\sqrt{3}}{2}, \frac{1}{2}\right)$.

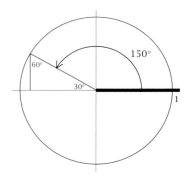

31. $-\frac{\pi}{4}$ radians

SOLUTION For this exercise it may be easier to convert to degrees. Thus we translate $-\frac{\pi}{4}$ radians to −45°.

The radius making a −45° angle with the positive horizontal axis is shown below. Draw a

perpendicular line segment from the endpoint of the radius to the horizontal axis, forming a right triangle as shown below. We already know that one angle of this right triangle is 45°; thus the other angle must also be 45°, as labeled below.

The hypotenuse of this right triangle is a radius of the unit circle and thus has length 1. The other two sides each have length $\frac{\sqrt{2}}{2}$. Looking at the figure below, we see that the first coordinate of the endpoint of the radius is $\frac{\sqrt{2}}{2}$ and the second coordinate of the endpoint of the radius is $-\frac{\sqrt{2}}{2}$. Thus the endpoint of the radius is $\left(\frac{\sqrt{2}}{2}, -\frac{\sqrt{2}}{2}\right)$.

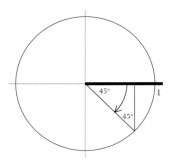

33. $\frac{5\pi}{2}$ radians

SOLUTION Note that $\frac{5\pi}{2} = 2\pi + \frac{\pi}{2}$. Thus the radius making an angle of $\frac{5\pi}{2}$ radians with the positive horizontal axis is obtained by starting at the horizontal axis, making one complete counterclockwise rotation (which is 2π radians), and then continuing for another $\frac{\pi}{2}$ radians. The resulting radius is shown below. Its endpoint is $(0, 1)$.

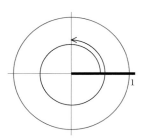

| 5.3 | *Cosine and Sine* |

SECTION OBJECTIVES

By the end of this section you should

- understand the definitions of cosine and sine;
- be able to compute the cosine and sine of any multiple of 30° or 45° ($\frac{\pi}{6}$ radians or $\frac{\pi}{4}$ radians);
- be able to determine whether the cosine (or sine) of an angle is positive or negative from the location of the corresponding radius;
- understand why $(\cos\theta)^2 + (\sin\theta)^2 = 1$.

Definition of Cosine and Sine

The table below shows the endpoint of the radius of the unit circle corresponding to some special angles (as usual, angles are measured counterclockwise from the positive horizontal axis). This table comes from tables in Sections 5.1 and 5.2.

θ (radians)	θ (degrees)	endpoint of radius with angle θ
0	0°	$(1,0)$
$\frac{\pi}{6}$	30°	$(\frac{\sqrt{3}}{2},\frac{1}{2})$
$\frac{\pi}{4}$	45°	$(\frac{\sqrt{2}}{2},\frac{\sqrt{2}}{2})$
$\frac{\pi}{3}$	60°	$(\frac{1}{2},\frac{\sqrt{3}}{2})$
$\frac{\pi}{2}$	90°	$(0,1)$
π	180°	$(-1,0)$

Coordinates of the endpoint of the radius of the unit circle corresponding to some special angles.

We might consider extending the table above to other angles. For example, suppose we want to know the endpoint of the radius corresponding to an angle of $\frac{\pi}{18}$ radians (which equals 10°). Unfortunately the coordinates of the endpoint of that radius do not have a nice form—neither coordinate is a rational number or even the square root of a rational number. The cosine and sine functions, which we are about to introduce, were invented to help us extend the table above to arbitrary angles.

The endpoint of the radius corresponding to $\frac{\pi}{18}$ radians is approximately $(0.9848, 0.1736)$.

The following figure shows a radius of the unit circle that makes an angle of θ with the positive horizontal axis (θ might be measured in either radians or degrees):

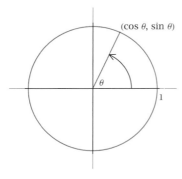

This figure defines the cosine and sine.

The coordinates of the endpoint of this radius are used to define the cosine and sine, as follows:

Cosine

The **cosine** of an angle θ, denoted $\cos \theta$, is defined to be the first coordinate of the endpoint of the radius of the unit circle that makes an angle of θ with the positive horizontal axis.

Sine

The **sine** of an angle θ, denoted $\sin \theta$, is defined to be the second coordinate of the endpoint of the radius of the unit circle that makes an angle of θ with the positive horizontal axis.

The two definitions above can be combined into a single statement, as follows:

With these defini-tions, the previous marginal note implies that $\cos \frac{\pi}{18} \approx 0.9848$ and $\sin \frac{\pi}{18} \approx 0.1736$, which could also be expressed as $\cos 10° \approx 0.9848$ and $\sin 10° \approx 0.1736$.

Cosine and sine

The endpoint of the radius of the unit circle that makes an angle of θ with the positive horizontal axis has coordinates $(\cos \theta, \sin \theta)$.

As an example of using these definitions, note that the radius that makes an angle of $\frac{\pi}{2}$ radians (which equals $90°$) with the positive horizontal axis has its endpoint at $(0, 1)$. Thus we can write

$$\cos \tfrac{\pi}{2} = 0 \quad \text{and} \quad \sin \tfrac{\pi}{2} = 1,$$

or equivalently we could write

$$\cos 90° = 0 \quad \text{and} \quad \sin 90° = 1.$$

Notice that we wrote $\cos \frac{\pi}{2} = 0$ above rather than the more cumbersome but more accurate expression $\cos(\frac{\pi}{2} \text{ radians}) = 0$. Here and in the marginal note above we are taking advantage of the common assumption that if no units are given for an angle, then the units are assumed to be radians.

Angles without units

If no units are given for an angle, then assume that the units are radians.

Sketch a radius of the unit circle making an angle θ with the positive horizontal axis such that $\cos \theta = 0.4$.

EXAMPLE 1

SOLUTION   Because $\cos \theta$ is the first coordinate of the radius of the unit circle corresponding to the angle θ, we need to find a radius of the unit circle whose first coordinate equals 0.4. To do this, start with the point corresponding to 0.4 on the horizontal axis and then move vertically either up or down to find a point on the unit circle whose first coordinate equals 0.4. Finally, draw the radius from the origin to one of the two points on the unit circle whose first coordinate equals 0.4.

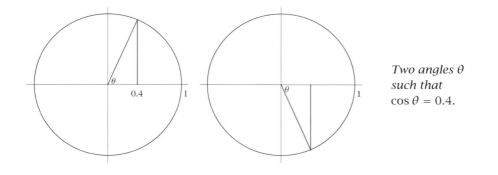

Two angles θ such that $\cos \theta = 0.4$.

Cosine and Sine of Special Angles

The table below gives the cosine and sine of some special angles. This table is obtained from the table on the first page of this section by breaking the last column of that earlier table into two columns, with the first coordinate labeled as the cosine and the second coordinate labeled as the sine. Look at both tables and make sure that you understand what is going on here.

Most calculators can be set to work in either radians or degrees. Whenever you use a calculator to compute values of cosine or sine, be sure that your calculator is set to work in the appropriate units.

θ (radians)	θ (degrees)	$\cos \theta$	$\sin \theta$
0	0°	1	0
$\frac{\pi}{6}$	30°	$\frac{\sqrt{3}}{2}$	$\frac{1}{2}$
$\frac{\pi}{4}$	45°	$\frac{\sqrt{2}}{2}$	$\frac{\sqrt{2}}{2}$
$\frac{\pi}{3}$	60°	$\frac{1}{2}$	$\frac{\sqrt{3}}{2}$
$\frac{\pi}{2}$	90°	0	1
π	180°	-1	0

Cosine and sine of some special angles.

The table above giving the cosine and sine of special angles could be greatly extended. For example, consider the radius making an angle of $-\frac{\pi}{2}$ radians (which equals $-90°$) with the positive horizontal axis, as shown below. The endpoint of this radius equals $(0, -1)$. Thus we see that

$$\cos(-\tfrac{\pi}{2}) = 0 \quad \text{and} \quad \sin(-\tfrac{\pi}{2}) = -1,$$

or equivalently we could write

$$\cos(-90°) = 0 \quad \text{and} \quad \sin(-90°) = -1.$$

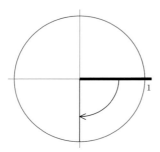

The radius making an angle of $-\frac{\pi}{2}$ with the positive horizontal axis has endpoint $(0, -1)$.

One of the few items that you do need to memorize from this section is that the cosine corresponds to the first coordinate of the endpoint of the corresponding radius and the sine corresponds to the second endpoint, rather than the other way around. One way of remembering this is to keep cosine and sine in alphabetical order, so that cosine (corresponding to the first coordinate) comes first.

In addition to adding a row for $-\frac{\pi}{2}$ radians (which equals $-90°$), we could add many more entries to the table for the cosine and sine of special angles. Possibilities would include $\frac{2\pi}{3}$ radians (which equals $120°$), $\frac{5\pi}{6}$ radians (which equals $150°$), the negatives of all the angles already in the table, and so on. This would quickly become far too much information to memorize. Instead of memorizing the table above, concentrate on understanding the definitions of cosine and sine. Then you will be able to figure out the cosine and sine of any of the special angles, as needed.

Similarly, do not become dependent on a calculator for evaluating the cosine and sine of special angles. If you need numeric values for $\cos 2$ or $\sin 17°$, then you will need to use a calculator. But if you get in the habit of using a calculator for evaluating expressions such as $\cos 0$ or $\sin(-180°)$, then cosine and sine will become simply buttons on your calculator and you will not be able to use these functions meaningfully.

The Signs of Cosine and Sine

The coordinate axes divide the coordinate plane into four regions, often called **quadrants**. The quadrant in which a radius lies determines whether the cosine and sine of the corresponding angle are positive or negative. The figure below shows the sign of the cosine and the sign of the sine in each of the four quadrants. Thus, for example, an angle corresponding to a radius lying in the region marked "cos < 0, sin > 0" will have a cosine that is negative and a sine that is positive.

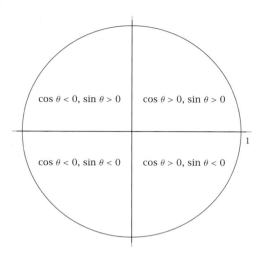

The quadrant in which a radius lies determines whether the cosine and sine of the corresponding angle are positive or negative.

There is no need to memorize this figure, because you can always reconstruct it if you understand the definitions of cosine and sine.

Recall that the cosine of an angle is the first coordinate of the endpoint of the corresponding radius and the sine is the second coordinate. Thus the cosine is positive in the two quadrants where the first coordinate is positive and the cosine is negative in the two quadrants where the first coordinate is negative. Similarly, the sine is positive in the two quadrants where the second coordinate is positive and the sine is negative in the two quadrants where the second coordinate is negative.

The example below should help you understand how the quadrant determines the sign of the cosine and sine.

(a) Evaluate $\cos\frac{\pi}{4}$ and $\sin\frac{\pi}{4}$.

(b) Evaluate $\cos\frac{3\pi}{4}$ and $\sin\frac{3\pi}{4}$.

(c) Evaluate $\cos(-\frac{\pi}{4})$ and $\sin(-\frac{\pi}{4})$.

(d) Evaluate $\cos(-\frac{3\pi}{4})$ and $\sin(-\frac{3\pi}{4})$.

EXAMPLE 2

SOLUTION   The four angles $\frac{\pi}{4}$, $\frac{3\pi}{4}$, $-\frac{\pi}{4}$, and $-\frac{3\pi}{4}$ radians (or, equivalently, 45°, 135°, −45°, and −135°), are shown below. Each coordinate of the radius corresponding to each of these angles is either $\frac{\sqrt{2}}{2}$ or $-\frac{\sqrt{2}}{2}$; the only issue to worry about in computing the cosine and sine of these angles is the sign.

Angles of $\frac{\pi}{4}$, $\frac{3\pi}{4}$, $-\frac{\pi}{4}$, and $-\frac{3\pi}{4}$ radians
(or, equivalently, 45°, 135°, −45°, and −135°).

(a) Both coordinates of the endpoint of the radius corresponding to $\frac{\pi}{4}$ are positive. Thus $\cos\frac{\pi}{4} = \sin\frac{\pi}{4} = \frac{\sqrt{2}}{2}$.

(b) The first coordinate of the endpoint of the radius corresponding to $\frac{3\pi}{4}$ is negative and the second coordinate of the endpoint is positive. Thus $\cos\frac{3\pi}{4} = -\frac{\sqrt{2}}{2}$ and $\sin\frac{3\pi}{4} = \frac{\sqrt{2}}{2}$.

(c) The first coordinate of the endpoint of the radius corresponding to $-\frac{\pi}{4}$ is positive and the second coordinate of the endpoint is negative. Thus we have $\cos(-\frac{\pi}{4}) = \frac{\sqrt{2}}{2}$ and $\sin(-\frac{\pi}{4}) = -\frac{\sqrt{2}}{2}$.

(d) Both coordinates of the endpoint of the radius corresponding to $-\frac{3\pi}{4}$ are negative. Thus we have $\cos(-\frac{3\pi}{4}) = \sin(-\frac{3\pi}{4}) = -\frac{\sqrt{2}}{2}$.

The Key Equation Connecting Cosine and Sine

The figure defining cosine and sine is sufficiently important that we should look at it again:

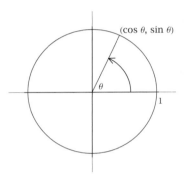

The point $(\cos\theta, \sin\theta)$ *is on the unit circle.*

The first known table of values of trigonometric functions was compiled by the Greek astronomer Hipparchus over two thousand years ago.

By definition of cosine and sine, the point $(\cos\theta, \sin\theta)$ is on the unit circle, which is the set of points in the coordinate plane such that the sum of the squares of the coordinates equals 1. In the xy-plane, the unit circle is described by the equation
$$x^2 + y^2 = 1.$$

Thus the following crucial equation holds:

> ### Relationship between cosine and sine
> $$(\cos\theta)^2 + (\sin\theta)^2 = 1$$
> for every angle θ.

Given either $\cos\theta$ or $\sin\theta$, the equation above can be used to solve for the other quantity, provided that we have enough additional information to determine the sign. The following example illustrates this procedure.

Suppose θ is an angle such that $\sin\theta = 0.6$, and suppose also that $\frac{\pi}{2} < \theta < \pi$. Evaluate $\cos\theta$.

EXAMPLE 3

SOLUTION   The equation above implies that

$$(\cos\theta)^2 + (0.6)^2 = 1.$$

Because $(0.6)^2 = 0.36$, this implies that

$$(\cos\theta)^2 = 0.64.$$

Thus $\cos\theta = 0.8$ or $\cos\theta = -0.8$. The additional information that $\frac{\pi}{2} < \theta < \pi$ implies that $\cos\theta$ is negative. Thus $\cos\theta = -0.8$.

The Graphs of Cosine and Sine

Before graphing the cosine and sine functions, we should think carefully about the domain and range of these functions. Recall that for each real number θ, there is a radius of the unit circle whose angle with the positive horizontal axis equals θ. As usual, positive angles are measured by moving counterclockwise from the positive horizontal axis and negative angles are measured by moving clockwise. Also as usual, we assume that angles are measured in radians (because no other units are given).

Recall also that the coordinates of the endpoints of the radius corresponding to the angle θ are labeled $(\cos\theta, \sin\theta)$, thus defining the cosine and sine functions. These functions are defined for every real number θ. Thus the domain of both cosine and sine is the set of real numbers.

As we have already noted, a consequence of $(\cos\theta, \sin\theta)$ lying on the unit circle is the equation

$$(\cos\theta)^2 + (\sin\theta)^2 = 1.$$

Because $(\cos\theta)^2$ and $(\sin\theta)^2$ are both nonnegative, the equation above implies that

$$(\cos\theta)^2 \le 1 \quad \text{and} \quad (\sin\theta)^2 \le 1.$$

These inequalities can be used as a crude test of the plausibility of a result. For example, suppose you do a calculation involving an angle θ and determine that $\cos\theta = 2$. Because the cosine of every angle is between -1 and 1, this is impossible. Thus you must have made a mistake in your calculation.

Thus $\cos\theta$ and $\sin\theta$ must both be between -1 and 1:

Cosine and sine are between −1 and 1

$$-1 \le \cos\theta \le 1 \quad \text{and} \quad -1 \le \sin\theta \le 1$$

for every angle θ.

These inequalities could also be written in the following form:

$$|\cos\theta| \le 1 \quad \text{and} \quad |\sin\theta| \le 1.$$

A figure of the unit circle shows that every point of the unit circle has a first coordinate in the interval $[-1, 1]$. Conversely, every number in the interval $[-1, 1]$ is the first coordinate of some point on the unit circle. The first coordinates of the points of the unit circle are precisely the values of the cosine function. Thus we can conclude that the range of the cosine function is the interval $[-1, 1]$. A similar conclusion holds for the sine function (use second coordinates instead of first coordinates).

We can summarize our results concerning the domain and range of the cosine and sine as follows:

Domain and range of cosine and sine

- The domain of both cosine and sine is the set of real numbers.

- The range of both functions is the interval $[-1, 1]$.

Because the domain of the cosine and the sine is the set of real numbers, we cannot show the graph of these functions on their entire domain. To understand what the graphs of these functions look like, we start by looking at the graph of cosine on the interval $[-6\pi, 6\pi]$:

The graph of cosine on the interval $[-6\pi, 6\pi]$.

The graphs in this book were generated by the computer algebra software Mathematica.

Let's begin examining the graph above by noting that the point $(0, 1)$ is on the graph, as expected from the equation $\cos 0 = 1$. Note that the horizontal axis has been called the θ-axis.

Moving to the right along the θ-axis from the origin, we see that the graph crosses the θ-axis at the point $(\frac{\pi}{2}, 0)$, as expected from the equation $\cos \frac{\pi}{2} = 0$. Continuing further to the right, we see that the graph hits its lowest value when $\theta = \pi$, as expected from the equation $\cos \pi = -1$. The graph then crosses the θ-axis again at the point $(\frac{3\pi}{2}, 0)$, as expected from the equation $\cos \frac{3\pi}{2} = 0$. Then the graph hits its highest value again when $\theta = 2\pi$, as expected from the equation $\cos 2\pi = 1$.

The most striking feature of the graph above is its periodic nature—the graph repeats itself. To understand why the graph of cosine exhibits this periodic behavior, consider a radius of the unit circle starting along the positive horizontal axis and moving counterclockwise. As the radius moves, the first coordinate of its endpoint gives the value of the cosine of the corresponding angle. After the radius moves through an angle of 2π, it returns to its original position. Then it begins the cycle again, returning to its original position after moving through a total angle of 4π, and so on. Thus we see the periodic behavior of the graph of cosine.

Later in this chapter we will return to examine the properties of cosine and its graph more deeply. For now, let's turn to the graph of sine. Here is the graph of sine on the interval $[-6\pi, 6\pi]$:

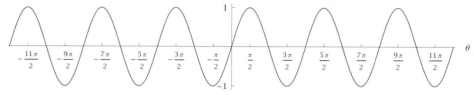

The graph of sine on the interval $[-6\pi, 6\pi]$.

This graph goes through the origin, as expected because $\sin 0 = 0$. Moving to the right along the θ-axis from the origin, we see that the graph hits its highest value when $\theta = \frac{\pi}{2}$, as expected because $\sin \frac{\pi}{2} = 1$. Continuing further to the right, we see that the graph crosses the θ-axis at the point $(\pi, 0)$, as expected because $\sin \pi = 0$. The graph then hits its lowest value when $\theta = \frac{3\pi}{2}$, as expected because $\sin \frac{3\pi}{2} = -1$. Then the graph crosses the θ-axis again at $(2\pi, 0)$, as expected because $\sin 2\pi = 0$.

The word "sine" comes from the Latin word "sinus", which means curve.

Surely you have noticed that the graph of sine looks much like the graph of cosine. It appears that shifting one graph somewhat to the left or right produces the other graph. We will see that this is indeed the case when we delve more deeply into properties of cosine and sine later in this chapter.

EXERCISES

Give exact values for the quantities in Exercises 1–10. Do not use a calculator for any of these exercises—otherwise you will likely get decimal approximations for some solutions rather than exact answers. More importantly, good understanding will come from working these exercises by hand.

1. (a) $\cos 3\pi$ (b) $\sin 3\pi$

2. (a) $\cos(-\frac{3\pi}{2})$ (b) $\sin(-\frac{3\pi}{2})$

3. (a) $\cos \frac{11\pi}{4}$ (b) $\sin \frac{11\pi}{4}$

4. (a) $\cos \frac{15\pi}{4}$ (b) $\sin \frac{15\pi}{4}$

5. (a) $\cos \frac{2\pi}{3}$ (b) $\sin \frac{2\pi}{3}$

6. (a) $\cos \frac{4\pi}{3}$ (b) $\sin \frac{4\pi}{3}$

7. (a) $\cos 210°$ (b) $\sin 210°$

8. (a) $\cos 300°$ (b) $\sin 300°$

9. (a) $\cos 360045°$ (b) $\sin 360045°$

10. (a) $\cos(-360030°)$ (b) $\sin(-360030°)$

11. Find the smallest number θ larger than 4π such that $\cos \theta = 0$.

12. Find the smallest number θ larger than 6π such that $\sin \theta = \frac{\sqrt{2}}{2}$.

13. Find the four smallest positive numbers θ such that $\cos \theta = 0$.

14. Find the four smallest positive numbers θ such that $\sin \theta = 0$.

15. Find the four smallest positive numbers θ such that $\sin \theta = 1$.

16. Find the four smallest positive numbers θ such that $\cos \theta = 1$.

17. Find the four smallest positive numbers θ such that $\cos \theta = -1$.

18. Find the four smallest positive numbers θ such that $\sin \theta = -1$.

19. Find the four smallest positive numbers θ such that $\sin \theta = \frac{1}{2}$.

20. Find the four smallest positive numbers θ such that $\cos \theta = \frac{1}{2}$.

21. Suppose $0 < \theta < \frac{\pi}{2}$ and $\cos \theta = \frac{2}{5}$. Evaluate $\sin \theta$.

22. Suppose $0 < \theta < \frac{\pi}{2}$ and $\sin \theta = \frac{3}{7}$. Evaluate $\cos \theta$.

23. Suppose $\frac{\pi}{2} < \theta < \pi$ and $\sin \theta = \frac{2}{9}$. Evaluate $\cos \theta$.

24. Suppose $\frac{\pi}{2} < \theta < \pi$ and $\sin \theta = \frac{3}{8}$. Evaluate $\cos \theta$.

25. ✐ Suppose $-\frac{\pi}{2} < \theta < 0$ and $\cos \theta = 0.1$. Evaluate $\sin \theta$.

26. ✐ Suppose $-\frac{\pi}{2} < \theta < 0$ and $\cos \theta = 0.3$. Evaluate $\sin \theta$.

27. Find the smallest number x such that $\sin(e^x) = 0$.

28. Find the smallest number x such that $\cos(e^x + 1) = 0$.

29. ✐ Find the smallest positive number x such that
$$\sin(x^2 + x + 4) = 0.$$

30. ✐ Find the smallest positive number x such that
$$\cos(x^2 + 2x + 6) = 0.$$

PROBLEMS

31. (a) Sketch a radius of the unit circle making an angle θ with the positive horizontal axis such that $\cos \theta = \frac{6}{7}$.

    (b) Sketch another radius, different from the one in part (a), also illustrating $\cos \theta = \frac{6}{7}$.

32. (a) Sketch a radius of the unit circle making an angle θ with the positive horizontal axis such that $\sin \theta = -0.8$.

    (b) Sketch another radius, different from the one in part (a), also illustrating $\sin \theta = -0.8$.

33. Find angles u and v such that $\cos u = \cos v$ but $\sin u \neq \sin v$.

34. Find angles u and v such that $\sin u = \sin v$ but $\cos u \neq \cos v$.

35. Suppose you have borrowed two calculators from friends, but you do not know whether they are set to work in radians or degrees. Thus you ask each calculator to evaluate $\cos 3.14$. One calculator replies with an answer of -0.999999; the other calculator replies with an answer of 0.998499. Without further use of a calculator, how would you decide which calculator is using radians and which calculator is using degrees? Explain your answer.

36. Suppose you have borrowed two calculators from friends, but you do not know whether they are set to work in radians or degrees. Thus you ask each calculator to evaluate $\sin 1$. One calculator replies with an answer of 0.017452; the other calculator replies with an answer of 0.841471. Without further use of a calculator, how would you decide which calculator is using radians and which calculator is using degrees? Explain your answer.

37. Explain why $e^{\cos x} < 3$ for every real number x.

38. Explain why the equation
$$(\sin x)^2 - 4 \sin x + 4 = 0$$
has no solutions.

39. Explain why there does not exist a real number x such that $e^{\sin x} = \frac{1}{4}$.

40. Explain why the equation
$$(\cos x)^{99} + 4 \cos x - 6 = 0$$
has no solutions.

41. Explain why there does not exist a number θ such that $\log \cos \theta = 0.1$.

WORKED-OUT SOLUTIONS *to Odd-numbered Exercises*

Give exact values for the quantities in Exercises 1–10. Do not use a calculator for any of these exercises—otherwise you will likely get decimal approximations for some solutions rather than exact answers. More importantly, good understanding will come from working these exercises by hand.

1. (a) $\cos 3\pi$ (b) $\sin 3\pi$

SOLUTION   Because $3\pi = 2\pi + \pi$, an angle of 3π radians (as measured counterclockwise from the positive horizontal axis) consists of a complete revolution around the circle (2π radians) followed by another π radians (180°), as shown below. The endpoint of the corresponding radius is $(-1, 0)$. Thus $\cos 3\pi = -1$ and $\sin 3\pi = 0$.

3. (a) $\cos \frac{11\pi}{4}$ (b) $\sin \frac{11\pi}{4}$

SOLUTION   Because $\frac{11\pi}{4} = 2\pi + \frac{\pi}{2} + \frac{\pi}{4}$, an angle of $\frac{11\pi}{4}$ radians (as measured counterclockwise from the positive horizontal axis) consists of a complete revolution around the circle (2π radians) followed by another $\frac{\pi}{2}$ radians (90°), followed by another $\frac{\pi}{4}$ radians (45°), as shown below. Hence the endpoint of the corresponding radius is $(-\frac{\sqrt{2}}{2}, \frac{\sqrt{2}}{2})$. Thus $\cos \frac{11\pi}{4} = -\frac{\sqrt{2}}{2}$ and $\sin \frac{11\pi}{4} = \frac{\sqrt{2}}{2}$.

5. (a) $\cos \frac{2\pi}{3}$ (b) $\sin \frac{2\pi}{3}$

SOLUTION   Because $\frac{2\pi}{3} = \frac{\pi}{2} + \frac{\pi}{6}$, an angle of $\frac{2\pi}{3}$ radians (as measured counterclockwise from the positive horizontal axis) consists of $\frac{\pi}{2}$ radians (90° radians) followed by another $\frac{\pi}{6}$ radians (30°), as shown below. The endpoint of the corresponding radius is $(-\frac{1}{2}, \frac{\sqrt{3}}{2})$. Thus $\cos \frac{2\pi}{3} = -\frac{1}{2}$ and $\sin \frac{2\pi}{3} = \frac{\sqrt{3}}{2}$.

7. (a) $\cos 210°$ (b) $\sin 210°$

SOLUTION   Because $210 = 180 + 30$, an angle of 210° (as measured counterclockwise from the positive horizontal axis) consists of 180° followed by another 30°, as shown below. The endpoint of the corresponding radius is $(-\frac{\sqrt{3}}{2}, -\frac{1}{2})$. Thus $\cos 210° = -\frac{\sqrt{3}}{2}$ and $\sin 210° = -\frac{1}{2}$.

9. (a) $\cos 360045°$ (b) $\sin 360045°$

SOLUTION   Because $360045 = 360 \times 1000 + 45$, an angle of 360045° (as measured counterclockwise from the positive horizontal axis) consists of 1000 complete revolutions around the circle followed by another 45°. The endpoint of the corresponding radius is $(\frac{\sqrt{2}}{2}, \frac{\sqrt{2}}{2})$. Thus

$$\cos 360045° = \frac{\sqrt{2}}{2} \quad \text{and} \quad \sin 360045° = \frac{\sqrt{2}}{2}.$$

11. Find the smallest number θ larger than 4π such that $\cos \theta = 0$.

    SOLUTION Note that
    $$0 = \cos \frac{\pi}{2} = \cos \frac{3\pi}{2} = \cos \frac{5\pi}{2} = \cdots$$
    and that the only numbers whose cosine equals 0 are of the form $\frac{(2n+1)\pi}{2}$, where n is an integer. The smallest number of this form larger than 4π is $\frac{9\pi}{2}$. Thus $\frac{9\pi}{2}$ is the smallest number larger than 4π whose cosine equals 0.

13. Find the four smallest positive numbers θ such that $\cos \theta = 0$.

    SOLUTION Think of a radius of the unit circle whose endpoint is $(1, 0)$. If this radius moves counterclockwise, forming an angle of θ with the positive horizontal axis, the first coordinate of its endpoint first becomes 0 when θ equals $\frac{\pi}{2}$ (which equals 90°), then again when θ equals $\frac{3\pi}{2}$ (which equals 270°), then again when θ equals $\frac{5\pi}{2}$ (which equals 360° + 90°, or 450°), then again when θ equals $\frac{7\pi}{2}$ (which equals 360° + 270°, or 630°), and so on. Thus the four smallest positive numbers θ such that $\cos \theta = 0$ are $\frac{\pi}{2}$, $\frac{3\pi}{2}$, $\frac{5\pi}{2}$, and $\frac{7\pi}{2}$.

15. Find the four smallest positive numbers θ such that $\sin \theta = 1$.

    SOLUTION Think of a radius of the unit circle whose endpoint is $(1, 0)$. If this radius moves counterclockwise, forming an angle of θ with the positive horizontal axis, then the second coordinate of its endpoint first becomes 1 when θ equals $\frac{\pi}{2}$ (which equals 90°), then again when θ equals $\frac{5\pi}{2}$ (which equals 360° + 90°, or 450°), then again when θ equals $\frac{9\pi}{2}$ (which equals $2 \times 360° + 90°$, or 810°), then again when θ equals $\frac{13\pi}{2}$ (which equals $3 \times 360° + 90°$, or 1170°), and so on. Thus the four smallest positive numbers θ such that $\sin \theta = 1$ are $\frac{\pi}{2}$, $\frac{5\pi}{2}$, $\frac{9\pi}{2}$, and $\frac{13\pi}{2}$.

17. Find the four smallest positive numbers θ such that $\cos \theta = -1$.

    SOLUTION Think of a radius of the unit circle whose endpoint is $(1, 0)$. If this radius moves

counterclockwise, forming an angle of θ with the positive horizontal axis, the first coordinate of its endpoint first becomes -1 when θ equals π (which equals 180°), then again when θ equals 3π (which equals 360° + 180°, or 540°), then again when θ equals 5π (which equals $2 \times 360° + 180°$, or 900°), then again when θ equals 7π (which equals $3 \times 360° + 180°$, or 1260°), and so on. Thus the four smallest positive numbers θ such that $\cos \theta = -1$ are π, 3π, 5π, and 7π.

19. Find the four smallest positive numbers θ such that $\sin \theta = \frac{1}{2}$.

    SOLUTION Think of a radius of the unit circle whose endpoint is $(1, 0)$. If this radius moves counterclockwise, forming an angle of θ with the positive horizontal axis, the second coordinate of its endpoint first becomes $\frac{1}{2}$ when θ equals $\frac{\pi}{6}$ (which equals 30°), then again when θ equals $\frac{5\pi}{6}$ (which equals 150°), then again when θ equals $\frac{13\pi}{6}$ (which equals 360° + 30°, or 390°), then again when θ equals $\frac{17\pi}{6}$ (which equals 360° + 150°, or 510°), and so on. Thus the four smallest positive numbers θ such that $\sin \theta = \frac{1}{2}$ are $\frac{\pi}{6}$, $\frac{5\pi}{6}$, $\frac{13\pi}{6}$, and $\frac{17\pi}{6}$.

21. Suppose $0 < \theta < \frac{\pi}{2}$ and $\cos \theta = \frac{2}{5}$. Evaluate $\sin \theta$.

    SOLUTION We know that
    $$(\cos \theta)^2 + (\sin \theta)^2 = 1.$$
    Thus
    $$\begin{aligned} (\sin \theta)^2 &= 1 - (\cos \theta)^2 \\ &= 1 - \left(\frac{2}{5}\right)^2 \\ &= \frac{21}{25}. \end{aligned}$$
    Because $0 < \theta < \frac{\pi}{2}$, we know that $\sin \theta > 0$. Thus taking square roots of both sides of the equation above gives
    $$\sin \theta = \frac{\sqrt{21}}{5}.$$

23. Suppose $\frac{\pi}{2} < \theta < \pi$ and $\sin \theta = \frac{2}{9}$. Evaluate $\cos \theta$.

    SOLUTION We know that

$$(\cos \theta)^2 + (\sin \theta)^2 = 1.$$

Thus

$$(\cos \theta)^2 = 1 - (\sin \theta)^2$$

$$= 1 - \left(\frac{2}{9}\right)^2$$

$$= \frac{77}{81}.$$

Because $\frac{\pi}{2} < \theta < \pi$, we know that $\cos \theta < 0$. Thus taking square roots of both sides of the equation above gives

$$\cos \theta = -\frac{\sqrt{77}}{9}.$$

25. Suppose $-\frac{\pi}{2} < \theta < 0$ and $\cos \theta = 0.1$. Evaluate $\sin \theta$.

SOLUTION   We know that

$$(\cos \theta)^2 + (\sin \theta)^2 = 1.$$

Thus

$$(\sin \theta)^2 = 1 - (\cos \theta)^2$$

$$= 1 - (0.1)^2$$

$$= 0.99.$$

Because $-\frac{\pi}{2} < \theta < 0$, we know that $\sin \theta < 0$. Thus taking square roots of both sides of the equation above gives

$$\sin \theta = -\sqrt{0.99} \approx -0.995.$$

27. Find the smallest number x such that $\sin(e^x) = 0$.

SOLUTION   Note that e^x is an increasing function. Because e^x is positive for every real number x, and because π is the smallest positive number whose sine equals 0, we want to choose x so that $e^x = \pi$. Thus $x = \ln \pi$.

29. Find the smallest positive number x such that

$$\sin(x^2 + x + 4) = 0.$$

SOLUTION   Note that $x^2 + x + 4$ is an increasing function on the interval $[0, \infty)$. If x is positive, then $x^2 + x + 4 > 4$. Because 4 is larger than π but less than 2π, the smallest number bigger than 4 whose sine equals 0 is 2π. Thus we want to choose x so that $x^2 + x + 4 = 2\pi$. In other words, we need to solve the equation

$$x^2 + x + (4 - 2\pi) = 0.$$

Using the quadratic formula, we see that the solutions to this equation are

$$x = \frac{-1 \pm \sqrt{8\pi - 15}}{2}.$$

A calculator shows that choosing the plus sign in the equation above gives $x \approx 1.0916$ and choosing the minus sign gives $x \approx -2.0916$. We seek only positive values of x, and thus we choose the plus sign in the equation above, getting $x \approx 1.0916$.

| 5.4 | *More Trigonometric Functions* |

SECTION OBJECTIVES

By the end of this section you should

- understand the definition of the tangent of an angle;
- be able to compute the tangent of any multiple of 30° or 45° ($\frac{\pi}{6}$ radians or $\frac{\pi}{4}$ radians);
- be able to determine whether the tangent of an angle is positive or negative from the location of the corresponding radius;
- be able to compute $\cos\theta$, $\sin\theta$, and $\tan\theta$ if given just one of these quantities and the location of the corresponding radius.

The last section introduced the cosine and the sine, the two most important trigonometric functions. This section introduces the tangent, another important trigonometric function, along with three more trigonometric functions.

Definition of Tangent

Recall that $\cos\theta$ and $\sin\theta$ are defined to be the first and second coordinates of the endpoint of the radius of the unit circle that makes an angle of θ with the positive horizontal axis. The ratio of these two numbers, with the cosine in the denominator, turns out to be sufficiently useful to deserve its own name.

Tangent

The **tangent** of an angle θ, denoted $\tan\theta$, is defined by

$$\tan\theta = \frac{\sin\theta}{\cos\theta}.$$

Recall that the slope of the line segment connecting (x_1, y_1) and (x_2, y_2) is $\frac{y_2 - y_1}{x_2 - x_1}$.

The radius of the unit circle that makes an angle of θ with the positive horizontal axis has its initial point at $(0, 0)$ and its endpoint at $(\cos\theta, \sin\theta)$. Thus the slope of this line segment equals $\frac{\sin\theta - 0}{\cos\theta - 0}$, which equals $\frac{\sin\theta}{\cos\theta}$, which equals $\tan\theta$. In other words, we have the following interpretation of the tangent of an angle:

Tangent as slope

$\tan\theta$ equals the slope of the radius of the unit circle that makes an angle of θ with the positive horizontal axis.

The following figure illustrates how the cosine, sine, and tangent of an angle are defined:

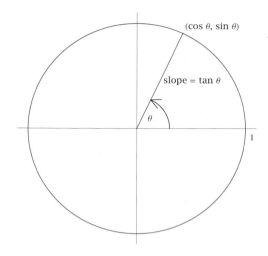

The radius that makes an angle of θ with the positive horizontal axis has slope tan θ.

Most of what you need to know about trigonometry can be derived from careful consideration of this figure.

Sketch a radius of the unit circle making an angle θ with the positive horizontal axis such that tan θ = $\frac{1}{2}$.

EXAMPLE 1

SOLUTION Because tan θ is the slope of the radius of the unit circle corresponding to the angle θ, we seek a radius of the unit circle whose slope equals $\frac{1}{2}$. One such radius is shown in the figure below on the left, and another such radius is shown below in the figure on the right:

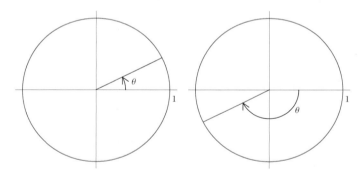

Two radii making an angle of θ with the positive horizontal axis such that tan θ = $\frac{1}{2}$. *Each of these radii has slope* $\frac{1}{2}$.

Tangent of Special Angles

As our first example of computing the tangent of an angle, note that the radius that makes an angle of $\frac{\pi}{4}$ radians (which equals 45°) with the positive horizontal axis has its endpoint at $(\frac{\sqrt{2}}{2}, \frac{\sqrt{2}}{2})$. For this point, the second coordinate divided by the first coordinate equals 1. Thus

$$\tan \frac{\pi}{4} = \tan 45° = 1.$$

The equation above is no surprise, because the line through the origin that makes a 45° angle with the positive horizontal axis has slope 1.

The table below gives the tangent of some special angles. This table is obtained from the table of cosines and sines of special angles in Section 5.3 simply by dividing the sine of each angle by its cosine.

θ (radians)	θ (degrees)	$\tan \theta$
0	$0°$	0
$\frac{\pi}{6}$	$30°$	$\frac{\sqrt{3}}{3}$
$\frac{\pi}{4}$	$45°$	1
$\frac{\pi}{3}$	$60°$	$\sqrt{3}$
$\frac{\pi}{2}$	$90°$	undefined
π	$180°$	0

Tangent of some special angles.

If you have trouble remembering whether $\tan \theta$ equals $\frac{\sin \theta}{\cos \theta}$ or $\frac{\cos \theta}{\sin \theta}$, note that the wrong choice would lead to $\tan 0$ being undefined, which is not desirable.

As can be seen in the table above, the tangent of $\frac{\pi}{2}$ radians (or equivalently the tangent of 90°) is not defined. The reason for this is that division by 0 is not defined. Specifically, the radius of the unit circle that makes an angle of $\frac{\pi}{2}$ radians with the positive horizontal axis has endpoint $(0, 1)$. Thus $\cos \frac{\pi}{2} = 0$ and $\sin \frac{\pi}{2} = 1$. According to our definition, $\tan \frac{\pi}{2}$ should equal 1 divided by 0, but this makes no sense. Thus we simply leave $\tan \frac{\pi}{2}$ as undefined.

Similarly, $\tan \theta$ is not defined for each angle θ such that $\cos \theta = 0$. In other words, $\tan \theta$ is not defined for $\theta = \pm \frac{\pi}{2}, \pm \frac{3\pi}{2}, \pm \frac{5\pi}{2}, \ldots$.

The Sign of Tangent

The quadrant in which a radius lies determines whether the tangent of the corresponding angle is positive or negative. The figure below shows the sign of the tangent in each of the four quadrants:

There is no need to memorize this figure, because you can always reconstruct it if you understand the definition of tangent.

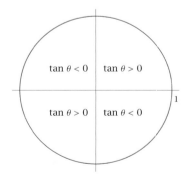

The quadrant in which a radius lies determines whether the tangent of the corresponding angle is positive or negative.

Recall that the tangent of an angle is the second coordinate of the endpoint of the corresponding radius divided by the first coordinate. Thus the tangent is positive in the quadrant where both coordinates are positive and also in the quadrant where both coordinates are negative. The tangent is negative in the quadrants where one coordinate is positive and the other coordinate is negative.

Connections between Cosine, Sine, and Tangent

Given any one of $\cos\theta$ or $\sin\theta$ or $\tan\theta$, the equations

$$(\cos\theta)^2 + (\sin\theta)^2 = 1 \quad \text{and} \quad \tan\theta = \frac{\sin\theta}{\cos\theta}$$

can be used to solve for the other two quantities, provided that we have enough additional information to determine the sign. Suppose, for example, that we know $\cos\theta$ (and the quadrant in which the angle θ lies). Knowing $\cos\theta$, we can use the first equation above to calculate $\sin\theta$ (as we did in the last section), and then we can use the second equation above to calculate $\tan\theta$.

The example below shows how to calculate $\cos\theta$ and $\sin\theta$ from $\tan\theta$ and the information about the quadrant of the angle.

EXAMPLE 2

Suppose $\pi < \theta < \frac{3\pi}{2}$ and $\tan\theta = 4$. Evaluate $\cos\theta$ and $\sin\theta$.

SOLUTION   In solving such problems, a sketch can help us understand what is going on. In this case, we know that the angle θ is between π radians (which equals $180°$) and $\frac{3\pi}{2}$ radians (which equals $270°$). Furthermore, the corresponding radius has a fairly steep slope of 4. Thus the sketch here gives a good depiction of the situation.

To solve this problem, rewrite the information that $\tan\theta = 4$ in the form

$$\frac{\sin\theta}{\cos\theta} = 4.$$

Multiplying both sides of this equation by $\cos\theta$, we get

$$\sin\theta = 4\cos\theta.$$

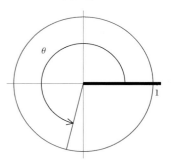

The angle between π and $\frac{3\pi}{2}$ whose tangent equals 4.

In the equation $(\cos\theta)^2 + (\sin\theta)^2 = 1$, substitute the expression above for $\sin\theta$, getting

$$(\cos\theta)^2 + (4\cos\theta)^2 = 1,$$

which is equivalent to the equation $17(\cos\theta)^2 = 1$. Thus $\cos\theta = \frac{1}{\sqrt{17}}$ or $\cos\theta = -\frac{1}{\sqrt{17}}$. A glance at the figure above shows that $\cos\theta$ is negative. Thus we must have $\cos\theta = -\frac{1}{\sqrt{17}}$.

The equation $\sin\theta = 4\cos\theta$ now implies that $\sin\theta = -\frac{4}{\sqrt{17}}$.

If we want to remove the square roots from the denominators, then our solution could be written in the form $\cos\theta = -\frac{\sqrt{17}}{17}$, $\sin\theta = -\frac{4\sqrt{17}}{17}$.

The Graph of Tangent

Before graphing the tangent function, we should think carefully about its domain and range. We have already noted that the tangent is defined for all real numbers except odd multiples of $\frac{\pi}{2}$.

The tangent of an angle is the slope of the corresponding radius of the unit circle. Because every real number is the slope of some radius of the unit circle, we see that every number is the tangent of some angle. In other words, the range of the tangent function equals the set of real numbers.

We can summarize our conclusions concerning the domain and range of the tangent as follows:

Domain and range of tangent

- The domain of the tangent function is the set of real numbers that are not odd multiples of $\frac{\pi}{2}$.

- The range of the tangent function is the set of real numbers.

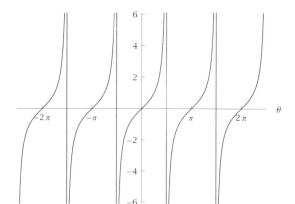

The graph of tangent on the interval $(-\frac{5}{2}\pi, \frac{5}{2}\pi)$.

This graph has been vertically truncated to show only values of the tangent that have absolute value less than 6.

Let's begin examining the graph above by noting that the graph goes through the origin, as expected from the equation $\tan 0 = 0$. Moving to the right along the θ-axis (the horizontal axis) from the origin, we see that the point $(\frac{\pi}{4}, 1)$ is on the graph, as expected from the equation $\tan \frac{\pi}{4} = 1$.

Continuing further to the right along the θ-axis toward the point where $\theta = \frac{\pi}{2}$, we see that as θ gets close to $\frac{\pi}{2}$, the values of $\tan \theta$ rapidly become very large. In fact, the values of $\tan \theta$ become too large to be shown on the figure above while maintaining a reasonable scale on the vertical axis.

To understand why $\tan \theta$ is large when θ is slightly less than a right angle, consider the figure in the margin, which shows an angle a bit less than $\frac{\pi}{2}$. We know that the red line segment has slope $\tan \theta$. Thus the red line segment lies on the line $y = (\tan \theta)x$. Hence the point on the red line segment with $x = 1$ has $y = \tan \theta$. In other words, the blue line segment has length $\tan \theta$.

Clearly the blue line segment will become very long when the red line segment comes close to making a right angle with the positive horizontal axis. Thus $\tan \theta$ becomes large when θ is just slightly less than a right angle.

This behavior can also be seen numerically as well as graphically. For example,

$$\sin(\tfrac{\pi}{2} - 0.01) \approx 0.99995 \quad \text{and} \quad \cos(\tfrac{\pi}{2} - 0.01) \approx 0.0099998.$$

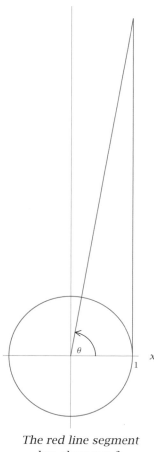

The red line segment has slope $\tan \theta$.
The blue line segment has length $\tan \theta$.

Thus $\tan(\frac{\pi}{2} - 0.01)$, which is the ratio of the two numbers above, is approximately 100.

What's happening here is that if θ is a number just slightly less than $\frac{\pi}{2}$ (for example, θ might be $\frac{\pi}{2} - 0.01$ as in the example above), then $\sin \theta$ is just slightly less than 1 and $\cos \theta$ is just slightly more than 0. Thus the ratio $\frac{\sin \theta}{\cos \theta}$, which equals $\tan \theta$, will be large.

In addition to the behavior of the graph near the lines where θ is an odd multiple of $\frac{\pi}{2}$, another striking feature of the graph above is its periodic nature. We will discuss this property of the graph of the tangent later in this chapter when we examine the properties of the tangent more deeply.

Three More Trigonometric Functions

The three main trigonometric functions are cosine, sine, and tangent. Three more trigonometric functions are sometimes used. These functions are simply the multiplicative inverses of the functions we have already defined. Here are the formal definitions:

Secant

The **secant** of an angle θ, denoted $\sec \theta$, is defined by

$$\sec \theta = \frac{1}{\cos \theta}.$$

The secant, cosecant, and cotangent functions do not exist in France, in the sense that students there do not learn about these functions.

Cosecant

The **cosecant** of an angle θ, denoted $\csc \theta$, is defined by

$$\csc \theta = \frac{1}{\sin \theta}.$$

Cotangent

The **cotangent** of an angle θ, denoted $\cot \theta$, is defined by

$$\cot \theta = \frac{\cos \theta}{\sin \theta}.$$

In all three of these definitions, the function is not defined for values of θ that would result in a division by 0.

Because the cotangent is defined to be the cosine divided by the sine and the tangent is defined to be the sine divided by the cosine, we have the following consequence of the definitions:

> ### Tangent and cotangent are multiplicative inverses.
>
> If θ is an angle such that both $\tan \theta$ and $\cot \theta$ are defined, then
>
> $$\cot \theta = \frac{1}{\tan \theta}.$$

Many books place too much emphasis on the secant, cosecant, and cotangent. You will rarely need to know anything about these functions beyond their definitions. Whenever you do encounter one of these functions, simply replace it by its definition in terms of cosine, sine, and tangent and then use your knowledge of those more familiar functions. By concentrating on cosine, sine, and tangent rather than all six trigonometric functions, you will attain a better understanding with less clutter in your mind.

So that you will be comfortable with these functions in case you encounter them elsewhere, some of the exercises in this section require you to use the secant, cosecant, or cotangent. However, after this section we will rarely use these functions in this book.

EXERCISES

1. Find the four smallest positive numbers θ such that $\tan \theta = 1$.

2. Find the four smallest positive numbers θ such that $\tan \theta = -1$.

3. Suppose $0 < \theta < \frac{\pi}{2}$ and $\cos \theta = \frac{1}{5}$. Evaluate:
   (a) $\sin \theta$ (b) $\tan \theta$

4. Suppose $0 < \theta < \frac{\pi}{2}$ and $\sin \theta = \frac{1}{4}$. Evaluate:
   (a) $\cos \theta$ (b) $\tan \theta$

5. Suppose $\frac{\pi}{2} < \theta < \pi$ and $\sin \theta = \frac{2}{3}$. Evaluate:
   (a) $\cos \theta$ (b) $\tan \theta$

6. Suppose $\frac{\pi}{2} < \theta < \pi$ and $\sin \theta = \frac{3}{4}$. Evaluate:
   (a) $\cos \theta$ (b) $\tan \theta$

7. Suppose $-\frac{\pi}{2} < \theta < 0$ and $\cos \theta = \frac{4}{5}$. Evaluate:
   (a) $\sin \theta$ (b) $\tan \theta$

8. Suppose $-\frac{\pi}{2} < \theta < 0$ and $\cos \theta = \frac{1}{5}$. Evaluate:
   (a) $\sin \theta$ (b) $\tan \theta$

9. Suppose $0 < \theta < \frac{\pi}{2}$ and $\tan \theta = \frac{1}{4}$. Evaluate:
   (a) $\cos \theta$ (b) $\sin \theta$

10. Suppose $0 < \theta < \frac{\pi}{2}$ and $\tan \theta = \frac{2}{3}$. Evaluate:
    (a) $\cos \theta$ (b) $\sin \theta$

11. Suppose $-\frac{\pi}{2} < \theta < 0$ and $\tan \theta = -3$. Evaluate:
    (a) $\cos \theta$ (b) $\sin \theta$

12. Suppose $-\frac{\pi}{2} < \theta < 0$ and $\tan \theta = -2$. Evaluate:
    (a) $\cos \theta$ (b) $\sin \theta$

Given that

$$\cos 15° = \frac{\sqrt{2 + \sqrt{3}}}{2} \quad and \quad \sin 22.5° = \frac{\sqrt{2 - \sqrt{2}}}{2},$$

in Exercises 13–22 find exact expressions for the indicated quantities.
[These values for $\cos 15°$ *and* $\sin 22.5°$ *will be derived in Examples 4 and 5 in Section 6.3.]*

13. $\sin 15°$

14. $\cos 22.5°$

15. $\tan 15°$

16. $\tan 22.5°$

17. $\cot 15°$

18. $\cot 22.5°$

19. $\csc 15°$

20. $\csc 22.5°$

21. $\sec 15°$

22. $\sec 22.5°$

Suppose u and v are in the interval $(0, \frac{\pi}{2})$, with

$$\tan u = 2 \quad and \quad \tan v = 3.$$

In Exercises 23–32, find exact expressions for the indicated quantities.

23. $\cot u$ 27. $\sin u$ 31. $\sec u$
24. $\cot v$ 28. $\sin v$ 32. $\sec v$
25. $\cos u$ 29. $\csc u$
26. $\cos v$ 30. $\csc v$

33. Find the smallest number x such that $\tan e^x = 0$.

34. Find the smallest number x such that $\tan e^x$ is undefined.

PROBLEMS

35. (a) Sketch a radius of the unit circle making an angle θ with the positive horizontal axis such that $\tan \theta = \frac{1}{7}$.
    (b) Sketch another radius, different from the one in part (a), also illustrating $\tan \theta = \frac{1}{7}$.

36. (a) Sketch a radius of the unit circle making an angle θ with the positive horizontal axis such that $\tan \theta = 7$.
    (b) Sketch another radius, different from the one in part (a), also illustrating $\tan \theta = 7$.

37. Suppose a radius of the unit circle makes an angle with the positive horizontal axis whose tangent equals 5, and another radius of the unit circle makes an angle with the positive horizontal axis whose tangent equals $-\frac{1}{5}$. Explain why these two radii are perpendicular to each other.

38. Explain why
$$\tan(\theta + \tfrac{\pi}{2}) = -\frac{1}{\tan \theta}$$
for every number θ that is not an integer multiple of $\frac{\pi}{2}$.

39. Explain why the previous problem excluded integer multiples of $\frac{\pi}{2}$ from the allowable values for θ.

40. Suppose you have borrowed two calculators from friends, but you do not know whether they are set to work in radians or degrees. Thus you ask each calculator to evaluate $\tan 89.9$. One calculator replies with an answer of -2.62; the other calculator replies with an answer of 572.96. Without further use of a calculator, how would you decide which calculator is using radians and which calculator is using degrees? Explain your answer.

41. Suppose you have borrowed two calculators from friends, but you do not know whether they are set to work in radians or degrees. Thus you ask each calculator to evaluate $\tan 1$. One calculator replies with an answer of 0.017455; the other calculator replies with an answer of 1.557408. Without further use of a calculator, how would you decide which calculator is using radians and which calculator is using degrees? Explain your answer.

42. Find a number θ such that the tangent of θ degrees is larger than 50000.

43. Find a positive number θ such that the tangent of θ degrees is less than -90000.

44. Explain why
$$|\sin \theta| \leq |\tan \theta|$$
for all θ such that $\tan \theta$ is defined.

45. Suppose θ is not an odd multiple of $\frac{\pi}{2}$. Explain why the point $(\tan \theta, 1)$ is on the line containing the point $(\sin \theta, \cos \theta)$ and the origin.

46. In 1768 the Swiss mathematician Johann Lambert proved that if θ is a rational number in the interval $(0, \frac{\pi}{2})$, then $\tan \theta$ is irrational. Explain why this result implies that π is irrational.

    [*Lambert's result provided the first proof that π is irrational.*]

WORKED-OUT SOLUTIONS *to Odd-numbered Exercises*

1. Find the four smallest positive numbers θ such that $\tan \theta = 1$.

   SOLUTION Think of a radius of the unit circle whose endpoint is $(1,0)$. If this radius moves counterclockwise, forming an angle of θ with the positive horizontal axis, then the first and second coordinates of its endpoint first become equal (which is equivalent to having $\tan \theta = 1$) when θ equals $\frac{\pi}{4}$ (which equals $45°$), then again when θ equals $\frac{5\pi}{4}$ (which equals $225°$), then again when θ equals $\frac{9\pi}{4}$ (which equals $360° + 45°$, or $405°$), then again when θ equals $\frac{13\pi}{4}$ (which equals $360° + 225°$, or $585°$), and so on.

   Thus the four smallest positive numbers θ such that $\tan \theta = 1$ are $\frac{\pi}{4}$, $\frac{5\pi}{4}$, $\frac{9\pi}{4}$, and $\frac{13\pi}{4}$.

3. Suppose $0 < \theta < \frac{\pi}{2}$ and $\cos \theta = \frac{1}{5}$. Evaluate:

   (a) $\sin \theta$ (b) $\tan \theta$

   SOLUTION The figure below gives a sketch of the angle involved in this exercise:

   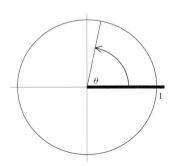

   The angle between 0 and $\frac{\pi}{2}$ whose cosine equals $\frac{1}{5}$.

   (a) We know that

   $$(\cos \theta)^2 + (\sin \theta)^2 = 1.$$

   Thus $\left(\frac{1}{5}\right)^2 + (\sin \theta)^2 = 1$. Solving this equation for $(\sin \theta)^2$ gives

   $$(\sin \theta)^2 = \frac{24}{25}.$$

   The sketch above shows that $\sin \theta > 0$. Thus taking square roots of both sides of the equation above gives

   $$\sin \theta = \frac{\sqrt{24}}{5} = \frac{\sqrt{4 \cdot 6}}{5} = \frac{2\sqrt{6}}{5}.$$

(b)
   $$\tan \theta = \frac{\sin \theta}{\cos \theta} = \frac{\frac{2\sqrt{6}}{5}}{\frac{1}{5}} = 2\sqrt{6}.$$

5. Suppose $\frac{\pi}{2} < \theta < \pi$ and $\sin \theta = \frac{2}{3}$. Evaluate:

   (a) $\cos \theta$ (b) $\tan \theta$

   SOLUTION The figure below gives a sketch of the angle involved in this exercise:

   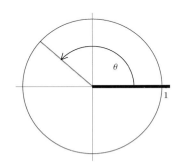

   The angle between $\frac{\pi}{2}$ and π whose sine equals $\frac{2}{3}$.

   (a) We know that

   $$(\cos \theta)^2 + (\sin \theta)^2 = 1.$$

   Thus $(\cos \theta)^2 + \left(\frac{2}{3}\right)^2 = 1$. Solving this equation for $(\cos \theta)^2$ gives

   $$(\cos \theta)^2 = \frac{5}{9}.$$

   The sketch above shows that $\cos \theta < 0$. Thus taking square roots of both sides of the equation above gives

   $$\cos \theta = -\frac{\sqrt{5}}{3}.$$

(b)
   $$\tan \theta = \frac{\sin \theta}{\cos \theta} = -\frac{\frac{2}{3}}{\frac{\sqrt{5}}{3}} = -\frac{2}{\sqrt{5}} = -\frac{2\sqrt{5}}{5}.$$

7. Suppose $-\frac{\pi}{2} < \theta < 0$ and $\cos \theta = \frac{4}{5}$. Evaluate:

   (a) $\sin \theta$ (b) $\tan \theta$

   SOLUTION The figure below gives a sketch of the angle involved in this exercise:

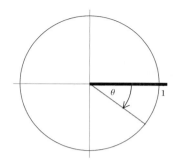

The angle between $-\frac{\pi}{2}$ and 0 whose cosine equals $\frac{4}{5}$.

(a) We know that

$$(\cos\theta)^2 + (\sin\theta)^2 = 1.$$

Thus $\left(\frac{4}{5}\right)^2 + (\sin\theta)^2 = 1$. Solving this equation for $(\sin\theta)^2$ gives

$$(\sin\theta)^2 = \frac{9}{25}.$$

The sketch above shows that $\sin\theta < 0$. Thus taking square roots of both sides of the equation above gives

$$\sin\theta = -\frac{3}{5}.$$

(b)

$$\tan\theta = \frac{\sin\theta}{\cos\theta} = -\frac{\frac{3}{5}}{\frac{4}{5}} = -\frac{3}{4}.$$

9. Suppose $0 < \theta < \frac{\pi}{2}$ and $\tan\theta = \frac{1}{4}$. Evaluate:

(a) $\cos\theta$ (b) $\sin\theta$

SOLUTION   The figure below gives a sketch of the angle involved in this exercise:

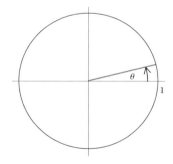

The angle between 0 and $\frac{\pi}{2}$ whose tangent equals $\frac{1}{4}$.

(a) Rewrite the equation $\tan\theta = \frac{1}{4}$ in the form $\frac{\sin\theta}{\cos\theta} = \frac{1}{4}$. Multiplying both sides of this equation by $\cos\theta$, we get

$$\sin\theta = \frac{1}{4}\cos\theta.$$

Substitute this expression for $\sin\theta$ into the equation $(\cos\theta)^2 + (\sin\theta)^2 = 1$, getting

$$(\cos\theta)^2 + \frac{1}{16}(\cos\theta)^2 = 1,$$

which is equivalent to

$$(\cos\theta)^2 = \frac{16}{17}.$$

The sketch above shows that $\cos\theta > 0$. Thus taking square roots of both sides of the equation above gives

$$\cos\theta = \frac{4}{\sqrt{17}} = \frac{4\sqrt{17}}{17}.$$

(b) We have already noted that $\sin\theta = \frac{1}{4}\cos\theta$. Thus

$$\sin\theta = \frac{\sqrt{17}}{17}.$$

11. Suppose $-\frac{\pi}{2} < \theta < 0$ and $\tan\theta = -3$. Evaluate:

(a) $\cos\theta$ (b) $\sin\theta$

SOLUTION   The figure below gives a sketch of the angle involved in this exercise:

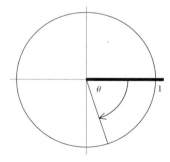

The angle between $-\frac{\pi}{2}$ and 0 whose tangent equals -3.

(a) Rewrite the equation $\tan\theta = -3$ in the form $\frac{\sin\theta}{\cos\theta} = -3$. Multiplying both sides of this equation by $\cos\theta$, we get

$$\sin\theta = -3\cos\theta.$$

Substitute this expression for $\sin\theta$ into the equation $(\cos\theta)^2 + (\sin\theta)^2 = 1$, getting

$$(\cos\theta)^2 + 9(\cos\theta)^2 = 1,$$

which is equivalent to

$$(\cos\theta)^2 = \frac{1}{10}.$$

The sketch above shows that $\cos\theta > 0$. Thus taking square roots of both sides of the equation above gives

$$\cos\theta = \frac{1}{\sqrt{10}} = \frac{\sqrt{10}}{10}.$$

(b) We have already noted that $\sin\theta = -3\cos\theta$. Thus

$$\sin\theta = -\frac{3\sqrt{10}}{10}.$$

Given that

$$\cos 15° = \frac{\sqrt{2+\sqrt{3}}}{2} \quad \textit{and} \quad \sin 22.5° = \frac{\sqrt{2-\sqrt{2}}}{2},$$

in Exercises 13–22 find exact expressions for the indicated quantities.

13. $\sin 15°$

SOLUTION We know that

$$(\cos 15°)^2 + (\sin 15°)^2 = 1.$$

Thus

$$(\sin 15°)^2 = 1 - (\cos 15°)^2$$

$$= 1 - \left(\frac{\sqrt{2+\sqrt{3}}}{2}\right)^2$$

$$= 1 - \frac{2+\sqrt{3}}{4}$$

$$= \frac{2-\sqrt{3}}{4}.$$

Because $\sin 15° > 0$, taking square roots of both sides of the equation above gives

$$\sin 15° = \frac{\sqrt{2-\sqrt{3}}}{2}.$$

15. $\tan 15°$

SOLUTION

$$\tan 15° = \frac{\sin 15°}{\cos 15°}$$

$$= \frac{\sqrt{2-\sqrt{3}}}{\sqrt{2+\sqrt{3}}}$$

$$= \frac{\sqrt{2-\sqrt{3}}}{\sqrt{2+\sqrt{3}}} \cdot \frac{\sqrt{2-\sqrt{3}}}{\sqrt{2-\sqrt{3}}}$$

$$= \frac{2-\sqrt{3}}{\sqrt{4-3}}$$

$$= 2-\sqrt{3}$$

17. $\cot 15°$

SOLUTION

$$\cot 15° = \frac{1}{\tan 15°}$$

$$= \frac{1}{2-\sqrt{3}}$$

$$= \frac{1}{2-\sqrt{3}} \cdot \frac{2+\sqrt{3}}{2+\sqrt{3}}$$

$$= \frac{2+\sqrt{3}}{4-3}$$

$$= 2+\sqrt{3}$$

19. $\csc 15°$

SOLUTION

$$\csc 15° = \frac{1}{\sin 15°}$$

$$= \frac{2}{\sqrt{2-\sqrt{3}}}$$

$$= \frac{2}{\sqrt{2-\sqrt{3}}} \cdot \frac{\sqrt{2+\sqrt{3}}}{\sqrt{2+\sqrt{3}}}$$

$$= \frac{2\sqrt{2+\sqrt{3}}}{\sqrt{4-3}}$$

$$= 2\sqrt{2+\sqrt{3}}$$

21. $\sec 15°$

SOLUTION

$$\sec 15° = \frac{1}{\cos 15°}$$

$$= \frac{2}{\sqrt{2+\sqrt{3}}}$$

$$= \frac{2}{\sqrt{2+\sqrt{3}}} \cdot \frac{\sqrt{2-\sqrt{3}}}{\sqrt{2-\sqrt{3}}}$$

$$= \frac{2\sqrt{2-\sqrt{3}}}{\sqrt{4-3}}$$

$$= 2\sqrt{2-\sqrt{3}}$$

Suppose u and v are in the interval (0, $\frac{\pi}{2}$), with

$$\tan u = 2 \quad and \quad \tan v = 3.$$

In Exercises 23–32, find exact expressions for the indicated quantities.

23. $\cot u$

SOLUTION
$$\cot u = \frac{1}{\tan u}$$
$$= \frac{1}{2}$$

25. $\cos u$

SOLUTION   We know that

$$2 = \tan u$$
$$= \frac{\sin u}{\cos u}.$$

To find $\cos u$, make the substitution $\sin u = \sqrt{1 - (\cos u)^2}$ in the equation above (this substitution is valid because we know that $0 < u < \frac{\pi}{2}$ and thus $\sin u > 0$), getting

$$2 = \frac{\sqrt{1 - (\cos u)^2}}{\cos u}.$$

Now square both sides of the equation above, then multiply both sides by $(\cos u)^2$ and rearrange to get the equation

$$5(\cos u)^2 = 1.$$

Because $0 < u < \frac{\pi}{2}$, we see that $\cos u > 0$. Thus taking square roots of both sides of the equation above gives $\cos u = \frac{1}{\sqrt{5}}$, which can be rewritten as $\cos u = \frac{\sqrt{5}}{5}$.

27. $\sin u$

SOLUTION

$$\sin u = \sqrt{1 - (\cos u)^2}$$
$$= \sqrt{1 - \frac{1}{5}}$$
$$= \sqrt{\frac{4}{5}}$$
$$= \frac{2}{\sqrt{5}}$$
$$= \frac{2\sqrt{5}}{5}$$

29. $\csc u$

SOLUTION
$$\csc u = \frac{1}{\sin u}$$
$$= \frac{\sqrt{5}}{2}$$

31. $\sec u$

SOLUTION
$$\sec u = \frac{1}{\cos u}$$
$$= \sqrt{5}$$

33. Find the smallest number x such that $\tan e^x = 0$.

SOLUTION   Note that e^x is an increasing function. Because e^x is positive for every real number x, and because π is the smallest positive number whose tangent equals 0, we want to choose x so that $e^x = \pi$. Thus $x = \ln \pi \approx 1.14473$.

Trigonometry in Right Triangles

SECTION OBJECTIVES

By the end of this section you should

- understand the right triangle characterization of cosine, sine, and tangent;

- be able to compute the cosine, sine, and tangent of any angle of a right triangle if given the lengths of two sides of the triangle;

- be able to compute the lengths of all three sides of a right triangle if given any angle (in addition to the right angle) and the length of any side.

The word "trigonome-try" first appeared in English in 1614 in a translation of a book written in Latin by the German mathematician Bartholomeo Pitiscus. A prominent crater on the moon is named for him.

Trigonometry originated in the study of triangles. In this section we study trigonometry in the context of right triangles. In the next chapter we will deal with general triangles.

Trigonometric Functions via Right Triangles

Consider a radius of the unit circle making an angle of θ radians with the positive horizontal axis, where $0 < \theta < \frac{\pi}{2}$ (in degrees, this angle is between $0°$ and $90°$), as shown here.

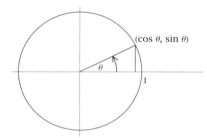

In the figure above, a vertical line segment has been dropped from the endpoint of the radius to the horizontal axis, producing a right triangle. The hypotenuse of this right triangle is a radius of the unit circle and hence has length 1. Because the endpoint of this radius has coordinates $(\cos\theta, \sin\theta)$, the horizontal side of the triangle has length $\cos\theta$ and the vertical side of the triangle has length $\sin\theta$. To get a clearer picture of what is going on, this triangle is displayed here, without the unit circle or the coordinate axes cluttering the figure (and for additional clarity, the scale has been enlarged).

If we apply the Pythagorean Theorem to the triangle above, we get

$$(\cos\theta)^2 + (\sin\theta)^2 = 1,$$

which is a familiar equation.

Using the same angle θ as above, consider now a right triangle where one of the angles is θ but where the hypotenuse does not necessarily have length 1. Let c denote the length of the hypotenuse of this right triangle. Let a denote the length of the other side of the triangle adjacent to the angle θ, and let b denote the length of the side opposite the angle θ, as shown here.

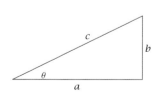

The two triangles shown above have the same angles. Thus these two triangles are similar. This similarity implies that the ratio of the lengths of any two sides of one of the triangles equals the ratio of the lengths of the corresponding sides of the other triangle.

For example, in our first triangle consider the horizontal side and the hypotenuse. These two sides have lengths $\cos\theta$ and 1. Thus the ratio of their lengths is $\frac{\cos\theta}{1}$, which equals $\cos\theta$. In our second triangle, the corresponding sides have lengths a and c. Their ratio (in the same order as used for the first triangle) is $\frac{a}{c}$. Setting these ratios from the two similar triangles equal to each other, we have

$$\cos\theta = \frac{a}{c}.$$

Similarly, in our first triangle above consider the vertical side and the hypotenuse. These two sides have lengths $\sin\theta$ and 1. Thus the ratio of their lengths is $\frac{\sin\theta}{1}$, which equals $\sin\theta$. In our second triangle, the corresponding sides have lengths b and c. Their ratio (in the same order as used for the first triangle) is $\frac{b}{c}$. Setting these ratios from the two similar triangles equal to each other, we have

$$\sin\theta = \frac{b}{c}.$$

Finally, in our first triangle consider the vertical side and the horizontal side. These two sides have lengths $\sin\theta$ and $\cos\theta$. Thus the ratio of their lengths is $\frac{\sin\theta}{\cos\theta}$, which equals $\tan\theta$. In our second triangle, the corresponding sides have lengths b and a. Their ratio (in the same order as used for the first triangle) is $\frac{b}{a}$. Setting these ratios from the two similar triangles equal to each other, we have

$$\tan\theta = \frac{b}{a}.$$

The last three equations displayed above form the basis of what is called right-triangle trigonometry. The box below restates these three equations using words rather than symbols.

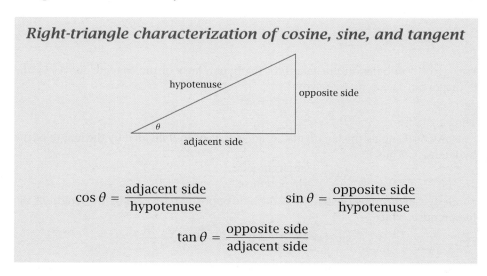

Right-triangle characterization of cosine, sine, and tangent

$$\cos\theta = \frac{\text{adjacent side}}{\text{hypotenuse}} \qquad \sin\theta = \frac{\text{opposite side}}{\text{hypotenuse}}$$

$$\tan\theta = \frac{\text{opposite side}}{\text{adjacent side}}$$

Here the word "hypotenuse" is shorthand for "the length of the hypotenuse". Similarly, "adjacent side" is shorthand for "the length of the nonhypotenuse side adjacent to the angle θ". Finally, "opposite side" is shorthand for "the length of the side opposite the angle θ".

Caution: The characterizations of cos θ, sin θ, and tan θ in the box above are valid only in right triangles, not in arbitrary triangles.

The figure and the equations in the box above capture the fundamentals of right-triangle trigonometry. Be sure that you thoroughly internalize the contents of the box above and that you can comfortably use these characterizations of the trigonometric functions.

Recall that we defined the cosine, sine, and tangent of an angle by using the unit circle and the radius made by the angle with the positive horizontal axis. The equations in the box above are a consequence of our definitions and of the properties of similar triangles.

Some books with more limited aims use the equations in the box above as the definitions of cosine, sine, and tangent. That approach makes sense only when θ is between 0 radians and $\frac{\pi}{2}$ radians (or between 0° and 90°), because there do not exist right triangles with angles bigger than $\frac{\pi}{2}$ radians (or 90°), just as there do not exist right triangles with negative angles.

However, the domain of the cosine and sine functions should be the entire real line for use in calculus. Thus the definitions given here using the unit circle are needed for calculus. The characterizations of cosine, sine, and tangent given in the box above are highly useful, but keep in mind that the box above is valid only when θ is a positive angle less than $\frac{\pi}{2}$ radians (or 90°).

Two Sides of a Right Triangle

Given the lengths of any two sides of a right triangle, the Pythagorean Theorem allows us to find the length of the third side. Once we know the lengths of all three sides of a right triangle, we can find the cosine, sine, and tangent of any angle of the triangle. The example below illustrates this procedure.

EXAMPLE 1

Find the length of the hypotenuse and evaluate $\cos\theta$, $\sin\theta$, and $\tan\theta$ in this triangle.

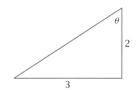

In this example the side opposite the angle θ is the horizontal side of the triangle rather than the vertical side. This illustrates the usefulness of thinking in terms of opposite and adjacent sides rather than specific letters such as a, b, and c.

SOLUTION   Let c denote the length of the hypotenuse of the triangle above. By the Pythagorean Theorem, we have
$$c^2 = 3^2 + 2^2.$$
Thus $c = \sqrt{13}$.

Now $\cos\theta$ equals the length of the side adjacent to θ divided by the length of the hypotenuse. Thus
$$\cos\theta = \frac{\text{adjacent side}}{\text{hypotenuse}} = \frac{2}{\sqrt{13}} = \frac{2\sqrt{13}}{13}.$$
Similarly, $\sin\theta$ equals the length of the side opposite θ divided by the length of the hypotenuse. Thus
$$\sin\theta = \frac{\text{opposite side}}{\text{hypotenuse}} = \frac{3}{\sqrt{13}} = \frac{3\sqrt{13}}{13}.$$

Finally, $\tan\theta$ equals the length of the side opposite θ divided by the length of the side adjacent to θ. Thus

$$\tan\theta = \frac{\text{opposite side}}{\text{adjacent side}} = \frac{3}{2}.$$

Later in this chapter we will see how to find the angle θ from the knowledge of either its cosine, its sine, or its tangent.

One Side and One Angle of a Right Triangle

Given the length of any side of a right triangle and any angle (in addition to the right angle), we can find the lengths of the other two sides of the triangle. The example below illustrates this procedure.

EXAMPLE 2

Find the lengths of the other two sides of this triangle.

SOLUTION   The other two sides of the triangle are not labeled. Thus in the figure above, let a denote the length of the side adjacent to the 28° angle and let c denote the length of the hypotenuse. You may want to write these labels on the figure above.

Because we know the length of the side opposite the 28° angle, we will start with the sine. We have

$$\sin 28° = \frac{\text{opposite side}}{\text{hypotenuse}} = \frac{4}{c}.$$

Solving for c, we get

$$c = \frac{4}{\sin 28°} \approx 8.52,$$

where the approximation was obtained with the aid of a calculator.

Now we can find the length of the side adjacent to the 28° angle by using our characterization of the tangent. We have

$$\tan 28° = \frac{\text{opposite side}}{\text{adjacent side}} = \frac{4}{a}.$$

Solving for a, we get

$$a = \frac{4}{\tan 28°} \approx 7.52,$$

where the approximation was obtained with the aid of a calculator.

Real-world problems often do not come with labels attached. Thus sometimes the first step toward a solution is the assignment of appropriate labels.

EXERCISES

Use the right triangle below for Exercises 1-76. This triangle is not drawn to scale corresponding to the data in the exercises.

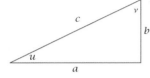

1. Suppose $a = 2$ and $b = 7$. Evaluate c.

2. Suppose $a = 3$ and $b = 5$. Evaluate c.

3. Suppose $a = 2$ and $b = 7$. Evaluate $\cos u$.

4. Suppose $a = 3$ and $b = 5$. Evaluate $\cos u$.

5. Suppose $a = 2$ and $b = 7$. Evaluate $\sin u$.

6. Suppose $a = 3$ and $b = 5$. Evaluate $\sin u$.

7. Suppose $a = 2$ and $b = 7$. Evaluate $\tan u$.

8. Suppose $a = 3$ and $b = 5$. Evaluate $\tan u$.

9. Suppose $a = 2$ and $b = 7$. Evaluate $\cos v$.

10. Suppose $a = 3$ and $b = 5$. Evaluate $\cos v$.

11. Suppose $a = 2$ and $b = 7$. Evaluate $\sin v$.

12. Suppose $a = 3$ and $b = 5$. Evaluate $\sin v$.

13. Suppose $a = 2$ and $b = 7$. Evaluate $\tan v$.

14. Suppose $a = 3$ and $b = 5$. Evaluate $\tan v$.

15. Suppose $b = 2$ and $c = 7$. Evaluate a.

16. Suppose $b = 4$ and $c = 6$. Evaluate a.

17. Suppose $b = 2$ and $c = 7$. Evaluate $\cos u$.

18. Suppose $b = 4$ and $c = 6$. Evaluate $\cos u$.

19. Suppose $b = 2$ and $c = 7$. Evaluate $\sin u$.

20. Suppose $b = 4$ and $c = 6$. Evaluate $\sin u$.

21. Suppose $b = 2$ and $c = 7$. Evaluate $\tan u$.

22. Suppose $b = 4$ and $c = 6$. Evaluate $\tan u$.

23. Suppose $b = 2$ and $c = 7$. Evaluate $\cos v$.

24. Suppose $b = 4$ and $c = 6$. Evaluate $\cos v$.

25. Suppose $b = 2$ and $c = 7$. Evaluate $\sin v$.

26. Suppose $b = 4$ and $c = 6$. Evaluate $\sin v$.

27. Suppose $b = 2$ and $c = 7$. Evaluate $\tan v$.

28. Suppose $b = 4$ and $c = 6$. Evaluate $\tan v$.

29. Suppose $a = 5$ and $u = 17°$. Evaluate b.

30. Suppose $b = 3$ and $v = 38°$. Evaluate a.

31. Suppose $a = 5$ and $u = 17°$. Evaluate c.

32. Suppose $b = 3$ and $v = 38°$. Evaluate c.

33. Suppose $u = 17°$. Evaluate $\cos v$.

34. Suppose $v = 38°$. Evaluate $\cos u$.

35. Suppose $u = 17°$. Evaluate $\sin v$.

36. Suppose $v = 38°$. Evaluate $\sin u$.

37. Suppose $u = 17°$. Evaluate $\tan v$.

38. Suppose $v = 38°$. Evaluate $\tan u$.

39. Suppose $c = 8$ and $u = 1$ radian. Evaluate a.

40. Suppose $c = 3$ and $v = 0.2$ radians. Evaluate a.

41. Suppose $c = 8$ and $u = 1$ radian. Evaluate b.

42. Suppose $c = 3$ and $v = 0.2$ radians. Evaluate b.

43. Suppose $u = 1$ radian. Evaluate $\cos v$.

44. Suppose $v = 0.2$ radians. Evaluate $\cos u$.

45. Suppose $u = 1$ radian. Evaluate $\sin v$.

46. Suppose $v = 0.2$ radians. Evaluate $\sin u$.

47. Suppose $u = 1$ radian. Evaluate $\tan v$.

48. Suppose $v = 0.2$ radians. Evaluate $\tan u$.

49. Suppose $c = 4$ and $\cos u = \frac{1}{5}$. Evaluate a.

50. Suppose $c = 5$ and $\cos u = \frac{2}{3}$. Evaluate a.

51. Suppose $c = 4$ and $\cos u = \frac{1}{5}$. Evaluate b.

52. Suppose $c = 5$ and $\cos u = \frac{2}{3}$. Evaluate b.

53. Suppose $\cos u = \frac{1}{5}$. Evaluate $\sin u$.

54. Suppose $\cos u = \frac{2}{3}$. Evaluate $\sin u$.

55. Suppose $\cos u = \frac{1}{5}$. Evaluate $\tan u$.

56. Suppose $\cos u = \frac{2}{3}$. Evaluate $\tan u$.

57. Suppose $\cos u = \frac{1}{5}$. Evaluate $\cos v$.

58. Suppose $\cos u = \frac{2}{3}$. Evaluate $\cos v$.

59. Suppose $\cos u = \frac{1}{5}$. Evaluate $\sin v$.

60. Suppose $\cos u = \frac{2}{3}$. Evaluate $\sin v$.

61. Suppose $\cos u = \frac{1}{5}$. Evaluate $\tan v$.

62. Suppose $\cos u = \frac{2}{3}$. Evaluate $\tan v$.

63. Suppose $b = 4$ and $\sin v = \frac{1}{3}$. Evaluate a.

64. Suppose $b = 2$ and $\sin v = \frac{3}{7}$. Evaluate a.

65. Suppose $b = 4$ and $\sin v = \frac{1}{3}$. Evaluate c.

66. Suppose $b = 2$ and $\sin v = \frac{3}{7}$. Evaluate c.

67. Suppose $\sin v = \frac{1}{3}$. Evaluate $\cos u$.

68. Suppose $\sin v = \frac{3}{7}$. Evaluate $\cos u$.

69. Suppose $\sin v = \frac{1}{3}$. Evaluate $\sin u$.

70. Suppose $\sin v = \frac{3}{7}$. Evaluate $\sin u$.

71. Suppose $\sin v = \frac{1}{3}$. Evaluate $\tan u$.

72. Suppose $\sin v = \frac{3}{7}$. Evaluate $\tan u$.

73. Suppose $\sin v = \frac{1}{3}$. Evaluate $\cos v$.

74. Suppose $\sin v = \frac{3}{7}$. Evaluate $\cos v$.

75. Suppose $\sin v = \frac{1}{3}$. Evaluate $\tan v$.

76. Suppose $\sin v = \frac{3}{7}$. Evaluate $\tan v$.

77. Suppose a 25-foot ladder is leaning against a wall, making a 63° angle with the ground (as measured from a perpendicular line from the base of the ladder to the wall). How high up the wall is the end of the ladder?

78. Suppose a 19-foot ladder is leaning against a wall, making a 71° angle with the ground (as measured from a perpendicular line from the base of the ladder to the wall). How high up the wall is the end of the ladder?

79. Suppose you need to find the height of a tall building. Standing 20 meters away from the base of the building, you aim a laser pointer at the closest part of the top of the building. You measure that the laser pointer is 4° tilted from pointing straight up. The laser pointer is held 2 meters above the ground. How tall is the building?

80. Suppose you need to find the height of a tall building. Standing 15 meters away from the base of the building, you aim a laser pointer at the closest part of the top of the building. You measure that the laser pointer is 7° tilted from pointing straight up. The laser pointer is held 2 meters above the ground. How tall is the building?

PROBLEMS

81. In doing several of the exercises in this section, you should have noticed a relationship between $\cos u$ and $\sin v$, along with a relationship between $\sin u$ and $\cos v$. What are these relationships? Explain why they hold.

82. In doing several of the exercises in this section, you should have noticed a relationship between $\tan u$ and $\tan v$. What is this relationship? Explain why it holds.

WORKED-OUT SOLUTIONS *to Odd-numbered Exercises*

Use the right triangle below for Exercises 1–76. This triangle is not drawn to scale corresponding to the data in the exercises.

1. Suppose $a = 2$ and $b = 7$. Evaluate c.

    SOLUTION   The Pythagorean Theorem implies that $c^2 = 2^2 + 7^2$. Thus

    $$c = \sqrt{2^2 + 7^2} = \sqrt{53}.$$

3. Suppose $a = 2$ and $b = 7$. Evaluate $\cos u$.

    SOLUTION

    $$\cos u = \frac{\text{adjacent side}}{\text{hypotenuse}} = \frac{a}{c} = \frac{2}{\sqrt{53}} = \frac{2\sqrt{53}}{53}$$

5. Suppose $a = 2$ and $b = 7$. Evaluate $\sin u$.

    SOLUTION

    $$\sin u = \frac{\text{opposite side}}{\text{hypotenuse}} = \frac{b}{c} = \frac{7}{\sqrt{53}} = \frac{7\sqrt{53}}{53}$$

7. Suppose $a = 2$ and $b = 7$. Evaluate $\tan u$.

SOLUTION

$$\tan u = \frac{\text{opposite side}}{\text{adjacent side}} = \frac{b}{a} = \frac{7}{2}$$

9. Suppose $a = 2$ and $b = 7$. Evaluate $\cos v$.

SOLUTION

$$\cos v = \frac{\text{adjacent side}}{\text{hypotenuse}} = \frac{b}{c} = \frac{7}{\sqrt{53}} = \frac{7\sqrt{53}}{53}$$

11. Suppose $a = 2$ and $b = 7$. Evaluate $\sin v$.

SOLUTION

$$\sin v = \frac{\text{opposite side}}{\text{hypotenuse}} = \frac{a}{c} = \frac{2}{\sqrt{53}} = \frac{2\sqrt{53}}{53}$$

13. Suppose $a = 2$ and $b = 7$. Evaluate $\tan v$.

SOLUTION

$$\tan v = \frac{\text{opposite side}}{\text{adjacent side}} = \frac{a}{b} = \frac{2}{7}$$

15. Suppose $b = 2$ and $c = 7$. Evaluate a.

SOLUTION The Pythagorean Theorem implies that $a^2 + 2^2 = 7^2$. Thus

$$a = \sqrt{7^2 - 2^2} = \sqrt{45} = \sqrt{9 \cdot 5} = \sqrt{9} \cdot \sqrt{5} = 3\sqrt{5}.$$

17. Suppose $b = 2$ and $c = 7$. Evaluate $\cos u$.

SOLUTION

$$\cos u = \frac{\text{adjacent side}}{\text{hypotenuse}} = \frac{a}{c} = \frac{3\sqrt{5}}{7}$$

19. Suppose $b = 2$ and $c = 7$. Evaluate $\sin u$.

SOLUTION

$$\sin u = \frac{\text{opposite side}}{\text{hypotenuse}} = \frac{b}{c} = \frac{2}{7}$$

21. Suppose $b = 2$ and $c = 7$. Evaluate $\tan u$.

SOLUTION

$$\tan u = \frac{\text{opposite side}}{\text{adjacent side}} = \frac{b}{a} = \frac{2}{3\sqrt{5}} = \frac{2\sqrt{5}}{15}$$

23. Suppose $b = 2$ and $c = 7$. Evaluate $\cos v$.

SOLUTION

$$\cos v = \frac{\text{adjacent side}}{\text{hypotenuse}} = \frac{b}{c} = \frac{2}{7}$$

25. Suppose $b = 2$ and $c = 7$. Evaluate $\sin v$.

SOLUTION

$$\sin v = \frac{\text{opposite side}}{\text{hypotenuse}} = \frac{a}{c} = \frac{3\sqrt{5}}{7}$$

27. Suppose $b = 2$ and $c = 7$. Evaluate $\tan v$.

SOLUTION

$$\tan v = \frac{\text{opposite side}}{\text{adjacent side}} = \frac{a}{b} = \frac{3\sqrt{5}}{2}$$

29. Suppose $a = 5$ and $u = 17°$. Evaluate b.

SOLUTION We have

$$\tan 17° = \frac{\text{opposite side}}{\text{adjacent side}} = \frac{b}{5}.$$

Solving for b, we get $b = 5 \tan 17° \approx 1.53$.

31. Suppose $a = 5$ and $u = 17°$. Evaluate c.

SOLUTION We have

$$\cos 17° = \frac{\text{adjacent side}}{\text{hypotenuse}} = \frac{5}{c}.$$

Solving for c, we get

$$c = \frac{5}{\cos 17°} \approx 5.23.$$

33. Suppose $u = 17°$. Evaluate $\cos v$.

SOLUTION Because $v = 90° - u$, we have $v = 73°$. Thus $\cos v = \cos 73° \approx 0.292$.

35. Suppose $u = 17°$. Evaluate $\sin v$.

SOLUTION $\sin v = \sin 73° \approx 0.956$

37. Suppose $u = 17°$. Evaluate $\tan v$.

SOLUTION $\tan v = \tan 73° \approx 3.27$

39. Suppose $c = 8$ and $u = 1$ radian. Evaluate a.

SOLUTION We have

$$\cos 1 = \frac{\text{adjacent side}}{\text{hypotenuse}} = \frac{a}{8}.$$

Solving for a, we get

$$a = 8\cos 1 \approx 4.32.$$

When using a calculator to do the approximation above, be sure that your calculator is set to operate in radian mode.

41. 📱 Suppose $c = 8$ and $u = 1$ radian. Evaluate b.

SOLUTION   We have
$$\sin 1 = \frac{\text{opposite side}}{\text{hypotenuse}} = \frac{b}{8}.$$
Solving for b, we get
$$b = 8\sin 1 \approx 6.73.$$

43. 📱 Suppose $u = 1$ radian. Evaluate $\cos v$.

SOLUTION   Because $v = \frac{\pi}{2} - u$, we have $v = \frac{\pi}{2} - 1$. Thus
$$\cos v = \cos(\tfrac{\pi}{2} - 1) \approx 0.841.$$

45. 📱 Suppose $u = 1$ radian. Evaluate $\sin v$.

SOLUTION
$$\sin v = \sin(\tfrac{\pi}{2} - 1) \approx 0.540$$

47. 📱 Suppose $u = 1$ radian. Evaluate $\tan v$.

SOLUTION
$$\tan v = \tan(\tfrac{\pi}{2} - 1) \approx 0.642$$

49. Suppose $c = 4$ and $\cos u = \frac{1}{5}$. Evaluate a.

SOLUTION   We have
$$\frac{1}{5} = \cos u = \frac{\text{adjacent side}}{\text{hypotenuse}} = \frac{a}{4}.$$
Solving this equation for a, we get
$$a = \frac{4}{5}.$$

51. Suppose $c = 4$ and $\cos u = \frac{1}{5}$. Evaluate b.

SOLUTION   The Pythagorean Theorem implies that $\left(\frac{4}{5}\right)^2 + b^2 = 4^2$. Thus
$$b = \sqrt{16 - \frac{16}{25}} = 4\sqrt{1 - \frac{1}{25}} = 4\sqrt{\frac{24}{25}} = \frac{8\sqrt{6}}{5}.$$

53. Suppose $\cos u = \frac{1}{5}$. Evaluate $\sin u$.

SOLUTION
$$\sin u = \sqrt{1 - (\cos u)^2} = \sqrt{1 - \frac{1}{25}}$$
$$= \sqrt{\frac{24}{25}} = \frac{2\sqrt{6}}{5}$$

55. Suppose $\cos u = \frac{1}{5}$. Evaluate $\tan u$.

SOLUTION
$$\tan u = \frac{\sin u}{\cos u} = \frac{\frac{2\sqrt{6}}{5}}{\frac{1}{5}} = 2\sqrt{6}$$

57. Suppose $\cos u = \frac{1}{5}$. Evaluate $\cos v$.

SOLUTION
$$\cos v = \frac{b}{c} = \sin u = \frac{2\sqrt{6}}{5}$$

59. Suppose $\cos u = \frac{1}{5}$. Evaluate $\sin v$.

SOLUTION
$$\sin v = \frac{a}{c} = \cos u = \frac{1}{5}$$

61. Suppose $\cos u = \frac{1}{5}$. Evaluate $\tan v$.

SOLUTION
$$\tan v = \frac{\sin v}{\cos v} = \frac{\frac{1}{5}}{\frac{2\sqrt{6}}{5}} = \frac{1}{2\sqrt{6}} = \frac{\sqrt{6}}{12}$$

63. Suppose $b = 4$ and $\sin v = \frac{1}{3}$. Evaluate a.

SOLUTION   We have
$$\frac{1}{3} = \sin v = \frac{\text{opposite side}}{\text{hypotenuse}} = \frac{a}{c}.$$
Thus
$$c = 3a.$$
By the Pythagorean Theorem, we also have
$$c^2 = a^2 + 16.$$
Substituting $3a$ for c in this equation gives
$$9a^2 = a^2 + 16.$$
Solving the equation above for a shows that $a = \sqrt{2}$.

65. Suppose $b = 4$ and $\sin v = \frac{1}{3}$. Evaluate c.

SOLUTION We have
$$\frac{1}{3} = \sin v = \frac{a}{c}.$$
Thus
$$c = 3a = 3\sqrt{2}.$$

67. Suppose $\sin v = \frac{1}{3}$. Evaluate $\cos u$.

SOLUTION
$$\cos u = \frac{a}{c} = \sin v = \frac{1}{3}$$

69. Suppose $\sin v = \frac{1}{3}$. Evaluate $\sin u$.

SOLUTION
$$\sin u = \sqrt{1 - (\cos u)^2} = \sqrt{1 - \left(\frac{1}{3}\right)^2}$$
$$= \sqrt{\frac{8}{9}} = \frac{2\sqrt{2}}{3}$$

71. Suppose $\sin v = \frac{1}{3}$. Evaluate $\tan u$.

SOLUTION
$$\tan u = \frac{\sin u}{\cos u} = \frac{\frac{2\sqrt{2}}{3}}{\frac{1}{3}} = 2\sqrt{2}$$

73. Suppose $\sin v = \frac{1}{3}$. Evaluate $\cos v$.

SOLUTION
$$\cos v = \sqrt{1 - (\sin v)^2} = \sqrt{1 - \left(\frac{1}{3}\right)^2}$$
$$= \sqrt{\frac{8}{9}} = \frac{2\sqrt{2}}{3}$$

75. Suppose $\sin v = \frac{1}{3}$. Evaluate $\tan v$.

SOLUTION
$$\tan v = \frac{\sin v}{\cos v} = \frac{\frac{1}{3}}{\frac{2\sqrt{2}}{3}} = \frac{1}{2\sqrt{2}} = \frac{\sqrt{2}}{4}$$

77. Suppose a 25-foot ladder is leaning against a wall, making a 63° angle with the ground (as measured from a perpendicular line from the

base of the ladder to the wall). How high up the wall is the end of the ladder?

SOLUTION

In the sketch here, the vertical line represents the wall and the hypotenuse represents the ladder. As labeled here, the ladder touches the wall at height b; thus we need to evaluate b.

We have $\sin 63° = \frac{b}{25}$. Solving this equation for b, we get
$$b = 25 \sin 63° \approx 22.28.$$

Thus the ladder touches the wall at a height of approximately 22.28 feet. Because $0.28 \times 12 = 3.36$, this is approximately 22 feet, 3 inches.

79. Suppose you need to find the height of a tall building. Standing 20 meters away from the base of the building, you aim a laser pointer at the closest part of the top of the building. You measure that the laser pointer is 4° tilted from pointing straight up. The laser pointer is held 2 meters above the ground. How tall is the building?

SOLUTION

In the sketch here, the right-most vertical line represents the building and the hypotenuse represents the path of the laser beam. Because the laser pointer is 4° tilted from pointing straight up, the angle formed by the laser beam and a line parallel to the ground is 86°, as indicated in the figure (which is not drawn to scale).

The side of the right triangle opposite the 86° angle has been labeled b. Thus the height of the building is $b + 2$.

We have $\tan 86° = \frac{b}{20}$. Solving this equation for b, we get
$$b = 20 \tan 86° \approx 286.$$

Adding 2 to this result, we see that the height of the building is approximately 288 meters.

5.6 | *Trigonometric Identities*

SECTION OBJECTIVES

By the end of this section you should

- understand how to derive and work with trigonometric identities;
- be able to use the trigonometric identities for $-\theta$;
- be able to use the trigonometric identities for $\frac{\pi}{2} - \theta$;
- be able to use the trigonometric identities for $\theta + \pi$ and $\theta + 2\pi$.

Equations come in two flavors. One flavor is an equation such as

$$x^2 = 4x - 3,$$

which holds for only certain special values of the variable x. We can talk about solving such equations, which means finding the special values of the variable (or variables) that make the equations valid. For example, the equation above is valid only if $x = 1$ or $x = 3$.

A second flavor is an equation such as

$$(x + 3)^2 = x^2 + 6x + 9,$$

which is valid for all numbers x. An equation such as this is called an **identity** because it is identically true without regard to the value of any variables. As another example, the logarithmic identity

$$\log(xy) = \log x + \log y$$

holds for all positive numbers x and y.

In this section we focus on basic trigonometric identities, which are identities that involve trigonometric functions. Such identities are often useful for simplifying trigonometric expressions and for converting information about one trigonometric function to information about another trigonometric function. We will deal with additional trigonometric identities later, particularly in Sections 6.3 and 6.4.

Throughout this book, identities generally appear in blue to distinguish them from equations of the first flavor.

Do not memorize the many dozen useful trigonometric identities. Concentrate on understanding why these identities hold. Then you will be able to derive the ones you need in any particular situation.

The Relationship Between Cosine and Sine

We have already used the most important trigonometric identity, which is $(\cos\theta)^2 + (\sin\theta)^2 = 1$. Recall that this identity arises from the definition of $(\cos\theta, \sin\theta)$ as a point on the unit circle, whose equation is $x^2 + y^2 = 1$.

Most books use the notation $\cos^2\theta$ instead of $(\cos\theta)^2$ and $\sin^2\theta$ instead of $(\sin\theta)^2$. We have been using the notation $(\cos\theta)^2$ and $(\sin\theta)^2$ to emphasize the meaning of these terms. Now it is time to switch to the more common notation. Keep in mind, however, that an expression such as $\cos^2\theta$ really means $(\cos\theta)^2$.

Notation for powers of cosine, sine, and tangent

If n is a positive integer, then

- $\cos^n \theta$ means $(\cos \theta)^n$;

- $\sin^n \theta$ means $(\sin \theta)^n$;

- $\tan^n \theta$ means $(\tan \theta)^n$.

With our new notation, the most important trigonometric identity can be rewritten as follows:

Relationship between cosine and sine

$$\cos^2 \theta + \sin^2 \theta = 1$$

for every angle θ.

Given either $\cos \theta$ or $\sin \theta$, we can use these equations to evaluate the other provided that we also have enough information to choose between positive and negative values.

The trigonometric identity above implies that

$$\cos \theta = \pm\sqrt{1 - \sin^2 \theta}$$

and

$$\sin \theta = \pm\sqrt{1 - \cos^2 \theta},$$

with the choices between the plus and minus signs depending on the quadrant in which θ lies.

The equations above can be used, for example, to write $\tan \theta$ solely in terms of $\cos \theta$, as follows:

$$\tan \theta = \frac{\sin \theta}{\cos \theta} = \pm\frac{\sqrt{1 - \cos^2 \theta}}{\cos \theta}.$$

If both sides of the key trigonometric identity $\cos^2 \theta + \sin^2 \theta = 1$ are divided by $\cos^2 \theta$ and then we rewrite $\frac{\sin^2 \theta}{\cos^2 \theta}$ as $\tan^2 \theta$, we get another useful identity:

$$1 + \tan^2 \theta = \frac{1}{\cos^2 \theta}.$$

Using one of the three less common trigonometric functions, we could also write this identity in the form

$$1 + \tan^2 \theta = \sec^2 \theta,$$

where $\sec^2 \theta$ denotes, of course, $(\sec \theta)^2$.

Simplifying a trigonometric expression often involves doing a bit of algebraic manipulation and using an appropriate trigonometric identity, as in the following example.

Simplify the expression

EXAMPLE 1

$$(\tan^2\theta)\Big(\frac{1}{1-\cos\theta}+\frac{1}{1+\cos\theta}\Big).$$

SOLUTION

$$(\tan^2\theta)\Big(\frac{1}{1-\cos\theta}+\frac{1}{1+\cos\theta}\Big)=(\tan^2\theta)\Big(\frac{(1+\cos\theta)+(1-\cos\theta)}{(1-\cos\theta)(1+\cos\theta)}\Big)$$

$$=(\tan^2\theta)\Big(\frac{2}{1-\cos^2\theta}\Big)$$

$$=(\tan^2\theta)\Big(\frac{2}{\sin^2\theta}\Big)$$

$$=\Big(\frac{\sin^2\theta}{\cos^2\theta}\Big)\Big(\frac{2}{\sin^2\theta}\Big)$$

$$=\frac{2}{\cos^2\theta}$$

Trigonometric Identities for the Negative of an Angle

By the definitions of cosine and sine, the endpoint of the radius of the unit circle making an angle of θ with the positive horizontal axis has coordinates $(\cos\theta,\sin\theta)$. Similarly, the endpoint of the radius of the unit circle making an angle of $-\theta$ with the positive horizontal axis has coordinates $(\cos(-\theta),\sin(-\theta))$, as shown in the figure below:

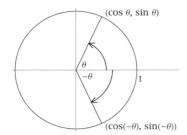
(cos θ, sin θ)

θ
−θ
1

(cos(−θ), sin(−θ))

The radius corresponding to the angle $-\theta$ is the reflection through the horizontal axis of the radius corresponding to the angle θ.

Each of the two radii in the figure above is the reflection of the other through the horizontal axis. Thus the endpoints of the two radii in the figure above have the same first coordinate, and their second coordinates are the negative of each other. In other words, the figure above shows that

$$\cos(-\theta)=\cos\theta \quad \text{and} \quad \sin(-\theta)=-\sin\theta.$$

Using these equations and the definition of the tangent, we see that

$$\tan(-\theta)=\frac{\sin(-\theta)}{\cos(-\theta)}=\frac{-\sin\theta}{\cos\theta}=-\tan\theta.$$

Collecting the three identities we have just derived gives the following:

An identity involving the tangent can often be derived from the corresponding identities for cosine and sine.

> ## *Trigonometric identities with $-\theta$*
>
> $$\cos(-\theta) = \cos\theta$$
>
> $$\sin(-\theta) = -\sin\theta$$
>
> $$\tan(-\theta) = -\tan\theta$$

As we have just seen, the cosine of the negative of an angle is the same as the cosine of the angle. This explains why the graph of the cosine is symmetric with respect to the vertical axis. Specifically, along with the typical point $(\theta, \cos\theta)$ on the graph of the cosine we also have the point $(-\theta, \cos(-\theta))$, which equals $(-\theta, \cos\theta)$.

The graph of cosine is symmetric with respect to the vertical axis.

In contrast to the behavior of the cosine, the sine of the negative of an angle is the negative of the sine of the angle. This explains why the graph of the sine is symmetric with respect to the origin. Specifically, along with the typical point $(\theta, \sin\theta)$ on the graph of the sine we also have the point $(-\theta, \sin(-\theta))$, which equals $(-\theta, -\sin\theta)$.

*The graphs of sine (left) and tangent (right)
are symmetric with respect to the origin.*

Similarly, the graph of the tangent is also symmetric with respect to the origin because the tangent of the negative of an angle is the negative of the tangent of the angle.

Trigonometric Identities with $\frac{\pi}{2}$

*A positive angle is called **acute** if it is less than a right angle, which means less than $\frac{\pi}{2}$ radians or, equivalently, less than $90°$.*

Suppose $0 < \theta < \frac{\pi}{2}$, and consider a right triangle with an angle of θ radians. Because the angles of a triangle add up to π radians, the triangle's other acute angle is $\frac{\pi}{2} - \theta$ radians, as shown in the figure below. If we were working in degrees rather than radians, then we would be stating that a right triangle with an angle of $\theta°$ also has an angle of $(90 - \theta)°$.

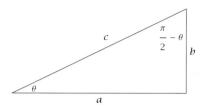

In a right triangle with an angle of θ radians, the other acute angle is $\frac{\pi}{2} - \theta$ radians.

In the triangle above, let c denote the length of the hypotenuse, let a denote the length of the side adjacent to the angle θ, and let b denote the length of the side opposite the angle θ. Focusing on the angle θ, our characterization from the last section of cosine, sine, and tangent in terms of right triangles shows that

$$\cos \theta = \tfrac{a}{c} \quad \text{and} \quad \sin \theta = \tfrac{b}{c} \quad \text{and} \quad \tan \theta = \tfrac{b}{a}.$$

Now focusing instead on the angle $\frac{\pi}{2} - \theta$ in the triangle above, our right-triangle characterization of the trigonometric functions shows that

$$\cos(\tfrac{\pi}{2} - \theta) = \tfrac{b}{c} \quad \text{and} \quad \sin(\tfrac{\pi}{2} - \theta) = \tfrac{a}{c} \quad \text{and} \quad \tan(\tfrac{\pi}{2} - \theta) = \tfrac{a}{b}.$$

Comparing the last two sets of displayed equations, we get the following identities:

> ### Trigonometric identities with $\frac{\pi}{2} - \theta$
>
> $$\cos(\tfrac{\pi}{2} - \theta) = \sin \theta$$
>
> $$\sin(\tfrac{\pi}{2} - \theta) = \cos \theta$$
>
> $$\tan(\tfrac{\pi}{2} - \theta) = \frac{1}{\tan \theta}$$

We have derived the identities above under the assumption that $0 < \theta < \frac{\pi}{2}$, but the first two identities hold for all values of θ. The third identity above holds for all values of θ except the integer multiples of $\frac{\pi}{2}$ [either $\tan(\frac{\pi}{2} - \theta)$ or $\tan \theta$ is not defined for such angles].

Note that if $\tan \theta = 0$ (which happens when θ is an integer multiple of π), then $\tan(\frac{\pi}{2} - \theta)$ is undefined.

As an example of the formulas above, suppose $\theta = \frac{\pi}{6}$. Then

$$\tfrac{\pi}{2} - \theta = \tfrac{\pi}{2} - \tfrac{\pi}{6} = \tfrac{3\pi}{6} - \tfrac{\pi}{6} = \tfrac{2\pi}{6} = \tfrac{\pi}{3}.$$

For these angles $\frac{\pi}{6}$ and $\frac{\pi}{3}$ (which equal $30°$ and $60°$), we already know the values of the trigonometric functions:

$$\cos \tfrac{\pi}{6} = \tfrac{\sqrt{3}}{2} \quad \text{and} \quad \sin \tfrac{\pi}{6} = \tfrac{1}{2} \quad \text{and} \quad \tan \tfrac{\pi}{6} = \tfrac{\sqrt{3}}{3}$$

and

$$\cos \tfrac{\pi}{3} = \tfrac{1}{2} \quad \text{and} \quad \sin \tfrac{\pi}{3} = \tfrac{\sqrt{3}}{2} \quad \text{and} \quad \tan \tfrac{\pi}{3} = \sqrt{3}.$$

Thus we see here the expected pattern when we consider an angle θ along with the angle $\frac{\pi}{2} - \theta$: the values of cosine and sine are interchanged, and the values of tangent are multiplicative inverses of each other (note that $\frac{1}{\sqrt{3}} = \frac{\sqrt{3}}{3}$).

Rewriting the identities in the box above in terms of degrees rather than radians, we obtain the following identities:

Trigonometric identities with $(90 - \theta)°$

These identities imply, for example, that $\cos 81° = \sin 9°$, $\sin 81° = \cos 9°$, and $\tan 81° = \frac{1}{\tan 9°}$.

$$\cos(90 - \theta)° = \sin\theta°$$

$$\sin(90 - \theta)° = \cos\theta°$$

$$\tan(90 - \theta)° = \frac{1}{\tan\theta°}$$

Combining two or more trigonometric identities often leads to useful new identities, as shown in the following example.

EXAMPLE 2

Show that
$$\cos(\theta - \tfrac{\pi}{2}) = \sin\theta$$
for every number θ.

SOLUTION   Suppose θ is any real number. Then
$$\cos(\theta - \tfrac{\pi}{2}) = \cos(\tfrac{\pi}{2} - \theta)$$
$$= \sin\theta,$$

where the first equality above comes from the identity $\cos(-\theta) = \cos\theta$ (with θ replaced by $\frac{\pi}{2} - \theta$) and the second equality comes from one of the identities derived above.

The equation $\cos(\theta - \frac{\pi}{2}) = \sin\theta$ implies that the graph of sine is obtained by shifting the graph of cosine to the right by $\frac{\pi}{2}$ units, as can be seen in the figure below:

Shifting the graph of cosine (left) to the right by $\frac{\pi}{2}$ units produces the graph of sine (right).

Trigonometric Identities Involving a Multiple of π

Consider a typical angle θ and also the angle $\theta + \pi$. Because π radians (which equals $180°$) is a rotation half-way around the circle, the radius of the unit circle that makes an angle of $\theta + \pi$ with the positive horizontal axis forms a line with the radius that makes an angle of θ with the positive horizontal axis, as seen in the figure below.

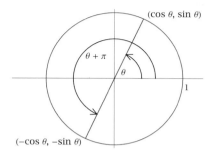

The radius corresponding to $\theta + \pi$ lies directly opposite the radius corresponding to θ. Thus the coordinates of the endpoints of these two radii are the negatives of each other.

By definition of the cosine and sine, the endpoint of the radius of the unit circle corresponding to θ has coordinates $(\cos \theta, \sin \theta)$, as shown above. The radius corresponding to $\theta + \pi$ lies directly opposite the radius corresponding to θ. Thus the coordinates of the endpoint of the radius corresponding to $\theta + \pi$ are the negatives of the coordinates of the endpoint of the radius corresponding to θ. In other words, the endpoint of the radius corresponding to $\theta + \pi$ has coordinates $(-\cos \theta, -\sin \theta)$, as shown in the figure above.

By definition of the cosine and sine, the endpoint of the radius of the unit circle corresponding to $\theta + \pi$ has coordinates $(\cos(\theta + \pi), \sin(\theta + \pi))$. Thus $(\cos(\theta + \pi), \sin(\theta + \pi)) = (-\cos \theta, -\sin \theta)$. This implies that

$$\cos(\theta + \pi) = -\cos \theta \quad \text{and} \quad \sin(\theta + \pi) = -\sin \theta.$$

Recall that $\tan \theta$ equals the slope of the radius of the unit circle corresponding to θ. Similarly, $\tan(\theta + \pi)$ equals the slope of the radius corresponding to $\theta + \pi$. However, these two radii lie on the same line, as can be seen in the figure above. Thus these two radii have the same slope. Hence

$$\tan(\theta + \pi) = \tan \theta.$$

Another way to reach the same conclusion is to use the definition of the tangent as the ratio of the sine and cosine, along with the identities above:

$$\tan(\theta + \pi) = \frac{\sin(\theta + \pi)}{\cos(\theta + \pi)} = \frac{-\sin \theta}{-\cos \theta} = \frac{\sin \theta}{\cos \theta} = \tan \theta.$$

Collecting the trigonometric identities involving $\theta + \pi$, we have:

Trigonometric identities with $\theta + \pi$

$$\cos(\theta + \pi) = -\cos \theta$$

$$\sin(\theta + \pi) = -\sin \theta$$

$$\tan(\theta + \pi) = \tan \theta$$

The first two identities hold for all values of θ. The third identity holds for all values of θ except odd multiples of $\frac{\pi}{2}$, which must be excluded because $\tan(\theta + \pi)$ and $\tan \theta$ are not defined for such angles.

The trigonometric identity $\tan(\theta + \pi) = \tan\theta$ explains the periodic nature of the graph of the tangent, with the graph repeating the same shape after each interval of length π. This behavior is demonstrated in the graph below:

This graph has been vertically truncated to show only values of the tangent that have absolute value less than 6.

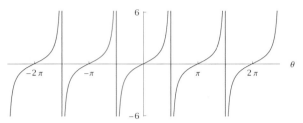

The graph of the tangent function. Because $\tan(\theta + \pi) = \tan\theta$, this graph repeats the same shape after each interval of length π.

Now we consider a typical angle θ and also the angle $\theta + 2\pi$. Because 2π radians (which equals $360°$) is a complete rotation all the way around the circle, the radius of the unit circle that makes an angle of $\theta + 2\pi$ with the positive horizontal axis is the same as the radius that makes an angle of θ with the positive horizontal axis.

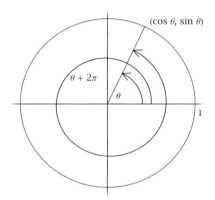

By definition of the cosine and sine, the endpoint of the radius of the unit circle corresponding to θ has coordinates $(\cos\theta, \sin\theta)$, as shown above. Because the radius corresponding to $\theta + 2\pi$ is the same as the radius corresponding to θ, we see that $(\cos(\theta + 2\pi), \sin(\theta + 2\pi)) = (\cos\theta, \sin\theta)$. This implies that

$$\cos(\theta + 2\pi) = \cos\theta \quad \text{and} \quad \sin(\theta + 2\pi) = \sin\theta.$$

Recall that $\tan\theta$ equals the slope of the radius of the unit circle corresponding to θ. Similarly, $\tan(\theta + 2\pi)$ equals the slope of the radius corresponding to $\theta + 2\pi$. However, these two radii are the same. Thus

$$\tan(\theta + 2\pi) = \tan\theta.$$

Another way to reach the same conclusion is to use the definition of the tangent as the ratio of the sine and cosine, along with the identities above:

$$\tan(\theta + 2\pi) = \frac{\sin(\theta + 2\pi)}{\cos(\theta + 2\pi)} = \frac{\sin\theta}{\cos\theta} = \tan\theta.$$

Yet another way to reach the same conclusion is to use (twice!) the identity concerning the tangent of an angle plus π:

$$\tan(\theta + 2\pi) = \tan((\theta + \pi) + \pi) = \tan(\theta + \pi) = \tan \theta.$$

Collecting the trigonometric identities involving $\theta + 2\pi$, we have:

> ### Trigonometric identities with $\theta + 2\pi$
>
> $$\cos(\theta + 2\pi) = \cos \theta$$
>
> $$\sin(\theta + 2\pi) = \sin \theta$$
>
> $$\tan(\theta + 2\pi) = \tan \theta$$

The first two identities hold for all values of θ. The third identity holds for all values of θ except odd multiples of $\frac{\pi}{2}$, which must be excluded because $\tan(\theta + \pi)$ and $\tan \theta$ are not defined for such angles.

The trigonometric identities $\cos(\theta + 2\pi) = \cos \theta$ and $\sin(\theta + 2\pi) = \sin \theta$ explain the periodic nature of the graphs of cosine and sine, with the graphs repeating the same shape after each interval of length 2π. This behavior is demonstrated in the graphs below:

The graphs of the cosine (left) and sine (right).
Because $\cos(\theta + 2\pi) = \cos \theta$ and $\sin(\theta + 2\pi) = \sin \theta$,
these graphs repeat the same shape after each interval of length 2π.

In the box above, 2π could be replaced by any even multiple of π. For example, the radius corresponding to $\theta + 6\pi$ is obtained by starting with the radius corresponding to θ and then making three complete rotations around the circle, ending up with the same radius. Thus $\cos(\theta + 6\pi) = \cos \theta$, $\sin(\theta + 6\pi) = \sin \theta$, and $\tan(\theta + 6\pi) = \tan \theta$. More generally, if n is an even integer, then the radius of the unit circle corresponding to the angle $\theta + n\pi$ is the same as the radius corresponding to the angle θ. Thus if n is an even integer, then the values of the trigonometric functions at $\theta + n\pi$ are the same as the values at θ.

Similarly, in our trigonometric formulas for $\theta + \pi$, we could replace π by any odd multiple of π. For example, the radius corresponding to $\theta + 5\pi$ is obtained by starting with the radius corresponding to θ and then making two-and-one-half rotations around the circle, ending up with the opposite radius. Thus $\cos(\theta + 5\pi) = -\cos \theta$, $\sin(\theta + 5\pi) = -\sin \theta$, and $\tan(\theta + 5\pi) = \tan \theta$. More generally, if n is an odd integer, then the radius of the unit circle corresponding to the angle $\theta + n\pi$ lies directly opposite the radius corresponding to θ. Thus if n is an odd integer, then the values of cosine and sine at $\theta + n\pi$ are the negatives of the values at θ, and the value of tangent at $\theta + n\pi$ is the same as the value at θ.

The trigonometric identities involving an integer multiple of π can be summarized as follows:

> ## Trigonometric identities with $\theta + n\pi$
>
> $$\cos(\theta + n\pi) = \begin{cases} \cos\theta & \text{if } n \text{ is an even integer} \\ -\cos\theta & \text{if } n \text{ is an odd integer} \end{cases}$$
>
> $$\sin(\theta + n\pi) = \begin{cases} \sin\theta & \text{if } n \text{ is an even integer} \\ -\sin\theta & \text{if } n \text{ is an odd integer} \end{cases}$$
>
> $$\tan(\theta + n\pi) = \tan\theta \quad \text{if } n \text{ is an integer}$$

The first two identities above hold for all values of θ. The third identity above holds for all values of θ except the odd multiples of $\frac{\pi}{2}$; these values must be excluded because $\tan(\theta + \pi)$ and $\tan\theta$ are not defined for such angles.

EXERCISES

1. For $\theta = 7°$, evaluate each of the following:

   (a) $\cos^2\theta$ (b) $\cos(\theta^2)$

   [*Exercises 1 and 2 emphasize that* $\cos^2\theta$ *does not equal* $\cos(\theta^2)$*.*]

2. For $\theta = 5$ radians, evaluate each of the following:

   (a) $\cos^2\theta$ (b) $\cos(\theta^2)$

3. For $\theta = 4$ radians, evaluate each of the following:

   (a) $\sin^2\theta$ (b) $\sin(\theta^2)$

   [*Exercises 3 and 4 emphasize that* $\sin^2\theta$ *does not equal* $\sin(\theta^2)$*.*]

4. For $\theta = -8°$, evaluate each of the following:

   (a) $\sin^2\theta$ (b) $\sin(\theta^2)$

In Exercises 5–38, find exact expressions for the indicated quantities, given that

$$\cos\frac{\pi}{12} = \frac{\sqrt{2+\sqrt{3}}}{2} \quad \text{and} \quad \sin\frac{\pi}{8} = \frac{\sqrt{2-\sqrt{2}}}{2}.$$

[*These values for* $\cos\frac{\pi}{12}$ *and* $\sin\frac{\pi}{8}$ *will be derived in Examples 4 and 5 in Section 6.3.*]

5. $\cos(-\frac{\pi}{12})$
6. $\sin(-\frac{\pi}{8})$
7. $\sin\frac{\pi}{12}$
8. $\cos\frac{\pi}{8}$
9. $\sin(-\frac{\pi}{12})$
10. $\cos(-\frac{\pi}{8})$
11. $\tan\frac{\pi}{12}$
12. $\tan\frac{\pi}{8}$
13. $\tan(-\frac{\pi}{12})$
14. $\tan(-\frac{\pi}{8})$
15. $\cos\frac{25\pi}{12}$
16. $\cos\frac{17\pi}{8}$
17. $\sin\frac{25\pi}{12}$
18. $\sin\frac{17\pi}{8}$
19. $\tan\frac{25\pi}{12}$
20. $\tan\frac{17\pi}{8}$
21. $\cos\frac{13\pi}{12}$

22. $\cos\frac{9\pi}{8}$
23. $\sin\frac{13\pi}{12}$
24. $\sin\frac{9\pi}{8}$
25. $\tan\frac{13\pi}{12}$
26. $\tan\frac{9\pi}{8}$
27. $\cos\frac{5\pi}{12}$
28. $\cos\frac{3\pi}{8}$
29. $\cos(-\frac{5\pi}{12})$
30. $\cos(-\frac{3\pi}{8})$
31. $\sin\frac{5\pi}{12}$
32. $\sin\frac{3\pi}{8}$
33. $\sin(-\frac{5\pi}{12})$
34. $\sin(-\frac{3\pi}{8})$
35. $\tan\frac{5\pi}{12}$
36. $\tan\frac{3\pi}{8}$
37. $\tan(-\frac{5\pi}{12})$
38. $\tan(-\frac{3\pi}{8})$

Suppose u and v are in the interval $(\frac{\pi}{2}, \pi)$, with

$$\tan u = -2 \quad \text{and} \quad \tan v = -3.$$

In Exercises 39–66, find exact expressions for the indicated quantities.

39. $\tan(-u)$

40. $\tan(-v)$

41. $\cos u$

42. $\cos v$

43. $\cos(-u)$

44. $\cos(-v)$

45. $\sin u$

46. $\sin v$

47. $\sin(-u)$

48. $\sin(-v)$

49. $\cos(u + 4\pi)$

50. $\cos(v - 6\pi)$

51. $\sin(u - 6\pi)$

52. $\sin(v + 10\pi)$

53. $\tan(u + 8\pi)$

54. $\tan(v - 4\pi)$

55. $\cos(u - 3\pi)$

56. $\cos(v + 5\pi)$

57. $\sin(u + 5\pi)$

58. $\sin(v - 7\pi)$

59. $\tan(u - 9\pi)$

60. $\tan(v + 3\pi)$

61. $\cos(\frac{\pi}{2} - u)$

62. $\cos(\frac{\pi}{2} - v)$

63. $\sin(\frac{\pi}{2} - u)$

64. $\sin(\frac{\pi}{2} - v)$

65. $\tan(\frac{\pi}{2} - u)$

66. $\tan(\frac{\pi}{2} - v)$

PROBLEMS

67. Show that

$$(\cos\theta + \sin\theta)^2 = 1 + 2\cos\theta\sin\theta$$

for every number θ.
[*Expressions such as* $\cos\theta\sin\theta$ *mean* $(\cos\theta)(\sin\theta)$, *not* $\cos(\theta\sin\theta)$.]

68. Show that

$$\frac{\sin x}{1 - \cos x} = \frac{1 + \cos x}{\sin x}$$

for every number x that is not an integer multiple of π.

69. Show that

$$\cos^3\theta + \cos^2\theta\sin\theta + \cos\theta\sin^2\theta + \sin^3\theta$$

$$= \cos\theta + \sin\theta$$

for every number θ.
[*Hint:* Try replacing the $\cos^2\theta$ term above with $1 - \sin^2\theta$ and replacing the $\sin^2\theta$ term above with $1 - \cos^2\theta$.]

70. Show that

$$\sin^2\theta = \frac{\tan^2\theta}{1 + \tan^2\theta}$$

for all θ except odd multiples of $\frac{\pi}{2}$.

71. Find a formula for $\cos\theta$ solely in terms of $\tan\theta$.

72. Find a formula for $\tan\theta$ solely in terms of $\sin\theta$.

73. Is cosine an even function, an odd function, or neither?

74. Is sine an even function, an odd function, or neither?

75. Is tangent an even function, an odd function, or neither?

76. Explain why $\sin 3° + \sin 357° = 0$.

77. Explain why $\cos 85° + \cos 95° = 0$.

78. Pretend that you are living in the time before calculators and computers existed, and that you have a table showing the cosines and sines of $1°$, $2°$, $3°$, and so on, up to the cosine and sine of $45°$. Explain how you would find the cosine and sine of $71°$, which are beyond the range of your table.

79. Suppose n is an integer. Find formulas for $\sec(\theta + n\pi)$, $\csc(\theta + n\pi)$, and $\cot(\theta + n\pi)$ in terms of $\sec\theta$, $\csc\theta$, and $\cot\theta$.

80. Restate all the results in boxes in the subsection on *Trigonometric Identities Involving a Multiple of* π in terms of degrees instead of in terms of radians.

81. Show that

$$\cos(\pi - \theta) = -\cos\theta$$

for every angle θ.

82. Show that

$$\sin(\pi - \theta) = \sin\theta$$

for every angle θ.

83. Show that

$$\cos(x + \frac{\pi}{2}) = -\sin x$$

for every number x.

84. Show that

$$\sin(t + \frac{\pi}{2}) = \cos t$$

for every number t.

85. Show that

$$\tan(\theta + \frac{\pi}{2}) = -\frac{1}{\tan\theta}$$

for every angle θ that is not an integer multiple of $\frac{\pi}{2}$. Interpret this result in terms of the characterization of the slopes of perpendicular lines.

WORKED-OUT SOLUTIONS *to Odd-numbered Exercises*

1. 📱 For $\theta = 7°$, evaluate each of the following:

   (a) $\cos^2\theta$ (b) $\cos(\theta^2)$

   SOLUTION

   (a) Using a calculator working in degrees, we have

   $$\cos^2 7° = (\cos 7°)^2 \approx (0.992546)^2 \approx 0.985148.$$

   (b) Note that $7^2 = 49$. Using a calculator working in degrees, we have

   $$\cos 49° \approx 0.656059.$$

3. 📱 For $\theta = 4$ radians, evaluate each of the following:

   (a) $\sin^2\theta$ (b) $\sin(\theta^2)$

   SOLUTION

   (a) Using a calculator working in radians, we have

   $$\sin^2 4 = (\sin 4)^2 \approx (-0.756802)^2 \approx 0.57275.$$

   (b) Note that $4^2 = 16$. Using a calculator working in radians, we have

   $$\sin 16 \approx -0.287903.$$

In Exercises 5-38, find exact expressions for the indicated quantities, given that

$$\cos \frac{\pi}{12} = \frac{\sqrt{2 + \sqrt{3}}}{2} \quad \textit{and} \quad \sin \frac{\pi}{8} = \frac{\sqrt{2 - \sqrt{2}}}{2}.$$

5. $\cos(-\frac{\pi}{12})$

   SOLUTION

   $$\cos(-\tfrac{\pi}{12}) = \cos \tfrac{\pi}{12} = \frac{\sqrt{2 + \sqrt{3}}}{2}$$

7. $\sin \frac{\pi}{12}$

   SOLUTION   We know that

   $$\cos^2 \tfrac{\pi}{12} + \sin^2 \tfrac{\pi}{12} = 1.$$

   Thus

$$\sin^2 \tfrac{\pi}{12} = 1 - \cos^2 \tfrac{\pi}{12}$$

$$= 1 - \left(\frac{\sqrt{2 + \sqrt{3}}}{2}\right)^2$$

$$= 1 - \frac{2 + \sqrt{3}}{4}$$

$$= \frac{2 - \sqrt{3}}{4}.$$

Because $\sin \frac{\pi}{12} > 0$, taking square roots of both sides of the equation above gives

$$\sin \frac{\pi}{12} = \frac{\sqrt{2 - \sqrt{3}}}{2}.$$

9. $\sin(-\frac{\pi}{12})$

   SOLUTION

   $$\sin(-\tfrac{\pi}{12}) = -\sin \tfrac{\pi}{12} = -\frac{\sqrt{2 - \sqrt{3}}}{2}$$

11. $\tan \frac{\pi}{12}$

   SOLUTION

   $$\tan \frac{\pi}{12} = \frac{\sin \frac{\pi}{12}}{\cos \frac{\pi}{12}}$$

   $$= \frac{\sqrt{2 - \sqrt{3}}}{\sqrt{2 + \sqrt{3}}}$$

   $$= \frac{\sqrt{2 - \sqrt{3}}}{\sqrt{2 + \sqrt{3}}} \cdot \frac{\sqrt{2 - \sqrt{3}}}{\sqrt{2 - \sqrt{3}}}$$

   $$= \frac{2 - \sqrt{3}}{\sqrt{4 - 3}}$$

   $$= 2 - \sqrt{3}$$

13. $\tan(-\frac{\pi}{12})$

   SOLUTION

   $$\tan(-\tfrac{\pi}{12}) = -\tan \tfrac{\pi}{12} = -(2 - \sqrt{3}) = \sqrt{3} - 2$$

15. $\cos \frac{25\pi}{12}$

   SOLUTION   Because $\frac{25\pi}{12} = \frac{\pi}{12} + 2\pi$, we have

$$\cos \frac{25\pi}{12} = \cos(\frac{\pi}{12} + 2\pi)$$
$$= \cos \frac{\pi}{12}$$
$$= \frac{\sqrt{2 + \sqrt{3}}}{2}.$$

17. $\sin \frac{25\pi}{12}$

SOLUTION   Because $\frac{25\pi}{12} = \frac{\pi}{12} + 2\pi$, we have

$$\sin \frac{25\pi}{12} = \sin(\frac{\pi}{12} + 2\pi)$$
$$= \sin \frac{\pi}{12}$$
$$= \frac{\sqrt{2 - \sqrt{3}}}{2}.$$

19. $\tan \frac{25\pi}{12}$

SOLUTION   Because $\frac{25\pi}{12} = \frac{\pi}{12} + 2\pi$, we have

$$\tan \frac{25\pi}{12} = \tan(\frac{\pi}{12} + 2\pi)$$
$$= \tan \frac{\pi}{12}$$
$$= 2 - \sqrt{3}.$$

21. $\cos \frac{13\pi}{12}$

SOLUTION   Because $\frac{13\pi}{12} = \frac{\pi}{12} + \pi$, we have

$$\cos \frac{13\pi}{12} = \cos(\frac{\pi}{12} + \pi)$$
$$= -\cos \frac{\pi}{12}$$
$$= -\frac{\sqrt{2 + \sqrt{3}}}{2}.$$

23. $\sin \frac{13\pi}{12}$

SOLUTION   Because $\frac{13\pi}{12} = \frac{\pi}{12} + \pi$, we have

$$\sin \frac{13\pi}{12} = \sin(\frac{\pi}{12} + \pi)$$
$$= -\sin \frac{\pi}{12}$$
$$= -\frac{\sqrt{2 - \sqrt{3}}}{2}.$$

25. $\tan \frac{13\pi}{12}$

SOLUTION   Because $\frac{13\pi}{12} = \frac{\pi}{12} + \pi$, we have

$$\tan \frac{13\pi}{12} = \tan(\frac{\pi}{12} + \pi)$$
$$= \tan \frac{\pi}{12}$$
$$= 2 - \sqrt{3}.$$

27. $\cos \frac{5\pi}{12}$

SOLUTION

$$\cos \frac{5\pi}{12} = \sin(\frac{\pi}{2} - \frac{5\pi}{12}) = \sin \frac{\pi}{12} = \frac{\sqrt{2 - \sqrt{3}}}{2}$$

29. $\cos(-\frac{5\pi}{12})$

SOLUTION

$$\cos(-\frac{5\pi}{12}) = \cos \frac{5\pi}{12} = \frac{\sqrt{2 - \sqrt{3}}}{2}$$

31. $\sin \frac{5\pi}{12}$

SOLUTION

$$\sin \frac{5\pi}{12} = \cos(\frac{\pi}{2} - \frac{5\pi}{12}) = \cos \frac{\pi}{12} = \frac{\sqrt{2 + \sqrt{3}}}{2}$$

33. $\sin(-\frac{5\pi}{12})$

SOLUTION

$$\sin(-\frac{5\pi}{12}) = -\sin \frac{5\pi}{12} = -\frac{\sqrt{2 + \sqrt{3}}}{2}$$

35. $\tan \frac{5\pi}{12}$

SOLUTION

$$\tan \frac{5\pi}{12} = \frac{1}{\tan(\frac{\pi}{2} - \frac{5\pi}{12})}$$
$$= \frac{1}{\tan \frac{\pi}{12}}$$
$$= \frac{1}{2 - \sqrt{3}}$$
$$= \frac{1}{2 - \sqrt{3}} \cdot \frac{2 + \sqrt{3}}{2 + \sqrt{3}}$$
$$= \frac{2 + \sqrt{3}}{4 - 3}$$
$$= 2 + \sqrt{3}$$

37. $\tan(-\frac{5\pi}{12})$

SOLUTION

$$\tan(-\frac{5\pi}{12}) = -\tan \frac{5\pi}{12} = -2 - \sqrt{3}$$

Suppose u and v are in the interval $(\frac{\pi}{2}, \pi)$, with

$$\tan u = -2 \quad and \quad \tan v = -3.$$

In Exercises 39–66, find exact expressions for the indicated quantities.

39. $\tan(-u)$

SOLUTION $\tan(-u) = -\tan u = -(-2) = 2$

41. $\cos u$

SOLUTION We know that

$$-2 = \tan u$$

$$= \frac{\sin u}{\cos u}.$$

To find $\cos u$, make the substitution $\sin u = \sqrt{1 - \cos^2 u}$ in the equation above (this substitution is valid because $\frac{\pi}{2} < u < \pi$, which implies that $\sin u > 0$), getting

$$-2 = \frac{\sqrt{1 - \cos^2 u}}{\cos u}.$$

Now square both sides of the equation above, then multiply both sides by $\cos^2 u$ and rearrange to get the equation

$$5\cos^2 u = 1.$$

Thus $\cos u = -\frac{1}{\sqrt{5}}$ (the possibility that $\cos u$ equals $\frac{1}{\sqrt{5}}$ is eliminated because $\frac{\pi}{2} < u < \pi$, which implies that $\cos u < 0$). This can be written as $\cos u = -\frac{\sqrt{5}}{5}$.

43. $\cos(-u)$

SOLUTION $\cos(-u) = \cos u = -\dfrac{\sqrt{5}}{5}$

45. $\sin u$

SOLUTION
$$\sin u = \sqrt{1 - \cos^2 u}$$

$$= \sqrt{1 - \frac{1}{5}}$$

$$= \sqrt{\frac{4}{5}}$$

$$= \frac{2}{\sqrt{5}}$$

$$= \frac{2\sqrt{5}}{5}$$

47. $\sin(-u)$

SOLUTION $\sin(-u) = -\sin u = -\dfrac{2\sqrt{5}}{5}$

49. $\cos(u + 4\pi)$

SOLUTION $\cos(u + 4\pi) = \cos u = -\dfrac{\sqrt{5}}{5}$

51. $\sin(u - 6\pi)$

SOLUTION $\sin(u - 6\pi) = \sin u = \dfrac{2\sqrt{5}}{5}$

53. $\tan(u + 8\pi)$

SOLUTION $\tan(u + 8\pi) = \tan u = -2$

55. $\cos(u - 3\pi)$

SOLUTION $\cos(u - 3\pi) = -\cos u = \dfrac{\sqrt{5}}{5}$

57. $\sin(u + 5\pi)$

SOLUTION $\sin(u + 5\pi) = -\sin u = -\dfrac{2\sqrt{5}}{5}$

59. $\tan(u - 9\pi)$

SOLUTION $\tan(u - 9\pi) = \tan u = -2$

61. $\cos(\frac{\pi}{2} - u)$

SOLUTION $\cos(\frac{\pi}{2} - u) = \sin u = \dfrac{2\sqrt{5}}{5}$

63. $\sin(\frac{\pi}{2} - u)$

SOLUTION $\sin(\frac{\pi}{2} - u) = \cos u = -\dfrac{\sqrt{5}}{5}$

65. $\tan(\frac{\pi}{2} - u)$

SOLUTION $\tan(\frac{\pi}{2} - u) = \dfrac{1}{\tan u} = -\dfrac{1}{2}$

5.7 | *Inverse Trigonometric Functions*

SECTION OBJECTIVES

By the end of this section you should

- understand the definitions of $\cos^{-1}$, $\sin^{-1}$, and $\tan^{-1}$;
- understand the domain and range of $\cos^{-1}$, $\sin^{-1}$, and $\tan^{-1}$;
- be able to sketch the radius of the unit circle corresponding to the arccosine, arcsine, and arctangent of a number;
- be able to use the inverse trigonometric functions to find angles in a right triangle, given the lengths of two sides.

Several of the most important functions in mathematics are defined as the inverse functions of familiar functions. For example, the square root is defined as the inverse function of x^2, and the logarithm with base b is defined as the inverse of b^x.

In this section, we will define the inverses of the cosine, sine, and tangent functions. These inverse functions are called the arccosine, the arcsine, and the arctangent. Roughly speaking, arccosine is the inverse function of the cosine, arcsine is the inverse function of the sine, and arctangent is the inverse function of the tangent. However, neither cosine nor sine nor tangent is one-to-one when defined on its usual domain. Thus we will need to restrict the domains of these functions to obtain one-to-one functions that have inverses.

As usual, we will assume throughout this section that all angles are measured in radians unless explicitly stated otherwise.

The Arccosine Function

We begin by considering the cosine. The domain of the cosine function is the entire real line. As can be seen from the graph below, the cosine function is not one-to-one (because there are horizontal lines that intersect the graph in more than one point):

The graph of cosine on the interval $[-2\pi, 2\pi]$.

For example, suppose we are told that x is a number such that $\cos x = 0$, and we are asked to find the value of x. Of course $\cos \frac{\pi}{2} = 0$, but also $\cos \frac{3\pi}{2} = 0$; we also have $\cos(-\frac{\pi}{2}) = 0$ and $\cos(-\frac{3\pi}{2}) = 0$ and so on. Thus with the information given we have no way to determine a unique value of x such that $\cos x = 0$. Hence the cosine function does not have an inverse.

We faced a similar dilemma when we wanted to define the square root function as the inverse of x^2. The domain of the function x^2 is the entire real line. This function is not one-to-one; thus it does not have an inverse.

For example, if we are told that $x^2 = 16$, then we cannot determine whether $x = 4$ or $x = -4$. We solved this problem by restricting the domain of x^2 to $[0, \infty)$; the resulting function is one-to-one, and its inverse is called the square root function. Roughly speaking, we say that the square root function is the inverse of x^2.

We will follow a similar process with the cosine. To decide how to restrict the domain of the cosine, we start by declaring that we want 0 to be in the domain of the restricted function. Looking at the graph above of cosine, we see that starting at 0 and moving to the right, π is the farthest we can go while staying within an interval on which cosine is one-to-one. Once we decide that $[0, \pi]$ will be in the domain of our restricted cosine function, then we cannot move at all to the left from 0 and still have a one-to-one function. Thus $[0, \pi]$ is the natural domain to choose to get an inverse for the cosine.

The graph of cosine on the interval $[0, \pi]$.

If we restrict the domain of cosine to $[0, \pi]$, we obtain the one-to-one function whose graph is shown here. The inverse of this function is called the arccosine, which is often abbreviated as $\cos^{-1}$. Here is the formal definition:

Arccosine

For t in $[-1, 1]$, the **arccosine** of t, denoted $\cos^{-1} t$, is the unique angle in $[0, \pi]$ whose cosine equals t. In other words, the equation

$$\cos^{-1} t = \theta$$

means θ is the unique angle in $[0, \pi]$ such that

$$\cos \theta = t.$$

In defining $\cos^{-1} t$, we must restrict t to be in the interval $[-1, 1]$ because otherwise there is no angle whose cosine equals t.

EXAMPLE 1

(a) Evaluate $\cos^{-1} 0$.

(b) Evaluate $\cos^{-1} 1$.

(c) Explain why the expression $\cos^{-1} 2$ makes no sense.

SOLUTION

(a) Because $\frac{\pi}{2}$ is the unique angle in the interval $[0, \pi]$ whose cosine equals 0, we have $\cos^{-1} 0 = \frac{\pi}{2}$.

(b) Because 0 is the unique angle in the interval $[0, \pi]$ whose cosine equals 1, we have $\cos^{-1} 1 = 0$.

(c) The expression $\cos^{-1} 2$ makes no sense because there is no angle whose cosine equals 2.

Do not confuse $\cos^{-1} t$ with $(\cos t)^{-1}$. Confusion can arise due to inconsistency in common notation. For example, $\cos^2 t$ is indeed equal to $(\cos t)^2$. However, we defined $\cos^n t$ to equal $(\cos t)^n$ only when n is a positive integer (see Section 5.6). This restriction concerning $\cos^n t$ was made precisely so that $\cos^{-1} t$ could be defined with $\cos^{-1}$ interpreted as an inverse function.

Be sure you understand that $\cos^{-1} t$ is not equal to $\frac{1}{\cos t}$.

The notation $\cos^{-1}$ to denote the arccosine function is consistent with our notation f^{-1} to denote the inverse of a function f. Even here a bit of explanation helps. The usual domain of the cosine function is the real line. However, when we write $\cos^{-1}$ we do mean not the inverse of the usual cosine function (which has no inverse because it is not one-to-one). Instead, $\cos^{-1}$ means the inverse of the cosine function whose domain is restricted to the interval $[0, \pi]$.

Sketch the radius of the unit circle corresponding to the angle $\cos^{-1} 0.3$.

EXAMPLE 2

SOLUTION We seek an angle in $[0, \pi]$ whose cosine equals 0.3. This means that the first coordinate of the endpoint of the corresponding radius will equal 0.3. Thus we start with 0.3 on the horizontal axis, as shown here, and extend a line upward until it intersects the unit circle. That point of intersection is the endpoint of the radius corresponding to the angle $\cos^{-1} 0.3$, as shown here.

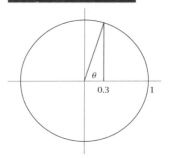

Here $\theta = \cos^{-1} 0.3$, or equivalently $\cos \theta = 0.3$.

The definition above implies that the domain and range of the arccosine function are as follows:

> ### Domain and range of arccosine
>
> - The domain of $\cos^{-1}$ is $[-1, 1]$.
>
> - The range of $\cos^{-1}$ is $[0, \pi]$.

To help remember the range of $\cos^{-1}$, think of a radius of the unit circle starting along the positive horizontal axis and moving counterclockwise. The first coordinate of the endpoint of this radius is the cosine of the associated angle. As the radius moves from an angle of 0 radians (along the positive horizontal axis) to an angle of π radians (along the negative horizontal axis), the first coordinate of the endpoint of this radius takes on each value in the interval $[-1, 1]$ exactly once. This would not be true if we considered angles in any interval larger than $[0, \pi]$ or in any interval smaller than $[0, \pi]$.

Some books use the notation $\arccos t$ instead of $\cos^{-1} t$.

The graph of $\cos^{-1}$ can be obtained in the usual way when dealing with inverse functions. Specifically, the graph shown here is the reflection of the graph of the cosine (restricted to the interval $[0, \pi]$) through the line with slope 1 that contains the origin.

Given the lengths of the hypotenuse and another side of a right triangle, you can use the arccosine function to determine the angle between those two sides. The example below illustrates the procedure.

The graph of $\cos^{-1}$.

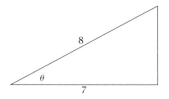

EXAMPLE 3

In this right triangle, evaluate the angle θ in radians.

SOLUTION Because the cosine of an angle in a right triangle equals the length of the adjacent side divided by the length of the hypotenuse, we have $\cos\theta = \frac{7}{8}$. Using a calculator working in radians, we then have

$$\theta = \cos^{-1}\frac{7}{8} \approx 0.505 \text{ radians.}$$

The Arcsine Function

Now we consider the sine function, whose graph is shown below:

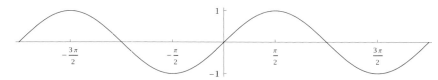

The graph of sine on the interval $[-2\pi, 2\pi]$.

Again, we need to restrict the domain to obtain a one-to-one function. We again start by declaring that we want 0 to be in the domain of the restricted function. Looking at the graph above of sine, we see that $[-\frac{\pi}{2}, \frac{\pi}{2}]$ is the largest interval containing 0 on which sine is one-to-one.

If we restrict the domain of sine to $[-\frac{\pi}{2}, \frac{\pi}{2}]$, we obtain the one-to-one function whose graph is shown here. The inverse of this function is called the arcsine, which is often abbreviated as $\sin^{-1}$. Here is the formal definition:

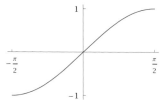

The graph of sine on the interval $[-\frac{\pi}{2}, \frac{\pi}{2}]$.

Arcsine

For t in $[-1, 1]$, the **arcsine** of t, denoted $\sin^{-1} t$, is the unique angle in $[-\frac{\pi}{2}, \frac{\pi}{2}]$ whose sine equals t. In other words, the equation

$$\sin^{-1} t = \theta$$

means θ is the unique angle in $[-\frac{\pi}{2}, \frac{\pi}{2}]$ such that

$$\sin\theta = t.$$

In defining $\sin^{-1} t$, we must restrict t to be in the interval $[-1, 1]$ because otherwise there is no angle whose sine equals t.

EXAMPLE 4

(a) Evaluate $\sin^{-1} 0$.

(b) Evaluate $\sin^{-1}(-1)$.

(c) Explain why the expression $\sin^{-1}(-3)$ makes no sense.

SOLUTION

(a) Because 0 is the unique angle in the interval $[-\frac{\pi}{2}, \frac{\pi}{2}]$ whose sine equals 0, we have $\sin^{-1} 0 = 0$.

(b) Because $-\frac{\pi}{2}$ is the unique angle in the interval $[-\frac{\pi}{2}, \frac{\pi}{2}]$ whose sine equals -1, we have $\sin^{-1}(-1) = -\frac{\pi}{2}$.

(c) The expression $\sin^{-1}(-3)$ makes no sense because there is no angle whose sine equals -3.

Do not confuse $\sin^{-1} t$ with $(\sin t)^{-1}$. The same comments that were made earlier about the notation $\cos^{-1}$ apply to $\sin^{-1}$. Specifically, $\sin^2 t$ means $(\sin t)^2$, but $\sin^{-1} t$ involves an inverse function.

Be sure you understand that $\sin^{-1} t$ is not equal to $\frac{1}{\sin t}$.

Sketch the radius of the unit circle corresponding to the angle $\sin^{-1} 0.3$.

EXAMPLE 5

SOLUTION We seek an angle in $[-\frac{\pi}{2}, \frac{\pi}{2}]$ whose sine equals 0.3. This means that the second coordinate of the endpoint of the corresponding radius will equal 0.3. Thus we start with 0.3 on the vertical axis, as shown below, and extend a line to the right until it intersects the unit circle. That point of intersection is the endpoint of the radius corresponding to the angle $\sin^{-1} 0.3$, as shown below:

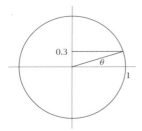

Here $\theta = \sin^{-1} 0.3$, or equivalently $\sin \theta = 0.3$.

The definition above implies that the domain and range of the arcsine function are as follows:

Domain and range of arcsine

- The domain of $\sin^{-1}$ is $[-1, 1]$.

- The range of $\sin^{-1}$ is $[-\frac{\pi}{2}, \frac{\pi}{2}]$.

To help remember the range of $\sin^{-1}$, think of a radius of the unit circle starting along the negative vertical axis and moving counterclockwise. The second coordinate of the endpoint of this radius is the sine of the associated angle. As the radius moves from an angle of $-\frac{\pi}{2}$ radians (along the negative vertical axis) to an angle of $\frac{\pi}{2}$ radians (along the positive vertical axis), the second coordinate of the endpoint of this radius takes on each value in the

Some books use the notation $\arcsin t$ instead of $\sin^{-1} t$.

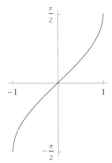

The graph of $\sin^{-1}$.

interval $[-1, 1]$ exactly once. This would not be true if we considered angles in any interval larger than $[-\frac{\pi}{2}, \frac{\pi}{2}]$ or in any interval smaller than $[-\frac{\pi}{2}, \frac{\pi}{2}]$.

The graph of $\sin^{-1}$ can be obtained in the usual way when dealing with inverse functions. Specifically, the graph shown here is the reflection of the graph of the sine (restricted to the interval $[-\frac{\pi}{2}, \frac{\pi}{2}]$) through the line with slope 1 that contains the origin.

Given the lengths of the hypotenuse and another side of a right triangle, you can use the arcsine function to determine the angle opposite the nonhypotenuse side. The example below illustrates the procedure.

EXAMPLE 6

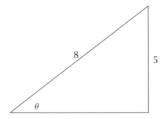

In this right triangle, evaluate the angle θ in degrees.

SOLUTION   Because the sine of an angle in a right triangle equals the length of the opposite side divided by the length of the hypotenuse, we have $\sin\theta = \frac{5}{8}$. Using a calculator working in degrees, we then have $\theta = \sin^{-1}\frac{5}{8} \approx 38.7°$.

The Arctangent Function

Now we consider the tangent function, whose graph is shown below:

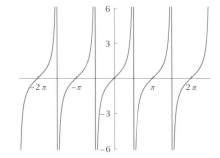

The graph of tangent on most of the interval $(-\frac{5}{2}\pi, \frac{5}{2}\pi)$. *Because* $|\tan\theta|$ *gets very large for* θ *close to odd multiples of* $\frac{\pi}{2}$, *it is not possible to show the entire graph on this interval.*

The graph of tangent on most of the interval $(-\frac{\pi}{2}, \frac{\pi}{2})$.

Again, we need to restrict the domain to obtain a one-to-one function. We again start by declaring that we want 0 to be in the domain of the restricted function. Looking at the graph above of tangent, we see that $(-\frac{\pi}{2}, \frac{\pi}{2})$ is the largest interval containing 0 on which tangent is one-to-one. This is an open interval that excludes the two endpoints $\frac{\pi}{2}$ and $-\frac{\pi}{2}$. Recall that the tangent function is not defined at $\frac{\pi}{2}$ or at $-\frac{\pi}{2}$; thus these numbers cannot be included in the domain.

If we restrict the domain of tangent to $(-\frac{\pi}{2}, \frac{\pi}{2})$, we obtain the one-to-one function most of whose graph is shown here. The inverse of this function is called the arctangent, which is often abbreviated as $\tan^{-1}$. Here is the formal definition:

Arctangent

The **arctangent** of t, denoted $\tan^{-1} t$, is the unique angle in $(-\frac{\pi}{2}, \frac{\pi}{2})$ whose tangent equals t. In other words, the equation

$$\tan^{-1} t = \theta$$

means θ is the unique angle in $(-\frac{\pi}{2}, \frac{\pi}{2})$ such that

$$\tan \theta = t.$$

Unlike $\cos^{-1} t$ and $\sin^{-1} t$, which make sense only when t is in $[-1, 1]$, $\tan^{-1} t$ makes sense for every real number t (because for every real number t there is an angle whose tangent equals t).

EXAMPLE 7

(a) Evaluate $\tan^{-1} 0$.

(b) Evaluate $\tan^{-1} 1$.

(c) Evaluate $\tan^{-1} \sqrt{3}$.

SOLUTION

(a) Because 0 is the unique angle in the interval $(-\frac{\pi}{2}, \frac{\pi}{2})$ whose tangent equals 0, we have $\tan^{-1} 0 = 0$.

(b) Because $\frac{\pi}{4}$ is the unique angle in the interval $(-\frac{\pi}{2}, \frac{\pi}{2})$ whose tangent equals 1, we have $\tan^{-1} 1 = \frac{\pi}{4}$.

(c) Because $\frac{\pi}{3}$ is the unique angle in the interval $(-\frac{\pi}{2}, \frac{\pi}{2})$ whose tangent equals $\sqrt{3}$, we have $\tan^{-1} \sqrt{3} = \frac{\pi}{3}$.

Do not confuse $\tan^{-1} t$ with $(\tan t)^{-1}$. The same comments that were made earlier about the notation $\cos^{-1}$ and $\sin^{-1}$ apply to $\tan^{-1}$. Specifically, $\tan^2 t$ means $(\tan t)^2$, but $\tan^{-1} t$ involves an inverse function.

Be sure you understand that $\tan^{-1} t$ is not equal to $\frac{1}{\tan t}$.

Sketch the radius of the unit circle corresponding to the angle $\tan^{-1}(-3)$.

EXAMPLE 8

SOLUTION   We seek an angle in $(-\frac{\pi}{2}, \frac{\pi}{2})$ whose tangent equals -3. This means that the slope of the corresponding radius will equal -3. The unit circle has two radii with slope -3; one of them is the radius shown below and the other is the radius in the opposite direction. But of these two radii, only the one shown below has a corresponding angle in the interval $(-\frac{\pi}{2}, \frac{\pi}{2})$. Notice that the indicated angle is negative because of the clockwise direction of the arrow below:

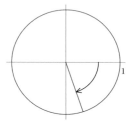

This radius has slope -3 *and thus makes an angle of* $\tan^{-1}(-3)$ *with the positive horizontal axis.*

The definition above implies that the domain and range of the arctangent function are as follows:

> ## Domain and range of arctangent
>
> - The domain of $\tan^{-1}$ is the set of real numbers.
> - The range of $\tan^{-1}$ is $(-\frac{\pi}{2}, \frac{\pi}{2})$.

Some books use the notation arctan t *instead of* $\tan^{-1} t$.

To help remember this, think of a radius of the unit circle starting along the negative vertical axis and moving counterclockwise. The slope of this radius is the tangent of the associated angle. As the radius moves from an angle of $-\frac{\pi}{2}$ radians (along the negative vertical axis, where the slope is undefined) to an angle of 0 radians (along the positive horizontal axis), the slope of this radius takes on each negative number exactly once. As the radius then moves from an angle of 0 radians (along the positive horizontal axis, where the slope is 0) to an angle of $\frac{\pi}{2}$ radians (along the positive vertical axis, where the slope is undefined), the slope of this radius takes on each positive number exactly once. This would not be true if we considered angles in any interval larger than $(-\frac{\pi}{2}, \frac{\pi}{2})$ or in any interval smaller than $(-\frac{\pi}{2}, \frac{\pi}{2})$.

The graph of $\tan^{-1}$ can be obtained in the usual way when dealing with inverse functions. Specifically, the graph shown here is the reflection of the graph of the tangent (restricted to an interval slightly smaller than $(-\frac{\pi}{2}, \frac{\pi}{2})$) through the line with slope 1 that contains the origin:

The graph of $\tan^{-1}$ *on the interval* $[-6, 6]$.

Given the lengths of the two nonhypotenuse sides of a right triangle, you can use the arctangent function to determine the angles of the triangle. The example below illustrates the procedure.

(a) In this right triangle, use the arctangent function to evaluate the angle u in degrees.

(b) In this right triangle, use the arctangent function to evaluate the angle v in degrees.

(c) As a check, compute the sum of the angles u and v obtained in parts (a) and (b). Does this sum have the expected value?

EXAMPLE 9

SOLUTION

(a) Because the tangent of an angle in a right triangle equals the length of the opposite side divided by the length of the adjacent side, we have $\tan u = \frac{5}{9}$. Using a calculator working in degrees, we then have

$$u = \tan^{-1} \tfrac{5}{9} \approx 29.1°.$$

(b) Because the tangent of an angle in a right triangle equals the length of the opposite side divided by the length of the adjacent side, we have $\tan v = \frac{9}{5}$. Using a calculator working in degrees, we then have

$$v = \tan^{-1} \tfrac{9}{5} \approx 60.9°.$$

(c) We have
$$u + v \approx 29.1° + 60.9° = 90°.$$

Thus the sum of the two acute angles in this right triangle is $90°$, just as expected.

EXERCISES

1. Evaluate $\cos^{-1} \frac{1}{2}$.

2. Evaluate $\sin^{-1} \frac{1}{2}$.

3. Evaluate $\tan^{-1}(-1)$.

4. Evaluate $\tan^{-1}(-\sqrt{3})$.

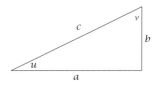

Use the right triangle above for Exercises 5–12. This triangle is not drawn to scale corresponding to the data in the exercises.

5. Suppose $a = 2$ and $c = 3$. Evaluate u in radians.

6. Suppose $a = 3$ and $c = 4$. Evaluate u in radians.

7. Suppose $a = 2$ and $c = 5$. Evaluate v in radians.

8. Suppose $a = 3$ and $c = 5$. Evaluate v in radians.

9. Suppose $a = 5$ and $b = 4$. Evaluate u in degrees.

10. Suppose $a = 5$ and $b = 6$. Evaluate u in degrees.

11. Suppose $a = 5$ and $b = 7$. Evaluate v in degrees.

12. Suppose $a = 7$ and $b = 6$. Evaluate v in degrees.

13. Find the smallest positive number t such that $10^{\cos t} = 6$.

14. Find the smallest positive number t such that $10^{\sin t} = 7$.

15. 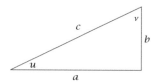 Find the smallest positive number t such that $e^{\tan t} = 15$.

16. Find the smallest positive number t such that $e^{\tan t} = 500$.

17. Find the smallest positive number y such that $\cos(\tan y) = 0.2$.

18. Find the smallest positive number y such that $\sin(\tan y) = 0.6$.

19. Find the smallest positive number x such that

$$\sin^2 x - 3\sin x + 1 = 0.$$

20. Find the smallest positive number x such that

$$\sin^2 x - 4\sin x + 2 = 0.$$

21. Find the smallest positive number x such that

$$\cos^2 x - 0.5\cos x + 0.06 = 0.$$

22. Find the smallest positive number x such that

$$\cos^2 x - 0.7\cos x + 0.12 = 0.$$

PROBLEMS

23. Explain why

$$\cos^{-1}\tfrac{3}{5} = \sin^{-1}\tfrac{4}{5} = \tan^{-1}\tfrac{4}{3}.$$

[*Hint:* Take $a = 3$ and $b = 4$ in the triangle above. Then find c and consider various ways to express u.]

24. Explain why

$$\cos^{-1}\tfrac{5}{13} = \sin^{-1}\tfrac{12}{13} = \tan^{-1}\tfrac{12}{5}.$$

25. Suppose a and b are numbers such that

$$\cos^{-1} a = \tfrac{\pi}{7} \quad \text{and} \quad \sin^{-1} b = \tfrac{\pi}{7}.$$

Explain why $a^2 + b^2 = 1$.

26. Without using a calculator, sketch the unit circle and the radius that makes an angle of $\cos^{-1} 0.1$ with the positive horizontal axis.

27. Without using a calculator, sketch the unit circle and the radius that makes an angle of $\sin^{-1}(-0.1)$ with the positive horizontal axis.

28. Without using a calculator, sketch the unit circle and the radius that makes an angle of $\tan^{-1} 4$ with the positive horizontal axis.

29. Find all numbers t such that

$$\cos^{-1} t = \sin^{-1} t.$$

30. There exist angles θ such that $\cos\theta = -\sin\theta$ (for example, $-\tfrac{\pi}{4}$ and $\tfrac{3\pi}{4}$ are two such angles). However, explain why there do not exist any numbers t such that

$$\cos^{-1} t = -\sin^{-1} t.$$

WORKED-OUT SOLUTIONS *to Odd-numbered Exercises*

1. Evaluate $\cos^{-1}\tfrac{1}{2}$.

   SOLUTION $\cos\tfrac{\pi}{3} = \tfrac{1}{2}$; thus $\cos^{-1}\tfrac{1}{2} = \tfrac{\pi}{3}$.

3. Evaluate $\tan^{-1}(-1)$.

   SOLUTION $\tan(-\tfrac{\pi}{4}) = -1$; thus

   $$\tan^{-1}(-1) = -\tfrac{\pi}{4}.$$

Use the right triangle above for Exercises 5–12. This triangle is not drawn to scale corresponding to the data in the exercises.

5. 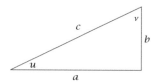 Suppose $a = 2$ and $c = 3$. Evaluate u in radians.

SOLUTION Because the cosine of an angle in a right triangle equals the length of the adjacent side divided by the length of the hypotenuse, we have $\cos u = \frac{2}{3}$. Using a calculator working in radians, we then have

$$u = \cos^{-1}\frac{2}{3} \approx 0.841 \text{ radians.}$$

7. ✐ Suppose $a = 2$ and $c = 5$. Evaluate v in radians.

SOLUTION Because the sine of an angle in a right triangle equals the length of the opposite side divided by the length of the hypotenuse, we have $\sin v = \frac{2}{5}$. Using a calculator working in radians, we then have

$$v = \sin^{-1}\frac{2}{5} \approx 0.412 \text{ radians.}$$

9. ✐ Suppose $a = 5$ and $b = 4$. Evaluate u in degrees.

SOLUTION Because the tangent of an angle in a right triangle equals the length of the opposite side divided by the length of the adjacent side, we have $\tan u = \frac{4}{5}$. Using a calculator working in degrees, we then have

$$u = \tan^{-1}\frac{4}{5} \approx 38.7°.$$

11. ✐ Suppose $a = 5$ and $b = 7$. Evaluate v in degrees.

SOLUTION Because the tangent of an angle in a right triangle equals the length of the opposite side divided by the length of the adjacent side, we have $\tan v = \frac{5}{7}$. Using a calculator working in degrees, we then have

$$v = \tan^{-1}\frac{5}{7} \approx 35.5°.$$

13. ✐ Find the smallest positive number t such that $10^{\cos t} = 6$.

SOLUTION The equation above implies that $\cos t = \log 6$. Thus we take $t = \cos^{-1}(\log 6) \approx 0.67908$.

15. ✐ Find the smallest positive number t such that $e^{\tan t} = 15$.

SOLUTION The equation above implies that $\tan t = \ln 15$. Thus we take $t = \tan^{-1}(\ln 15) \approx 1.21706$.

17. ✐ Find the smallest positive number y such that $\cos(\tan y) = 0.2$.

SOLUTION The equation above implies that we should choose $\tan y = \cos^{-1} 0.2 \approx 1.36944$. Thus we should choose $y \approx \tan^{-1} 1.36944 \approx 0.94007$.

19. ✐ Find the smallest positive number x such that
$$\sin^2 x - 3\sin x + 1 = 0.$$

SOLUTION Write $y = \sin x$. Then the equation above can be rewritten as

$$y^2 - 3y + 1 = 0.$$

Using the quadratic formula, we find that the solutions to this equation are

$$y = \frac{3 + \sqrt{5}}{2} \approx 2.61803$$

and

$$y = \frac{3 - \sqrt{5}}{2} \approx 0.38197.$$

Thus $\sin x \approx 2.61803$ or $\sin x \approx 0.381966$. However, there is no real number x such that $\sin x \approx 2.61803$ (because $\sin x$ is at most 1 for every real number x), and thus we must have $\sin x \approx 0.381966$. Thus $x \approx \sin^{-1} 0.381966 \approx 0.39192$.

21. ✐ Find the smallest positive number x such that
$$\cos^2 x - 0.5\cos x + 0.06 = 0.$$

SOLUTION Write $y = \cos x$. Then the equation above can be rewritten as

$$y^2 - 0.5y + 0.06 = 0.$$

Using the quadratic formula or factorization, we find that the solutions to this equation are

$$y = 0.2 \quad \text{and} \quad y = 0.3.$$

Thus $\cos x = 0.2$ or $\cos x = 0.3$, which suggests that we choose $x = \cos^{-1} 0.2$ or $x = \cos^{-1} 0.3$. Because arccosine is a decreasing function, $\cos^{-1} 0.3$ is smaller than $\cos^{-1} 0.2$. Because we want to find the smallest positive value of x satisfying the original equation, we choose $x = \cos^{-1} 0.3 \approx 1.2661$.

5.8 | *Inverse Trigonometric Identities*

SECTION OBJECTIVES

By the end of this section you should

- understand how to derive and work with inverse trigonometric identities;
- be able to use the inverse trigonometric identities for $-t$;
- be able to use the identity for $\tan^{-1}\frac{1}{t}$;
- be able to compute the composition, in either order, of a trigonometric function and its inverse function;
- be able to compute the composition of a trigonometric function with the inverse of a different trigonometric function.

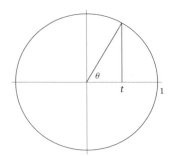

This radius makes an angle of $\cos^{-1} t$ with the positive horizontal axis.

Inverse trigonometric identities are identities involving inverse trigonometric functions. In this section we develop the most useful inverse trigonometric identities.

The Arccosine, Arcsine, and Arctangent of $-t$: Graphical Approach

We begin by finding a formula for $\cos^{-1}(-t)$ in terms of $\cos^{-1} t$. To do this, suppose $0 < t < 1$. Let $\theta = \cos^{-1} t$, which implies that $\cos\theta = t$. Consider the radius of the unit circle that makes an angle of θ with the positive horizontal axis. The first coordinate of the endpoint of this radius will equal t, as shown above.

To find $\cos^{-1}(-t)$, we need to find a radius whose first coordinate equals $-t$. This radius is obtained by reflecting the radius above through the vertical axis, obtaining the figure below.

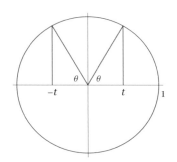

From the figure here, we see that the radius whose endpoint has first coordinate equal to $-t$ forms an angle of θ with the negative horizontal axis; thus this radius makes an angle of $\pi - \theta$ with the positive horizontal axis. In other words, we have $\cos^{-1}(-t) = \pi - \theta$, which we can rewrite as

$$\cos^{-1}(-t) = \pi - \cos^{-1} t.$$

Note that $\pi - \theta$ is in $[0, \pi]$ whenever θ is in $[0, \pi]$. Thus $\pi - \cos^{-1} t$ is in the right interval to be the arccosine of some number.

EXAMPLE 1

Evaluate $\cos^{-1}(-\cos\frac{\pi}{7})$.

SOLUTION   Using the formula above with $t = \cos\frac{\pi}{7}$, we have

$$\cos^{-1}(-\cos\tfrac{\pi}{7}) = \pi - \cos^{-1}(\cos\tfrac{\pi}{7})$$

$$= \pi - \tfrac{\pi}{7}$$

$$= \tfrac{6\pi}{7}.$$

We now turn to the problem of finding a formula for $\sin^{-1}(-t)$ in terms of $\sin^{-1} t$. To do this, suppose $0 < t < 1$. Let $\theta = \sin^{-1} t$, which implies that $\sin \theta = t$. Consider the radius of the unit circle that makes an angle of θ with the positive horizontal axis. The second coordinate of the endpoint of this radius will equal t, as shown here.

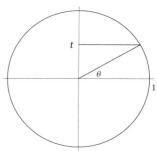

This radius makes an angle of $\sin^{-1} t$ *with the positive horizontal axis.*

To find $\sin^{-1}(-t)$, we need to find a radius whose second coordinate equals $-t$. This radius is obtained by reflecting the radius above through the horizontal axis, obtaining the figure here. From this figure, we see that the radius whose endpoint has second coordinate equal to $-t$ forms an angle of $-\theta$ with the positive horizontal axis.

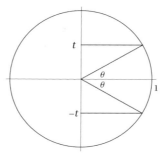

In other words, we have $\sin^{-1}(-t) = -\theta$, which we can rewrite as

$$\sin^{-1}(-t) = -\sin^{-1} t.$$

Note that $-\theta$ is in $[-\frac{\pi}{2}, \frac{\pi}{2}]$ whenever θ is in $[-\frac{\pi}{2}, \frac{\pi}{2}]$. Thus $-\sin^{-1} t$ is in the right interval to be the arcsine of some number.

Evaluate $\sin^{-1}(-\sin \frac{\pi}{7})$.

EXAMPLE 2

SOLUTION   Using the formula above with $t = \sin \frac{\pi}{7}$, we have

$$\sin^{-1}(-\sin \tfrac{\pi}{7}) = -\sin^{-1}(\sin \tfrac{\pi}{7})$$

$$= -\tfrac{\pi}{7}.$$

We now turn to the problem of finding a formula for $\tan^{-1}(-t)$ in terms of $\tan^{-1} t$. To do this, suppose $t > 0$. Let $\theta = \tan^{-1} t$, which implies that $\tan \theta = t$. Consider the radius of the unit circle that makes an angle of θ with the positive horizontal axis. This radius, which is shown in the margin, has slope t.

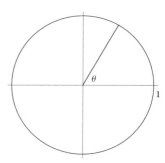

This radius with slope t makes an angle of $\tan^{-1} t$ *with the positive horizontal axis.*

To find $\tan^{-1}(-t)$, we need to find a radius whose slope equals $-t$. We can obtain a radius with slope $-t$ from the radius with slope t via a reflection through the horizontal axis (which leaves the first coordinate of the endpoint unchanged and multiplies the second coordinate by -1), as shown here.

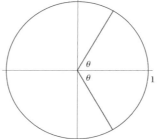

From the figure here, we see that the radius with slope $-t$ forms an angle of $-\theta$ with the positive horizontal axis. In other words, we have $\tan^{-1}(-t) = -\theta$, which we can rewrite as

$$\tan^{-1}(-t) = -\tan^{-1} t.$$

Note that $-\theta$ is in $(-\frac{\pi}{2}, \frac{\pi}{2})$ whenever θ is in $(-\frac{\pi}{2}, \frac{\pi}{2})$. Thus $-\tan^{-1} t$ is in the right interval to be the arctangent of some number.

In summary, we have found the following identities for computing the inverse trigonometric functions of $-t$:

> ### Inverse trigonometric identities for $-t$
>
> $$\cos^{-1}(-t) = \pi - \cos^{-1} t$$
>
> $$\sin^{-1}(-t) = -\sin^{-1} t$$
>
> $$\tan^{-1}(-t) = -\tan^{-1} t$$

We derived the first two identities above from figures using the assumption that $0 < t < 1$; for the last identity above our illustration assumed that $t > 0$. However, the algebraic approach, to which we now turn, shows that the first two identities above are actually valid whenever $-1 \le t \le 1$, and the last identity above is valid for all values of t.

The Arccosine, Arcsine, and Arctangent of $-t$: Algebraic Approach

Sometimes a second approach to a subject leads to better understanding.

In this subsection we will again derive the inverse trigonometric identities above, but this time using an algebraic approach that uses our previous trigonometric identities. We begin with an algebraic derivation of the identity for $\cos^{-1}(-t)$.

Suppose $-1 \le t \le 1$. Let $\theta = \cos^{-1} t$. Thus $\cos \theta = t$ and θ is in $[0, \pi]$ (which implies that $\pi - \theta$ is in $[0, \pi]$). Furthermore

$$\cos(\pi - \theta) = \cos(\theta - \pi) = -\cos \theta = -t,$$

where the first equality above comes from our identity for the cosine of the negative of an angle (Section 5.6) and the second equality comes from our identity for $\cos(\theta + n\pi)$ (also Section 5.6; here we are taking $n = -1$). Because $\pi - \theta$ is an angle in $[0, \pi]$ whose cosine equals $-t$ (by the equation above), we conclude that $\cos^{-1}(-t) = \pi - \theta$. This can be rewritten as

$$\cos^{-1}(-t) = \pi - \cos^{-1} t,$$

completing our second derivation of this identity.

Now we turn to an algebraic derivation of the identity for $\sin^{-1}(-t)$. Suppose $-1 \le t \le 1$. Let $\theta = \sin^{-1} t$. Thus θ is in $[-\frac{\pi}{2}, \frac{\pi}{2}]$ (which implies that $-\theta$ is in $[-\frac{\pi}{2}, \frac{\pi}{2}]$) and $\sin \theta = t$. Furthermore

$$\sin(-\theta) = -\sin \theta = -t,$$

where the first equality above comes from our identity for the sine of the negative of an angle (Section 5.6). Because $-\theta$ is an angle in $[-\frac{\pi}{2}, \frac{\pi}{2}]$ whose sine equals $-t$ (by the equation above), we conclude that $\sin^{-1}(-t) = -\theta$. This can be rewritten as

$$\sin^{-1}(-t) = -\sin^{-1} t,$$

completing our second derivation of this identity.

Finally, we turn to an algebraic derivation of the identity for $\tan^{-1}(-t)$. Suppose t is any real number. Let $\theta = \tan^{-1} t$. Thus θ is in $(-\frac{\pi}{2}, \frac{\pi}{2})$ [which implies that $-\theta$ is in $(-\frac{\pi}{2}, \frac{\pi}{2})$] and $\tan \theta = t$. Furthermore

$$\tan(-\theta) = -\tan \theta = -t,$$

where the first equality above comes from our identity for the tangent of the negative of an angle (Section 5.6). Because $-\theta$ is an angle in $(-\frac{\pi}{2}, \frac{\pi}{2})$ whose tangent equals $-t$ (by the equation above), we conclude that $\tan^{-1}(-t) = -\theta$. This can be rewritten as

$$\tan^{-1}(-t) = -\tan^{-1} t,$$

completing our second derivation of this identity.

Arccosine Plus Arcsine

Suppose $-1 \le t \le 1$ and $\theta = \cos^{-1} t$. Thus θ is in $[0, \pi]$ and $\cos \theta = t$. Now

$$\sin(\frac{\pi}{2} - \theta) = \cos \theta = t,$$

where the first equality comes from one of our identities in Section 5.6. The equation above shows that $\frac{\pi}{2} - \theta$ is an angle whose sine equals t. Furthermore, $\frac{\pi}{2} - \theta$ is in $[-\frac{\pi}{2}, \frac{\pi}{2}]$ (because θ is in $[0, \pi]$). Thus $\sin^{-1} t = \frac{\pi}{2} - \theta$, which can be rewritten as $\sin^{-1} t = \frac{\pi}{2} - \cos^{-1} t$. Adding $\cos^{-1} t$ to both sides of this equation produces a more symmetric version of this important identity.

Arccosine plus arcsine
$$\cos^{-1} t + \sin^{-1} t = \frac{\pi}{2}$$
for all t in $[-1, 1]$.

For example, $\cos^{-1} \frac{1}{2} = \frac{\pi}{3}$ and $\sin^{-1} \frac{1}{2} = \frac{\pi}{6}$. Adding these together, we have $\frac{\pi}{3} + \frac{\pi}{6}$ equals $\frac{\pi}{2}$, which agrees with this identity.

The Arctangent of $\frac{1}{t}$

Suppose $t > 0$ and $\theta = \tan^{-1} t$. Thus θ is in $(0, \frac{\pi}{2})$ and $\tan \theta = t$. Now

$$\tan(\frac{\pi}{2} - \theta) = \frac{1}{\tan \theta} = \frac{1}{t},$$

where the first equality comes from one of our identities in Section 5.6. The equation above shows that $\frac{\pi}{2} - \theta$ is an angle whose tangent equals $\frac{1}{t}$. Furthermore, $\frac{\pi}{2} - \theta$ is in $(0, \frac{\pi}{2})$ [because θ is in $(0, \frac{\pi}{2})$]. Thus $\tan^{-1} \frac{1}{t} = \frac{\pi}{2} - \theta$, which can be rewritten as

$$\tan^{-1} \frac{1}{t} = \frac{\pi}{2} - \tan^{-1} t.$$

Somewhat surprisingly, the formula derived in the paragraph above for $\tan^{-1} \frac{1}{t}$ does not hold when t is negative. To find the correct formula in this case, suppose $t < 0$. Then

$$\tan^{-1} \frac{1}{t} = \tan^{-1}\left(-\frac{1}{(-t)}\right)$$
$$= -\tan^{-1}\left(\frac{1}{(-t)}\right)$$
$$= -\left(\frac{\pi}{2} - \tan^{-1}(-t)\right)$$
$$= -\left(\frac{\pi}{2} + \tan^{-1} t\right)$$
$$= -\frac{\pi}{2} - \tan^{-1} t,$$

where the second and fourth equalities above come from the identity we found earlier in this section for the arctangent of the negative of a number and the third identity above comes from applying the result of the previous paragraph to the positive number $-t$.

Putting together the results from the last two paragraphs, we have the following identity for $\tan^{-1} \frac{1}{t}$:

For example, a calculator shows that $\tan^{-1} 5 \approx 1.3734$. Thus $\tan^{-1} \frac{1}{5} = \frac{\pi}{2} - 1.3734 \approx 1.5708 - 1.3734 = 0.1974$.

Arctangent of $\frac{1}{t}$

$$\tan^{-1} \frac{1}{t} = \begin{cases} \frac{\pi}{2} - \tan^{-1} t & \text{if } t > 0 \\ -\frac{\pi}{2} - \tan^{-1} t & \text{if } t < 0 \end{cases}$$

Composition of Trigonometric Functions and Their Inverses

Recall that if f is a one-to-one function, then $f \circ f^{-1}$ is the identity function on the range of f, meaning that $f(f^{-1}(t)) = t$ for every t in the range of f. In the case of the trigonometric functions (or more precisely, the trigonometric functions restricted to the appropriate domain) and their inverses, this gives the following set of equations:

Trigonometric functions composed with their inverses

$$\cos(\cos^{-1} t) = t \quad \text{for every } t \text{ in } [-1, 1]$$

$$\sin(\sin^{-1} t) = t \quad \text{for every } t \text{ in } [-1, 1]$$

$$\tan(\tan^{-1} t) = t \quad \text{for every real number } t$$

The left sides of the first two equations above make no sense unless t is in $[-1, 1]$ because $\cos^{-1}$ and the $\sin^{-1}$ are only defined on the interval $[-1, 1]$.

Recall also that if f is a one-to-one function, then $f^{-1} \circ f$ is the identity function on the domain of f, meaning that $f^{-1}(f(\theta)) = \theta$ for every θ in the domain of f. In the case of the trigonometric functions (or more precisely, the trigonometric functions restricted to the appropriate domain) and their inverses, this gives the following set of equations:

> ### *Inverse trigonometric functions composed with their inverses*
>
> $$\cos^{-1}(\cos \theta) = \theta \quad \text{for every } \theta \text{ in } [0, \pi]$$
>
> $$\sin^{-1}(\sin \theta) = \theta \quad \text{for every } \theta \text{ in } [-\tfrac{\pi}{2}, \tfrac{\pi}{2}]$$
>
> $$\tan^{-1}(\tan \theta) = \theta \quad \text{for every } \theta \text{ in } (-\tfrac{\pi}{2}, \tfrac{\pi}{2})$$

Pay attention to the restrictions on θ needed for these identities to hold.

The next example shows why the restrictions above on θ are necessary.

Evaluate $\cos^{-1}(\cos(2\pi))$.

EXAMPLE 3

SOLUTION   The key point here is that the first equation above is not valid because 2π is not in the allowable range for θ. However, we can evaluate this expression directly. Because $\cos(2\pi) = 1$, we have

$$\cos^{-1}(\cos(2\pi)) = \cos^{-1} 1 = 0.$$

The example above shows that $\cos^{-1}(\cos \theta)$ does not equal θ if $\theta = 2\pi$. Some of the worked-out exercises in this section show how to deal with these compositions when θ is not in the required range.

More Compositions with Inverse Trigonometric Functions

In the previous subsection we discussed the composition of a trigonometric function with its inverse function. In this subsection we will discuss the composition of a trigonometric function with the inverse of a different trigonometric function.

For example, consider the problem of evaluating $\cos(\sin^{-1} \tfrac{2}{3})$. One way to approach this problem would be to evaluate $\sin^{-1} \tfrac{2}{3}$, then evaluate the cosine of that angle. However, no one knows how to find an exact expression for $\sin^{-1} \tfrac{2}{3}$.

A calculator could give an approximate answer. A calculator working in radians shows that

$$\sin^{-1} \tfrac{2}{3} \approx 0.729728.$$

Using a calculator again to take cosine of the number above, we see that

$$\cos(\sin^{-1} \tfrac{2}{3}) \approx 0.745356.$$

When working with trigonometric functions, an accurate numerical approximation such as computed above is sometimes the best that can be done. However, for compositions of the type discussed above, exact answers are possible to obtain. The example below shows how to do this.

EXAMPLE 4

In general we know that $\cos \theta = \pm\sqrt{1 - \sin^2\theta}$. Here we can choose the plus sign because this θ is in $[-\frac{\pi}{2}, \frac{\pi}{2}]$, which implies that $\cos \theta \geq 0$.

Evaluate $\cos(\sin^{-1} \tfrac{2}{3})$.

SOLUTION Let $\theta = \sin^{-1} \tfrac{2}{3}$. Thus θ is in $[-\frac{\pi}{2}, \frac{\pi}{2}]$ and $\sin \theta = \tfrac{2}{3}$. Now

$$\cos(\sin^{-1} \tfrac{2}{3}) = \cos \theta$$
$$= \sqrt{1 - \sin^2\theta}$$
$$= \sqrt{1 - \left(\tfrac{2}{3}\right)^2}$$
$$= \sqrt{\tfrac{5}{9}}$$
$$= \tfrac{\sqrt{5}}{3}.$$

A calculator shows that $\frac{\sqrt{5}}{3} \approx 0.745356$. Thus the exact value we just obtained for $\cos(\sin^{-1} \tfrac{2}{3})$ is consistent with the approximate value obtained earlier.

The method used in the example above might be called the algebraic approach. The example below solves the same problem using a right-triangle approach. Some people prefer the algebraic approach; others prefer the right-triangle approach. Use whichever method seems clearer to you.

EXAMPLE 5

Evaluate $\cos(\sin^{-1} \tfrac{2}{3})$.

SOLUTION Let $\theta = \sin^{-1} \tfrac{2}{3}$; thus $\sin \theta = \tfrac{2}{3}$. Recall that

$$\sin \theta = \frac{\text{opposite side}}{\text{hypotenuse}}$$

in a right triangle with an angle of θ, where "opposite side" means the length of the side opposite the angle θ. The easiest choices for side lengths to have $\sin \theta = \tfrac{2}{3}$ are shown in the triangle below:

We could also have chosen sides of length 4 and 6, or $\tfrac{2}{3}$ and 1, or any pair of numbers whose ratio equals $\tfrac{2}{3}$. But choosing sides of length 2 and 3 is the simplest choice.

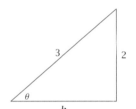

A right triangle with $\sin \theta = \tfrac{2}{3}$.

We need to evaluate $\cos \theta$. In terms of the figure above, we have

$$\cos \theta = \frac{\text{adjacent side}}{\text{hypotenuse}} = \frac{b}{3}.$$

Applying the Pythagorean Theorem to the triangle above, we have $b^2 + 4 = 9$, which implies that $b = \sqrt{5}$. Thus $\cos \theta = \frac{\sqrt{5}}{3}$. In other words, $\cos(\sin^{-1} \frac{2}{3}) = \frac{\sqrt{5}}{3}$.

The procedures used in the examples above can be used to find identities for the composition of a trigonometric function and the inverse of another trigonometric function. We first illustrate this procedure using the algebraic approach.

Find a formula for $\tan(\cos^{-1} t)$.

EXAMPLE 6

SOLUTION Suppose $-1 \le t \le 1$ with $t \neq 0$ (we are excluding $t = 0$ because in that case we would have $\cos^{-1} t = \frac{\pi}{2}$, but $\tan \frac{\pi}{2}$ is undefined). Let $\theta = \cos^{-1} t$. Thus θ is in $[0, \pi]$ and $\cos \theta = t$. Now

$$\tan(\cos^{-1} t) = \tan \theta$$

$$= \frac{\sin \theta}{\cos \theta}$$

$$= \frac{\sqrt{1 - \cos^2 \theta}}{\cos \theta}$$

$$= \frac{\sqrt{1 - t^2}}{t}.$$

In general we know that $\sin \theta = \pm\sqrt{1 - \cos^2 \theta}$. Here we can choose the plus sign because this θ is in $[0, \pi]$, which implies that $\sin \theta \geq 0$.

Thus the formula we seek is

$$\tan(\cos^{-1} t) = \frac{\sqrt{1 - t^2}}{t}.$$

Next, we derive the same identity using the right-triangle approach. Again, you should use whichever method you find clearer.

Find a formula for $\tan(\cos^{-1} t)$.

EXAMPLE 7

SOLUTION Let $\theta = \cos^{-1} t$; thus $\cos \theta = t$. Recall that

$$\cos \theta = \frac{\text{adjacent side}}{\text{hypotenuse}}$$

in a right triangle with an angle of θ, where "adjacent side" means the length of the (nonhypotenuse) side adjacent to the angle θ. The easiest choices for side lengths to have $\cos \theta = t$ are shown in the triangle here.

We need to evaluate $\tan \theta$. In terms of the figure here, we have

$$\tan \theta = \frac{\text{opposite side}}{\text{adjacent side}} = \frac{b}{t}.$$

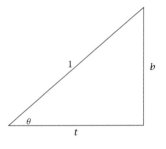

A right triangle with $\cos \theta = t$.

Applying the Pythagorean Theorem to the triangle above, we have $t^2 + b^2 = 1$, which implies that $b = \sqrt{1-t^2}$. Thus $\tan\theta = \frac{\sqrt{1-t^2}}{t}$. In other words, we have the identity

$$\tan(\cos^{-1} t) = \frac{\sqrt{1-t^2}}{t}.$$

In the examples above, we derived the identity

$$\tan(\cos^{-1} t) = \frac{\sqrt{1-t^2}}{t},$$

which holds whenever $-1 \le t \le 1$ with $t \ne 0$. There are five more such identities, involving the composition of a trigonometric function and the inverse of another trigonometric function. The problems in this section ask you to derive those five additional identities, which can be done using the same methods as for the identity above. Memorizing these identities is not a good use of your mental energy, but be sure that you understand how to derive them.

EXERCISES

1. Suppose t is such that $\cos^{-1} t = 2$. Evaluate the following:
   (a) $\cos^{-1}(-t)$
   (b) $\sin^{-1} t$
   (c) $\sin^{-1}(-t)$

2. Suppose t is such that $\sin^{-1} t = -\frac{2\pi}{7}$. Evaluate the following:
   (a) $\sin^{-1}(-t)$
   (b) $\cos^{-1} t$
   (c) $\cos^{-1}(-t)$

3. Suppose t is such that $\tan^{-1} t = \frac{3\pi}{7}$. Evaluate the following:
   (a) $\tan^{-1} \frac{1}{t}$
   (b) $\tan^{-1}(-t)$
   (c) $\tan^{-1}(-\frac{1}{t})$

4. Suppose t is such that $\tan^{-1} t = -\frac{4\pi}{11}$. Evaluate the following:
   (a) $\tan^{-1} \frac{1}{t}$
   (b) $\tan^{-1}(-t)$
   (c) $\tan^{-1}(-\frac{1}{t})$

5. Evaluate $\cos(\cos^{-1} \frac{1}{4})$.

6. Evaluate $\tan(\tan^{-1} 5)$.

7. Evaluate $\sin^{-1}(\sin \frac{2\pi}{7})$.

8. Evaluate $\cos^{-1}(\cos \frac{1}{2})$.

9. Evaluate $\cos^{-1}(\cos 3\pi)$.

10. Evaluate $\sin^{-1}(\sin \frac{9\pi}{4})$.

11. Evaluate $\tan^{-1}(\tan \frac{11\pi}{5})$.

12. Evaluate $\tan^{-1}(\tan \frac{17\pi}{7})$.

13. Evaluate $\sin(-\sin^{-1} \frac{3}{13})$.

14. Evaluate $\tan(-\tan^{-1} \frac{7}{11})$.

15. Evaluate $\sin(\cos^{-1} \frac{1}{3})$.

16. Evaluate $\cos(\sin^{-1} \frac{2}{5})$.

17. Evaluate $\tan(\cos^{-1} \frac{1}{3})$.

18. Evaluate $\tan(\sin^{-1} \frac{2}{5})$.

19. Evaluate $\cos(\tan^{-1}(-4))$.

20. Evaluate $\sin(\tan^{-1}(-9))$.

21. Evaluate $\sin^{-1}(\cos \frac{2\pi}{5})$.

22. Evaluate $\cos^{-1}(\sin \frac{4\pi}{9})$.

PROBLEMS

23. Is arccosine an even function, an odd function, or neither?

24. Is arcsine an even function, an odd function, or neither?

25. Is arctangent an even function, an odd function, or neither?

26. Show that

$$\tan^{-1} \tfrac{1}{t} = \tfrac{t}{|t|} \tfrac{\pi}{2} - \tan^{-1} t$$

   for all $t \neq 0$.

27. Show that

$$\cos(\sin^{-1} t) = \sqrt{1 - t^2}$$

   whenever $-1 \leq t \leq 1$.

28. Find an identity expressing $\sin(\cos^{-1} t)$ as a nice function of t.

29. Find an identity expressing $\tan(\sin^{-1} t)$ as a nice function of t.

30. Show that

$$\cos(\tan^{-1} t) = \frac{1}{\sqrt{1 + t^2}}$$

   for every number t.

31. Find an identity expressing $\sin(\tan^{-1} t)$ as a nice function of t.

32. Explain why

$$\cos^{-1} t = \sin^{-1} \sqrt{1 - t^2}$$

   whenever $0 \leq t \leq 1$.

33. Explain why

$$\cos^{-1} t = \tan^{-1} \frac{\sqrt{1-t^2}}{t}$$

   whenever $0 < t \leq 1$.

34. Explain why

$$\sin^{-1} t = \tan^{-1} \frac{t}{\sqrt{1-t^2}}$$

   whenever $-1 < t < 1$.

35. Explain what is wrong with the following "proof" that $\theta = -\theta$:

   Let θ be any angle. Then

$$\cos \theta = \cos(-\theta).$$

   Apply $\cos^{-1}$ to both sides of the equation above, getting

$$\cos^{-1}(\cos \theta) = \cos^{-1}(\cos(-\theta)).$$

   Because $\cos^{-1}$ is the inverse of cos, the equation above implies that

$$\theta = -\theta.$$

WORKED-OUT SOLUTIONS *to Odd-numbered Exercises*

1. Suppose t is such that $\cos^{-1} t = 2$. Evaluate the following:

   (a) $\cos^{-1}(-t)$ (c) $\sin^{-1}(-t)$

   (b) $\sin^{-1} t$

   SOLUTION

   (a) $\cos^{-1}(-t) = \pi - \cos^{-1} t = \pi - 2$

   (b) $\sin^{-1} t = \frac{\pi}{2} - \cos^{-1} t = \frac{\pi}{2} - 2$

   (c) $\sin^{-1}(-t) = -\sin^{-1} t = 2 - \frac{\pi}{2}$

3. Suppose t is such that $\tan^{-1} t = \frac{3\pi}{7}$. Evaluate the following:

   (a) $\tan^{-1} \frac{1}{t}$ (c) $\tan^{-1}(-\frac{1}{t})$

   (b) $\tan^{-1}(-t)$

   SOLUTION

   (a) Because $t = \tan \frac{3\pi}{7}$, we see that $t > 0$. Thus

$$\tan^{-1} \tfrac{1}{t} = \tfrac{\pi}{2} - \tan^{-1} t = \tfrac{\pi}{2} - \tfrac{3\pi}{7} = \tfrac{\pi}{14}.$$

   (b) $\tan^{-1}(-t) = -\tan^{-1} t = -\frac{3\pi}{7}$

   (c) $\tan^{-1}(-\frac{1}{t}) = -\tan^{-1}(\frac{1}{t}) = -\frac{\pi}{14}$

5. Evaluate $\cos(\cos^{-1} \frac{1}{4})$.

   SOLUTION   Let $\theta = \cos^{-1} \frac{1}{4}$. Thus θ is the angle in $[0, \pi]$ such that $\cos \theta = \frac{1}{4}$. Thus $\cos(\cos^{-1} \frac{1}{4}) = \cos \theta = \frac{1}{4}$.

7. Evaluate $\sin^{-1}(\sin\frac{2\pi}{7})$.

SOLUTION Let $\theta = \sin^{-1}(\sin\frac{2\pi}{7})$. Thus θ is the unique angle in the interval $[-\frac{\pi}{2}, \frac{\pi}{2}]$ such that

$$\sin\theta = \sin\frac{2\pi}{7}.$$

Because $-\frac{1}{2} \le \frac{2}{7} \le \frac{1}{2}$, we see that $\frac{2\pi}{7}$ is in $[-\frac{\pi}{2}, \frac{\pi}{2}]$. Thus the equation above implies that $\theta = \frac{2\pi}{7}$.

9. Evaluate $\cos^{-1}(\cos 3\pi)$.

SOLUTION Because $\cos 3\pi = -1$, we see that

$$\cos^{-1}(\cos 3\pi) = \cos^{-1}(-1).$$

Because $\cos\pi = -1$, we have $\cos^{-1}(-1) = \pi$ ($\cos 3\pi$ also equals -1, but $\cos^{-1}(-1)$ must be in the interval $[0, \pi]$). Thus $\cos^{-1}(\cos 3\pi) = \pi$.

11. Evaluate $\tan^{-1}(\tan\frac{11\pi}{5})$.

SOLUTION Because $\tan^{-1}$ is the inverse of tan, it may be tempting to think that $\tan^{-1}(\tan\frac{11\pi}{5})$ equals $\frac{11\pi}{5}$. However, the values of $\tan^{-1}$ must be between $-\frac{\pi}{2}$ and $\frac{\pi}{2}$. Because $\frac{11\pi}{5} > \frac{\pi}{2}$, we conclude that $\tan^{-1}(\tan\frac{11\pi}{5})$ cannot equal $\frac{11\pi}{5}$.

Note that

$$\tan\frac{11\pi}{5} = \tan(2\pi + \frac{\pi}{5}) = \tan\frac{\pi}{5}.$$

Because $\frac{\pi}{5}$ is in $(-\frac{\pi}{2}, \frac{\pi}{2})$, we have $\tan^{-1}(\tan\frac{\pi}{5}) = \frac{\pi}{5}$. Thus

$$\tan^{-1}(\tan\frac{11\pi}{5}) = \tan^{-1}(\tan\frac{\pi}{5}) = \frac{\pi}{5}.$$

13. Evaluate $\sin(-\sin^{-1}\frac{3}{13})$.

SOLUTION

$$\sin(-\sin^{-1}\frac{3}{13}) = -\sin(\sin^{-1}\frac{3}{13})$$

$$= -\frac{3}{13}$$

15. Evaluate $\sin(\cos^{-1}\frac{1}{3})$.

SOLUTION We give two ways to work this exercise: the algebraic approach and the right-triangle approach.

Algebraic approach: Let $\theta = \cos^{-1}\frac{1}{3}$. Thus θ is the angle in $[0, \pi]$ such that $\cos\theta = \frac{1}{3}$. Note that $\sin\theta \ge 0$ because θ is in $[0, \pi]$. Thus

$$\sin(\cos^{-1}\frac{1}{3}) = \sin\theta$$

$$= \sqrt{1 - \cos^2\theta}$$

$$= \sqrt{1 - \frac{1}{9}}$$

$$= \sqrt{\frac{8}{9}}$$

$$= \frac{2\sqrt{2}}{3}.$$

Right-triangle approach: Let $\theta = \cos^{-1}\frac{1}{3}$; thus $\cos\theta = \frac{1}{3}$. Because

$$\cos\theta = \frac{\text{adjacent side}}{\text{hypotenuse}}$$

in a right triangle with an angle of θ, the following figure (which is not drawn to scale) illustrates the situation:

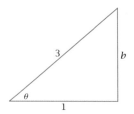

We need to evaluate $\sin\theta$. In terms of the figure above, we have

$$\sin\theta = \frac{\text{opposite side}}{\text{hypotenuse}} = \frac{b}{3}.$$

Applying the Pythagorean Theorem to the triangle above, we have $b^2 + 1 = 9$, which implies that $b = \sqrt{8} = 2\sqrt{2}$. Thus $\sin\theta = \frac{2\sqrt{2}}{3}$. In other words, $\sin(\cos^{-1}\frac{1}{3}) = \frac{2\sqrt{2}}{3}$.

17. Evaluate $\tan(\cos^{-1}\frac{1}{3})$.

SOLUTION We give two ways to work this exercise: the algebraic approach and the right-triangle approach.

Algebraic approach: From Exercise 15, we already know that

$$\sin(\cos^{-1}\frac{1}{3}) = \frac{2\sqrt{2}}{3}.$$

Thus

$$\tan(\cos^{-1}\tfrac{1}{3}) = \frac{\sin(\cos^{-1}\tfrac{1}{3})}{\cos(\cos^{-1}\tfrac{1}{3})}$$

$$= \frac{\frac{2\sqrt{2}}{3}}{\frac{1}{3}}$$

$$= 2\sqrt{2}.$$

Right-triangle approach: Let $\theta = \cos^{-1}\tfrac{1}{3}$; thus $\cos\theta = \tfrac{1}{3}$. Because

$$\cos\theta = \frac{\text{adjacent side}}{\text{hypotenuse}}$$

in a right triangle with an angle of θ, the following figure (which is not drawn to scale) illustrates the situation:

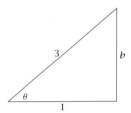

We need to evaluate $\tan\theta$. In terms of the figure above, we have

$$\tan\theta = \frac{\text{opposite side}}{\text{adjacent side}} = b.$$

Applying the Pythagorean Theorem to the triangle above, we have $b^2 + 1 = 9$, which implies that $b = \sqrt{8} = 2\sqrt{2}$. Thus $\tan\theta = 2\sqrt{2}$. In other words, $\tan(\cos^{-1}\tfrac{1}{3}) = 2\sqrt{2}$.

19. Evaluate $\cos(\tan^{-1}(-4))$.

SOLUTION We give two ways to work this exercise: the algebraic approach and the right-triangle approach.

Algebraic approach: Let $\theta = \tan^{-1}(-4)$. Thus θ is the angle in $(-\tfrac{\pi}{2}, \tfrac{\pi}{2})$ such that $\tan\theta = -4$. Note that $\cos\theta > 0$ because θ is in $(-\tfrac{\pi}{2}, \tfrac{\pi}{2})$.

Recall that dividing both sides of the identity $\cos^2\theta + \sin^2\theta = 1$ by $\cos^2\theta$ produces the equation $1 + \tan^2\theta = \frac{1}{\cos^2\theta}$. Solving this equation for $\cos\theta$ gives the following:

$$\cos(\tan^{-1}(-4)) = \cos\theta$$

$$= \frac{1}{\sqrt{1 + \tan^2\theta}}$$

$$= \frac{1}{\sqrt{1 + (-4)^2}}$$

$$= \frac{1}{\sqrt{17}} = \frac{\sqrt{17}}{17}.$$

Right-triangle approach: Sides with a negative length make no sense in a right triangle. Thus first we use some identities to get rid of the minus sign, as follows:

$$\cos(\tan^{-1}(-4)) = \cos(-\tan^{-1}4)$$

$$= \cos(\tan^{-1}4).$$

Thus we need to evaluate $\cos(\tan^{-1}4)$.

Now let $\theta = \tan^{-1}4$; thus $\tan\theta = 4$. Because

$$\tan\theta = \frac{\text{opposite side}}{\text{adjacent side}}$$

in a right triangle with an angle of θ, the following figure (which is not drawn to scale) illustrates the situation:

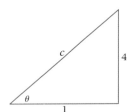

We need to evaluate $\cos\theta$. In terms of the figure above, we have

$$\cos\theta = \frac{\text{adjacent side}}{\text{hypotenuse}} = \frac{1}{c}.$$

Applying the Pythagorean Theorem to the triangle above, we have $c^2 = 1 + 16$, which implies that $c = \sqrt{17}$. Thus $\cos\theta = \frac{1}{\sqrt{17}} = \frac{\sqrt{17}}{17}$. In other words, $\cos(\tan^{-1}4) = \frac{\sqrt{17}}{17}$. Thus $\cos(\tan^{-1}(-4)) = \frac{\sqrt{17}}{17}$.

21. Evaluate $\sin^{-1}(\cos\tfrac{2\pi}{5})$.

SOLUTION

$$\sin^{-1}(\cos\tfrac{2\pi}{5}) = \tfrac{\pi}{2} - \cos^{-1}(\cos\tfrac{2\pi}{5})$$

$$= \tfrac{\pi}{2} - \tfrac{2\pi}{5} = \tfrac{\pi}{10}$$

CHAPTER SUMMARY

To check that you have mastered the most important concepts and skills covered in this chapter,
make sure that you can do each item in the following list:

- Explain what it means for an angle to be negative.

- Explain how an angle can be larger than 360°.

- Convert angles from radians to degrees.

- Convert angles from degrees to radians.

- Compute the length of a circular arc.

- Compute the cosine, sine, and tangent of any multiple of 30° or 45° ($\frac{\pi}{6}$ radians or $\frac{\pi}{4}$ radians).

- Explain why $\cos^2\theta + \sin^2\theta = 1$ for every angle θ.

- Compute $\cos\theta$, $\sin\theta$, and $\tan\theta$ if given just one of these quantities and the location of the corresponding radius.

- Compute the cosine, sine, and tangent of any angle of a right triangle if given the lengths of two sides of the triangle.

- Compute the lengths of all three sides of a right triangle if given any angle (in addition to the right angle) and the length of any side.

- Use the basic trigonometric identities involving $-\theta$, $\frac{\pi}{2} - \theta$, and $\theta + \pi$.

- Give the domain and range of the cosine, sine, and tangent functions.

- Give the domain and range of $\cos^{-1}$, $\sin^{-1}$, and $\tan^{-1}$.

- Compute the composition of a trigonometric function and an inverse trigonometric function.

To review a chapter, go through the list above to find items that you do not know how to do,
then reread the material in the chapter about those items. Then try to answer the chapter
review questions below without looking back at the chapter.

CHAPTER REVIEW QUESTIONS

1. Find all points where the line through the origin with slope 5 intersects the unit circle.

2. Sketch a unit circle and the radius of that circle that makes an angle of $-70°$ with the positive horizontal axis.

3. Explain how to convert an angle from degrees to radians.

4. Convert 27° to radians.

5. Explain how to convert an angle from radians to degrees.

6. Convert $\frac{7\pi}{9}$ radians to degrees.

7. Give the domain and range of each of the following functions: cos, sin, and tan.

8. Find three distinct angles, expressed in degrees, whose cosine equals $\frac{1}{2}$.

9. Find three distinct angles, expressed in radians, whose sine equals $-\frac{1}{2}$.

10. Find three distinct angles, expressed in radians, whose tangent equals 1.

11. Explain why $\cos^2\theta + \sin^2\theta = 1$ for every angle θ.

12. Explain why $\cos(\theta + 2\pi) = \cos\theta$ for every angle θ.

13. Suppose $\frac{\pi}{2} < x < \pi$ and $\tan x = -4$. Evaluate $\cos x$ and $\sin x$.

14. 📱 Find the lengths of both circular arcs of the unit circle connecting the points $(\frac{3}{5}, \frac{4}{5})$ and $(\frac{5}{13}, \frac{12}{13})$.

Use the right triangle below for Questions 15–35. This triangle is not drawn to scale corresponding to the data in the questions.

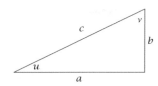

15. Suppose $a = 4$ and $b = 9$. Evaluate c.

16. Suppose $a = 4$ and $b = 9$. Evaluate $\cos u$.

17. Suppose $a = 4$ and $b = 9$. Evaluate $\sin u$.

18. Suppose $a = 4$ and $b = 9$. Evaluate $\tan u$.

19. Suppose $a = 4$ and $b = 9$. Evaluate $\cos v$.

20. Suppose $a = 4$ and $b = 9$. Evaluate $\sin v$.

21. Suppose $a = 4$ and $b = 9$. Evaluate $\tan v$.

22. Suppose $a = 3$ and $c = 8$. Evaluate b.

23. Suppose $a = 3$ and $c = 8$. Evaluate $\cos u$.

24. Suppose $a = 3$ and $c = 8$. Evaluate $\sin u$.

25. Suppose $a = 3$ and $c = 8$. Evaluate $\tan u$.

26. Suppose $a = 3$ and $c = 8$. Evaluate $\cos v$.

27. Suppose $a = 3$ and $c = 8$. Evaluate $\sin v$.

28. Suppose $a = 3$ and $c = 8$. Evaluate $\tan v$.

29. 📱 Suppose $b = 4$ and $u = 28°$. Evaluate a.

30. 📱 Suppose $b = 4$ and $u = 28°$. Evaluate c.

31. 📱 Suppose $u = 28°$. Evaluate $\cos v$.

32. 📱 Suppose $u = 28°$. Evaluate $\sin v$.

33. 📱 Suppose $u = 28°$. Evaluate $\tan v$.

34. 📱 Suppose $a = 4$ and $c = 7$. Evaluate u and v in radians.

35. 📱 Suppose $a = 6$ and $b = 7$. Evaluate u and v in degrees.

36. Suppose θ is an angle such that $\cos \theta = \frac{3}{8}$. Evaluate $\cos(-\theta)$.

37. Suppose x is a number such that $\sin x = \frac{4}{7}$. Evaluate $\sin(-x)$.

38. Suppose y is a number such that $\tan y = -\frac{2}{9}$. Evaluate $\tan(-y)$.

39. Suppose u is a number such that $\cos u = -\frac{2}{5}$. Evaluate $\cos(u + \pi)$.

40. Suppose θ is an angle such that $\tan \theta = \frac{5}{6}$. Evaluate $\tan(\frac{\pi}{2} - \theta)$.

41. Find a formula for $\tan \theta$ solely in terms of $\cos \theta$.

42. Give the domain and range of each of the following functions: $\cos^{-1}$, $\sin^{-1}$, and $\tan^{-1}$.

43. Evaluate $\cos^{-1} \frac{\sqrt{3}}{2}$.

44. Evaluate $\sin^{-1} \frac{\sqrt{3}}{2}$.

45. Evaluate $\cos(\cos^{-1} \frac{2}{5})$.

46. Without using a calculator, sketch the unit circle and the radius that makes an angle of $\cos^{-1}(-0.8)$ with the positive horizontal axis.

47. Explain why your calculator is likely to be unhappy if you ask it to evaluate $\cos^{-1} 3$.

48. 📱 Find the smallest positive number x such that
$$3 \sin^2 x - 4 \sin x + 1 = 0.$$

49. Evaluate $\sin^{-1}(\sin \frac{19\pi}{8})$.

50. Evaluate $\cos(\tan^{-1} 5)$.

Tides on a Florida beach follow a periodic pattern modeled by trigonometric functions.

Applications of Trigonometry

This chapter focuses on applications of the trigonometry that was introduced in the last chapter. The chapter begins by showing how trigonometry can be used to compute areas of various regions. Then we will see how trigonometry enables us to compute all the angles and the lengths of all the sides of a triangle given only some of this information.

The double-angle and half-angle formulas for the trigonometric functions will allow us to compute exact expressions for quantities such as $\cos 15°$ and $\sin 18°$. The addition and subtraction formulas for the trigonometric functions will help us discover new identities.

Transformations of trigonometric functions are used to model periodic events. Redoing function transformations in the context of trigonometric functions will also help us review the key concepts of function transformations from Chapter 1.

This chapter concludes an optional section giving an introduction to polar coordinates, which are based on trigonometry, and another optional section on vectors and the complex plane.

6.1 *Using Trigonometry to Compute Area*

SECTION OBJECTIVES

By the end of this section you should

- be able to compute the area of a triangle given the lengths of two sides and the angle between them;
- understand the ambiguous angle problem that sometimes arises when trying to find the angle between two sides of a triangle;
- understand the formula for the area of a parallelogram;
- be able to compute the area of a regular polygon.

The Area of a Triangle via Trigonometry

Suppose we know the lengths of two sides of a triangle and the angle between those two sides. How can we find the area of the triangle? The example below shows how a knowledge of trigonometry helps solve this problem.

Find the area of a triangle that has sides of length 4 and 7 and an angle of 49° between those two sides.

EXAMPLE 1

SOLUTION We will consider the side of length 7 to be the base of the triangle. Let h denote the corresponding height of the triangle, as shown here.

Looking at the figure above, we see that $\sin 49° = \frac{h}{4}$. Solving for h, we have $h = 4 \sin 49°$. Thus the triangle has area

$$\tfrac{1}{2} \cdot 7h = \tfrac{1}{2} \cdot 7 \cdot 4 \sin 49° = 14 \sin 49° \approx 10.566.$$

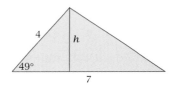

To find a formula for the area of a triangle given the lengths of two sides of a triangle and the angle between those two sides, we repeat the process used in the example above. We know that the area of a triangle is one-half the base times the height. Thus we will begin by finding a formula for the height of a triangle in terms of the lengths of two sides and the angle between them.

Consider a triangle with sides of length a and b and an angle θ between those two sides. We will consider b to be the base of the triangle. Let h denote the corresponding height of this triangle.

We want to write the height h in terms of the known measurements of the triangle, which are a, b, and θ. Looking at the figure here, we see that $\sin \theta = \frac{h}{a}$. Solving for h, we have

$$h = a \sin \theta.$$

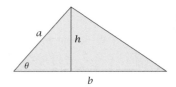

A triangle with base b and height h.

The area of the triangle above is $\frac{1}{2}bh$. Substituting $a \sin \theta$ for h shows that the area of the triangle equals $\frac{1}{2}ab \sin \theta$. Thus we have arrived at our desired formula giving the area of a triangle in terms of the lengths of two sides and the angle between those sides.

Area of a triangle

A triangle with sides of length a and b and with angle θ between those two sides has area

$$\tfrac{1}{2}ab \sin \theta.$$

Whenever we encounter a new formula we should check that it agrees with previously known formulas in cases where both formulas apply. The formula above allows us to compute the area of a triangle whenever we know the lengths of two sides and the angle between those sides. We already knew how to do this when the angle in question is a right angle. Specifically, we already knew that the right triangle shown here has area $\tfrac{1}{2}ab$ (which is half the area of a rectangle with sides of length a and b).

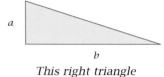

This right triangle has area $\tfrac{1}{2}ab$.

To apply our new formula to the right triangle above, we take $\theta = \tfrac{\pi}{2}$. Because $\sin \tfrac{\pi}{2} = 1$, the expression $\tfrac{1}{2}ab \sin \theta$ becomes $\tfrac{1}{2}ab$. In other words, our new formula for the area of a triangle gives the same result as our previous formula for the area of a right triangle. Thus the two formulas are consistent (if they had been inconsistent, then we would know that one of them was incorrect).

Ambiguous Angles

Suppose a triangle has sides of lengths a and b, an angle θ between those sides, and area R. Given any three of a, b, θ, and R, we can use the equation

$$R = \tfrac{1}{2}ab \sin \theta$$

to solve for the other quantity. This process is mostly straightforward—the exercises at the end of this section provide some practice in this procedure.

However, a subtlety arises when we know the lengths a, b and the area R and we need to find the angle θ. Solving the equation above for $\sin \theta$, we get

$$\sin \theta = \frac{2R}{ab}.$$

Thus θ is an angle whose sine equals $\frac{2R}{ab}$, and it would seem that we finish by taking $\theta = \sin^{-1} \frac{2R}{ab}$. Sometimes this is correct, but not always. Let's look at an example to see what can happen.

EXAMPLE 2   Suppose a triangle with area 6 has sides of lengths 3 and 8. Find the angle between those two sides.

SOLUTION   Solving for $\sin \theta$ as above, we have

$$\sin \theta = \frac{2R}{ab} = \frac{2 \cdot 6}{3 \cdot 8} = \frac{1}{2}.$$

Now $\sin^{-1} \tfrac{1}{2}$ equals $\tfrac{\pi}{6}$ radians, which equals $30°$. Thus it appears that our triangle should look like this:

This triangle has area 6.

However, the sine of $150°$ also equals $\frac{1}{2}$. Thus the following triangle with sides of lengths 3 and 8 also has area 6:

This triangle also has area 6.

If the only information available is that the triangle has area 6 and sides of length 3 and 8, then there is no way to decide which of the two possibilities above truly represents the triangle.

Do not mistakenly think that because $\sin^{-1}\frac{1}{2}$ is defined to equal $\frac{\pi}{6}$ radians (which equals $30°$), the preferred solution in the example above is to choose $\theta = 30°$. We defined the arcsine of a number to be in the interval $[-\frac{\pi}{2}, \frac{\pi}{2}]$ because some choice needed to be made in order to obtain a well-defined inverse for the sine. However, remember that given a number t in $[-1, 1]$, there are angles other than $\sin^{-1} t$ whose sine equals t (although there is only one such angle in the interval $[-\frac{\pi}{2}, \frac{\pi}{2}]$).

In the example above, we had $30°$ and $150°$ as two angles whose sine equals $\frac{1}{2}$. More generally, given any number t in $[-1, 1]$ and an angle θ such that $\sin\theta = t$, we also have $\sin(\pi - \theta) = t$. This follows from the identity $\sin(\pi - \theta) = \sin\theta$, which can be derived as follows:

$$\sin(\pi - \theta) = -(\sin(\theta - \pi))$$

$$= -(-\sin\theta)$$

$$= \sin\theta,$$

where the first identity above follows from our identity for the sine of the negative of an angle (Section 5.6) and the second identity follows from our formula for the sine of $\theta + n\pi$, with $n = -1$ (also Section 5.6).

When working in degrees instead of radians, the result in the paragraph above should be restated to say that the angles $\theta°$ and $(180 - \theta)°$ have the same sine.

Returning to the example above, note that in addition to $30°$ and $150°$, there are other angles whose sine equals $\frac{1}{2}$. For example, $-330°$ and $390°$ are two such angles. But a triangle cannot have a negative angle, and a triangle cannot have an angle larger than $180°$. Thus neither $-330°$ nor $390°$ is a viable possibility for the angle θ in the triangle in question.

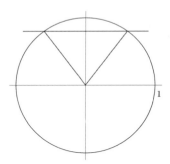

The two radii shown here have endpoints with the same second coordinate; thus the corresponding angles have the same sine.

The Area of a Parallelogram via Trigonometry

The procedure for finding the area of a parallelogram, given an angle of the parallelogram and the lengths of the two adjacent sides, is the same as the procedure followed for a triangle. Consider a parallelogram with sides of length a and b and an angle θ between those two sides, as shown here. We will consider b to be the base of the parallelogram, and we let h denote the height of the parallelogram.

A parallelogram with base b and height h.

We want to write the height h in terms of what we assume are the known measurements of the parallelogram, which are a, b, and θ. Looking at the figure above, we see that $\sin\theta = \frac{h}{a}$. Solving for h, we have

$$h = a\sin\theta.$$

The area of the parallelogram above is bh. Substituting $a\sin\theta$ for h shows that the area equals $ab\sin\theta$. Thus we have the following formula:

> ### Area of a parallelogram
>
> A parallelogram with adjacent sides of length a and b and with angle θ between those two sides has area
>
> $$ab\sin\theta.$$

Suppose a parallelogram has adjacent sides of lengths a and b, an angle θ between those sides, and area R. Given any three of a, b, θ, and R, we can use the equation

$$R = ab\sin\theta$$

to solve for the other quantity. As with the case of a triangle, if we know the lengths a and b and the area R, then there can be two possible choices for θ. For a parallelogram, both choices can be correct, as illustrated in the example below.

EXAMPLE 3

In a parallelogram that has area 40 and pairs of sides with lengths 5 and 10, as shown here, find the angle between the sides of lengths 5 and 10.

SOLUTION Solving the area formula above for $\sin\theta$, we have

$$\sin\theta = \frac{R}{ab} = \frac{40}{5\cdot10} = \frac{4}{5}.$$

A calculator shows that $\sin^{-1}\frac{4}{5} \approx 0.927$ radians, which is approximately 53.1°. An angle of $\pi - \sin^{-1}\frac{4}{5}$, which is approximately 126.9°, also has a sine equal to $\frac{4}{5}$.

To determine whether $\theta \approx 53.1°$ or whether $\theta \approx 126.9°$, we need to look at the figure here. As you can see, two angles have been labeled θ—both angles are between sides of length 5 and 10, reflecting the ambiguity in the statement of the problem. Although the ambiguity makes this a poorly stated problem, our formula has found both possible answers!

Specifically, if what was meant was the acute angle θ above (the leftmost angle labeled θ), then $\theta \approx 53.1°$; if what was meant was the obtuse angle θ above (the rightmost angle labeled θ), then $\theta \approx 126.9°$.

An angle θ measured in degrees is called **obtuse** *if $90° < \theta < 180°$.*

The Area of a Polygon

One way to find the area of a polygon is to decompose the polygon into triangles and then compute the sum of the areas of the triangles. This procedure works particularly well for a **regular polygon**, which is a polygon all of whose sides have the same length and all of whose angles are equal. For example, a regular polygon with four sides is a square. As another example, the figure here shows a regular octagon inscribed inside a circle.

The following example illustrates the procedure for finding the area of a regular polygon.

Find the area of a regular octagon whose vertices are eight equally spaced points on the unit circle.

EXAMPLE 4

SOLUTION The figure here shows how the octagon can be decomposed into triangles by drawing line segments from the center of the circle (the origin) to the vertices.

Each triangle shown here has two sides that are radii of the unit circle; thus those two sides of the triangle each have length 1. The angle between those two radii is $\frac{2\pi}{8}$ radians (because one rotation around the entire circle is an angle of 2π radians, and each of the eight triangles has an angle that takes up one-eighth of the total). Now $\frac{2\pi}{8}$ radians equals $\frac{\pi}{4}$ radians (or 45°). Thus each of the eight triangles has area

$$\tfrac{1}{2} \cdot 1 \cdot 1 \cdot \sin \tfrac{\pi}{4},$$

which equals $\frac{\sqrt{2}}{4}$. Thus the sum of the areas of the eight triangles equals $8 \cdot \frac{\sqrt{2}}{4}$, which equals $2\sqrt{2}$. In other words, the octagon has area $2\sqrt{2}$.

Once we know the area of a regular octagon inscribed in the unit circle, we can find the area of a regular octagon of any size. The idea is first to find the length of each side of a regular octagon inscribed in the unit circle, then scale appropriately, remembering that area is proportional to the square of side lengths. The example below illustrates this procedure.

(a) Find the length of each side of a regular octagon whose vertices are eight equally spaced points on the unit circle.

EXAMPLE 5

(b) Find the area of a regular octagon with sides of length s.

SOLUTION

(a) Suppose one of the vertices of the regular octagon is the point $(1, 0)$, as shown in the figure above. If we move counterclockwise along the unit circle, the next vertex is the point $(\cos \frac{2\pi}{8}, \sin \frac{2\pi}{8})$, which equals $(\frac{\sqrt{2}}{2}, \frac{\sqrt{2}}{2})$. Thus the length of each side of this regular octagon equals the distance between $(1, 0)$ and $(\frac{\sqrt{2}}{2}, \frac{\sqrt{2}}{2})$, which equals

$$\sqrt{(1 - \tfrac{\sqrt{2}}{2})^2 + (\tfrac{\sqrt{2}}{2})^2}.$$

Simplifying the expression above, we conclude that each side of this regular octagon has length

$$\sqrt{2 - \sqrt{2}}.$$

(b) The Area Stretch Theorem (see Section 4.2) implies that there is a constant c such that a regular octagon with sides of length s has area cs^2. From the previous example and from part (a) of this example, we know that the area equals $2\sqrt{2}$ if $s = \sqrt{2 - \sqrt{2}}$. Thus

$$2\sqrt{2} = c\left(\sqrt{2 - \sqrt{2}}\right)^2 = c(2 - \sqrt{2}).$$

Solving this equation for c, we have

$$c = \frac{2\sqrt{2}}{2 - \sqrt{2}} = \frac{2\sqrt{2}}{2 - \sqrt{2}} \cdot \frac{2 + \sqrt{2}}{2 + \sqrt{2}} = 2\sqrt{2} + 2.$$

Thus a regular octagon with sides of length s has area

$$(2\sqrt{2} + 2)s^2.$$

Most coins are round, but a few countries have coins that are regular polygons. The picture in the margin shows the one-dollar Canadian coin, which is an 11-sided regular polygon. The techniques used in the example above will allow you to compute the area of a face of this coin, as you are asked to do in Exercise 38.

EXERCISES

1. Find the area of a triangle that has sides of length 3 and 4, with an angle of 37° between those sides.

2. Find the area of a triangle that has sides of length 4 and 5, with an angle of 41° between those sides.

3. Find the area of a triangle that has sides of length 2 and 7, with an angle of 3 radians between those sides.

4. Find the area of a triangle that has sides of length 5 and 6, with an angle of 2 radians between those sides.

For Exercises 5–12 use the following figure (which is not drawn to scale):

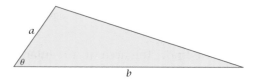

5. Find the value of b if $a = 3$, $\theta = 30°$, and the area of the triangle equals 5.

6. Find the value of a if $b = 5$, $\theta = 45°$, and the area of the triangle equals 8.

7. Find the value of a if $b = 7$, $\theta = \frac{\pi}{4}$, and the area of the triangle equals 10.

8. Find the value of b if $a = 9$, $\theta = \frac{\pi}{3}$, and the area of the triangle equals 4.

9. Find the value of θ (in radians) if $a = 7$, $b = 6$, the area of the triangle equals 15, and $\theta < \frac{\pi}{2}$.

10. 📱 Find the value of θ (in radians) if $a = 5$, $b = 4$, the area of the triangle equals 3, and $\theta < \frac{\pi}{2}$.

11. 📱 Find the value of θ (in degrees) if $a = 6$, $b = 3$, the area of the triangle equals 5, and $\theta > 90°$.

12. 📱 Find the value of θ (in degrees) if $a = 8$, $b = 5$, and the area of the triangle equals 12, and $\theta > 90°$.

13. 📱 Find the area of a parallelogram that has pairs of sides of lengths 6 and 9, with an angle of $81°$ between two of those sides.

14. 📱 Find the area of a parallelogram that has pairs of sides of lengths 5 and 11, with an angle of $28°$ between two of those sides.

15. Find the area of a parallelogram that has pairs of sides of lengths 4 and 10, with an angle of $\frac{\pi}{6}$ radians between two of those sides.

16. Find the area of a parallelogram that has pairs of sides of lengths 3 and 12, with an angle of $\frac{\pi}{3}$ radians between two of those sides.

For Exercises 17–24, use the following figure (which is not drawn to scale except that u is indeed meant to be an acute angle and v is indeed meant to be an obtuse angle):

17. Find the value of b if $a = 4$, $v = 135°$, and the area of the parallelogram equals 7.

18. Find the value of a if $b = 6$, $v = 120°$, and the area of the parallelogram equals 11.

19. Find the value of a if $b = 10$, $u = \frac{\pi}{3}$, and the area of the parallelogram equals 7.

20. Find the value of b if $a = 5$, $u = \frac{\pi}{4}$, and the area of the parallelogram equals 9.

21. 📱 Find the value of u (in radians) if $a = 3$, $b = 4$, and the area of the parallelogram equals 10.

22. 📱 Find the value of u (in radians) if $a = 4$, $b = 6$, and the area of the parallelogram equals 19.

23. 📱 Find the value of v (in degrees) if $a = 6$, $b = 7$, and the area of the parallelogram equals 31.

24. 📱 Find the value of v (in degrees) if $a = 8$, $b = 5$, and the area of the parallelogram equals 12.

25. What is the largest possible area for a triangle that has one side of length 4 and one side of length 7?

26. What is the largest possible area for a parallelogram that has pairs of sides with lengths 5 and 9?

27. Sketch the regular hexagon whose vertices are six equally spaced points on the unit circle, with one of the vertices at the point $(1, 0)$.

28. Sketch the regular dodecagon whose vertices are twelve equally spaced points on the unit circle, with one of the vertices at the point $(1, 0)$. [A **dodecagon** *is a twelve-sided polygon.*]

29. Find the coordinates of all six vertices of the regular hexagon whose vertices are six equally spaced points on the unit circle, with $(1, 0)$ as one of the vertices. List the vertices in counterclockwise order starting at $(1, 0)$.

30. Find the coordinates of all twelve vertices of the dodecagondodecagon whose vertices are twelve equally spaced points on the unit circle, with $(1, 0)$ as one of the vertices. List the vertices in counterclockwise order starting at $(1, 0)$.

31. Find the area of a regular hexagon whose vertices are six equally spaced points on the unit circle.

32. Find the area of a regular dodecagon whose vertices are twelve equally spaced points on the unit circle.

33. Find the perimeter of a regular hexagon whose vertices are six equally spaced points on the unit circle.

34. Find the perimeter of a regular dodecagon-dodecagon whose vertices are twelve equally spaced points on the unit circle.

35. Find the area of a regular hexagon with sides of length s.

36. Find the area of a regular dodecagon with sides of length s.

37. 🖊 Find the area of a regular 13-sided polygon whose vertices are 13 equally spaced points on a circle of radius 4.

38. 🖊 The face of a Canadian one-dollar coin is a regular 11-sided polygon (see the picture just before the start of these exercises). The distance from the center of this polygon to one of the vertices is 1.325 centimeters. Find the area of the face of this coin.

PROBLEMS

Some problems require considerably more thought than the exercises.
Unlike exercises, problems usually have more than one correct answer.

39. What is the area of a triangle whose sides all have length r?

40. Explain why there does not exist a triangle with area 15 having one side of length 4 and one side of length 7.

41. Show that if a triangle has area R, sides of length A, B, and C, and angles a, b, and c, then

$$R^3 = \tfrac{1}{8} A^2 B^2 C^2 (\sin a)(\sin b)(\sin c).$$

[*Hint:* Write three formulas for the area R, and then multiply these formulas together.]

42. Find numbers b and c such that an isosceles triangle with sides of length b, b, and c has perimeter and area that are both integers.

43. Explain why the solution to Exercise 32 is somewhat close to π.

44. 🖊 Use a calculator to evaluate numerically the exact solution you obtained to Exercise 34. Then explain why this number is somewhat close to 2π.

45. Explain why a regular polygon with n sides whose vertices are n equally spaced points on the unit circle has area $\frac{n}{2} \sin \frac{2\pi}{n}$.

46. Explain why the result stated in the previous problem implies that

$$\sin \tfrac{2\pi}{n} \approx \tfrac{2\pi}{n}$$

for large positive integers n.

47. 🖊 Choose three large values of n, and use a calculator to verify that $\sin \frac{2\pi}{n} \approx \frac{2\pi}{n}$ for each of those three large values of n.

48. Show that each edge of a regular polygon with n sides whose vertices are n equally spaced points on the unit circle has length

$$\sqrt{2 - 2\cos \tfrac{2\pi}{n}}.$$

49. Explain why a regular polygon with n sides, each with length s, has area

$$\frac{n \sin \frac{2\pi}{n}}{4(1 - \cos \frac{2\pi}{n})} s^2.$$

50. Verify that for $n = 4$, the formula given by the previous problem reduces to the usual formula for the area of a square.

51. Explain why a regular polygon with n sides whose vertices are n equally spaced points on the unit circle has perimeter

$$n\sqrt{2 - 2\cos \tfrac{2\pi}{n}}.$$

52. Explain why the result stated in the previous problem implies that

$$n\sqrt{2 - 2\cos \tfrac{2\pi}{n}} \approx 2\pi$$

for large positive integers n.

53. 🖊 Choose three large values of n, and use a calculator to verify that $n\sqrt{2 - 2\cos \frac{2\pi}{n}} \approx 2\pi$ for each of those three large values of n.

54. Show that

$$\cos \tfrac{2\pi}{n} \approx 1 - \tfrac{2\pi^2}{n^2}$$

if n is a large positive integer.

WORKED-OUT SOLUTIONS *to Odd-numbered Exercises*

Do not read these worked-out solutions before first struggling to do the exercises yourself. Otherwise you risk the danger of mimicking the techniques shown here without understanding the ideas.

Best way to learn: Carefully read the section of the textbook, then do all the odd-numbered exercises (even if they have not been assigned) and check your answers here. If you get stuck on an exercise, reread the section of the textbook—then try the exercise again. If you are still stuck, then look at the worked-out solution here.

1. Find the area of a triangle that has sides of length 3 and 4, with an angle of 37° between those sides.

   SOLUTION The area of this triangle equals $\frac{3 \cdot 4 \cdot \sin 37°}{2}$, which equals $6 \sin 37°$. A calculator shows that this is approximately 3.61 (make sure that your calculator is computing in degrees, or first convert to radians, when doing this calculation).

3. Find the area of a triangle that has sides of length 2 and 7, with an angle of 3 radians between those sides.

   SOLUTION The area of this triangle equals $\frac{2 \cdot 7 \cdot \sin 3}{2}$, which equals $7 \sin 3$. A calculator shows that this is approximately 0.988 (make sure that your calculator is computing in radians, or first convert to degrees, when doing this calculation).

For Exercises 5–12 use the following figure (which is not drawn to scale):

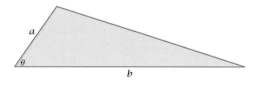

5. Find the value of b if $a = 3$, $\theta = 30°$, and the area of the triangle equals 5.

   SOLUTION Because the area of the triangle equals 5, we have
   $$5 = \frac{ab \sin \theta}{2} = \frac{3b \sin 30°}{2} = \frac{3b}{4}.$$
   Solving the equation above for b, we get $b = \frac{20}{3}$.

7. Find the value of a if $b = 7$, $\theta = \frac{\pi}{4}$, and the area of the triangle equals 10.

   SOLUTION Because the area of the triangle equals 10, we have
   $$10 = \frac{ab \sin \theta}{2} = \frac{7a \sin \frac{\pi}{4}}{2} = \frac{7a}{2\sqrt{2}}.$$
   Solving the equation above for a, we get $a = \frac{20\sqrt{2}}{7}$.

9. Find the value of θ (in radians) if $a = 7$, $b = 6$, the area of the triangle equals 15, and $\theta < \frac{\pi}{2}$.

   SOLUTION Because the area of the triangle equals 15, we have
   $$15 = \frac{ab \sin \theta}{2} = \frac{7 \cdot 6 \cdot \sin \theta}{2} = 21 \sin \theta.$$
   Solving the equation above for $\sin \theta$, we get $\sin \theta = \frac{5}{7}$. Thus $\theta = \sin^{-1} \frac{5}{7} \approx 0.7956$.

11. Find the value of θ (in degrees) if $a = 6$, $b = 3$, the area of the triangle equals 5, and $\theta > 90°$.

    SOLUTION Because the area of the triangle equals 5, we have
    $$5 = \frac{ab \sin \theta}{2} = \frac{6 \cdot 3 \cdot \sin \theta}{2} = 9 \sin \theta.$$
    Solving the equation above for $\sin \theta$, we get $\sin \theta = \frac{5}{9}$. Thus θ equals $\pi - \sin^{-1} \frac{5}{9}$ radians. Converting this to degrees, we have
    $$\theta = 180° - (\sin^{-1} \tfrac{5}{9})\frac{180°}{\pi} \approx 146.25°.$$

13. Find the area of a parallelogram that has pairs of sides of lengths 6 and 9, with an angle of 81° between two of those sides.

    SOLUTION The area of this parallelogram equals $6 \cdot 9 \cdot \sin 81°$, which equals $54 \sin 81°$.

A calculator shows that this is approximately 53.34.

15. Find the area of a parallelogram that has pairs of sides of lengths 4 and 10, with an angle of $\frac{\pi}{6}$ radians between two of those sides.

SOLUTION The area of this parallelogram equals $4 \cdot 10 \cdot \sin \frac{\pi}{6}$, which equals 20.

For Exercises 17–24, use the following figure (which is not drawn to scale except that u is indeed meant to be an acute angle and v is indeed meant to be an obtuse angle):

17. Find the value of b if $a = 4$, $v = 135°$, and the area of the parallelogram equals 7.

SOLUTION Because the area of the parallelogram equals 7, we have

$$7 = ab \sin v = 4b \sin 135° = 2\sqrt{2}b.$$

Solving the equation above for b, we get $b = \frac{7}{2\sqrt{2}} = \frac{7\sqrt{2}}{4}$.

19. Find the value of a if $b = 10$, $u = \frac{\pi}{3}$, and the area of the parallelogram equals 7.

SOLUTION Because the area of the parallelogram equals 7, we have

$$7 = ab \sin u = 10a \sin \frac{\pi}{3} = 5a\sqrt{3}.$$

Solving the equation above for a, we get $a = \frac{7}{5\sqrt{3}} = \frac{7\sqrt{3}}{15}$.

21. Find the value of u (in radians) if $a = 3$, $b = 4$, and the area of the parallelogram equals 10.

SOLUTION Because the area of the parallelogram equals 10, we have

$$10 = ab \sin u = 3 \cdot 4 \cdot \sin u = 12 \sin u.$$

Solving the equation above for $\sin u$, we get $\sin u = \frac{5}{6}$. Thus

$$u = \sin^{-1} \frac{5}{6} \approx 0.9851.$$

23. Find the value of v (in degrees) if $a = 6$, $b = 7$, and the area of the parallelogram equals 31.

SOLUTION Because the area of the parallelogram equals 31, we have

$$31 = ab \sin v = 6 \cdot 7 \cdot \sin v = 42 \sin v.$$

Solving the equation above for $\sin v$, we get $\sin v = \frac{31}{42}$. Because v is an obtuse angle, we thus have $v = \pi - \sin^{-1} \frac{31}{42}$ radians. Converting this to degrees, we have $v = 180° - (\sin^{-1} \frac{31}{42}) \frac{180°}{\pi} \approx 132.43°$.

25. What is the largest possible area for a triangle that has one side of length 4 and one side of length 7?

SOLUTION In a triangle that has one side of length 4 and one side of length 7, let θ denote the angle between those two sides. Thus the area of the triangle will equal

$$14 \sin \theta.$$

We need to choose θ to make this area as large as possible. The largest possible value of $\sin \theta$ is 1, which occurs when $\theta = \frac{\pi}{2}$ (or $\theta = 90°$ if we are working in degrees). Thus we choose $\theta = \frac{\pi}{2}$, which gives us a right triangle with sides of length 4 and 7 around the right angle.

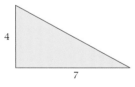

This right triangle has area 14, which is the largest area of any triangle with sides of length 4 and 7.

27. Sketch the regular hexagon whose vertices are six equally spaced points on the unit circle, with one of the vertices at the point $(1, 0)$.

SOLUTION

29. Find the coordinates of all six vertices of the regular hexagon whose vertices are six equally spaced points on the unit circle, with $(1,0)$ as one of the vertices. List the vertices in counterclockwise order starting at $(1,0)$.

SOLUTION   The coordinates of the six vertices, listed in counterclockwise order starting at $(1,0)$, are $(\cos \frac{2\pi m}{6}, \sin \frac{2\pi m}{6})$, with m going from 0 to 5. Evaluating the trigonometric functions, we get the following list of coordinates of vertices: $(1,0)$, $(\frac{1}{2}, \frac{\sqrt{3}}{2})$, $(-\frac{1}{2}, \frac{\sqrt{3}}{2})$, $(-1,0)$, $(-\frac{1}{2}, -\frac{\sqrt{3}}{2})$, $(\frac{1}{2}, -\frac{\sqrt{3}}{2})$.

31. Find the area of a regular hexagon whose vertices are six equally spaced points on the unit circle.

SOLUTION   Decompose the hexagon into triangles by drawing line segments from the center of the circle (the origin) to the vertices. Each triangle has two sides that are radii of the unit circle; thus those two sides of the triangle each have length 1. The angle between those two radii is $\frac{2\pi}{6}$ radians (because one rotation around the entire circle is an angle of 2π radians, and each of the six triangles has an angle that takes up one-sixth of the total). Now $\frac{2\pi}{6}$ radians equals $\frac{\pi}{3}$ radians (or $60°$). Thus each of the six triangles has area

$$\tfrac{1}{2} \cdot 1 \cdot 1 \cdot \sin \tfrac{\pi}{3},$$

which equals $\frac{\sqrt{3}}{4}$. Thus the sum of the areas of the six triangles equals $6 \cdot \frac{\sqrt{3}}{4}$, which equals $\frac{3\sqrt{3}}{2}$. In other words, the hexagon has area $\frac{3\sqrt{3}}{2}$.

33. Find the perimeter of a regular hexagon whose vertices are six equally spaced points on the unit circle.

SOLUTION   If we assume that one of the vertices of the hexagon is the point $(1,0)$, then the next vertex in the counterclockwise direction is the point $(\frac{1}{2}, \frac{\sqrt{3}}{2})$. Thus the length of each side of the hexagon equals the distance between $(1,0)$ and $(\frac{1}{2}, \frac{\sqrt{3}}{2})$, which equals

$$\sqrt{(1 - \tfrac{1}{2})^2 + (\tfrac{\sqrt{3}}{2})^2},$$

which equals 1. Thus the perimeter of the hexagon equals $6 \cdot 1$, which equals 6.

35. Find the area of a regular hexagon with sides of length s.

SOLUTION   There is a constant c such that a regular hexagon with sides of length s has area cs^2. From Exercises 31 and 33, we know that the area equals $\frac{3\sqrt{3}}{2}$ if $s = 1$. Thus

$$\tfrac{3\sqrt{3}}{2} = c \cdot 1^2 = c.$$

Thus a regular hexagon with sides of length s has area $\frac{3\sqrt{3}}{2} s^2$.

37. Find the area of a regular 13-sided polygon whose vertices are 13 equally spaced points on a circle of radius 4.

SOLUTION   Decompose the 13-sided polygon into triangles by drawing line segments from the center of the circle to the vertices. Each triangle has two sides that are radii of the circle with radius 4; thus those two sides of the triangle each have length 4. The angle between those two radii is $\frac{2\pi}{13}$ radians (because one rotation around the entire circle is an angle of 2π radians, and each of the 13 triangles has an angle that takes up one-thirteenth of the total). Thus each of the 13 triangles has area

$$\tfrac{1}{2} \cdot 4 \cdot 4 \cdot \sin \tfrac{2\pi}{13},$$

which equals $8 \sin \frac{2\pi}{13}$. The area of the 13-sided polygon is the sum of the areas of the 13 triangles, which equals $13 \cdot 8 \sin \frac{2\pi}{13}$, which is approximately 48.3.

(c) Use the law of sines in the form

$$\frac{\sin A}{a} = \frac{\sin C}{c},$$

which in this case becomes the equation

$$\frac{\sin \frac{\pi}{7}}{6} = \frac{\sin \frac{2\pi}{7}}{c}.$$

Solve the equation above for c, getting

$$c = \frac{6\sin \frac{2\pi}{7}}{\sin \frac{\pi}{7}} \approx 10.81.$$

5. $\boxed{}$ Suppose $a = 3$, $b = 5$, and $c = 6$. Evaluate:

   (a) A (b) B (c) C

SOLUTION The law of cosines allows us to solve for the angles of the triangle when we know the lengths of all the sides. Note the check that is performed below after part (c).

(a) To find A, use the law of cosines in the form

$$a^2 = b^2 + c^2 - 2bc\cos A,$$

which in this case becomes the equation

$$3^2 = 5^2 + 6^2 - 2 \cdot 5 \cdot 6 \cdot \cos A,$$

which can be rewritten as

$$9 = 61 - 60\cos A.$$

Solve the equation above for $\cos A$, getting

$$\cos A = \tfrac{13}{15}.$$

Thus $A = \cos^{-1}\tfrac{13}{15}$. Use a calculator to evaluate $\cos^{-1}\tfrac{13}{15}$ in radians, and then multiply that result by $\frac{180°}{\pi}$ to convert to degrees, getting

$$A = \cos^{-1}\tfrac{13}{15} \approx 0.522 \text{ radians} \approx 29.9°.$$

(b) To find B, use the law of cosines in the form

$$b^2 = a^2 + c^2 - 2ac\cos B,$$

which in this case becomes the equation

$$25 = 45 - 36\cos B.$$

Solve the equation above for $\cos B$, getting

$$\cos B = \tfrac{5}{9}.$$

Thus $B = \cos^{-1}\tfrac{5}{9}$. Use a calculator to evaluate $\cos^{-1}\tfrac{5}{9}$ in radians, and then multiply that result by $\frac{180°}{\pi}$ to convert to degrees, getting

$$B = \cos^{-1}\tfrac{5}{9} \approx 0.982 \text{ radians} \approx 56.3°.$$

(c) To find C, use the law of cosines in the form

$$c^2 = a^2 + b^2 - 2ab\cos C,$$

which in this case becomes the equation

$$36 = 34 - 30\cos C.$$

Solve the equation above for $\cos C$, getting

$$\cos C = -\tfrac{1}{15}.$$

Thus $C = \cos^{-1}(-\tfrac{1}{15})$. Use a calculator to evaluate $\cos^{-1}(-\tfrac{1}{15})$ in radians, and then multiply that result by $\frac{180°}{\pi}$ to convert to degrees, getting

$$C = \cos^{-1}(-\tfrac{1}{15}) \approx 1.638 \text{ radians} \approx 93.8°.$$

CHECK The angles in a triangle add up to $180°$. Thus we can check for mistakes by seeing if our values of A, B, and C add up to $180°$:

$$A + B + C \approx 29.9° + 56.3° + 93.8° = 180.0°.$$

Because the sum above equals $180.0°$, this check uncovers no problems. If the sum had differed from $180.0°$ by more than $0.1°$ (a small difference might arise due to using approximate values rather than exact values), then we would know that an error had been made.

7. $\boxed{}$ Suppose $a = 5$, $b = 6$, and $c = 9$. Evaluate:

   (a) A (b) B (c) C

SOLUTION The law of cosines allows us to solve for the angles of the triangle when we know the lengths of all the sides. Note the check that is performed below after part (c).

(a) To find A, use the law of cosines in the form

$$a^2 = b^2 + c^2 - 2bc\cos A,$$

which in this case becomes the equation

$$5^2 = 6^2 + 9^2 - 2 \cdot 6 \cdot 9 \cdot \cos A,$$

which can be rewritten as

$$25 = 117 - 108\cos A.$$

Solve the equation above for $\cos A$, getting

$$\cos A = \tfrac{23}{27}.$$

Thus $A = \cos^{-1}\tfrac{23}{27}$. Use a calculator to evaluate $\cos^{-1}\tfrac{23}{27}$ in radians, and then multiply that result by $\frac{180°}{\pi}$ to convert to degrees, getting

$$A = \cos^{-1}\tfrac{23}{27} \approx 0.551 \text{ radians} \approx 31.6°.$$

(b) To find B, use the law of cosines in the form

$$b^2 = a^2 + c^2 - 2ac \cos B,$$

which in this case becomes the equation

$$36 = 106 - 90 \cos B.$$

Solve the equation above for $\cos B$, getting

$$\cos B = \tfrac{7}{9}.$$

Thus $B = \cos^{-1} \tfrac{7}{9}$. Use a calculator to evaluate $\cos^{-1} \tfrac{7}{9}$ in radians, and then multiply that result by $\frac{180°}{\pi}$ to convert to degrees, getting

$$B = \cos^{-1} \tfrac{7}{9} \approx 0.680 \text{ radians} \approx 38.9°.$$

(c) To find C, use the law of cosines in the form

$$c^2 = a^2 + b^2 - 2ab \cos C,$$

which in this case becomes the equation

$$81 = 61 - 60 \cos C.$$

Solve the equation above for $\cos C$, getting

$$\cos C = -\tfrac{1}{3}.$$

Thus $C = \cos^{-1}(-\tfrac{1}{3})$. Use a calculator to evaluate $\cos^{-1}(-\tfrac{1}{3})$ in radians, and then multiply that result by $\frac{180°}{\pi}$ to convert to degrees, getting

$$C = \cos^{-1}(-\tfrac{1}{3}) \approx 1.911 \text{ radians} \approx 109.5°.$$

CHECK   The angles in a triangle add up to $180°$. Thus we can check for mistakes by seeing if our values of A, B, and C add up to $180°$:

$$A + B + C \approx 31.6° + 38.9° + 109.5° = 180.0°.$$

Because the sum above equals $180.0°$, this check uncovers no problems. If the sum had differed from $180.0°$ by more than $0.1°$ (a small difference might arise due to using approximate values rather than exact values), then we would know that an error had been made.

9. Suppose $a = 2$, $b = 3$, and $C = 37°$. Evaluate:

(a) c (b) A (c) B

SOLUTION   Note the check that is performed below after part (c).

(a) To find c, use the law of cosines in the form

$$c^2 = a^2 + b^2 - 2ab \cos C,$$

which in this case becomes the equation

$$c^2 = 2^2 + 3^2 - 2 \cdot 2 \cdot 3 \cdot \cos 37°,$$

which can be rewritten as

$$c^2 = 13 - 12 \cos 37°.$$

Thus

$$c = \sqrt{13 - 12 \cos 37°} \approx 1.848.$$

(b) To find A, use the law of cosines in the form

$$a^2 = b^2 + c^2 - 2bc \cos A,$$

which in this case becomes the approximate equation

$$4 \approx 12.415 - 11.088 \cos A,$$

where we have an approximation rather than an exact equality because we have used an approximate value for c. Solve the equation above for $\cos A$, getting

$$\cos A \approx 0.7589.$$

Thus $A \approx \cos^{-1} 0.7589$. Use a calculator to evaluate $\cos^{-1} 0.7589$ in radians, and then multiply that result by $\frac{180°}{\pi}$ to convert to degrees, getting

$$A \approx \cos^{-1} 0.7589 \approx 0.7092 \text{ radians} \approx 40.6°.$$

(c) The angles in a triangle add up to $180°$. Thus $A + B + C = 180°$. Solving for B, we have

$$B = 180° - A - C \approx 180° - 40.6° - 37° = 102.4°.$$

Multiplying by $\frac{\pi}{180°}$ to convert to radians gives

$$B \approx 102.4° \approx 1.787 \text{ radians}.$$

CHECK   We will check our results by computing B by a different method. Specifically, we will use the law of cosines rather than the simpler method used above in part (c).

We use the law of cosines in the form

$$b^2 = a^2 + c^2 - 2ac \cos B,$$

which in this case becomes the approximate equation

$$9 \approx 7.4151 - 7.392 \cos B,$$

where we have an approximation rather than an exact equality because we have used the approximate value 1.848 for c. Solve the equation above for $\cos B$, getting

$$\cos B \approx -0.2144.$$

Thus $B \approx \cos^{-1}(-0.2144)$. Use a calculator to evaluate $\cos^{-1}(-0.2144)$ in radians, and then multiply that result by $\frac{180°}{\pi}$ to convert to degrees, getting

$$B \approx \cos^{-1}(-0.2144) \approx 1.787 \text{ radians} \approx 102.4°.$$

In part (c) above, we also obtained a value of $102.4°$ for B. Thus this check uncovers no problems. If the two methods for computing B had produced results differing by more than $0.1°$ (a small difference might arise due to using approximate values rather than exact values), then we would know that an error had been made.

11. ☏ Suppose $a = 3$, $b = 4$, and $C = 1$ radian. Evaluate:

    (a) c (b) A (c) B

SOLUTION   Note the check that is performed below after part (c).

(a)   To find c, use the law of cosines in the form

$$c^2 = a^2 + b^2 - 2ab \cos C,$$

which in this case becomes the equation

$$c^2 = 3^2 + 4^2 - 2 \cdot 3 \cdot 4 \cdot \cos 1,$$

which can be rewritten as

$$c^2 = 25 - 24 \cos 1.$$

Thus
$$c = \sqrt{25 - 24 \cos 1} \approx 3.469.$$

(b)   To find A, use the law of cosines in the form

$$a^2 = b^2 + c^2 - 2bc \cos A,$$

which in this case becomes the approximate equation

$$9 \approx 28.034 - 27.752 \cos A,$$

where we have an approximation rather than an exact equality because we have used an approximate value for c. Solve the equation above for $\cos A$, getting

$$\cos A \approx 0.6859.$$

Thus $A \approx \cos^{-1} 0.6859$. Use a calculator to evaluate $\cos^{-1} 0.6859$ in radians, and then multiply that result by $\frac{180°}{\pi}$ to convert to degrees, getting

$$A \approx \cos^{-1} 0.6859 \approx 0.8150 \text{ radians} \approx 46.7°.$$

(c)   The angles in a triangle add up to π radians. Thus $A + B + C = \pi$. Solving for B, we have

$$B = \pi - A - C \approx \pi - 0.8150 - 1 \approx 1.3266.$$

Multiplying by $\frac{180°}{\pi}$ to convert to radians gives

$$B \approx 1.3266 \text{ radians} \approx 76.0°.$$

CHECK   We will check our results by computing B by a different method. Specifically, we will use the law of cosines rather than the simpler method used above in part (c).

We use the law of cosines in the form

$$b^2 = a^2 + c^2 - 2ac \cos B,$$

which in this case becomes the approximate equation

$$16 \approx 21.034 - 20.814 \cos B,$$

where we have an approximation rather than an exact equality because we have used the approximate value 3.469 for c. Solve the equation above for $\cos B$, getting

$$\cos B \approx 0.2419.$$

Thus $B \approx \cos^{-1} 0.2419$. Use a calculator to evaluate $\cos^{-1} 0.2419$ in radians, getting

$$B \approx \cos^{-1} 0.2419 \approx 1.3265 \text{ radians}.$$

In part (c) above, we obtained a value of 1.3266 radians for B. Thus the two methods for computing B differed by only 0.0001 radians. This tiny difference is almost certainly due to using approximate values rather than exact values. Thus this check uncovers no problems.

13. ☏ Suppose $a = 4$, $b = 3$, and $B = 30°$. Evaluate:

(a) A (assume that $A < 90°$)

(b) C

(c) c

SOLUTION

(a) Use the law of sines in the form

$$\frac{\sin A}{a} = \frac{\sin B}{b},$$

which in this case becomes the equation

$$\frac{\sin A}{4} = \frac{\frac{1}{2}}{3}.$$

Solve the equation above for $\sin A$, getting

$$\sin A = \tfrac{2}{3}.$$

The assumption that $A < 90°$ now implies that

$$A = \sin^{-1}\tfrac{2}{3} \approx 0.7297 \text{ radians} \approx 41.8°.$$

(b) The angles in a triangle add up to $180°$. Thus $A + B + C = 180°$. Solving for C, we have

$$C = 180° - A - B \approx 180° - 41.8° - 30° = 108.2°.$$

Multiplying by $\frac{\pi}{180°}$ to convert to radians gives

$$C \approx 108.2° \approx 1.888 \text{ radians}.$$

(c) Use the law of sines in the form

$$\frac{\sin A}{a} = \frac{\sin C}{c},$$

which in this case becomes the equation

$$\frac{\frac{2}{3}}{4} \approx \frac{\sin 108.2°}{c},$$

where we have an approximation rather than an exact equality because we have used the approximate value $108.2°$ for C (our solution in part (a) showed that $\sin A$ has the exact value $\frac{2}{3}$; thus the left side above is not an approximation). Solving the equation above for c, we get

$$c \approx 5.70.$$

(a) A (assume that $A > 90°$)

(b) C

(c) c

SOLUTION

(a) Use the law of sines in the form

$$\frac{\sin A}{a} = \frac{\sin B}{b},$$

which in this case becomes the equation

$$\frac{\sin A}{4} = \frac{\frac{1}{2}}{3}.$$

Solve the equation above for $\sin A$, getting

$$\sin A = \tfrac{2}{3}.$$

The assumption that $A > 90°$ now implies that

$$A = \pi - \sin^{-1}\tfrac{2}{3} \approx 2.4119 \text{ radians} \approx 138.2°.$$

(b) The angles in a triangle add up to $180°$. Thus $A + B + C = 180°$. Solving for C, we have

$$C = 180° - A - B \approx 180° - 138.2° - 30° = 11.8°.$$

Multiplying by $\frac{\pi}{180°}$ to convert to radians gives

$$C \approx 11.8° \approx 0.206 \text{ radians}.$$

(c) Use the law of sines in the form

$$\frac{\sin A}{a} = \frac{\sin C}{c},$$

which in this case becomes the equation

$$\frac{\frac{2}{3}}{4} \approx \frac{\sin 11.8°}{c},$$

where we have an approximation rather than an exact equality because we have used the approximate value $11.8°$ for C (our solution in part (a) showed that $\sin A$ has the exact value $\frac{2}{3}$; thus the left side above is not an approximation). Solving the equation above for c, we get

$$c \approx 1.23.$$

15. ✐ Suppose $a = 4$, $b = 3$, and $B = 30°$. Evaluate:

6.3 | *Double-Angle and Half-Angle Formulas*

SECTION OBJECTIVES

By the end of this section you should

- ■ be able to use double-angle formulas for cosine, sine, and tangent;

- ■ be able to use half-angle formulas for cosine, sine, and tangent.

How are the values of $\cos(2\theta)$ and $\sin(2\theta)$ and $\tan(2\theta)$ related to the values of $\cos\theta$ and $\sin\theta$ and $\tan\theta$? What about the values of $\cos\frac{\theta}{2}$ and $\sin\frac{\theta}{2}$ and $\tan\frac{\theta}{2}$? In this section we will see how to answer these questions. We will begin with the double-angle formulas involving 2θ and then use those formulas to find the half-angle formulas involving $\frac{\theta}{2}$.

The Cosine of 2θ

Suppose $0 < \theta < \frac{\pi}{2}$, and consider a right triangle with a hypotenuse of length 1 and an angle of θ radians. The other angle of this right triangle will be $\frac{\pi}{2} - \theta$ radians. The side opposite the angle θ has length $\sin\theta$, as shown below (the unlabeled side of the triangle has length $\cos\theta$, but that side is not of interest right now):

Reflect the triangle above through the horizontal side, producing another right triangle with a hypotenuse of length 1 and angles of θ and $\frac{\pi}{2} - \theta$ radians, as shown below:

The triangle formed by the outer edges is an isosceles triangle with two sides of length 1 and an angle of 2θ between those two sides.

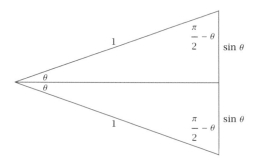

Now consider the isosceles triangle above formed by the union of the two right triangles. Two sides of this isosceles triangle have length 1. As can be seen above, the angle between these two sides is 2θ. As can also be seen above, the side opposite this angle has length $2\sin\theta$. Thus applying the law of cosines to this isosceles triangle gives

$$(2\sin\theta)^2 = 1^2 + 1^2 - 2 \cdot 1 \cdot 1 \cdot \cos(2\theta),$$

which can be rewritten as

$$4\sin^2\theta = 2 - 2\cos(2\theta).$$

Solving this equation for $\cos(2\theta)$ gives the equation

$$\cos(2\theta) = 1 - 2\sin^2\theta.$$

We just found a formula for $\cos(2\theta)$ in terms of $\sin\theta$. Sometimes we need a formula expressing $\cos(2\theta)$ in terms of $\cos\theta$. To obtain such a formula, replace $\sin^2\theta$ by $1 - \cos^2\theta$ in the equation above, getting

$$\cos(2\theta) = 2\cos^2\theta - 1.$$

Yet another formula for $\cos(2\theta)$ arises if we replace 1 in the formula above by $\cos^2\theta + \sin^2\theta$, getting

$$\cos(2\theta) = \cos^2\theta - \sin^2\theta.$$

Thus we have found three formulas for $\cos(2\theta)$, which are collected below:

> ### Double-angle formulas for cosine
> $$\cos(2\theta) = 1 - 2\sin^2\theta = 2\cos^2\theta - 1 = \cos^2\theta - \sin^2\theta$$

Never, ever, make the mistake of thinking that $\cos(2\theta)$ equals $2\cos\theta$.

In practice, use whichever of the three formulas is most convenient, as shown in the next example.

Suppose θ is an angle such that $\cos\theta = \frac{3}{4}$. Evaluate $\cos(2\theta)$.

EXAMPLE 1

SOLUTION   Because we know the value of $\cos\theta$, we use the second of the formulas given above for $\cos(2\theta)$:

$$\cos(2\theta) = 2\cos^2\theta - 1 = 2\left(\tfrac{3}{4}\right)^2 - 1 = 2 \cdot \tfrac{9}{16} - 1 = \tfrac{9}{8} - 1 = \tfrac{1}{8}.$$

The Sine of 2θ

To find a formula for $\sin(2\theta)$, we will apply the law of sines to the isosceles triangle in the last figure above. As we have already noted, this triangle has an angle of 2θ, with a side of length $2\sin\theta$ opposite this angle. The uppermost angle in the isosceles triangle is $\frac{\pi}{2} - \theta$ radians, with a side of length 1 opposite this angle. The law of sines now tells us that

$$\frac{\sin(2\theta)}{2\sin\theta} = \frac{\sin(\frac{\pi}{2} - \theta)}{1}.$$

Recall that $\sin(\frac{\pi}{2} - \theta) = \cos\theta$ (see Section 5.6). Thus the equation above can be rewritten as

$$\frac{\sin(2\theta)}{2\sin\theta} = \cos\theta.$$

Solving this equation for $\sin(2\theta)$ gives the following formula:

Expressions such as $\cos\theta\sin\theta$ should be interpreted to mean $(\cos\theta)(\sin\theta)$, not $\cos(\theta\sin\theta)$.

Double-angle formula for sine

$$\sin(2\theta) = 2\cos\theta\sin\theta$$

EXAMPLE 2

Using the information that $\cos 30° = \frac{\sqrt{3}}{2}$ and $\sin 30° = \frac{1}{2}$, use the double-angle formula for sine to evaluate $\sin 60°$.

SOLUTION   Using the double-angle formula for $\sin(2\theta)$ with $\theta = 30°$, we have

$$\sin 60° = 2\cos 30° \sin 30° = 2 \cdot \frac{\sqrt{3}}{2} \cdot \frac{1}{2} = \frac{\sqrt{3}}{2}.$$

REMARK   This is a truly terrible method for evaluating $\sin 60°$. Once we know that $\cos 30° = \frac{\sqrt{3}}{2}$, the information that $\sin 60° = \frac{\sqrt{3}}{2}$ follows immediately from the identity $\sin(90° - \theta) = \cos\theta$. The double-angle formula is used here to evaluate $\sin 60°$ only to help you get comfortable with the meaning of the double-angle formula.

The Tangent of 2θ

Now that we have found formulas for $\cos(2\theta)$ and $\sin(2\theta)$, we can find a formula for $\tan(2\theta)$ in the usual fashion of writing the tangent as a ratio of a sine and cosine. In doing so, we will find it more convenient to use the last of the three formulas we found for $\cos(2\theta)$. Specifically, we have

$$\tan(2\theta) = \frac{\sin(2\theta)}{\cos(2\theta)}$$

$$= \frac{2\cos\theta\sin\theta}{\cos^2\theta - \sin^2\theta}.$$

In the last expression, divide numerator and denominator by $\cos^2\theta$, getting

$$\tan(2\theta) = \frac{2\frac{\sin\theta}{\cos\theta}}{1 - \frac{\sin^2\theta}{\cos^2\theta}}.$$

Now replace $\frac{\sin\theta}{\cos\theta}$ above by $\tan\theta$, getting the following nice formula:

Double-angle formula for tangent

$$\tan(2\theta) = \frac{2\tan\theta}{1 - \tan^2\theta}$$

Suppose θ is an angle such that $\tan\theta = 5$. Evaluate $\tan(2\theta)$.

EXAMPLE 3

SOLUTION Because $\tan\theta = 5$, the formula above tells us that

$$\tan(2\theta) = \frac{2 \cdot 5}{1 - 5^2} = -\frac{10}{24} = -\frac{5}{12}.$$

We derived the double-angle formulas for cosine, sine, and tangent starting with the figure on the first page of this section. That figure assumes that θ is between 0 and $\frac{\pi}{2}$. Actually these double-angle formulas are valid for all values of θ, except that in the formula for $\tan(2\theta)$ we must exclude values of θ for which $\tan\theta$ or $\tan(2\theta)$ is undefined.

The Cosine and Sine of $\frac{\theta}{2}$

Now we are ready to find the half-angle formulas for evaluating $\cos\frac{\theta}{2}$ and $\sin\frac{\theta}{2}$. We start with the double-angle formula

$$\cos(2\theta) = 2\cos^2\theta - 1.$$

This formula allows us to find the value of $\cos(2\theta)$ if we know the value of $\cos\theta$. If instead we start out knowing the value of $\cos(2\theta)$, then the equation above could be solved for $\cos\theta$. The example below illustrates this procedure.

Find an exact expression for $\cos 15°$.

EXAMPLE 4

SOLUTION We know that $\cos 30° = \frac{\sqrt{3}}{2}$. We want to find the cosine of half of $30°$. Thus we set $\theta = 15°$ in the identity above, getting

$$\cos 30° = 2\cos^2 15° - 1.$$

In this equation, replace $\cos 30°$ with its value, getting

$$\frac{\sqrt{3}}{2} = 2\cos^2 15° - 1.$$

Now solve the equation above for $\cos 15°$, getting

$$\cos 15° = \sqrt{\frac{1 + \frac{\sqrt{3}}{2}}{2}} = \sqrt{\frac{(1 + \frac{\sqrt{3}}{2}) \cdot 2}{2 \cdot 2}} = \frac{\sqrt{2 + \sqrt{3}}}{2}.$$

This value for $\cos 15°$ (or $\cos\frac{\pi}{12}$ if we work in radians) was used in exercises in Sections 5.4 and 5.6.

REMARK In the first equality in the last line above, we did not need to worry about choosing a plus or minus sign associated with the square root because we know that $\cos 15°$ is positive.

To find a general formula for $\cos \frac{\theta}{2}$ in terms of $\cos \theta$, we will carry out the procedure followed in the example above. The key idea is that we can substitute any value for θ in the identity

$$\cos(2\theta) = 2\cos^2\theta - 1,$$

provided that we make the same substitution on both sides of the equation. We want to find a formula for $\cos \frac{\theta}{2}$. Thus we replace θ by $\frac{\theta}{2}$ on both sides of the equation above, getting

$$\cos \theta = 2\cos^2\frac{\theta}{2} - 1.$$

Now solve this equation for $\cos \frac{\theta}{2}$, getting the following half-angle formula:

Never, ever, make the mistake of thinking that $\cos \frac{\theta}{2}$ equals $\frac{\cos\theta}{2}$.

Half-angle formula for cosine

$$\cos \frac{\theta}{2} = \pm\sqrt{\frac{1 + \cos \theta}{2}}$$

The choice of the plus or minus sign in the formula above will need to depend on knowledge of the sign of $\cos \frac{\theta}{2}$. For example, if $0 < \theta < \pi$, then $0 < \frac{\theta}{2} < \frac{\pi}{2}$, which implies that $\cos \frac{\theta}{2}$ is positive (thus we would choose the plus sign in the formula above). As another example, if $\pi < \theta < 3\pi$, then $\frac{\pi}{2} < \frac{\theta}{2} < \frac{3\pi}{2}$, which implies that $\cos \frac{\theta}{2}$ is negative (thus we would choose the minus sign in the formula above).

To find a formula for $\sin \frac{\theta}{2}$, we start with the double-angle formula

$$\cos(2\theta) = 1 - 2\sin^2\theta.$$

In the identity above, replace θ by $\frac{\theta}{2}$ on both sides of the equation, getting

$$\cos \theta = 1 - 2\sin^2\frac{\theta}{2}.$$

Now solve this equation for $\sin \frac{\theta}{2}$, getting the following half-angle formula:

Half-angle formula for sine

$$\sin \frac{\theta}{2} = \pm\sqrt{\frac{1 - \cos \theta}{2}}$$

The choice of the plus or minus sign in the formula above will need to depend on knowledge of the sign of $\sin \frac{\theta}{2}$. The examples below illustrate this procedure.

Find an exact expression for $\sin \frac{\pi}{8}$.

EXAMPLE 5

SOLUTION We already know how to evaluate $\sin \frac{\pi}{4}$. Thus we take $\theta = \frac{\pi}{4}$ in the half-angle formula for sine, getting

This value for $\sin \frac{\pi}{8}$ (or $\sin 22.5°$ if we work in degrees) was used in exercises in Sections 5.4 and 5.6.

$$\sin \frac{\pi}{8} = \sqrt{\frac{1 - \cos \frac{\pi}{4}}{2}} = \sqrt{\frac{1 - \frac{\sqrt{2}}{2}}{2}} = \sqrt{\frac{2 - \sqrt{2}}{4}} = \frac{\sqrt{2 - \sqrt{2}}}{2}.$$

In the first equality above, we chose the plus sign in the half-angle formula because we know that $\sin \frac{\pi}{8}$ is positive.

The next example shows that sometimes the minus sign must be chosen when using a half-angle formula.

Suppose $-\frac{\pi}{2} < \theta < 0$ and $\cos \theta = \frac{2}{3}$. Evaluate $\sin \frac{\theta}{2}$.

EXAMPLE 6

SOLUTION Because $-\frac{\pi}{4} < \frac{\theta}{2} < 0$, we see that $\sin \frac{\theta}{2} < 0$. Thus we need to choose the negative sign in the identity above. We have

$$\sin \frac{\theta}{2} = -\sqrt{\frac{1 - \cos \theta}{2}} = -\sqrt{\frac{1 - \frac{2}{3}}{2}} = -\sqrt{\frac{1}{6}} = -\frac{\sqrt{6}}{6}.$$

The Tangent of $\frac{\theta}{2}$

We start with the equation

$$\tan \theta = \frac{\sin \theta}{\cos \theta}.$$

We could find a formula for $\tan \frac{\theta}{2}$ by writing $\tan \frac{\theta}{2}$ as $\sin \frac{\theta}{2}$ divided by $\cos \frac{\theta}{2}$ and using the half-angle formulas for cosine and sine. However, the process used here leads to a simpler formula.

Because we seek a formula involving $\sin(2\theta)$, we multiply numerator and denominator above by $2\cos \theta$, getting

$$\tan \theta = \frac{\sin \theta}{\cos \theta} = \frac{2 \cos \theta \sin \theta}{2 \cos^2 \theta}.$$

The numerator of the last term above equals $\sin(2\theta)$. Furthermore, the identity $\cos(2\theta) = 2 \cos^2 \theta - 1$ shows that the denominator of the last term above equals $1 + \cos(2\theta)$. Making these substitutions in the equation above gives

$$\tan \theta = \frac{\sin(2\theta)}{1 + \cos(2\theta)}.$$

In the equation above, replace θ by $\frac{\theta}{2}$ on both sides of the equation, getting the half-angle formula

$$\tan \frac{\theta}{2} = \frac{\sin \theta}{1 + \cos \theta}.$$

This formula is valid for all values of θ, except that we must exclude odd multiples of π (because we need to exclude cases where $\cos \theta = -1$ to avoid division by 0).

To find another formula for $\tan \frac{\theta}{2}$, note that

$$\frac{\sin \theta}{1 + \cos \theta} = \frac{\sin \theta}{1 + \cos \theta} \cdot \frac{1 - \cos \theta}{1 - \cos \theta}$$

$$= \frac{(\sin \theta)(1 - \cos \theta)}{1 - \cos^2 \theta}$$

$$= \frac{(\sin \theta)(1 - \cos \theta)}{\sin^2 \theta}$$

$$= \frac{1 - \cos \theta}{\sin \theta}.$$

Thus our identity above for $\tan \frac{\theta}{2}$ can be rewritten to give the half-angle formula

$$\tan \frac{\theta}{2} = \frac{1 - \cos \theta}{\sin \theta}.$$

This formula is valid for all values of θ, except that we must exclude multiples of π (because we need to exclude cases where $\sin \theta = 0$ to avoid division by 0).

For convenience, we now collect the half-angle formulas for tangent.

Half-angle formulas for tangent

$$\tan \frac{\theta}{2} = \frac{1 - \cos \theta}{\sin \theta} = \frac{\sin \theta}{1 + \cos \theta}$$

EXERCISES

1. For $\theta = 23°$, evaluate each of the following:
   (a) $\cos(2\theta)$ (b) $2 \cos \theta$

   [*This exercise and the next one emphasize that* $\cos(2\theta)$ *does not equal* $2 \cos \theta$.]

2. For $\theta = 7$ radians, evaluate each of the following:
   (a) $\cos(2\theta)$ (b) $2 \cos \theta$

3. For $\theta = -5$ radians, evaluate each of the following:
   (a) $\sin(2\theta)$ (b) $2 \sin \theta$

   [*This exercise and the next one emphasize that* $\sin(2\theta)$ *does not equal* $2 \sin \theta$.]

4. For $\theta = 100°$, evaluate each of the following:
   (a) $\sin(2\theta)$ (b) $2 \sin \theta$

5. For $\theta = 6$ radians, evaluate each of the following:
   (a) $\cos \frac{\theta}{2}$ (b) $\frac{\cos \theta}{2}$

   [*This exercise and the next one emphasize that* $\cos \frac{\theta}{2}$ *does not equal* $\frac{\cos \theta}{2}$.]

6. For $\theta = -80°$, evaluate each of the following:
   (a) $\cos \frac{\theta}{2}$ (b) $\frac{\cos \theta}{2}$

7. For $\theta = 65°$, evaluate each of the following:
   (a) $\sin \frac{\theta}{2}$ (b) $\frac{\sin \theta}{2}$

[*This exercise and the next one emphasize that* $\sin\frac{\theta}{2}$ *does not equal* $\frac{\sin\theta}{2}$.]

8. 📱 For $\theta = 9$ radians, evaluate each of the following:

    (a) $\sin\frac{\theta}{2}$
        (b) $\frac{\sin\theta}{2}$

9. Given that $\sin 18° = \frac{\sqrt{5}-1}{4}$, find an exact expression for $\cos 36°$.

    [*The value used here for* $\sin 18°$ *is derived in Problem 101 in this section.*]

10. Given that $\sin\frac{3\pi}{10} = \frac{\sqrt{5}+1}{4}$, find an exact expression for $\cos\frac{3\pi}{5}$.

    [*Problem 71 asks you to explain how the value for* $\sin\frac{3\pi}{10}$ *used here follows from the solution to Exercise 9.*]

For Exercises 11–26, evaluate the given quantities assuming that u and v are both in the interval $(0, \frac{\pi}{2})$ and

$$\cos u = \tfrac{1}{3} \quad and \quad \sin v = \tfrac{1}{4}.$$

11. $\sin u$	17. $\sin(2u)$	23. $\sin\frac{u}{2}$
12. $\cos v$	18. $\sin(2v)$	24. $\sin\frac{v}{2}$
13. $\tan u$	19. $\tan(2u)$	25. $\tan\frac{u}{2}$
14. $\tan v$	20. $\tan(2v)$	26. $\tan\frac{v}{2}$
15. $\cos(2u)$	21. $\cos\frac{u}{2}$	
16. $\cos(2v)$	22. $\cos\frac{v}{2}$	

For Exercises 27–42, evaluate the given quantities assuming that u and v are both in the interval $(\frac{\pi}{2}, \pi)$ and

$$\sin u = \tfrac{1}{5} \quad and \quad \sin v = \tfrac{1}{6}.$$

27. $\cos u$	33. $\sin(2u)$	39. $\sin\frac{u}{2}$
28. $\cos v$	34. $\sin(2v)$	40. $\sin\frac{v}{2}$
29. $\tan u$	35. $\tan(2u)$	41. $\tan\frac{u}{2}$
30. $\tan v$	36. $\tan(2v)$	42. $\tan\frac{v}{2}$
31. $\cos(2u)$	37. $\cos\frac{u}{2}$	
32. $\cos(2v)$	38. $\cos\frac{v}{2}$	

For Exercises 43–58, evaluate the given quantities assuming that u and v are both in the interval $(-\frac{\pi}{2}, 0)$ and

$$\tan u = -\tfrac{1}{7} \quad and \quad \tan v = -\tfrac{1}{8}.$$

43. $\cos u$	49. $\sin(2u)$	55. $\sin\frac{u}{2}$
44. $\cos v$	50. $\sin(2v)$	56. $\sin\frac{v}{2}$
45. $\sin u$	51. $\tan(2u)$	57. $\tan\frac{u}{2}$
46. $\sin v$	52. $\tan(2v)$	58. $\tan\frac{v}{2}$
47. $\cos(2u)$	53. $\cos\frac{u}{2}$	
48. $\cos(2v)$	54. $\cos\frac{v}{2}$	

59. 📱 Suppose $0 < \theta < \frac{\pi}{2}$ and $\sin\theta = 0.4$.

    (a) Without using a double-angle formula, evaluate $\sin(2\theta)$.

    (b) Without using an inverse trigonometric function, evaluate $\sin(2\theta)$ again.

[*Your solutions to (a) and (b), which are obtained through different methods, should be the same, although they might differ by a tiny amount due to using approximations rather than exact amounts.*]

60. 📱 Suppose $0 < \theta < \frac{\pi}{2}$ and $\sin\theta = 0.2$.

    (a) Without using a double-angle formula, evaluate $\sin(2\theta)$.

    (b) Without using an inverse trigonometric function, evaluate $\sin(2\theta)$ again.

61. 📱 Suppose $-\frac{\pi}{2} < \theta < 0$ and $\cos\theta = 0.3$.

    (a) Without using a double-angle formula, evaluate $\cos(2\theta)$.

    (b) Without using an inverse trigonometric function, evaluate $\cos(2\theta)$ again.

62. 📱 Suppose $-\frac{\pi}{2} < \theta < 0$ and $\cos\theta = 0.8$.

    (a) Without using a double-angle formula, evaluate $\cos(2\theta)$.

    (b) Without using an inverse trigonometric function, evaluate $\cos(2\theta)$ again.

63. Find an exact expression for $\sin 15°$.

64. Find an exact expression for $\cos 22.5°$.

65. Find an exact expression for $\sin\frac{\pi}{24}$.

66. Find an exact expression for $\cos\frac{\pi}{16}$.

67. Find a formula for $\sin(4\theta)$ in terms of $\cos\theta$ and $\sin\theta$.

68. Find a formula for $\cos(4\theta)$ in terms of $\cos\theta$.

69. Find constants a, b, and c such that

$$\cos^4\theta = a + b\cos(2\theta) + c\cos(4\theta)$$

for all θ.

70. Find constants a, b, and c such that

$$\sin^4\theta = a + b\cos(2\theta) + c\cos(4\theta)$$

for all θ.

PROBLEMS

71. Explain how the equation $\sin \frac{3\pi}{10} = \frac{\sqrt{5}+1}{4}$ follows from the solution to Exercise 9.

72. Show that
$$(\cos x + \sin x)^2 = 1 + \sin(2x)$$
for every number x.

73. Show that
$$\cos(2\theta) \leq \cos^2 \theta$$
for every angle θ.

74. Show that
$$|\sin(2\theta)| \leq 2|\sin \theta|$$
for every angle θ.

75. Do not ever make the mistake of thinking that
$$\frac{\sin(2\theta)}{2} = \sin \theta$$
is a valid identity. Although the equation above is false in general, it is true for some special values of θ. Find all values of θ that satisfy the equation above.

76. Explain why there does not exist an angle θ such that $\cos \theta \sin \theta = \frac{2}{3}$.

77. Show that
$$|\cos \theta \sin \theta| \leq \frac{1}{2}$$
for every angle θ.

78. Do not ever make the mistake of thinking that
$$\frac{\cos(2\theta)}{2} = \cos \theta$$
is a valid identity.

   (a) Show that the equation above is false whenever $0 < \theta < \frac{\pi}{2}$.

   (b) Show that there exists an angle θ in the interval $(\frac{\pi}{2}, \pi)$ satisfying the equation above.

79. Without doing any algebraic manipulations, explain why
$$(2 \cos^2 \theta - 1)^2 + (2 \cos \theta \sin \theta)^2 = 1$$
for every angle θ.

80. Find angles u and v such that $\cos(2u) = \cos(2v)$ but $\cos u \neq \cos v$.

81. Show that if $\cos(2u) = \cos(2v)$, then $|\cos u| = |\cos v|$.

82. Find angles u and v such that $\sin(2u) = \sin(2v)$ but $|\sin u| \neq |\sin v|$.

83. Show that
$$\sin^2(2\theta) = 4(\sin^2 \theta - \sin^4 \theta)$$
for all θ.

84. Find a formula that expresses $\sin^2(2\theta)$ only in terms of $\cos \theta$.

85. Show that
$$(\cos \theta + \sin \theta)^2 (\cos \theta - \sin \theta)^2 + \sin^2(2\theta) = 1$$
for all angles θ.

86. Suppose θ is not an integer multiple of π. Explain why the point $(1, 2\cos \theta)$ is on the line containing the point $(\sin \theta, \sin(2\theta))$ and the origin.

87. Show that
$$\tan^2(2x) = \frac{4(\cos^2 x - \cos^4 x)}{(2\cos^2 x - 1)^2}$$
for all numbers x except odd multiples of $\frac{\pi}{4}$.

88. Find a formula that expresses $\tan^2(2\theta)$ only in terms of $\sin \theta$.

89. Find all numbers t such that
$$\frac{\cos^{-1} t}{2} = \sin^{-1} t.$$

90. Find all numbers t such that
$$\cos^{-1} t = \frac{\sin^{-1} t}{2}.$$

91. Show that
$$\tan \frac{\theta}{2} = \pm \sqrt{\frac{1 - \cos \theta}{1 + \cos \theta}}$$
for all θ except odd multiples of π.

92. Find a formula that expresses $\tan \frac{\theta}{2}$ only in terms of $\tan \theta$.

93. Suppose θ is an angle such that $\cos \theta$ is rational. Explain why $\cos(2\theta)$ is rational.

94. Give an example of an angle θ such that $\sin \theta$ is rational but $\sin(2\theta)$ is irrational.

95. Give an example of an angle θ such that both $\sin\theta$ and $\sin(2\theta)$ are rational.

Problems 96–101 will lead you to the discovery of an exact expression for the value of $\sin 18°$. ***For convenience, throughout these problems let***

$$t = \sin 18°.$$

96. Using a double-angle formula, show that $\cos 36° = 1 - 2t^2$.

97. Using a double-angle formula and the previous problem, show that

$$\cos 72° = 8t^4 - 8t^2 + 1.$$

98. Explain why $\sin 18° = \cos 72°$. Then using the previous problem, explain why

$$8t^4 - 8t^2 - t + 1 = 0.$$

99. Verify that

$$8t^4 - 8t^2 - t + 1 = (t-1)(2t+1)(4t^2 + 2t - 1).$$

100. Explain why the two previous problems imply that

$$t = 1, \quad t = -\frac{1}{2}, \quad t = \frac{-\sqrt{5}-1}{4}, \text{ or } t = \frac{\sqrt{5}-1}{4}.$$

101. Explain why the first three values in the previous problem are not possible values for $\sin 18°$. Conclude that

$$\sin 18° = \frac{\sqrt{5}-1}{4}.$$

[*This value for* $\sin 18°$ *(or* $\sin\frac{\pi}{10}$ *if we work in radians) was used in Exercise 9.*]

102. Use the result from the previous problem to show that

$$\cos 18° = \sqrt{\frac{\sqrt{5}+5}{8}}.$$

WORKED-OUT SOLUTIONS *to Odd-numbered Exercises*

1. 🖩 For $\theta = 23°$, evaluate each of the following:

   (a) $\cos(2\theta)$ (b) $2\cos\theta$

   SOLUTION

   (a) Note that $2 \times 23 = 46$. Using a calculator working in degrees, we have

   $$\cos 46° \approx 0.694658.$$

   (b) Using a calculator working in degrees, we have

   $$2\cos 23° \approx 2 \times 0.920505 = 1.841010.$$

3. 🖩 For $\theta = -5$ radians, evaluate each of the following:

   (a) $\sin(2\theta)$ (b) $2\sin\theta$

   SOLUTION

   (a) Note that $2 \times (-5) = -10$. Using a calculator working in radians, we have

   $$\sin(-10) \approx 0.544021.$$

   (b) Using a calculator working in radians, we have

   $$2\sin(-5) \approx 2 \times 0.9589 = 1.9178.$$

5. 🖩 For $\theta = 6$ radians, evaluate each of the following:

   (a) $\cos\frac{\theta}{2}$ (b) $\frac{\cos\theta}{2}$

   SOLUTION

   (a) Using a calculator working in radians, we have

   $$\cos\frac{6}{2} = \cos 3 \approx -0.989992.$$

   (b) Using a calculator working in radians, we have

   $$\frac{\cos 6}{2} \approx \frac{0.96017}{2} = 0.480085.$$

7. 🖩 For $\theta = 65°$, evaluate each of the following:

   (a) $\sin\frac{\theta}{2}$ (b) $\frac{\sin\theta}{2}$

   SOLUTION

   (a) Using a calculator working in degrees, we have

   $$\sin\frac{65°}{2} = \sin 32.5° \approx 0.537300.$$

   (b) Using a calculator working in degrees, we have

   $$\frac{\sin 65°}{2} \approx \frac{0.906308}{2} = 0.453154.$$

9. Given that $\sin 18° = \frac{\sqrt{5}-1}{4}$, find an exact expression for $\cos 36°$.

SOLUTION To evaluate $\cos 36°$, use one of the double-angle formulas for $\cos(2\theta)$ with $\theta = 18°$:

$$\cos 36° = 1 - 2\sin^2 18°$$

$$= 1 - 2\left(\tfrac{\sqrt{5}-1}{4}\right)^2 = 1 - 2\left(\tfrac{3-\sqrt{5}}{8}\right) = \tfrac{\sqrt{5}+1}{4}.$$

For Exercises 11–26, evaluate the given quantities assuming that u and v are both in the interval $(0, \frac{\pi}{2})$ and

$$\cos u = \tfrac{1}{3} \quad and \quad \sin v = \tfrac{1}{4}.$$

11. $\sin u$

SOLUTION Because $0 < u < \frac{\pi}{2}$, we know that $\sin u > 0$. Thus

$$\sin u = \sqrt{1 - \cos^2 u} = \sqrt{1 - \tfrac{1}{9}} = \sqrt{\tfrac{8}{9}} = \tfrac{2\sqrt{2}}{3}.$$

13. $\tan u$

SOLUTION To evaluate $\tan u$, use its definition as a ratio:

$$\tan u = \frac{\sin u}{\cos u} = \frac{\frac{2\sqrt{2}}{3}}{\frac{1}{3}} = 2\sqrt{2}.$$

15. $\cos(2u)$

SOLUTION To evaluate $\cos(2u)$, use one of the double-angle formulas for cosine:

$$\cos(2u) = 2\cos^2 u - 1 = \tfrac{2}{9} - 1 = -\tfrac{7}{9}.$$

17. $\sin(2u)$

SOLUTION To evaluate $\sin(2u)$, use the double-angle formula for sine:

$$\sin(2u) = 2\cos u \sin u = 2 \cdot \tfrac{1}{3} \cdot \tfrac{2\sqrt{2}}{3} = \tfrac{4\sqrt{2}}{9}.$$

19. $\tan(2u)$

SOLUTION To evaluate $\tan(2u)$, use its definition as a ratio:

$$\tan(2u) = \frac{\sin(2u)}{\cos(2u)} = \frac{\frac{4\sqrt{2}}{9}}{-\frac{7}{9}} = -\tfrac{4\sqrt{2}}{7}.$$

Alternatively, we could have used the double-angle formula for tangent, which will produce the same answer.

21. $\cos \frac{u}{2}$

SOLUTION Because $0 < \frac{u}{2} < \frac{\pi}{4}$, we know that $\cos \frac{u}{2} > 0$. Thus

$$\cos \frac{u}{2} = \sqrt{\frac{1 + \cos u}{2}}$$

$$= \sqrt{\frac{1 + \frac{1}{3}}{2}} = \sqrt{\frac{\frac{4}{3}}{2}} = \sqrt{\tfrac{2}{3}} = \tfrac{\sqrt{6}}{3}.$$

23. $\sin \frac{u}{2}$

SOLUTION Because $0 < \frac{u}{2} < \frac{\pi}{4}$, we know that $\sin \frac{u}{2} > 0$. Thus

$$\sin \frac{u}{2} = \sqrt{\frac{1 - \cos u}{2}}$$

$$= \sqrt{\frac{1 - \frac{1}{3}}{2}} = \sqrt{\frac{\frac{2}{3}}{2}} = \sqrt{\tfrac{1}{3}} = \tfrac{1}{\sqrt{3}} = \tfrac{\sqrt{3}}{3}.$$

25. $\tan \frac{u}{2}$

SOLUTION To evaluate $\tan \frac{u}{2}$, use its definition as a ratio:

$$\tan \frac{u}{2} = \frac{\sin \frac{u}{2}}{\cos \frac{u}{2}} = \frac{\frac{\sqrt{3}}{3}}{\frac{\sqrt{6}}{3}} = \tfrac{\sqrt{3}}{\sqrt{6}} = \tfrac{1}{\sqrt{2}} = \tfrac{\sqrt{2}}{2}.$$

Alternatively, we could have used the half-angle formula for tangent, which will produce the same answer.

For Exercises 27–42, evaluate the given quantities assuming that u and v are both in the interval $(\frac{\pi}{2}, \pi)$ and

$$\sin u = \tfrac{1}{5} \quad and \quad \sin v = \tfrac{1}{6}.$$

27. $\cos u$

SOLUTION Because $\frac{\pi}{2} < u < \pi$, we know that $\cos u < 0$. Thus

$$\cos u = -\sqrt{1 - \sin^2 u} = -\sqrt{1 - \tfrac{1}{25}} = -\sqrt{\tfrac{24}{25}}$$

$$= -\tfrac{2\sqrt{6}}{5}.$$

29. $\tan u$

SOLUTION   To evaluate $\tan u$, use its definition as a ratio:

$$\tan u = \frac{\sin u}{\cos u} = \frac{\frac{1}{5}}{-\frac{2\sqrt{6}}{5}} = -\frac{1}{2\sqrt{6}} = -\frac{\sqrt{6}}{12}.$$

31. $\cos(2u)$

SOLUTION   To evaluate $\cos(2u)$, use one of the double-angle formulas for cosine:

$$\cos(2u) = 1 - 2\sin^2 u = 1 - \frac{2}{25} = \frac{23}{25}.$$

33. $\sin(2u)$

SOLUTION   To evaluate $\sin(2u)$, use the double-angle formula for sine:

$$\sin(2u) = 2\cos u \sin u = 2 \cdot \left(-\frac{2\sqrt{6}}{5}\right) \cdot \frac{1}{5} = -\frac{4\sqrt{6}}{25}.$$

35. $\tan(2u)$

SOLUTION   To evaluate $\tan(2u)$, use its definition as a ratio:

$$\tan(2u) = \frac{\sin(2u)}{\cos(2u)} = \frac{-\frac{4\sqrt{6}}{25}}{\frac{23}{25}} = -\frac{4\sqrt{6}}{23}.$$

Alternatively, we could have used the double-angle formula for tangent, which will produce the same answer.

37. $\cos\frac{u}{2}$

SOLUTION   Because $\frac{\pi}{4} < \frac{u}{2} < \frac{\pi}{2}$, we know that $\cos\frac{u}{2} > 0$. Thus

$$\cos\frac{u}{2} = \sqrt{\frac{1 + \cos u}{2}}$$

$$= \sqrt{\frac{1 - \frac{2\sqrt{6}}{5}}{2}} = \sqrt{\frac{\frac{5 - 2\sqrt{6}}{5}}{2}} = \sqrt{\frac{5 - 2\sqrt{6}}{10}}.$$

39. $\sin\frac{u}{2}$

SOLUTION   Because $\frac{\pi}{4} < \frac{u}{2} < \frac{\pi}{2}$, we know that $\sin\frac{u}{2} > 0$. Thus

$$\sin\frac{u}{2} = \sqrt{\frac{1 - \cos u}{2}}$$

$$= \sqrt{\frac{1 + \frac{2\sqrt{6}}{5}}{2}} = \sqrt{\frac{\frac{5 + 2\sqrt{6}}{5}}{2}} = \sqrt{\frac{5 + 2\sqrt{6}}{10}}.$$

41. $\tan\frac{u}{2}$

SOLUTION   To evaluate $\tan\frac{u}{2}$, use one of the half-angle formulas for tangent:

$$\tan\frac{u}{2} = \frac{1 - \cos u}{\sin u} = \frac{1 + \frac{2\sqrt{6}}{5}}{\frac{1}{5}} = 5 + 2\sqrt{6}.$$

We could also have evaluated $\tan\frac{u}{2}$ by using its definition as the ratio of $\sin\frac{u}{2}$ and $\cos\frac{u}{2}$, but in this case that procedure would lead to a more complicated algebraic expression.

For Exercises 43–58, evaluate the given quantities assuming that u and v are both in the interval $(-\frac{\pi}{2}, 0)$ *and*

$$\tan u = -\frac{1}{7} \quad and \quad \tan v = -\frac{1}{8}.$$

43. $\cos u$

SOLUTION   Because $-\frac{\pi}{2} < u < 0$, we know that $\cos u > 0$ and $\sin u < 0$. Thus

$$-\frac{1}{7} = \tan u = \frac{\sin u}{\cos u} = \frac{-\sqrt{1 - \cos^2 u}}{\cos u}.$$

Squaring the first and last entries above gives

$$\frac{1}{49} = \frac{1 - \cos^2 u}{\cos^2 u}.$$

Multiplying both sides by $\cos^2 u$ and then by 49 gives

$$\cos^2 u = 49 - 49\cos^2 u.$$

Thus $50\cos^2 u = 49$, which implies that

$$\cos u = \sqrt{\frac{49}{50}} = \frac{7}{5\sqrt{2}} = \frac{7\sqrt{2}}{10}.$$

45. $\sin u$

SOLUTION   Solve the equation $\tan u = \frac{\sin u}{\cos u}$ for $\sin u$:

$$\sin u = \cos u \tan u = \frac{7\sqrt{2}}{10} \cdot \left(-\frac{1}{7}\right) = -\frac{\sqrt{2}}{10}.$$

47. $\cos(2u)$

SOLUTION   To evaluate $\cos(2u)$, use one of the double-angle formulas for cosine:

$$\cos(2u) = 2\cos^2 u - 1 = 2 \cdot \frac{49}{50} - 1 = \frac{24}{25}.$$

49. $\sin(2u)$

SOLUTION To evaluate $\sin(2u)$, use the double-angle formula for sine:

$$\sin(2u) = 2\cos u \sin u = 2 \cdot \frac{7\sqrt{2}}{10} \cdot \left(-\frac{\sqrt{2}}{10}\right) = -\frac{7}{25}.$$

51. $\tan(2u)$

SOLUTION To evaluate $\tan(2u)$, use the double-angle formula for tangent:

$$\tan(2u) = \frac{2\tan u}{1 - \tan^2 u} = \frac{-\frac{2}{7}}{\frac{48}{49}} = -\frac{7}{24}.$$

Alternatively, we could have evaluated $\tan(2u)$ by using its definition as a ratio of $\sin(2u)$ and $\cos(2u)$, producing the same answer.

53. $\cos\frac{u}{2}$

SOLUTION Because $-\frac{\pi}{4} < \frac{u}{2} < 0$, we know that $\cos\frac{u}{2} > 0$. Thus

$$\cos\frac{u}{2} = \sqrt{\frac{1 + \cos u}{2}}$$

$$= \sqrt{\frac{1 + \frac{7\sqrt{2}}{10}}{2}} = \sqrt{\frac{\frac{10+7\sqrt{2}}{10}}{2}} = \sqrt{\frac{10 + 7\sqrt{2}}{20}}.$$

55. $\sin\frac{u}{2}$

SOLUTION Because $-\frac{\pi}{4} < \frac{u}{2} < 0$, we know that $\sin\frac{u}{2} < 0$. Thus

$$\sin\frac{u}{2} = -\sqrt{\frac{1 - \cos u}{2}}$$

$$= -\sqrt{\frac{1 - \frac{7\sqrt{2}}{10}}{2}} = -\sqrt{\frac{\frac{10-7\sqrt{2}}{10}}{2}} = -\sqrt{\frac{10 - 7\sqrt{2}}{20}}.$$

57. $\tan\frac{u}{2}$

SOLUTION To evaluate $\tan\frac{u}{2}$, use one of the half-angle formulas for tangent:

$$\tan\frac{u}{2} = \frac{1 - \cos u}{\sin u} = \frac{1 - \frac{7\sqrt{2}}{10}}{-\frac{\sqrt{2}}{10}} = 7 - \frac{10}{\sqrt{2}} = 7 - 5\sqrt{2}.$$

We could also have evaluated $\tan\frac{u}{2}$ by using its definition as the ratio of $\sin\frac{u}{2}$ and $\cos\frac{u}{2}$, but in this case that procedure would lead to a more complicated algebraic expression.

59. ⏍ Suppose $0 < \theta < \frac{\pi}{2}$ and $\sin\theta = 0.4$.

(a) Without using a double-angle formula, evaluate $\sin(2\theta)$.

(b) Without using an inverse trigonometric function, evaluate $\sin(2\theta)$ again.

SOLUTION

(a) Because $0 < \theta < \frac{\pi}{2}$ and $\sin\theta = 0.4$, we see that

$$\theta = \sin^{-1} 0.4 \approx 0.411517 \text{ radians.}$$

Thus

$$2\theta \approx 0.823034 \text{ radians.}$$

Hence

$$\sin(2\theta) \approx \sin(0.823034) \approx 0.733212.$$

(b) To use the double-angle formula to evaluate $\sin(2\theta)$, we must first evaluate $\cos\theta$. Because $0 < \theta < \frac{\pi}{2}$, we know that $\cos\theta > 0$. Thus

$$\cos\theta = \sqrt{1 - \sin^2\theta} = \sqrt{1 - 0.16} = \sqrt{0.84}$$

$$\approx 0.916515.$$

Now

$$\sin(2\theta) = 2\cos\theta\sin\theta \approx 2(0.916515)(0.4)$$

$$= 0.733212.$$

61. ⏍ Suppose $-\frac{\pi}{2} < \theta < 0$ and $\cos\theta = 0.3$.

(a) Without using a double-angle formula, evaluate $\cos(2\theta)$.

(b) Without using an inverse trigonometric function, evaluate $\cos(2\theta)$ again.

SOLUTION

(a) Because $-\frac{\pi}{2} < \theta < 0$ and $\cos\theta = 0.3$, we see that

$$\theta = -\cos^{-1} 0.3 \approx -1.2661 \text{ radians.}$$

Thus

$$2\theta \approx -2.5322 \text{ radians.}$$

Hence

$$\cos(2\theta) \approx \cos(-2.5322) \approx -0.82.$$

(b) Using a double-angle formula, we have

$$\cos(2\theta) = 2\cos^2\theta - 1 \approx 2(0.3)^2 - 1$$

$$= -0.82.$$

63. Find an exact expression for $\sin 15°$.

    SOLUTION   Use the half-angle formula for $\sin \frac{\theta}{2}$ with $\theta = 30°$ (choose the plus sign associated with the square root because $\sin 15°$ is positive), getting

    $$\sin 15° = \sqrt{\frac{1 - \cos 30°}{2}}$$

    $$= \sqrt{\frac{1 - \frac{\sqrt{3}}{2}}{2}} = \sqrt{\frac{(1 - \frac{\sqrt{3}}{2}) \cdot 2}{2 \cdot 2}} = \frac{\sqrt{2 - \sqrt{3}}}{2}.$$

65. Find an exact expression for $\sin \frac{\pi}{24}$.

    SOLUTION   Using the half-angle formula for $\sin \frac{\theta}{2}$ with $\theta = \frac{\pi}{12}$ (and choosing the plus sign associated with the square root because $\sin \frac{\pi}{24}$ is positive), we have

    $$\sin \frac{\pi}{24} = \sqrt{\frac{1 - \cos \frac{\pi}{12}}{2}}.$$

    Note that $\frac{\pi}{12}$ radians equals $15°$. Substituting for $\cos \frac{\pi}{12}$ the value for $\cos 15°$ from Example 4 gives

    $$\sin \frac{\pi}{24} = \sqrt{\frac{1 - \frac{\sqrt{2+\sqrt{3}}}{2}}{2}} = \frac{\sqrt{2 - \sqrt{2 + \sqrt{3}}}}{2}.$$

67. Find a formula for $\sin(4\theta)$ in terms of $\cos \theta$ and $\sin \theta$.

    SOLUTION   Use the double-angle formula for sine, with θ replaced by 2θ, getting

    $$\sin(4\theta) = 2 \cos(2\theta) \sin(2\theta).$$

Now use the double-angle formulas for the expressions on the right side, getting

$$\sin(4\theta) = 2(2 \cos^2\theta - 1)(2 \cos \theta \sin \theta)$$

$$= 4(2 \cos^2\theta - 1) \cos \theta \sin \theta.$$

69. Find constants a, b, and c such that

    $$\cos^4\theta = a + b \cos(2\theta) + c \cos(4\theta)$$

    for all θ.

    SOLUTION   One of the double-angle formulas for $\cos(2\theta)$ can be written in the form

    $$\cos^2\theta = \frac{1 + \cos(2\theta)}{2}.$$

    Squaring both sides, we get

    $$\cos^4\theta = \frac{1 + 2 \cos(2\theta) + \cos^2(2\theta)}{4}.$$

    We now see that we need an expression for $\cos^2(2\theta)$, which we can obtain by replacing θ by 2θ in the formula above for $\cos^2\theta$:

    $$\cos^2(2\theta) = \frac{1 + \cos(4\theta)}{2}.$$

    Substituting this expression into the expression above for $\cos^4\theta$ gives

    $$\cos^4\theta = \frac{1 + 2 \cos(2\theta) + \frac{1+\cos(4\theta)}{2}}{4}$$

    $$= \tfrac{3}{8} + \tfrac{1}{2} \cos(2\theta) + \tfrac{1}{8} \cos(4\theta).$$

    Thus $a = \frac{3}{8}$, $b = \frac{1}{2}$, and $c = \frac{1}{8}$.

$$\boxed{6.4} \quad \textit{Addition and Subtraction Formulas}$$

SECTION OBJECTIVES

By the end of this section you should

- be able to use the addition and subtraction formulas for cosine;
- be able to use the addition and subtraction formulas for sine;
- be able to use the addition and subtraction formulas for tangent.

The Cosine of a Sum and Difference

Consider the figure below, which shows the unit circle along with a radius making an angle of u with the positive horizontal axis and a radius making an angle of $-v$ with the positive horizontal axis.

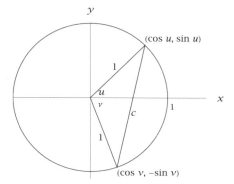

This figure has been carefully chosen to lead us to an easy derivation of the formula for $\cos(u + v)$.

We defined the cosine and sine so that the endpoint of the radius making an angle of u with the positive horizontal axis has coordinates $(\cos u, \sin u)$. The endpoint of the radius making an angle of $-v$ with the positive horizontal axis has coordinates $(\cos(-v), \sin(-v))$, which we have seen equals $(\cos v, -\sin v)$, as shown above.

The large triangle in the figure above has two sides that are radii of the unit circle and thus have length 1. The angle between these two sides is $u + v$. The length of the third side of this triangle has been labeled c. The idea now is that we can compute c^2 in two different ways: first by using the formula for the distance between two points, and second by using the law of cosines. We will then set these two computed values of c^2 equal to each other, obtaining a formula for $\cos(u + v)$.

To carry out the plan discussed in the paragraph above, note that one endpoint of the line segment above with length c has coordinates $(\cos u, \sin u)$ and the other endpoint has coordinates $(\cos v, -\sin v)$. Recall that the distance between two points is the square root of the sum of the squares of the differences of the coordinates. Thus

$$c = \sqrt{(\cos u - \cos v)^2 + (\sin u + \sin v)^2}.$$

Squaring both sides of this equation, we have

$$c^2 = (\cos u - \cos v)^2 + (\sin u + \sin v)^2$$
$$= \cos^2 u - 2\cos u \cos v + \cos^2 v$$
$$+ \sin^2 u + 2\sin u \sin v + \sin^2 v$$
$$= (\cos^2 u + \sin^2 u) + (\cos^2 v + \sin^2 v)$$
$$- 2\cos u \cos v + 2\sin u \sin v$$
$$= 2 - 2\cos u \cos v + 2\sin u \sin v.$$

To compute c^2 by another method, apply the law of cosines to the large triangle in the figure above, getting $c^2 = 1^2 + 1^2 - 2 \cdot 1 \cdot 1 \cos(u + v)$, which can be rewritten as

$$c^2 = 2 - 2\cos(u + v).$$

We have now found two expressions that equal c^2. Setting those expressions equal to each other, we have

$$2 - 2\cos(u + v) = 2 - 2\cos u \cos v + 2\sin u \sin v.$$

Subtracting 2 from both sides of the equation above and then dividing both sides by -2 gives the following result:

Never, ever, make the mistake of thinking that $\cos(u + v)$ equals $\cos u + \cos v$.

Addition formula for cosine

$$\cos(u + v) = \cos u \cos v - \sin u \sin v$$

We derived this formula using the figure above, which assumes that u and v are between 0 and $\frac{\pi}{2}$. However, the formula above is valid for all values of u and v.

Find an exact expression for $\cos 75°$.

EXAMPLE 1

SOLUTION   Note that $75° = 45° + 30°$, and we already know how to evaluate the cosine and sine of $45°$ and $30°$. Using the addition formula for cosine, we have

$$\cos 75° = \cos(45° + 30°)$$
$$= \cos 45° \cos 30° - \sin 45° \sin 30°$$
$$= \frac{\sqrt{2}}{2} \cdot \frac{\sqrt{3}}{2} - \frac{\sqrt{2}}{2} \cdot \frac{1}{2}$$
$$= \frac{\sqrt{6}-\sqrt{2}}{4}.$$

Notice that if $v = u$, the addition formula for cosine becomes

$$\cos(2u) = \cos^2 u - \sin^2 u,$$

which agrees with one of our previous double-angle formulas.

We can now find a formula for the cosine of the difference of two angles. In the formula for $\cos(u + v)$, replace v by $-v$ on both sides of the equation and use the identities $\cos(-v) = \cos v$ and $\sin(-v) = -\sin(v)$ to get the following result:

Subtraction formula for cosine

$$\cos(u - v) = \cos u \cos v + \sin u \sin v$$

| **EXAMPLE 2** | Find an exact expression for $\cos 15°$.

SOLUTION   Note that $15° = 45° - 30°$, and we already know how to evaluate the cosine and sine of $45°$ and $30°$. Using the subtraction formula for cosine, we have

$$\cos 15° = \cos(45° - 30°)$$

$$= \cos 45° \cos 30° + \sin 45° \sin 30°$$

$$= \frac{\sqrt{2}}{2} \cdot \frac{\sqrt{3}}{2} + \frac{\sqrt{2}}{2} \cdot \frac{1}{2}$$

$$= \frac{\sqrt{6} + \sqrt{2}}{4}.$$

Note that the expression produced by the subtraction formula for cosine is simpler than the expression produced by the half-angle formula for cosine.

REMARK Using a half-angle formula, in Example 4 in Section 6.3 we showed that

$$\cos 15° = \frac{\sqrt{2 + \sqrt{3}}}{2}.$$

Thus we have two seemingly different exact expressions for $\cos 15°$, one produced by the subtraction formula for cosine and the other produced by the half-angle formula for cosine. Problem 39 in this section asks you to verify that these two expressions for $\cos 15°$ are equal.

The Sine of a Sum and Difference

To find the formula for the sine of the sum of two angles, we will make use of the identities

$$\sin \theta = \cos(\tfrac{\pi}{2} - \theta) \quad \text{and} \quad \sin(\tfrac{\pi}{2} - \theta) = \cos \theta,$$

which you can review in Section 5.6. We begin by converting the sine into a cosine and then we use the identity just derived above:

$$\sin(u + v) = \cos(\tfrac{\pi}{2} - u - v)$$

$$= \cos((\tfrac{\pi}{2} - u) - v)$$

$$= \cos(\tfrac{\pi}{2} - u) \cos v + \sin(\tfrac{\pi}{2} - u) \sin v.$$

The equation above and the identities above now imply the following result:

Addition formula for sine

$$\sin(u + v) = \sin u \cos v + \cos u \sin v$$

Never, ever, make the mistake of thinking that $\sin(u + v)$ equals $\sin u + \sin v$.

Notice that if $v = u$, the addition formula for sine becomes

$$\sin(2u) = 2 \cos u \sin u,$$

which agrees with our previous double-angle formula for sine.

We can now find a formula for the sine of the difference of two angles. In the formula for $\sin(u + v)$, replace v by $-v$ on both sides of the equation and use the identities $\cos(-v) = \cos v$ and $\sin(-v) = -\sin(v)$ to get the following result:

Subtraction formula for sine

$$\sin(u - v) = \sin u \cos v - \cos u \sin v$$

Verify that the subtraction formula for sine gives the expected identity for $\sin(\tfrac{\pi}{2} - \theta)$.   **EXAMPLE 3**

SOLUTION   Using the subtraction formula for sine, we have

$$\sin(\tfrac{\pi}{2} - \theta) = \sin \tfrac{\pi}{2} \cos \theta - \cos \tfrac{\pi}{2} \sin \theta$$

$$= 1 \cdot \cos \theta - 0 \cdot \sin \theta$$

$$= \cos \theta.$$

The Tangent of a Sum and Difference

Now that we have found formulas for the cosine and sine of the sum of two angles, we can find a formula for the tangent of the sum of two angles in the usual fashion by writing the tangent as a ratio of a sine and cosine. Specifically, we have

$$\tan(u + v) = \frac{\sin(u + v)}{\cos(u + v)}$$

The last equality is obtained by dividing the numerator and denominator of the previous expression by $\cos u \cos v$.

$$= \frac{\sin u \cos v + \cos u \sin v}{\cos u \cos v - \sin u \sin v}$$

$$= \frac{\frac{\sin u}{\cos u} + \frac{\sin v}{\cos v}}{1 - \frac{\sin u \sin v}{\cos u \cos v}}.$$

Using the definition of the tangent, rewrite the equation above as follows:

Addition formula for tangent

$$\tan(u + v) = \frac{\tan u + \tan v}{1 - \tan u \tan v}$$

In this section we derive six addition and subtraction formulas. Memorizing all six would not be a good use of your time or mental energy. Instead, concentrate on learning the formulas for $\cos(u + v)$ and $\sin(u + v)$ and on understanding how the other formulas follow from those two.

The identity above is valid for all u, v such that $\tan u$, $\tan v$, and $\tan(u + v)$ are defined (in other words, avoid odd multiples of $\frac{\pi}{2}$).

Notice that if $v = u$, the addition formula for tangent becomes

$$\tan(2u) = \frac{2 \tan u}{1 - \tan^2 u},$$

which agrees with our previous double-angle formula for tangent.

We can now find a formula for the tangent of the difference of two angles. In the formula for $\tan(u + v)$, replace v by $-v$ on both sides of the equation and use the identity $\tan(-v) = -\tan v$ to get the following result:

Subtraction formula for tangent

$$\tan(u - v) = \frac{\tan u - \tan v}{1 + \tan u \tan v}$$

EXAMPLE 4

Use the subtraction formula for tangent to find a formula for $\tan(\pi - \theta)$.

SOLUTION Using the subtraction formula for tangent, we have

$$\tan(\pi - \theta) = \frac{\tan \pi - \tan \theta}{1 + \tan \pi \tan \theta}$$

$$= \frac{0 - \tan \theta}{1 + 0 \cdot \tan \theta}$$

$$= -\tan \theta.$$

We could have skipped the derivation of the double-angle formulas in the last section and instead we could have obtained the double-angle formulas as consequences of the addition formulas (in fact, your instructor may have done this). However, sometimes additional understanding comes from seeing multiple derivations of a formula.

EXERCISES

1. For $x = 19°$ and $y = 13°$, evaluate each of the following:
   (a) $\cos(x + y)$ (b) $\cos x + \cos y$
   [*This exercise and the next one emphasize that* $\cos(x + y)$ *does not equal* $\cos x + \cos y$.]

2. For $x = 1.2$ radians and $y = 3.4$ radians, evaluate each of the following:
   (a) $\cos(x + y)$ (b) $\cos x + \cos y$

3. For $x = 5.7$ radians and $y = 2.5$ radians, evaluate each of the following:
   (a) $\sin(x - y)$ (b) $\sin x - \sin y$
   [*This exercise and the next one emphasize that* $\sin(x - y)$ *does not equal* $\sin x - \sin y$.]

4. For $x = 79°$ and $y = 33°$, evaluate each of the following:
   (a) $\sin(x - y)$ (b) $\sin x - \sin y$

For Exercises 5-12, find exact expressions for the indicated quantities. The following information will be useful:

$$\cos 22.5° = \frac{\sqrt{2 + \sqrt{2}}}{2} \quad and \quad \sin 22.5° = \frac{\sqrt{2 - \sqrt{2}}}{2};$$

$$\cos 18° = \sqrt{\frac{\sqrt{5} + 5}{8}} \quad and \quad \sin 18° = \frac{\sqrt{5} - 1}{4}.$$

[*The value for* $\sin 22.5°$ *used here was derived in Example 5 in Section 6.3; the other values were derived in Exercise 64 and Problems 101 and 102 in Section 6.3.*]

5. $\cos 82.5°$ 9. $\cos 37.5°$

6. $\cos 48°$ 10. $\cos 12°$
   [*Hint:* $48 = 30 + 18$]   [*Hint:* $12 = 30 - 18$]

7. $\sin 82.5°$ 11. $\sin 37.5°$

8. $\sin 48°$ 12. $\sin 12°$

For Exercises 13-24, evaluate the indicated expressions assuming that

$$\cos x = \tfrac{1}{3} \quad and \quad \sin y = \tfrac{1}{4},$$

$$\sin u = \tfrac{2}{3} \quad and \quad \cos v = \tfrac{1}{5}.$$

Assume also that x *and* u *are in the interval* $(0, \frac{\pi}{2})$, *that* y *is in the interval* $(\frac{\pi}{2}, \pi)$, *and that* v *is in the interval* $(-\frac{\pi}{2}, 0)$.

13. $\cos(x + y)$ 19. $\sin(x - y)$

14. $\cos(u + v)$ 20. $\sin(u - v)$

15. $\cos(x - y)$ 21. $\tan(x + y)$

16. $\cos(u - v)$ 22. $\tan(u + v)$

17. $\sin(x + y)$ 23. $\tan(x - y)$

18. $\sin(u + v)$ 24. $\tan(u - v)$

25. Evaluate $\cos(\frac{\pi}{6} + \cos^{-1} \frac{3}{4})$.

26. Evaluate $\sin(\frac{\pi}{3} + \sin^{-1} \frac{2}{5})$.

27. Evaluate $\sin(\cos^{-1} \frac{1}{4} + \tan^{-1} 2)$.

28. Evaluate $\cos(\cos^{-1} \frac{2}{3} + \tan^{-1} 3)$.

29. Find a formula for $\cos(\theta + \frac{\pi}{2})$.

30. Find a formula for $\sin(\theta + \frac{\pi}{2})$.

31. Find a formula for $\cos(\theta + \frac{\pi}{4})$.

32. Find a formula for $\sin(\theta - \frac{\pi}{4})$.

33. Find a formula for $\tan(\theta + \frac{\pi}{4})$.

34. Find a formula for $\tan(\theta - \frac{\pi}{4})$.

35. Find a formula for $\tan(\theta + \frac{\pi}{2})$.

36. Find a formula for $\tan(\theta - \frac{\pi}{2})$.

PROBLEMS

37. Show (without using a calculator) that
$$\sin 10° \cos 20° + \cos 10° \sin 20° = \tfrac{1}{2}.$$

38. Show (without using a calculator) that
$$\sin \tfrac{\pi}{7} \cos \tfrac{4\pi}{21} + \cos \tfrac{\pi}{7} \sin \tfrac{4\pi}{21} = \tfrac{\sqrt{3}}{2}.$$

39. Show that
$$\frac{\sqrt{6} + \sqrt{2}}{4} = \frac{\sqrt{2 + \sqrt{3}}}{2}.$$

Do this without using a calculator and without using the knowledge that both expressions above are equal to $\cos 15°$ (see Example 2).

40. Show that

$$\cos(3\theta) = 4\cos^3\theta - 3\cos\theta$$

for all θ.

[*Hint:* $\cos(3\theta) = \cos(2\theta + \theta)$.]

41. Show that $\cos 20°$ is a zero of the polynomial $8x^3 - 6x - 1$.

[*Hint:* Set $\theta = 20°$ in the identity from the previous problem.]

42. Show that

$$\sin(3\theta) = 3\sin\theta - 4\sin^3\theta$$

for all θ.

43. Show that $\sin\frac{\pi}{18}$ is a zero of the polynomial $8x^3 - 6x + 1$.

[*Hint:* Use the identity from the previous problem.]

44. Show that

$$\cos(5\theta) = 16\cos^5\theta - 20\cos^3\theta + 5\cos\theta$$

for all θ.

45. Find a nice formula for $\sin(5\theta)$ in terms of $\sin\theta$.

46. Show that

$$\cos u \cos v = \frac{\cos(u+v) + \cos(u-v)}{2}$$

for all u, v.

[*Hint:* Add together the formulas for $\cos(u+v)$ and $\cos(u-v)$.]

47. Show that

$$\sin u \sin v = \frac{\cos(u-v) - \cos(u+v)}{2}$$

for all u, v.

48. Show that

$$\cos u \sin v = \frac{\sin(u+v) - \sin(u-v)}{2}$$

for all u, v.

49. Show that

$$\cos x + \cos y = 2\cos\tfrac{x+y}{2}\cos\tfrac{x-y}{2}$$

for all x, y.

[*Hint:* Take $u = \frac{x+y}{2}$ and $v = \frac{x-y}{2}$ in the formula given by Problem 46.]

50. Show that

$$\cos x - \cos y = 2\sin\tfrac{x+y}{2}\sin\tfrac{y-x}{2}$$

for all x, y.

51. Show that

$$\sin x - \sin y = 2\cos\tfrac{x+y}{2}\sin\tfrac{x-y}{2}$$

for all x, y.

52. Find a formula for $\sin x + \sin y$ analogous to the formula in the previous problem.

53. Suppose $u = \tan^{-1} 2$ and $v = \tan^{-1} 3$. Show that $\tan(u + v) = -1$.

54. Suppose $u = \tan^{-1} 2$ and $v = \tan^{-1} 3$. Using the previous problem, explain why $u + v = \frac{3\pi}{4}$.

55. Using the previous problem, derive the beautiful equation

$$\tan^{-1} 1 + \tan^{-1} 2 + \tan^{-1} 3 = \pi.$$

[*Problem 42 in Section 6.7 gives another derivation of the equation above.*]

WORKED-OUT SOLUTIONS *to Odd-numbered Exercises*

1. 📱 For $x = 19°$ and $y = 13°$, evaluate each of the following:

    (a) $\cos(x + y)$ (b) $\cos x + \cos y$

SOLUTION

(a) Using a calculator working in degrees, we have

$$\cos(19° + 13°) = \cos 32° \approx 0.84805.$$

(b) Using a calculator working in degrees, we have

$$\cos 19° + \cos 13° \approx 0.94552 + 0.97437$$

$$= 1.91989.$$

3. For $x = 5.7$ radians and $y = 2.5$ radians, evaluate each of the following:

    (a) $\sin(x - y)$ (b) $\sin x - \sin y$

SOLUTION

(a) Using a calculator working in radians, we have

$$\sin(5.7 - 2.5) = \sin 3.2 \approx -0.05837.$$

(b) Using a calculator working in radians, we have

$$\sin 5.7 - \sin 2.5 \approx -0.55069 - 0.59847$$

$$= -1.14916.$$

For Exercises 5–12, find exact expressions for the indicated quantities. The following information will be useful:

$$\cos 22.5° = \frac{\sqrt{2 + \sqrt{2}}}{2} \quad and \quad \sin 22.5° = \frac{\sqrt{2 - \sqrt{2}}}{2};$$

$$\cos 18° = \sqrt{\frac{\sqrt{5} + 5}{8}} \quad and \quad \sin 18° = \frac{\sqrt{5} - 1}{4}.$$

5. $\cos 82.5°$

SOLUTION

$$\cos 82.5° = \cos(60° + 22.5°)$$

$$= \cos 60° \cos 22.5° - \sin 60° \sin 22.5°$$

$$= \frac{1}{2} \cdot \frac{\sqrt{2 + \sqrt{2}}}{2} - \frac{\sqrt{3}}{2} \cdot \frac{\sqrt{2 - \sqrt{2}}}{2}$$

$$= \frac{\sqrt{2 + \sqrt{2}} - \sqrt{3}\sqrt{2 - \sqrt{2}}}{4}$$

7. $\sin 82.5°$

SOLUTION

$$\sin 82.5° = \sin(60° + 22.5°)$$

$$= \sin 60° \cos 22.5° + \cos 60° \sin 22.5°$$

$$= \frac{\sqrt{3}}{2} \cdot \frac{\sqrt{2 + \sqrt{2}}}{2} + \frac{1}{2} \cdot \frac{\sqrt{2 - \sqrt{2}}}{2}$$

$$= \frac{\sqrt{3}\sqrt{2 + \sqrt{2}} + \sqrt{2 - \sqrt{2}}}{4}$$

9. $\cos 37.5°$

SOLUTION

$$\cos 37.5° = \cos(60° - 22.5°)$$

$$= \cos 60° \cos 22.5° + \sin 60° \sin 22.5°$$

$$= \frac{1}{2} \cdot \frac{\sqrt{2 + \sqrt{2}}}{2} + \frac{\sqrt{3}}{2} \cdot \frac{\sqrt{2 - \sqrt{2}}}{2}$$

$$= \frac{\sqrt{2 + \sqrt{2}} + \sqrt{3}\sqrt{2 - \sqrt{2}}}{4}$$

11. $\sin 37.5°$

SOLUTION

$$\sin 37.5° = \sin(60° - 22.5°)$$

$$= \sin 60° \cos 22.5° - \cos 60° \sin 22.5°$$

$$= \frac{\sqrt{3}}{2} \cdot \frac{\sqrt{2 + \sqrt{2}}}{2} - \frac{1}{2} \cdot \frac{\sqrt{2 - \sqrt{2}}}{2}$$

$$= \frac{\sqrt{3}\sqrt{2 + \sqrt{2}} - \sqrt{2 - \sqrt{2}}}{4}$$

For Exercises 13–24, evaluate the indicated expressions assuming that

$$\cos x = \frac{1}{3} \quad and \quad \sin y = \frac{1}{4},$$

$$\sin u = \frac{2}{3} \quad and \quad \cos v = \frac{1}{5}.$$

Assume also that x and u are in the interval $(0, \frac{\pi}{2})$, that y is in the interval $(\frac{\pi}{2}, \pi)$, and that v is in the interval $(-\frac{\pi}{2}, 0)$.

13. $\cos(x + y)$

SOLUTION To use the addition formula for $\cos(x + y)$, we will need to know the cosine and sine of both x and y. Thus first we find those values, beginning with $\sin x$. Because $0 < x < \frac{\pi}{2}$, we know that $\sin x > 0$. Thus

$$\sin x = \sqrt{1 - \cos^2 x} = \sqrt{1 - \tfrac{1}{9}} = \sqrt{\tfrac{8}{9}} = \frac{\sqrt{4}\sqrt{2}}{\sqrt{9}}$$

$$= \tfrac{2\sqrt{2}}{3}.$$

Because $\frac{\pi}{2} < y < \pi$, we know that $\cos y < 0$. Thus

$$\cos y = -\sqrt{1 - \sin^2 y} = -\sqrt{1 - \frac{1}{16}} = -\sqrt{\frac{15}{16}}$$
$$= -\frac{\sqrt{15}}{4}.$$

Thus

$$\cos(x + y) = \cos x \cos y - \sin x \sin y$$
$$= \frac{1}{3} \cdot \left(-\frac{\sqrt{15}}{4}\right) - \frac{2\sqrt{2}}{3} \cdot \frac{1}{4}$$
$$= \frac{-\sqrt{15} - 2\sqrt{2}}{12}.$$

15. $\cos(x - y)$

SOLUTION

$$\cos(x - y) = \cos x \cos y + \sin x \sin y$$
$$= \frac{1}{3} \cdot \left(-\frac{\sqrt{15}}{4}\right) + \frac{2\sqrt{2}}{3} \cdot \frac{1}{4}$$
$$= \frac{2\sqrt{2} - \sqrt{15}}{12}$$

17. $\sin(x + y)$

SOLUTION

$$\sin(x + y) = \sin x \cos y + \cos x \sin y$$
$$= \frac{2\sqrt{2}}{3} \cdot \left(-\frac{\sqrt{15}}{4}\right) + \frac{1}{3} \cdot \frac{1}{4}$$
$$= \frac{1 - 2\sqrt{30}}{12}$$

19. $\sin(x - y)$

SOLUTION

$$\sin(x - y) = \sin x \cos y - \cos x \sin y$$
$$= \frac{2\sqrt{2}}{3} \cdot \left(-\frac{\sqrt{15}}{4}\right) - \frac{1}{3} \cdot \frac{1}{4}$$
$$= \frac{-1 - 2\sqrt{30}}{12}$$

21. $\tan(x + y)$

SOLUTION To use the addition formula for $\tan(x + y)$, we will need to know the tangent of both x and y. Thus first we find those values, beginning with $\tan x$:

$$\tan x = \frac{\sin x}{\cos x} = \frac{\frac{2\sqrt{2}}{3}}{\frac{1}{3}} = 2\sqrt{2}.$$

Also,

$$\tan y = \frac{\sin y}{\cos y} = \frac{\frac{1}{4}}{-\frac{\sqrt{15}}{4}} = -\frac{1}{\sqrt{15}} = -\frac{\sqrt{15}}{15}.$$

Thus

$$\tan(x + y) = \frac{\tan x + \tan y}{1 - \tan x \tan y}$$
$$= \frac{2\sqrt{2} - \frac{\sqrt{15}}{15}}{1 + 2\sqrt{2} \cdot \frac{\sqrt{15}}{15}}$$
$$= \frac{30\sqrt{2} - \sqrt{15}}{15 + 2\sqrt{30}},$$

where the last expression is obtained by multiplying the numerator and denominator of the previous expression by 15.

23. $\tan(x - y)$

SOLUTION

$$\tan(x - y) = \frac{\tan x - \tan y}{1 + \tan x \tan y}$$
$$= \frac{2\sqrt{2} + \frac{\sqrt{15}}{15}}{1 - 2\sqrt{2} \cdot \frac{\sqrt{15}}{15}}$$
$$= \frac{30\sqrt{2} + \sqrt{15}}{15 - 2\sqrt{30}},$$

where the last expression is obtained by multiplying the numerator and denominator of the middle expression by 15.

25. Evaluate $\cos(\frac{\pi}{6} + \cos^{-1}\frac{3}{4})$.

SOLUTION To use the addition formula for cosine, we will need to evaluate the cosine and sine of $\cos^{-1}\frac{3}{4}$. Thus we begin by computing those values.

The definition of $\cos^{-1}$ implies that

$$\cos(\cos^{-1}\frac{3}{4}) = \frac{3}{4}.$$

Evaluating $\sin(\cos^{-1}\frac{3}{4})$ takes a bit more work. Let $v = \cos^{-1}\frac{3}{4}$. Thus v is the angle in $[0, \pi]$ such that $\cos v = \frac{3}{4}$. Note that $\sin v \geq 0$ because v is in $[0, \pi]$. Thus

$$\sin(\cos^{-1}\frac{3}{4}) = \sin v = \sqrt{1 - \cos^2 v}$$
$$= \sqrt{1 - \frac{9}{16}} = \sqrt{\frac{7}{16}} = \frac{\sqrt{7}}{4}.$$

Using the addition formula for cosine, we now have

$$\cos(\tfrac{\pi}{6} + \cos^{-1}\tfrac{3}{4})$$

$$= \cos\tfrac{\pi}{6}\,\cos(\cos^{-1}\tfrac{3}{4}) - \sin\tfrac{\pi}{6}\,\sin(\cos^{-1}\tfrac{3}{4})$$

$$= \tfrac{\sqrt{3}}{2}\cdot\tfrac{3}{4} - \tfrac{1}{2}\cdot\tfrac{\sqrt{7}}{4}$$

$$= \tfrac{3\sqrt{3}-\sqrt{7}}{8}.$$

27. Evaluate $\sin(\cos^{-1}\tfrac{1}{4} + \tan^{-1}2)$.

SOLUTION   To use the addition formula for sine, we will need to evaluate the cosine and sine of $\cos^{-1}\tfrac{1}{4}$ and $\tan^{-1}2$. Thus we begin by computing those values.

The definition of $\cos^{-1}$ implies that

$$\cos(\cos^{-1}\tfrac{1}{4}) = \tfrac{1}{4}.$$

Evaluating $\sin(\cos^{-1}\tfrac{1}{4})$ takes a bit more work. Let $u = \cos^{-1}\tfrac{1}{4}$. Thus u is the angle in $[0, \pi]$ such that $\cos u = \tfrac{1}{4}$. Note that $\sin u \geq 0$ because u is in $[0, \pi]$. Thus

$$\sin(\cos^{-1}\tfrac{1}{4}) = \sin u = \sqrt{1 - \cos^2 u}$$

$$= \sqrt{1 - \tfrac{1}{16}} = \sqrt{\tfrac{15}{16}} = \tfrac{\sqrt{15}}{4}.$$

Now let $v = \tan^{-1}2$. Thus v is the angle in $(0, \tfrac{\pi}{2})$ such that $\tan v = 2$ (the range of $\tan^{-1}$ is the interval $(-\tfrac{\pi}{2}, \tfrac{\pi}{2})$, but for this particular v we know that $\tan v$ is positive, which excludes the interval $(-\tfrac{\pi}{2}, 0]$ from consideration). We have

$$2 = \tan v = \frac{\sin v}{\cos v} = \frac{\sqrt{1 - \cos^2 v}}{\cos v}.$$

Squaring the first and last terms above, we get

$$4 = \frac{1 - \cos^2 v}{\cos^2 v}.$$

Solving the equation above for $\cos v$ now gives

$$\cos(\tan^{-1}2) = \cos v = \tfrac{\sqrt{5}}{5}.$$

The identity $\sin v = \sqrt{1 - \cos^2 v}$ now implies that

$$\sin(\tan^{-1}2) = \sin v = \tfrac{2\sqrt{5}}{5}.$$

Using the addition formula for sine, we now have

$$\sin(\cos^{-1}\tfrac{1}{4} + \tan^{-1}2)$$

$$= \sin(\cos^{-1}\tfrac{1}{4})\,\cos(\tan^{-1}2)$$

$$\quad + \cos(\cos^{-1}\tfrac{1}{4})\,\sin(\tan^{-1}2)$$

$$= \tfrac{\sqrt{15}}{4}\cdot\tfrac{\sqrt{5}}{5} + \tfrac{1}{4}\cdot\tfrac{2\sqrt{5}}{5}$$

$$= \tfrac{5\sqrt{3}+2\sqrt{5}}{20}.$$

29. Find a formula for $\cos(\theta + \tfrac{\pi}{2})$.

SOLUTION

$$\cos(\theta + \tfrac{\pi}{2}) = \cos\theta\,\cos\tfrac{\pi}{2} - \sin\theta\,\sin\tfrac{\pi}{2}$$

$$= -\sin\theta.$$

31. Find a formula for $\cos(\theta + \tfrac{\pi}{4})$.

SOLUTION

$$\cos(\theta + \tfrac{\pi}{4}) = \cos\theta\,\cos\tfrac{\pi}{4} - \sin\theta\,\sin\tfrac{\pi}{4}$$

$$= \tfrac{\sqrt{2}}{2}(\cos\theta - \sin\theta)$$

33. Find a formula for $\tan(\theta + \tfrac{\pi}{4})$.

SOLUTION

$$\tan(\theta + \tfrac{\pi}{4}) = \frac{\tan\theta + \tan\tfrac{\pi}{4}}{1 - \tan\theta\,\tan\tfrac{\pi}{4}}$$

$$= \frac{\tan\theta + 1}{1 - \tan\theta}$$

35. Find a formula for $\tan(\theta + \tfrac{\pi}{2})$.

SOLUTION   Because $\tan\tfrac{\pi}{2}$ is undefined, we cannot use the formula for the tangent of the sum of two angles. But the following calculation works:

$$\tan(\theta + \tfrac{\pi}{2}) = \frac{\sin(\theta + \tfrac{\pi}{2})}{\cos(\theta + \tfrac{\pi}{2})}$$

$$= \frac{\sin\theta\,\cos\tfrac{\pi}{2} + \cos\theta\,\sin\tfrac{\pi}{2}}{\cos\theta\,\cos\tfrac{\pi}{2} - \sin\theta\,\sin\tfrac{\pi}{2}}$$

$$= \frac{\cos\theta}{-\sin\theta}$$

$$= -\frac{1}{\tan\theta}.$$

SECTION OBJECTIVES

By the end of this section you should

- understand the amplitude of a function and how function transformations affect it;

- understand the period of a function and how function transformations affect it;

- understand phase shift;

- be able to graph transformations of trigonometric functions that change the amplitude, period, and/or phase shift.

The phases of the moon, which repeat approximately monthly, provide an excellent example of periodic behavior.

Some events have patterns that repeat roughly periodically, such as tides (approximately daily), total daily nationwide ridership on mass transit (approximately weekly, with decreases on weekends as compared to weekdays), phases of the moon (approximately monthly), and the noon temperature in Chicago (approximately yearly, as the seasons change).

The cosine and sine functions are periodic functions and thus are particularly well suited for modeling such events. However, values of the cosine and sine, which are between -1 and 1, and the period of the cosine and sine, which is 2π, rarely fit the events being modeled. Thus transformations of these functions are needed.

In Section 1.3 we discussed various transformations of a function that could stretch the graph of the function vertically or horizontally, shift the graph to the left or right, or reflect the graph through the vertical or horizontal axis. In this section we will revisit function transformations, this time using trigonometric functions. Thus this section will help you review and solidify the concepts of function transformations introduced in Section 1.3 while also deepening your understanding of the behavior of the key trigonometric functions.

Amplitude

Recall that if f is a function, c is a positive number, and a function g is defined by $g(x) = cf(x)$, then the graph of g is obtained by vertically stretching the graph of f by a factor of c (see Section 1.3).

EXAMPLE 1

Here we are sloppily using $\cos x$ as an abbreviation for the function whose value at a number x equals $\cos x$.

(a) Sketch the graphs of the functions $\cos x$ and $3\cos x$ on the interval $[-4\pi, 4\pi]$.

(b) What is the range of the function $3\cos x$?

SOLUTION

(a) The graph of $3\cos x$ is obtained by vertically stretching the graph of $\cos x$ by a factor of 3:

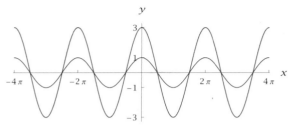

The graphs of cos *x (blue) and* 3 cos *x (red) on the interval* $[-4\pi, 4\pi]$.

For convenience, throughout this section different scales are used on the horizontal and vertical axes.

(b) The range of $3\cos x$ is obtained by multiplying each number in the range of $\cos x$ by 3. Thus the range of $3\cos x$ is the interval $[-3, 3]$.

We say that $3\cos x$ has amplitude 3. Here is the formal definition:

Amplitude

The **amplitude** of a function is one-half the difference between the maximum and minimum values of the function.

Not every function has an amplitude. For example, the tangent function defined on the interval $[0, \frac{\pi}{2})$ does not have a maximum value and thus does not have an amplitude.

For example, the function $3\cos x$ has a maximum value of 3 and a minimum value of -3. Thus the difference between the maximum and minimum values of $3\cos x$ is 6. Half of 6 is 3, and hence the function $3\cos x$ has amplitude 3.

The next example illustrates the effect of multiplying a trigonometric function by a negative number.

(a) Sketch the graphs of the functions $\sin x$ and $-3\sin x$ on the interval $[-4\pi, 4\pi]$.

(b) What is the range of the function $-3\sin x$?

(c) What is the amplitude of the function $-3\sin x$?

EXAMPLE 2

SOLUTION

(a) The graph of $-3\sin x$ is obtained by vertically stretching the graph of $\sin x$ by a factor of 3 and then reflecting through the horizontal axis:

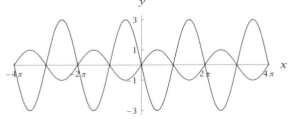

The graphs of sin *x (blue) and* -3 sin *x (red) on the interval* $[-4\pi, 4\pi]$.

(b) The range of $-3\sin x$ is obtained by multiplying each number in the range of $\sin x$ by -3. Thus the range of $-3\sin x$ is the interval $[-3, 3]$.

(c) The function $-3\sin x$ has a maximum value of 3 and a minimum value of -3. Thus the difference between the maximum and minimum values of $3\cos x$ is 6. Half of 6 is 3, and hence the function $-3\sin x$ has amplitude 3.

Recall that if f is a function, a is a positive number, and a function g is defined by $g(x) = f(x) + a$, then the graph of g is obtained by shifting the graph of f up a units (see Section 1.3). The next example illustrates a function whose graph is obtained from the graph of the cosine function by stretching vertically and shifting up.

EXAMPLE 3

(a) Sketch the graphs of $\cos x$ and $2 + 0.3 \cos x$ on the interval $[-4\pi, 4\pi]$.

(b) What is the range of the function $2 + 0.3 \cos x$?

(c) What is the amplitude of the function $2 + 0.3 \cos x$?

SOLUTION

(a) The graph of $2 + 0.3 \cos x$ is obtained by vertically stretching the graph of $\cos x$ by a factor of 0.3 and then shifting up by 2 units:

The graphs of $\cos x$ (blue) and $2 + 0.3 \cos x$ (red) on the interval $[-4\pi, 4\pi]$.

Even though $2 + 0.3 \cos x$ is larger than $\cos x$ for every real number x, the function $2 + 0.3 \cos x$ has a smaller amplitude than the function $\cos x$.

(b) The range of $2 + 0.3 \cos x$ is obtained by multiplying each number in the range of $\cos x$ by 0.3, which produces the interval $[-0.3, 0.3]$, and then adding 2 to each number. Thus the range of $2 + 0.3 \cos x$ is the interval $[1.7, 2.3]$, as can be seen in the graph above.

(c) The function $2 + 0.3 \cos x$ has a maximum value of 2.3 and a minimum value of 1.7. Thus the difference between the maximum and minimum values of $2 + 0.3 \cos x$ is 0.6. Half of 0.6 is 0.3, and hence the function $2 + 0.3 \cos x$ has amplitude 0.3.

Period

The graphs of the cosine and sine functions are periodic, meaning that they repeat their behavior at regular intervals. More specifically,

$$\cos(x + 2\pi) = \cos x \quad \text{and} \quad \sin(x + 2\pi) = \sin x$$

for every number x. In the equations above, we could have replaced 2π with 4π or 6π or 8π, and so on, but no positive number smaller than 2π would make these equations valid for all values of x. Thus we say that the cosine and sine functions have **period** 2π. Here is the formal definition:

Period

Suppose f is a function and $p > 0$. We say that f has **period** p if p is the smallest positive number such that

$$f(x + p) = f(x)$$

for every real number x in the domain of f.

Although the cosine and sine functions have period 2π, the tangent function has period π (see Section 5.6).

Some functions do not repeat their behavior at regular intervals and thus do not have a period. For example, the function f defined by $f(x) = x^2$ does not have a period. A function is called **periodic** if it has a period.

Recall that if f is a function, c is a positive number, and a function h is defined by $h(x) = f(cx)$, then the graph of h is obtained by horizontally stretching the graph of f by a factor of $\frac{1}{c}$ (see Section 1.3). This implies that if f has period p, then h has period $\frac{p}{c}$, as illustrated by the next example.

(a)   Sketch the graphs of $3 + \cos x$ and $\cos(2x)$ on the interval $[-4\pi, 4\pi]$.

(b)   What is the range of the function $\cos(2x)$?

(c)   What is the amplitude of the function $\cos(2x)$?

(d)   What is the period of the function $\cos(2x)$?

EXAMPLE 4

SOLUTION

(a)   The graph of $3 + \cos x$ is obtained by shifting the graph of $\cos x$ up by 3 units. The graph of $\cos(2x)$ is obtained by horizontally stretching the graph of $\cos x$ by a factor of $\frac{1}{2}$:

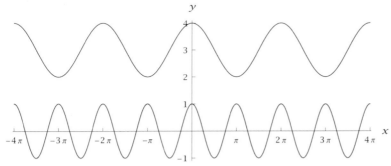

The graphs of $3 + \cos x$ (blue) and $\cos(2x)$ (red) on the interval $[-4\pi, 4\pi]$.

(b)   As x varies over the real numbers, $\cos x$ and $\cos(2x)$ take on the same values. Thus the range of $\cos(2x)$ is the interval $[-1, 1]$.

(c)   The function $\cos(2x)$ has a maximum value of 1 and a minimum value of -1. Thus the difference between the maximum and minimum values of $\cos(2x)$ is 2. Half of 2 is 1, and hence the function $\cos(2x)$ has amplitude 1.

(d) To find the period of $\cos(2x)$, we need to find the smallest positive number p such that
$$\cos(2(x + p)) = \cos(2x)$$
for every number x. The equation above can be rewritten as
$$\cos(2x + 2p) = \cos(2x).$$

If we think of the horizontal axis in the graph in part (a) above as representing time, then we can say that the graph of $\cos(2x)$ oscillates twice as fast as the graph of $\cos x$.

Because the cosine function has period 2π, to find the smallest positive number p that satisfies the equation above for all numbers x we need to solve the simple equation $2p = 2\pi$. Thus $p = \pi$, which means that $\cos(2x)$ has period π.

Another way to compute that $\cos(2x)$ has period π is to recall that the graph of $\cos(2x)$ is obtained by horizontally stretching the graph of $\cos x$ by a factor of $\frac{1}{2}$, as can be seen in the solution to part (a) above. Because the graph of $\cos x$ repeats its behavior in intervals of size 2π (and not in any intervals of smaller size), this means that the graph of $\cos(2x)$ repeats its behavior in intervals of size $\frac{1}{2}(2\pi)$ (and not in any intervals of smaller size); see the figure above. Thus $\cos(2x)$ has period π.

The next example illustrates a transformation of the sine function that changes both the amplitude and the period.

EXAMPLE 5

(a) Sketch the graph of the function $7\sin(2\pi x)$ on the interval $[-3, 3]$.

(b) What is the range of the function $7\sin(2\pi x)$?

(c) What is the amplitude of the function $7\sin(2\pi x)$?

(d) What is the period of the function $7\sin(2\pi x)$?

SOLUTION

(a) The graph of $7\sin(2\pi x)$ is obtained from the graph of $\sin x$ by stretching horizontally by a factor of $\frac{1}{2\pi}$ and stretching vertically by a factor of 7:

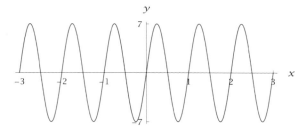

The graph of $7\sin(2\pi x)$ on the interval $[-3, 3]$.

(b) As x varies over the real numbers, $\sin(2\pi x)$ takes on the same values as $\sin x$. Hence the range of the function $\sin(2\pi x)$ is the interval $[-1, 1]$. The range of $7\sin(2\pi x)$ is obtained by multiplying each number in the range of $\sin(2\pi x)$ by 7. Thus the range of $\sin(2\pi x)$ is the interval $[-7, 7]$.

(c) The function $7\sin(2\pi x))$ has a maximum value of 7 and a minimum value of -7. Thus the difference between the maximum and minimum values of $7\sin(2\pi x)$ is 14. Half of 14 is 7, and hence the function $7\sin(2\pi x)$ has amplitude 7.

(d)   To find the period of $7\sin(2\pi x)$, we need to find the smallest positive number p such that

$$7\sin(2\pi(x+p)) = 7\sin(2\pi x)$$

for every number x. After dividing both sides by 7, we can rewrite the equation above as

$$\sin(2\pi x + 2\pi p) = \sin(2\pi x).$$

Because the sine function has period 2π, to find the smallest positive number p that satisfies the equation above for all numbers x we need to solve the simple equation $2\pi p = 2\pi$. Thus $p = 1$, which means that $7\sin(2\pi x)$ has period 1.

As this example shows, multiplying a function by a constant (in this case 7) changes the amplitude but has no effect on the period.

   Another way to compute that $7\sin(2\pi x)$ has period 1 is to recall that the graph of $7\sin(2\pi x)$ is obtained from the graph of $\sin x$ by stretching horizontally by a factor of $\frac{1}{2\pi}$ and stretching vertically by a factor of 7, as can be seen in the solution to part (a) above. Because the graph of $\sin x$ repeats its behavior in intervals of size 2π (and not in any intervals of smaller size), this means that the graph of $7\sin(2\pi x)$ repeats its behavior in intervals of size $\frac{1}{2\pi}(2\pi)$ (and not in any intervals of smaller size); see the figure above. Thus $7\sin(2\pi x)$ has period 1.

Phase Shift

Recall that if f is a function, b is a positive number, and a function g is defined by $g(x) = f(x - b)$, then the graph of g is obtained by shifting the graph of f right b units (see Section 1.3).

EXAMPLE 6

(a)   Sketch the graphs of $\cos x$ and $\cos(x - \frac{\pi}{3})$ on the interval $[-4\pi, 4\pi]$.

(b)   What is the range of the function $\cos(x - \frac{\pi}{3})$?

(c)   What is the amplitude of the function $\cos(x - \frac{\pi}{3})$?

(d)   What is the period of the function $\cos(x - \frac{\pi}{3})$?

(e)   By what fraction of the period of $\cos x$ has the graph been shifted right to obtain the graph of $\cos(x - \frac{\pi}{3})$?

SOLUTION

(a)   The graph of $\cos(x - \frac{\pi}{3})$ is obtained by shifting the graph of $\cos x$ right by $\frac{\pi}{3}$ units:

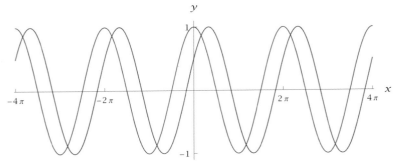

The graphs of $\cos x$ (blue) and $\cos(x - \frac{\pi}{3})$ (red) on the interval $[-4\pi, 4\pi]$.

As this example shows, shifting the graph of a function to the right or the left changes neither the range nor the amplitude nor the period.

(b) As x varies over the real numbers, $\cos x$ and $\cos(x - \frac{\pi}{3})$ take on the same values. Thus the range of $\cos(x - \frac{\pi}{3})$ is the interval $[-1, 1]$.

(c) The function $\cos(x - \frac{\pi}{3})$ has a maximum value of 1 and a minimum value of -1. Thus the difference between the maximum and minimum values of $\cos(x - \frac{\pi}{3})$ is 2. Half of 2 is 1, and hence the function $\cos(x - \frac{\pi}{3})$ has amplitude 1.

(d) Because the graph of $\cos(x - \frac{\pi}{3})$ is obtained by shifting the graph of $\cos x$ right by $\frac{\pi}{3}$ units, the graph of $\cos x$ repeats its behavior in intervals of the same size as the graph of $\cos x$. Because $\cos x$ has period 2π, this implies that $\cos(x - \frac{\pi}{3})$ also has period 2π.

(e) The graph of $\cos x$ is shifted right by $\frac{\pi}{3}$ units to obtain the graph of $\cos(x - \frac{\pi}{3})$. The period of $\cos x$ is 2π. Thus the fraction of the period of $\cos x$ by which the graph has been shifted is $\frac{\pi/3}{2\pi}$, which equals $\frac{1}{6}$.

In the solution to part (e) above, we saw that the graph of $\cos x$ is shifted right by one-sixth of a period to obtain the graph of $\cos(x - \frac{\pi}{3})$. Shifting the graph of a periodic function to the right or the left is often called a **phase shift** because the original function and the new function have the same period and the same behavior, although they are out of phase.

Here is how the $\cos x$ behaves with phase shifts of one-fourth its period, one-half its period, and all of its period:

- If the graph of $\cos x$ is shifted right by $\frac{\pi}{2}$ units, which is one-fourth of its period, then we obtain the graph of $\sin x$; this happens because $\cos(x - \frac{\pi}{2}) = \sin x$ (see Example 2 in Section 5.6).

- If the graph of $\cos x$ is shifted right by π units, which is one-half of its period, then we obtain the graph of $-\cos x$; this happens because $\cos(x - \pi) = -\cos x$ (using the formula in Section 5.6 for $\cos(\theta + n\pi)$, with $n = -1$).

- If the graph of $\cos x$ is shifted right by 2π units, which is its period, then we obtain the graph of $\cos x$; this happens because $\cos(x - 2\pi) = \cos x$.

The next example shows how to deal with a change in amplitude and a change in period and a phase shift.

EXAMPLE 7

(a) Sketch the graphs of the functions $5 \sin \frac{x}{2}$ and $5 \sin(\frac{x}{2} - \frac{\pi}{3})$ on the interval $[-4\pi, 4\pi]$.

(b) What is the range of the function $5 \sin(\frac{x}{2} - \frac{\pi}{3})$?

(c) What is the amplitude of the function $5 \sin(\frac{x}{2} - \frac{\pi}{3})$?

(d) What is the period of the function $5 \sin(\frac{x}{2} - \frac{\pi}{3})$?

(e) By what fraction of the period of $5 \sin \frac{x}{2}$ has the graph been shifted right to obtain the graph of $5 \sin(\frac{x}{2} - \frac{\pi}{3})$?

SOLUTION

(a) The graph of $5 \sin \frac{x}{2}$ is obtained from the graph of $\sin x$ by stretching vertically by a factor of 5 and stretching horizontally by a factor of 2, as shown below. To see how to construct the graph of $5 \sin(\frac{x}{2} - \frac{\pi}{3})$, define a function f by

$$f(x) = 5 \sin \frac{x}{2}.$$

Now

$$5 \sin(\tfrac{x}{2} - \tfrac{\pi}{3}) = 5 \sin \tfrac{x - \frac{2\pi}{3}}{2} = f(x - \tfrac{2\pi}{3}).$$

Thus the graph of $5 \sin(\frac{x}{2} - \frac{\pi}{3})$, shown below, is obtained by shifting the graph of $5 \sin \frac{x}{2}$ right by $\frac{2\pi}{3}$ units:

You may be surprised that the graph is shifted right by $\frac{2\pi}{3}$ units, not $\frac{\pi}{3}$ units. Take extra care with problems that involve both a change of period and a phase shift.

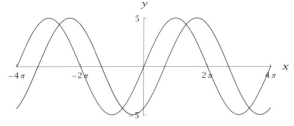

The graphs of $5 \sin \frac{x}{2}$ (blue) and $5 \sin(\frac{x}{2} - \frac{\pi}{3})$ (red) on the interval $[-4\pi, 4\pi]$.

(b) The range of $5 \sin(\frac{x}{2} - \frac{\pi}{3})$ is obtained by multiplying each number in the range of $\sin(\frac{x}{2} - \frac{\pi}{3})$ by 5. Thus the range of $5 \sin(\frac{x}{2} - \frac{\pi}{3})$ is the interval $[-5, 5]$.

(c) The function $5 \sin(\frac{x}{2} - \frac{\pi}{3})$ has a maximum value of 5 and a minimum value of -5. Thus the difference between the maximum and minimum values of $5 \sin(\frac{x}{2} - \frac{\pi}{3})$ is 10. Half of 10 is 5, and hence the function $5 \sin(\frac{x}{2} - \frac{\pi}{3})$ has amplitude 5.

(d) Because the graph of $5 \sin(\frac{x}{2} - \frac{\pi}{3})$ is obtained by shifting the graph of $5 \sin \frac{x}{2}$ right by $\frac{2\pi}{3}$ units, the graph of $5 \sin(\frac{x}{2} - \frac{\pi}{3})$ repeats its behavior in intervals of the same size as the graph of $5 \sin \frac{x}{2}$. Thus the period of $5 \sin(\frac{x}{2} - \frac{\pi}{3})$ equals the period of $5 \sin \frac{x}{2}$, which equals the period of $\sin \frac{x}{2}$ (because changing the amplitude does not change the period). The function $\sin \frac{x}{2}$ has period 4π, because its graph is obtained by horizontally stretching the graph of $\sin x$ (which has period 2π) by a factor of 2. Thus $5 \sin(\frac{x}{2} - \frac{\pi}{3})$ has period 4π.

(e) The graph of the function $5 \sin \frac{x}{2}$ is shifted right by $\frac{2\pi}{3}$ units to obtain the graph of $5 \sin(\frac{x}{2} - \frac{\pi}{3})$. The period of $5 \sin \frac{x}{2}$ is 4π. Thus the fraction of the period of $5 \sin \frac{x}{2}$ by which the graph has been shifted is $\frac{2\pi/3}{4\pi}$, which equals $\frac{1}{6}$.

EXERCISES

Use the following graph for Exercises 1–8:

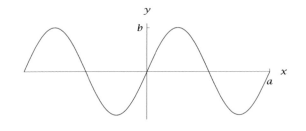

1. Suppose the figure above is part of the graph of the function $3 \sin x$. What is the value of b?

2. Suppose the figure above is part of the graph of the function $4 \sin(5x)$. What is the value of b?

3. Suppose the figure above is part of the graph of the function $\sin(7x)$. What is the value of a?

4. Suppose the figure above is part of the graph of the function $9\sin(6x)$. What is the value of a?

5. Find the smallest positive number c such that the figure above is part of the graph of the function $\sin(x+c)$.

6. Find the smallest positive number c such that the figure above is part of the graph of the function $\sin(x-c)$.

7. Find the smallest positive number c such that the figure above is part of the graph of the function $\cos(x-c)$.

8. Find the smallest positive number c such that the figure above is part of the graph of the function $\cos(x+c)$.
   [*Hint:* The correct answer is not $\frac{\pi}{2}$.]

9. Sketch the graphs of the functions $4\sin x$ and $\sin(4x)$ on the interval $[-\pi, \pi]$ (use the same coordinate axes for both graphs).

10. Sketch the graphs of the functions $-5\sin x$ and $\sin(-5x)$ on the interval $[-\pi, \pi]$ (use the same coordinate axes for both graphs).

11. What is the range of the function $4\sin x$?

12. What is the range of the function $-5\sin x$?

13. What is the range of the function $\sin(4x)$?

14. What is the range of the function $\sin(-5x)$?

15. What is the amplitude of the function $4\sin x$?

16. What is the amplitude of the function $-5\sin x$?

17. What is the amplitude of the function $\sin(4x)$?

18. What is the amplitude of the function $\sin(-5x)$?

19. What is the period of the function $4\sin x$?

20. What is the period of the function $-5\sin x$?

21. What is the period of the function $\sin(4x)$?

22. What is the period of the function $\sin(-5x)$?

23. Sketch the graphs of the functions $2 + \cos x$ and $\cos(2+x)$ on the interval $[-3\pi, 3\pi]$ (use the same coordinate axes for both graphs).

24. Sketch the graphs of the functions $4 - \cos x$ and $\cos(4-x)$ on the interval $[-3\pi, 3\pi]$ (use the same coordinate axes for both graphs).

25. What is the range of the function $\cos(2+x)$?

26. What is the range of the function $\cos(4-x)$?

27. What is the range of the function $2 + \cos x$?

28. What is the range of the function $4 - \cos x$?

29. What is the amplitude of the function $\cos(2+x)$?

30. What is the amplitude of the function $\cos(4-x)$?

31. What is the amplitude of the function $2 + \cos x$?

32. What is the amplitude of the function $4 - \cos x$?

33. What is the period of the function $\cos(2+x)$?

34. What is the period of the function $\cos(4-x)$?

35. What is the period of the function $2 + \cos x$?

36. What is the period of the function $4 - \cos x$?

37. Sketch the graph of the function $5\cos(\pi x)$ on the interval $[-4, 4]$.

38. Sketch the graph of the function $4\cos(3\pi x)$ on the interval $[-2, 2]$.

39. What is the range of the function $5\cos(\pi x)$?

40. What is the range of the function $4\cos(3\pi x)$?

41. What is the amplitude of the function $5\cos(\pi x)$?

42. What is the amplitude of the function $4\cos(3\pi x)$?

43. What is the period of the function $5\cos(\pi x)$?

44. What is the period of the function $4\cos(3\pi x)$?

45. Sketch the graph of the function $7\cos(\frac{\pi}{2}x + \frac{6\pi}{5})$ on the interval $[-8, 8]$.

46. Sketch the graph of the function $6\cos(\frac{\pi}{3}x + \frac{8\pi}{5})$ on the interval $[-9, 9]$.

47. What is the range of the function $7\cos(\frac{\pi}{2}x + \frac{6\pi}{5})$?

48. What is the range of the function $6\cos(\frac{\pi}{3}x + \frac{8\pi}{5})$?

49. What is the amplitude of the function $7\cos(\frac{\pi}{2}x + \frac{6\pi}{5})$?

50. What is the amplitude of the function $6\cos(\frac{\pi}{3}x + \frac{8\pi}{5})$?

51. What is the period of the function $7\cos(\frac{\pi}{2}x + \frac{6\pi}{5})$?

52. What is the period of the function $6\cos(\frac{\pi}{3}x + \frac{8\pi}{5})$?

53. By what fraction of the period of $7\cos(\frac{\pi}{2}x)$ has the graph been shifted left to obtain the graph of $7\cos(\frac{\pi}{2}x + \frac{6\pi}{5})$?

54. By what fraction of the period of $6\cos(\frac{\pi}{3}x)$ has the graph been shifted left to obtain the graph of $6\cos(\frac{\pi}{3}x + \frac{8\pi}{5})$?

55. Sketch the graph of the function $7\cos(\frac{\pi}{2}x + \frac{6\pi}{5}) + 3$ on the interval $[-8, 8]$.

56. Sketch the graph of the function $6\cos(\frac{\pi}{3}x + \frac{8\pi}{5}) + 7$ on the interval $[-9, 9]$.

For Exercises 57-66, assume that f is the function defined by

$$f(x) = a\cos(bx + c) + d,$$

where a, b, c, and d are constants.

57. Find two distinct values for a so that f has amplitude 3.

58. Find two distinct values for a so that f has amplitude $\frac{17}{5}$.

59. Find two distinct values for b so that f has period 4.

60. Find two distinct values for b so that f has period $\frac{7}{3}$.

61. Find values for a and d, with $a > 0$, so that f has range $[3, 11]$.

62. Find values for a and d, with $a > 0$, so that f has range $[-8, 6]$.

63. Find values for a, d, and c, with $a > 0$ and $0 \le c \le \pi$, so that f has range $[3, 11]$ and $f(0) = 10$.

64. Find values for a, d, and c, with $a > 0$ and $0 \le c \le \pi$, so that f has range $[-8, 6]$ and $f(0) = -2$.

65. Find values for a, d, c, and b, with $a > 0$ and $b > 0$ and $0 \le c \le \pi$, so that f has range $[3, 11]$, $f(0) = 10$, and f has period 7.

66. Find values for a, d, c, and b, with $a > 0$ and $b > 0$ and $0 \le c \le \pi$, so that f has range $[-8, 6]$, $f(0) = -2$, and f has period 8.

67. What is the range of the function $\sin^2 x$?

68. What is the range of the function $\cos^2(3x)$?

69. What is the amplitude of the function $\sin^2 x$?

70. What is the amplitude of the function $\cos^2(3x)$?

71. What is the period of the function $\sin^2 x$?

72. What is the period of the function $\cos^2(3x)$?

73. Sketch the graph of the function $\sin^2 x$ on the interval $[-3\pi, 3\pi]$.

74. Sketch the graph of the function $\cos^2(3x)$ on the interval $[-2\pi, 2\pi]$.

PROBLEMS

Use the following graph for Problems 75-77. Note that no scale is shown on the coordinate axes here. Do not assume that the scale is the same on the two coordinate axes:

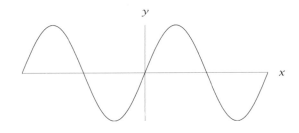

75. Explain why, with no scale on either axis, it is not possible to determine whether the figure above is the graph of $\sin x$, $3\sin x$, $\sin(5x)$, or $3\sin(5x)$.

76. Suppose you are told that the function graphed above is either $\sin x$ or $3\sin x$. To narrow the choice down to just one of these two functions, for which axis would you want to know the scale?

77. Suppose you are told that the function graphed above is either $\sin x$ or $\sin(5x)$. To narrow the choice down to just one of these two functions, for which axis would you want to know the scale?

78. Suppose f is the function whose value at x is the cosine of x degrees. Explain how the graph of f is obtained from the graph of $\cos x$.

79. Explain why a function of the form

$$-5\cos(bx + c),$$

where b and c are constants, can be rewritten in the form

$$5\cos(bx + \tilde{c}),$$

where $\tilde{c}$ is a constant. What is the relationship between $\tilde{c}$ and c?

80. Explain why a function of the form

$$a\cos(-7x + c),$$

where a and c are constants, can be rewritten in the form

$$a\cos(7x + \tilde{c}),$$

where $\tilde{c}$ is a constant. What is the relationship between $\tilde{c}$ and c?

81. Explain why a function of the form

$$a\cos(bx - 4),$$

where a and b are constants, can be rewritten in the form

$$a\cos(bx + \tilde{c}),$$

where $\tilde{c}$ is a positive constant.

82. Explain why a function of the form

$$a\cos(bx + c),$$

where a, b, and c are constants, can be rewritten in the form

$$\tilde{a}\cos(\tilde{b}x + \tilde{c}),$$

where $\tilde{a}$, $\tilde{b}$, and $\tilde{c}$ are nonnegative constants. What is the relationship between $\tilde{c}$ and c?

83. Explain why a function of the form

$$a\sin(bx + c),$$

where a, b, and c are constants, can be rewritten in the form

$$a\cos(bx + \tilde{c}),$$

where $\tilde{c}$ is a constant. What is the relationship between $\tilde{c}$ and c?

84. Explain why a function of the form

$$a\sin(bx + c),$$

where a, b, and c are constants, can be rewritten in the form

$$\tilde{a}\cos(\tilde{b}x + \tilde{c}),$$

where $\tilde{a}$, $\tilde{b}$, and $\tilde{c}$ are nonnegative constants.

85. Suppose f is a function with period p. Explain why

$$f(x + 2p) = f(x)$$

for every number x in the domain of f.

86. Suppose f is a function with period p. Explain why

$$f(x - p) = f(x)$$

for every number x such that $x - p$ is in the domain of f.

87. Suppose f is the function defined by $f(x) = \sin^4 x$. Is f a periodic function? Explain.

88. Suppose g is the function defined by $g(x) = \sin(x^4)$. Is g a periodic function? Explain.

89. Explain how the sine behaves with phase shifts of one-fourth its period, one-half its period, and all of its period, similarly to what was done for the cosine in the bulleted list that appears between Examples 6 and 7.

WORKED-OUT SOLUTIONS *to Odd-numbered Exercises*

Use the following graph for Exercises 1–8:

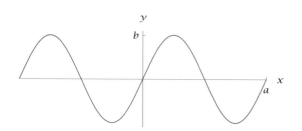

1. Suppose the figure above is part of the graph of the function $3\sin x$. What is the value of b?

   SOLUTION   The function shown in the graph has a maximum value of b. The function $3\sin x$ has a maximum value of 3. Thus $b = 3$.

3. Suppose the figure above is part of the graph of the function $\sin(7x)$. What is the value of a?

   SOLUTION   The function $\sin x$ has period 2π; thus the function $\sin(7x)$ has period $\frac{2\pi}{7}$. The function shown in the graph above has period a. Thus $a = \frac{2\pi}{7}$.

5. Find the smallest positive number c such that the figure above is part of the graph of the function $\sin(x + c)$.

   SOLUTION   The graph of $\sin(x + c)$ is obtained by shifting the graph of $\sin x$ left by c units. The graph above looks like the graph of $\sin x$ (for example, the graph goes through the origin and depicts a function that is increasing on an interval centered at 0).

   The graph above is indeed the graph of $\sin x$ if we take $a = 2\pi$ and $b = 1$. Because $\sin x$ has period 2π, taking $c = 2\pi$ gives the smallest positive number such that the figure above is part of the graph of the function $\sin(x + c)$.

7. Find the smallest positive number c such that the figure above is part of the graph of the function $\cos(x - c)$.

   SOLUTION   The graph of $\cos(x - c)$ is obtained by shifting the graph of $\cos x$ right by c units. Shifting the graph of $\cos x$ right by $\frac{\pi}{2}$ units gives the graph of $\sin x$; in other words, $\cos(x - \frac{\pi}{2}) = \sin x$, as can be verified from the subtraction formula for cosine.

   The graph above is indeed the graph of $\sin x$ if we take $a = 2\pi$ and $b = 1$. No positive number smaller than $\frac{\pi}{2}$ produces a graph of $\cos(x - c)$ that goes through the origin. Thus we must have $c = \frac{\pi}{2}$.

9. Sketch the graphs of the functions $4\sin x$ and $\sin(4x)$ on the interval $[-\pi, \pi]$ (use the same coordinate axes for both graphs).

   SOLUTION   The graph of $4\sin x$ is obtained by vertically stretching the graph of $\sin x$ by a factor of 4. The graph of $\sin(4x)$ is obtained by horizontally stretching the graph of $\sin x$ by a factor of $\frac{1}{4}$:

   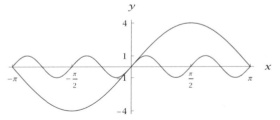

   The graphs of $4\sin x$ (blue) and $\sin(4x)$ (red) on the interval $[-\pi, \pi]$.

11. What is the range of the function $4\sin x$?

    SOLUTION   The range of $4\sin x$ is obtained by multiplying each number in the range of $\sin x$ by 4. Thus the range of $4\sin x$ is the interval $[-4, 4]$.

13. What is the range of the function $\sin(4x)$?

    SOLUTION   As x ranges over the real numbers, $\sin x$ and $\sin(4x)$ take on the same values. Thus the range of $\sin(4x)$ is the interval $[-1, 1]$.

15. What is the amplitude of the function $4\sin x$?

    SOLUTION   The function $4\sin x$ has a maximum value of 4 and a minimum value of -4. Thus the difference between the maximum and minimum values of $4\sin x$ is 8. Half of 8 is 4, and hence the function $4\sin x$ has amplitude 4.

17. What is the amplitude of the function $\sin(4x)$?

    SOLUTION   The function $\sin(4x)$ has a maximum value of 1 and a minimum value of -1. Thus the difference between the maximum and minimum values of $\sin(4x)$ is 2. Half of 2 is 1, and hence the function $\sin(4x)$ has amplitude 1.

19. What is the period of the function $4\sin x$?

    SOLUTION   The period of $4\sin x$ is the same as the period of $\sin x$. Thus $4\sin x$ has period 2π.

21. What is the period of the function $\sin(4x)$?

    SOLUTION The period of $\sin(4x)$ is the period of $\sin x$ divided by 4. Thus $\sin(4x)$ has period $\frac{2\pi}{4}$, which equals $\frac{\pi}{2}$. The figure above shows that $\sin(4x)$ indeed has period $\frac{\pi}{2}$.

23. Sketch the graphs of the functions $2 + \cos x$ and $\cos(2 + x)$ on the interval $[-3\pi, 3\pi]$ (use the same coordinate axes for both graphs).

    SOLUTION The graph of $2 + \cos x$ is obtained by shifting the graph of $\cos x$ up by 2 units. The graph of $\cos(2 + x)$ is obtained by shifting the graph of $\cos x$ left by 2 units:

    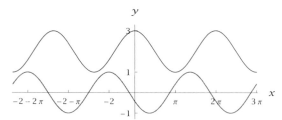

    The graphs of $2 + \cos x$ *(blue) and* $\cos(2 + x)$ *(red) on the interval* $[-3\pi, 3\pi]$.

25. What is the range of the function $\cos(2 + x)$?

    SOLUTION As x ranges over the real numbers, $\cos(2 + x)$ and $\cos x$ take on the same values. Thus the range of $\cos(2 + x)$ is the interval $[-1, 1]$.

27. What is the range of the function $2 + \cos x$?

    SOLUTION The range of $2 + \cos x$ is obtained by adding 2 to each number in the range of $\cos x$. Thus the range of $2 + \cos x$ is the interval $[1, 3]$.

29. What is the amplitude of the function $\cos(2 + x)$?

    SOLUTION The function $\cos(2 + x)$ has a maximum value of 1 and a minimum value of -1. Thus the difference between the maximum and minimum values of $\cos(2 + x)$ is 2. Half of 2 is 1, and hence the function $\cos(2 + x)$ has amplitude 1.

31. What is the amplitude of the function $2 + \cos x$?

    SOLUTION The function $2 + \cos x$ has a maximum value of 3 and a minimum value of 1. Thus the difference between the maximum and minimum values of $2 + \cos x$ is 2. Half of 2 is 1, and hence the function $2 + \cos x$ has amplitude 1.

33. What is the period of the function $\cos(2 + x)$?

    SOLUTION The period of $\cos(2 + x)$ is the same as the period of $\cos x$. Thus $\cos(2 + x)$ has period 2π.

35. What is the period of the function $2 + \cos x$?

    SOLUTION The period of $2 + \cos x$ is the same as the period of $\cos x$. Thus $2 + \cos x$ has period 2π.

37. Sketch the graph of the function $5 \cos(\pi x)$ on the interval $[-4, 4]$.

    SOLUTION The graph of $5 \cos(\pi x)$ is obtained by vertically stretching the graph of $\cos x$ by a factor of 5 and horizontally stretching by a factor of $\frac{1}{\pi}$:

    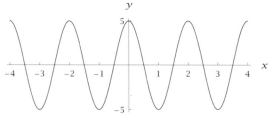

    The graph of $5 \cos(\pi x)$ *on the interval* $[-4, 4]$.

39. What is the range of the function $5 \cos(\pi x)$?

    SOLUTION The range of $5 \cos(\pi x)$ is obtained by multiplying each number in the range of $\cos(\pi x)$ by 5. Thus the range of $5 \cos(\pi x)$ is the interval $[-5, 5]$.

41. What is the amplitude of the function $5 \cos(\pi x)$?

    SOLUTION The function $5 \cos(\pi x)$ has a maximum value of 5 and a minimum value of -5. Thus the difference between the maximum and minimum values of $5 \cos(\pi x)$ is 10. Half of

10 is 5, and hence the function $5\cos(\pi x)$ has amplitude 5.

43. What is the period of the function $5\cos(\pi x)$?

    SOLUTION   The period of $5\cos(\pi x)$ is the period of $\cos x$ divided by π. Thus $5\cos(\pi x)$ has period $\frac{2\pi}{\pi}$, which equals 2. The figure above shows that $5\cos(\pi x)$ indeed has period 2.

45. Sketch the graph of the function $7\cos(\frac{\pi}{2}x + \frac{6\pi}{5})$ on the interval $[-8, 8]$.

    SOLUTION   The graph of $7\cos(\frac{\pi}{2}x)$ is obtained by vertically stretching the graph of $\cos x$ by a factor of 7 and horizontally stretching by a factor of $\frac{2}{\pi}$:

    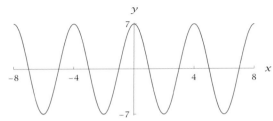

    The graph of $7\cos(\frac{\pi}{2}x)$ *on the interval* $[-8, 8]$.

    To see how to construct the graph of $7\cos(\frac{\pi}{2}x + \frac{6\pi}{5})$, define a function f by

    $$f(x) = 7\cos(\frac{\pi}{2}x).$$

    Now

    $$7\cos(\frac{\pi}{2}x + \frac{6\pi}{5}) = 7\cos(\frac{\pi}{2}(x + \frac{12}{5})) = f(x + \frac{12}{5}).$$

    Thus the graph of $7\cos(\frac{\pi}{2}x + \frac{6\pi}{5})$ is obtained by shifting the graph of $7\cos(\frac{\pi}{2}x)$ left by $\frac{12}{5}$ units:

    The graph of $7\cos(\frac{\pi}{2}x + \frac{6\pi}{5})$
    on the interval $[-8, 8]$.

Note that the peaks of the graph of the function $7\cos(\frac{\pi}{2}x)$ that occur at $x = -4$, at $x = 0$, at $x = 4$, and at $x = 8$ have been shifted by $\frac{12}{5}$ units to the left, now occurring in the graph at $x = -4 - \frac{12}{5}$ (which equals $-\frac{32}{5}$), at $x = 0 - \frac{12}{5}$ (which equals $-\frac{12}{5}$), at $x = 4 - \frac{12}{5}$ (which equals $\frac{8}{5}$), and at $x = 8 - \frac{12}{5}$ (which equals $\frac{28}{5}$).

47. What is the range of the function $7\cos(\frac{\pi}{2}x + \frac{6\pi}{5})$?

    SOLUTION   The range of the function $7\cos(\frac{\pi}{2}x + \frac{6\pi}{5})$ is obtained by multiplying each number in the range of $\cos(\frac{\pi}{2}x + \frac{6\pi}{5})$ by 7. Thus the range of the function $7\cos(\frac{\pi}{2}x + \frac{6\pi}{5})$ is the interval $[-7, 7]$.

49. What is the amplitude of the function $7\cos(\frac{\pi}{2}x + \frac{6\pi}{5})$?

    SOLUTION   The function $7\cos(\frac{\pi}{2}x + \frac{6\pi}{5})$ has a maximum value of 7 and a minimum value of -7. Thus the difference between the maximum and minimum values of $7\cos(\frac{\pi}{2}x + \frac{6\pi}{5})$ is 14. Half of 14 is 7, and hence the function $7\cos(\frac{\pi}{2}x + \frac{6\pi}{5})$ has amplitude 7.

51. What is the period of the function $7\cos(\frac{\pi}{2}x + \frac{6\pi}{5})$?

    SOLUTION   The period of $7\cos(\frac{\pi}{2}x + \frac{6\pi}{5})$ is the period of $\cos x$ divided by $\frac{\pi}{2}$. Thus $7\cos(\frac{\pi}{2}x + \frac{6\pi}{5})$ has period $(2\pi)/(\frac{\pi}{2})$, which equals 4. The figure above shows that $7\cos(\frac{\pi}{2}x + \frac{6\pi}{5})$ indeed has period 4.

53. By what fraction of the period of $7\cos(\frac{\pi}{2}x)$ has the graph been shifted left to obtain the graph of $7\cos(\frac{\pi}{2}x + \frac{6\pi}{5})$?

    SOLUTION   The graph of $7\cos(\frac{\pi}{2}x)$ is shifted left by $\frac{12}{5}$ units to obtain the graph of $7\cos(\frac{\pi}{2}x + \frac{6\pi}{5})$. The period of $7\cos(\frac{\pi}{2}x)$ is 4. Thus the fraction of the period of $7\cos(\frac{\pi}{2}x)$ by which the graph has been shifted is $\frac{12}{5}/4$, which equals $\frac{3}{5}$.

55. Sketch the graph of the function $7\cos(\frac{\pi}{2}x + \frac{6\pi}{5}) + 3$ on the interval $[-8, 8]$.

    SOLUTION   The graph of $7\cos(\frac{\pi}{2}x + \frac{6\pi}{5}) + 3$ is obtained by shifting the graph of $7\cos(\frac{\pi}{2}x + \frac{6\pi}{5})$ up by 3 units. Fortunately we already graphed the function $7\cos(\frac{\pi}{2}x + \frac{6\pi}{5})$ in Exercise 45. Shifting the graph obtained there up by 3 units, we obtain the following graph:

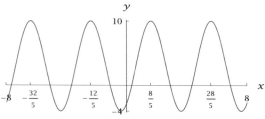

The graph of $7\cos(\frac{\pi}{2}x + \frac{6\pi}{5}) + 3$
on the interval $[-8, 8]$.

For Exercises 57–66, assume that f is the function defined by

$$f(x) = a\cos(bx + c) + d,$$

where a, b, c, and d are constants.

57. Find two distinct values for a so that f has amplitude 3.

SOLUTION The amplitude of a function is half the difference between its maximum and minimum values. The function $\cos(bx + c)$ has a maximum value of 1 and a minimum value of -1 (regardless of the values of b and c).

Thus the function $a\cos(bx + c)$ has a maximum value of $|a|$ and a minimum value of $-|a|$. Hence the function $a\cos(bx + c) + d$ has a maximum value of $|a| + d$ and a minimum value of $-|a| + d$. The difference between this maximum value and this minimum value is $2|a|$. Thus the amplitude of $a\cos(bx + c) + d$ is $|a|$ (notice that the value of d does not affect the amplitude).

Hence the function f has amplitude 3 if $|a| = 3$. Thus we can take $a = 3$ or $a = -3$.

59. Find two distinct values for b so that f has period 4.

SOLUTION The function $\cos x$ has period 2π. If $b > 0$, then the graph of $\cos(bx)$ is obtained by horizontally stretching the graph of $\cos x$ by a factor of $\frac{1}{b}$. Thus $\cos(bx)$ has period $\frac{2\pi}{b}$.

The graph of $\cos(bx + c)$ differs from the graph of $\cos(bx)$ only by a phase shift, which does

not change period. Thus $\cos(bx + c)$ also has period $\frac{2\pi}{b}$.

The graph of $a\cos(bx + c)$ is obtained from the graph of $\cos(bx + c)$ by stretching vertically, which changes the amplitude but not the period. Thus $a\cos(bx + c)$ also has period $\frac{2\pi}{b}$.

The graph of $a\cos(bx + c) + d$ is obtained by shifting the graph of $a\cos(bx + c)$ up or down (depending on whether d is positive or negative). Adding d changes neither the period nor the amplitude. Thus $a\cos(bx + c) + d$ also has period $\frac{2\pi}{b}$.

We want $a\cos(bx + c) + d$ to have period 4. Thus we solve the equation $\frac{2\pi}{b} = 4$, getting $b = \frac{\pi}{2}$. In other words, $a\cos(\frac{\pi}{2}x + c) + d$ has period 4, regardless of the values of a, c, and d.

Note that

$$a\cos(-\tfrac{\pi}{2}x + c) + d = a\cos(\tfrac{\pi}{2}x - c) + d,$$

and thus $a\cos(-\frac{\pi}{2}x + c) + d$ also has period 4. Hence to make f have period 4, we can take $b = \frac{\pi}{2}$ or $b = -\frac{\pi}{2}$.

61. Find values for a and d, with $a > 0$, so that f has range $[3, 11]$.

SOLUTION Because f has range $[3, 11]$, the maximum value of f is 11 and the minimum value of f is 3. Thus the difference between the maximum and minimum values of f is 8. Thus the amplitude of f is half of 8, which equals 4. Reasoning as in the solution to Exercise 57, we see that this implies $a = 4$ or $a = -4$. This exercise requires that $a > 0$, and thus we must take $a = 4$.

The function $4\cos(bx + c)$ has range $[-4, 4]$ (regardless of the values of b and c). Note that $[-4, 4]$ is an interval of length 8, just as $[3, 11]$ is an interval of length 8. We want to find a number d such that each number in the interval $[3, 11]$ is obtained by adding d to a number in the interval $[-4, 4]$. To find d, we can subtract either the left endpoints or the right endpoints of these two intervals. In other words, we can find d by evaluating $3 - (-4)$ or $11 - 4$. Either way, we obtain $d = 7$.

Thus the function $4\cos(bx + c) + 7$ has range $[3, 11]$ (regardless of the values of b and c).

63. Find values for a, d, and c, with $a > 0$ and $0 \le c \le \pi$, so that f has range $[3, 11]$ and $f(0) = 10$.

SOLUTION From the solution to Exercise 61, we see that we need to choose $a = 4$ and $d = 7$. Thus we have

$$f(x) = 4\cos(bx + c) + 7,$$

and we need to choose c so that $0 \le c \le \pi$ and $f(0) = 10$. Hence we need to choose c so that $0 \le c \le \pi$ and

$$4\cos c + 7 = 10.$$

Thus $\cos c = \frac{3}{4}$. Because $0 \le c \le \pi$, this means that $c = \cos^{-1}\frac{3}{4}$.

Thus the function $4\cos(bx + \cos^{-1}\frac{3}{4}) + 7$ has range $[3, 11]$ and $f(0) = 10$ (regardless of the value of b).

65. Find values for a, d, c, and b, with $a > 0$ and $b > 0$ and $0 \le c \le \pi$, so that f has range $[3, 11]$, $f(0) = 10$, and f has period 7.

SOLUTION From the solution to Exercise 63, we see that we need to choose $a = 4$, $c = \cos^{-1}\frac{3}{4}$, and $d = 7$. Thus we have

$$f(x) = 4\cos(bx + \cos^{-1}\frac{3}{4}) + 7,$$

and we need to choose $b > 0$ so that f has period 7. Because the cosine function has period 2π, this means that we need to choose $b = \frac{2\pi}{7}$.

Thus the function $4\cos(\frac{2\pi}{7}x + \cos^{-1}\frac{3}{4}) + 7$ has range $[3, 11]$, equals 10 when $x = 0$, and has period 7.

67. What is the range of the function $\sin^2 x$?

SOLUTION The sine function takes on all the values in the interval $[-1, 1]$; squaring the numbers in this interval gives the numbers in the interval $[0, 1]$. Thus the range of $\sin^2 x$ is the interval $[0, 1]$.

69. What is the amplitude of the function $\sin^2 x$?

SOLUTION The function $\sin^2 x$ has a maximum value of 1 and a minimum value of 0. The difference between this maximum value and this minimum value is 1. Thus the amplitude of $\sin^2 x$ is $\frac{1}{2}$.

71. What is the period of the function $\sin^2 x$?

SOLUTION We know that $\sin(x + \pi) = -\sin x$ for every number x (see Section 5.6). Squaring both sides of this equation, we get

$$\sin^2(x + \pi) = \sin^2 x.$$

No positive number p smaller than π can produce the identity

$$\sin^2(x + p) = \sin^2 x,$$

as can be seen by taking $x = 0$, in which case the equation above becomes $\sin^2 p = 0$. The smallest positive number p satisfying this last equation is π. Putting all this together, we conclude that the function $\sin^2 x$ has period π.

73. Sketch the graph of the function $\sin^2 x$ on the interval $[-3\pi, 3\pi]$.

SOLUTION The function $\sin^2 x$ takes on values between 0 and 1, has period π, equals 0 when x is an integer multiple of π, and equals 1 when x is halfway between two zeros of this function. Thus a sketch of the graph of $\sin^2 x$ should resemble the figure below:

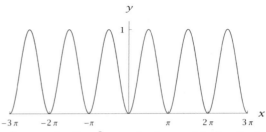

The graph of $\sin^2 x$ *on the interval* $[-3\pi, 3\pi]$.

<table>
</table>

| 6.6 | *Polar Coordinates* |

SECTION OBJECTIVES

By the end of this section you should

- understand polar coordinates;

- be able to convert from polar to rectangular coordinates;

- be able to convert from rectangular to polar coordinates;

- understand graphs in polar coordinates.

The usual rectangular coordinates (x, y) of a point in the coordinate plane tell us the horizontal and vertical displacement of the point from the origin. In this section we discuss another useful coordinate system, called polar coordinates, that focuses more directly on the line segment from the origin to a point. One of the polar coordinates tells us the length of this line segment; the other polar coordinate tells us the angle this line segment makes with the positive horizontal axis.

Defining Polar Coordinates

The two polar coordinates of a point are traditionally called r and θ. These coordinates have a simple geometric description in terms of the line segment from the origin to the point.

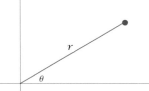

Polar coordinates

The **polar coordinates** r and θ of a point in the coordinate plane are characterized as follows:

- The polar coordinate r is the distance from the origin to the point.

- The polar coordinate θ is the angle between the positive horizontal axis and the line segment from the origin to the point.

EXAMPLE 1

Sketch the line segment from the origin to the point with polar coordinates $r = 3$ and $\theta = \frac{\pi}{4}$.

SOLUTION   The line segment is shown in the following figure. The length of the line segment is 3, and the line segment makes an angle of $\frac{\pi}{4}$ radians (which equals 45°) with the positive horizontal axis.

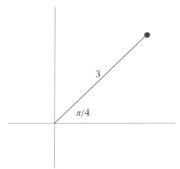

The endpoint of this line segment has polar coordinates $r = 3$ and $\theta = \frac{\pi}{4}$.

As another example, a point whose polar coordinate θ equals $\frac{\pi}{2}$ is on the positive vertical axis (because the positive vertical axis makes an angle of $\frac{\pi}{2}$ with the positive horizontal axis).

As usual, positive angles are measured counterclockwise from the positive horizontal axis. A negative angle corresponds to a movement clockwise from the positive horizontal axis. For example, a point whose polar coordinate θ equals $-\frac{\pi}{2}$ is on the negative vertical axis (because the negative vertical axis makes an angle of $-\frac{\pi}{2}$ with the positive horizontal axis).

Converting from Polar to Rectangular Coordinates

To obtain a formula for converting from polar to rectangular coordinates in the xy-plane, draw the line segment from the origin to the point in question, and then form the right triangle shown in the figure here.

Looking at this right triangle, we see that $\cos\theta = \frac{x}{r}$ and $\sin\theta = \frac{y}{r}$. Solving for x and y gives the following formulas:

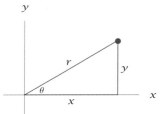

> ### Converting from polar to rectangular coordinates
>
> A point with polar coordinates r and θ has rectangular coordinates
>
> $$x = r\cos\theta \quad \text{and} \quad y = r\sin\theta.$$
>
> in the xy-plane.

Find the rectangular coordinates in the xy-plane of the point with polar coordinates $r = 5$ and $\theta = \frac{\pi}{3}$.

EXAMPLE 2

SOLUTION Using the formulas above, we have

$$x = 5\cos\frac{\pi}{3} = \frac{5}{2} \quad \text{and} \quad y = 5\sin\frac{\pi}{3} = \frac{5\sqrt{3}}{2}.$$

The point with polar coordinates $r = 6$ and $\theta = 0$ has rectangular coordinates $(6, 0)$, as does the point with polar coordinates $r = 6$ and $\theta = 2\pi$. More generally, adding any integer multiple of 2π to an angle does not change the cosine or sine of the angle. Thus the polar coordinates of a point are not unique.

Converting from Rectangular to Polar Coordinates

We have seen how to convert from polar to rectangular coordinates. Now we take up the question of converting in the other direction. In other words, given rectangular coordinates (x, y), how do we find the polar coordinates r and θ?

Recall that the polar coordinate r is the distance from the origin to the point (x, y). Thus

$$r = \sqrt{x^2 + y^2}.$$

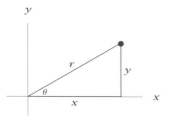

This figure shows that $\tan \theta = \frac{y}{x}$.

To see how to choose the polar coordinate θ given the rectangular coordinates (x, y), let's look once again at the standard figure showing the relationship between polar coordinates and rectangular coordinates.

Looking at the right triangle shown here, we see that $\tan \theta = \frac{y}{x}$. Thus it is tempting to choose $\theta = \tan^{-1} \frac{y}{x}$. However, there are two problems with the formula $\theta = \tan^{-1} \frac{y}{x}$. We now turn to a discussion of these problems.

The first problem involves the lack of uniqueness for the polar coordinate θ, as shown by the following example.

EXAMPLE 3

Find polar coordinates for the point with rectangular coordinates $(1, 1)$.

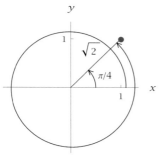

The point with rectangular coordinates $(1, 1)$ has polar coordinates $r = \sqrt{2}$ and $\theta = \frac{\pi}{4}$, but $\theta = \frac{\pi}{4} + 2\pi$ is also a valid choice.

SOLUTION There is no choice about the polar coordinate r for this point—we must take

$$r = \sqrt{1^2 + 1^2} = \sqrt{2}.$$

If we use the formula $\theta = \tan^{-1} \frac{y}{x}$ to obtain the polar coordinate θ for the point with rectangular coordinates $(1, 1)$, we get

$$\theta = \tan^{-1} \frac{1}{1} = \tan^{-1} 1 = \frac{\pi}{4}.$$

The point with polar coordinates $r = \sqrt{2}$ and $\theta = \frac{\pi}{4}$ indeed has rectangular coordinates $(1, 1)$, so it seems that all is well.

However, the point with polar coordinates $r = \sqrt{2}$ and $\theta = \frac{\pi}{4} + 2\pi$ also has rectangular coordinates $(1, 1)$, as shown here, as does the point with polar coordinates $r = \sqrt{2}$ and $\theta = \frac{\pi}{4} + 4\pi$. Or we could have chosen $\theta = \frac{\pi}{4} + 2\pi n$ for any integer n. Thus using the arctangent formula for the polar coordinate θ produced a correct answer in this case, but if we had been seeking one of the other correct choices for θ, the arctangent formula would not have provided it.

The second problem with the formula $\theta = \tan^{-1} \frac{y}{x}$ is more serious. To see how this problem arises, we will look at a few more examples.

Find polar coordinates for the point with rectangular coordinates $(1, -1)$.

EXAMPLE 4

SOLUTION Using the formula for the polar coordinate r, we get

$$r = \sqrt{1^2 + (-1)^2} = \sqrt{2}.$$

If we use the formula $\theta = \tan^{-1} \frac{y}{x}$ to obtain the polar coordinate θ for the point with rectangular coordinates $(1, -1)$, we get

$$\theta = \tan^{-1}\left(\frac{-1}{1}\right) = \tan^{-1}(-1) = -\frac{\pi}{4}.$$

The point with polar coordinates $r = \sqrt{2}$ and $\theta = -\frac{\pi}{4}$ indeed has rectangular coordinates $(1, -1)$. Thus in this case the formula $\theta = \tan^{-1} \frac{y}{x}$ has worked (although it ignored other possible correct choices for θ).

The point with rectangular coordinates $(1, -1)$ has polar coordinates $r = \sqrt{2}$ and $\theta = -\frac{\pi}{4}$ (along with other possible correct choices for θ).

The formula $\theta = \tan^{-1} \frac{y}{x}$ can be wrong, as shown in the next example.

Find polar coordinates for the point with rectangular coordinates $(-1, 1)$.

EXAMPLE 5

SOLUTION Using the formula for the polar coordinate r, we get

$$r = \sqrt{(-1)^2 + 1^2} = \sqrt{2}.$$

If we use the formula $\theta = \tan^{-1} \frac{y}{x}$ to obtain the polar coordinate θ for the point with rectangular coordinates $(-1, 1)$, we get

$$\theta = \tan^{-1}\left(\frac{1}{-1}\right) = \tan^{-1}(-1) = -\frac{\pi}{4}.$$

However, the point with polar coordinates $r = \sqrt{2}$ and $\theta = -\frac{\pi}{4}$ has rectangular coordinates $(1, -1)$, not $(-1, 1)$, which is what we seek now. The figure below shows that the correct choice of the polar coordinate θ for the point $(-1, 1)$ is $\theta = \frac{3\pi}{4}$ (or $\theta = \frac{3\pi}{4} + 2\pi n$ for any integer n).

In this example the formula $\theta = \tan^{-1} \frac{y}{x}$ gives an incorrect result.

The point with rectangular coordinates $(-1, 1)$ has polar coordinates $r = \sqrt{2}$ and $\theta = \frac{3\pi}{4}$ (along with other possible correct choices for θ).

The problem here is that although $\tan^{-1}\frac{y}{x}$ is an angle whose tangent equals $\frac{y}{x}$, there are also other angles whose tangent equals $\frac{y}{x}$. These other angles are obtained by adding an integer multiple of π to $\tan^{-1}\frac{y}{x}$.

The formula $\theta = \tan^{-1}\frac{y}{x}$ produced an incorrect answer when applied to the point $(-1, 1)$ in the example above. To understand why this happened, recall that $\tan^{-1}\frac{y}{x}$ is the angle in the interval $(-\frac{\pi}{2}, \frac{\pi}{2})$ whose tangent equals $\frac{y}{x}$. Note that $r\cos\theta > 0$ if $r > 0$ and $-\frac{\pi}{2} < \theta < \frac{\pi}{2}$. Thus the formula $\theta = \tan^{-1}\frac{y}{x}$ cannot produce a correct polar coordinate θ if $x < 0$.

In the case of the point with rectangular coordinates $(-1, 1)$, the formula $\theta = \tan^{-1}\frac{y}{x} = \tan^{-1}(-1)$ produces the angle $-\frac{\pi}{4}$, which indeed has tangent equal to -1. But the angle $\frac{3\pi}{4}$ (which equals $-\frac{\pi}{4} + \pi$) also has tangent equal to -1. The figure above shows that $\frac{3\pi}{4}$ (or $\frac{3\pi}{4} + 2\pi n$ for any integer n) is the angle that we need.

Another example may help show what is happening here.

EXAMPLE 6

Find polar coordinates for the point with rectangular coordinates $(-1, -1)$.

SOLUTION   Using the formula for the polar coordinate r, we get

$$r = \sqrt{(-1)^2 + (-1)^2} = \sqrt{2}.$$

If we use the formula $\theta = \tan^{-1}\frac{y}{x}$ to obtain the polar coordinate θ for the point with rectangular coordinates $(-1, -1)$, we get

$$\theta = \tan^{-1}\left(\frac{-1}{-1}\right) = \tan^{-1}1 = \frac{\pi}{4}.$$

However, the point with polar coordinates $r = \sqrt{2}$ and $\theta = \frac{\pi}{4}$ has rectangular coordinates $(1, 1)$, not $(-1, -1)$, which is what we seek now. The figure below shows that the correct choice of the polar coordinate θ for the point $(-1, -1)$ is $\theta = -\frac{3\pi}{4}$ (or $\theta = -\frac{3\pi}{4} + 2\pi n$ for any integer n). Note that $-\frac{3\pi}{4} = \frac{\pi}{4} - \pi$; thus the incorrect formula $\theta = \tan^{-1}\frac{y}{x}$ was off by an odd multiple of π.

The point with rectangular coordinates $(-1, -1)$ has polar coordinates $r = \sqrt{2}$ and $\theta = -\frac{3\pi}{4}$ (along with other possible correct choices for θ).

The examples presented in this section should help reinforce the idea that the equation $\tan\theta = t$ is not equivalent to the equation $\theta = \tan^{-1}t$.

The example above shows that the incorrect formula $\theta = \tan^{-1}\frac{y}{x}$ does not distinguish between $\tan^{-1}\frac{1}{1}$ and $\tan^{-1}\left(\frac{-1}{-1}\right)$, giving a result of $\frac{\pi}{4}$ in both cases. Thus we will state the formula for converting from rectangular to polar coordinates in terms of a requirement on $\tan\theta$ rather than a formula involving $\tan^{-1}$.

Although there are many angles θ satisfying $\tan\theta = \frac{y}{x}$, we will need to have $x = r\cos\theta$ and $y = r\sin\theta$. Because r is positive, this means that $\cos\theta$ will need to have the same sign as x and $\sin\theta$ will need to have the same sign as y. If we pick θ accordingly from among the angles whose tangent equals $\frac{y}{x}$, then we will have a correct choice of polar coordinates.

Converting from rectangular to polar coordinates

A point with rectangular coordinates (x, y), with $x \neq 0$, has polar coordinates r and θ that satisfy the equations

$$r = \sqrt{x^2 + y^2} \quad \text{and} \quad \tan \theta = \frac{y}{x},$$

where θ must be chosen so that $\cos \theta$ has the same sign as x and $\sin \theta$ has the same sign as y.

In the summary contained in the box above, we excluded the case where $x = 0$ (in other words, points on the vertical axis) to avoid division by 0 in the formula $\tan \theta = \frac{y}{x}$. To convert $(0, y)$ to polar coordinates, you can choose $\theta = \frac{\pi}{2}$ if $y > 0$ and $\theta = -\frac{\pi}{2}$ if $y < 0$. For example, the point with rectangular coordinates $(0, 5)$ has polar coordinates $r = 5$ and $\theta = \frac{\pi}{2}$. As another example, the point with rectangular coordinates $(0, -6)$ has polar coordinates $r = 6$ and $\theta = -\frac{\pi}{2}$.

The box below provides a convenient summary of how to choose the polar coordinate θ to be in the interval $(-\pi, \pi]$:

Choosing the polar coordinate θ in $(-\pi, \pi]$

The polar coordinate θ corresponding to a point with rectangular coordinates (x, y) can be chosen as follows:

- If $x > 0$, then $\theta = \tan^{-1} \frac{y}{x}$.

- If $x < 0$ and $y \geq 0$, then $\theta = \tan^{-1} \frac{y}{x} + \pi$.

- If $x < 0$ and $y < 0$, then $\theta = \tan^{-1} \frac{y}{x} - \pi$.

- If $x = 0$ and $y > 0$, then $\theta = \frac{\pi}{2}$.

- If $x = 0$ and $y < 0$, then $\theta = -\frac{\pi}{2}$.

Do not memorize this procedure. Instead, focus on understanding the meaning of polar coordinates. With that understanding, this procedure will be clear.

In the box above, none of the cases covers the origin, whose rectangular coordinates are $(0, 0)$. To express the origin in polar coordinates, we need to take $r = 0$. Then any choice of θ will satisfy the equations $0 = r \cos \theta$ and $0 = r \sin \theta$.

Find polar coordinates for the point with rectangular coordinates $(-4, 3)$. For the polar coordinate θ, use radians and choose θ to be in the interval $(-\pi, \pi]$.

EXAMPLE 7

SOLUTION Using the formula for the polar coordinate r, we have

$$r = \sqrt{(-4)^2 + 3^2} = \sqrt{16 + 9} = \sqrt{25} = 5.$$

Because the first coordinate of $(-4, 3)$ is negative and the second coordinate is positive, we have

$$\theta = \tan^{-1}\left(\tfrac{3}{-4}\right) + \pi \approx 2.498.$$

Graphs of Polar Equations

Some curves or regions in the coordinate plane can be described more simply by using polar coordinates instead of rectangular coordinates. Consider, for example, the circle of radius 3 centered at the origin. In rectangular coordinates in the xy-plane, this circle can be described by the equation

$$x^2 + y^2 = 9.$$

Recall that the polar coordinate r measures the distance to the origin. Because the circle of radius 3 centered at the origin equals the set of points whose distance to the origin equals 3, this circle above can be described in polar coordinates by the simpler equation

$$r = 3.$$

The circle described by the equation $r = 3$.

More generally, if c is a positive number, then the equation $r = c$ describes a circle of radius c centered at the origin.

As another example of the use of polar coordinates, the annular region in the xy-plane lying between the circle of radius 2 centered at the origin and the circle of radius 5 centered at the origin can be characterized by the inequalities

$$4 < x^2 + y^2 < 25.$$

In polar coordinates, this region can be characterized by the simpler inequalities

$$2 < r < 5;$$

this region is shown in the figure below.

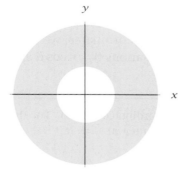

The region satisfying the inequalities $2 < r < 5$.

A point in the coordinate plane has polar coordinate θ equal to $\frac{\pi}{4}$ if and only if the line segment from the origin to the point makes an angle of $\frac{\pi}{4}$ radians (or 45°) with the positive horizontal axis. Thus the equation

$$\theta = \tfrac{\pi}{4}$$

describes the ray illustrated here.

So far our examples of equations in polar coordinates have involved only one of the two polar coordinates. As an example of an equation using both polar coordinates, consider the equation

$$r = \sin\theta.$$

This equation describes the set of points with polar coordinates r and θ, with $r = \sin\theta$. The table below shows a few values of θ and the corresponding values of r:

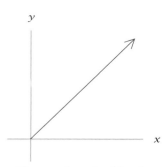

y

The ray described by the equation $\theta = \tfrac{\pi}{4}$. The ray continues without end; only part of it can be shown.

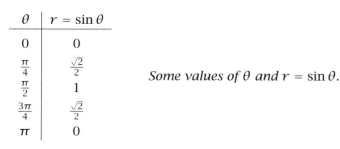

θ	$r = \sin\theta$
0	0
$\tfrac{\pi}{4}$	$\tfrac{\sqrt{2}}{2}$
$\tfrac{\pi}{2}$	1
$\tfrac{3\pi}{4}$	$\tfrac{\sqrt{2}}{2}$
π	0

Some values of θ and $r = \sin\theta$.

The first point in the table above is the origin (because this point has $r = 0$). The second point in the table above is on the ray $\theta = \tfrac{\pi}{4}$, a distance of $\tfrac{\sqrt{2}}{2}$ from the origin. The third point in the table above is on the positive vertical axis (corresponding to $\theta = \tfrac{\pi}{2}$), a distance of 1 from the origin, and so on.

Suppose that instead of considering values of θ in the interval $[0, \pi]$ separated by $\tfrac{\pi}{4}$ as in the table above, we consider values of θ in the interval $[0, \pi]$ separated by $\tfrac{\pi}{50}$. Plotting the resulting points leads to the figure shown here.

This figure appears to be part of a circle. To see that this is indeed a circle, multiply both sides of the equation $r = \sin\theta$ by r, obtaining

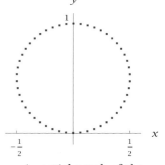

A partial graph of the polar equation $r = \sin\theta$.

$$r^2 = r\sin\theta.$$

Converting this equation to rectangular coordinates in the xy-plane gives

$$x^2 + y^2 = y.$$

Subtract y from both sides, getting

$$x^2 + y^2 - y = 0.$$

Completing the square, we can rewrite this equation as

$$x^2 + (y - \tfrac{1}{2})^2 = \tfrac{1}{4}.$$

Thus we see that the polar equation $r = \sin\theta$ describes a circle centered at $(0, \frac{1}{2})$ with radius $\frac{1}{2}$.

Because r represents the distance from the origin to the point, r cannot be negative. Hence for $\pi < \theta < 2\pi$, the equation $r = \sin\theta$ makes no sense because $\sin\theta$ is negative in this interval. Thus the graph of $r = \sin\theta$ contains no points corresponding to values of θ between π and 2π (in other words, the graph contains no points below the horizontal axis).

Some books allow r to be negative, which is contrary to the notion of r as the distance from the origin.

This restriction on θ to correspond to nonnegative values of r is similar to what happens when we graph the equation $y = \sqrt{x - 3}$. In graphing this equation, we do not consider values of x less than 3 because the equation $y = \sqrt{x - 3}$ makes no sense when $x < 3$. Similarly, the equation $r = \sin\theta$ makes no sense when $\pi < \theta < 2\pi$.

EXERCISES

In Exercises 1–12, convert the polar coordinates given for each point to rectangular coordinates in the xy-plane.

1. $r = \sqrt{19}, \theta = 5\pi$
2. $r = 3, \theta = 2^{1000}\pi$
3. $r = 4, \theta = \frac{\pi}{2}$
4. $r = 5, \theta = -\frac{\pi}{2}$
5. $r = 6, \theta = -\frac{\pi}{4}$
6. $r = 7, \theta = \frac{\pi}{4}$
7. $r = 8, \theta = \frac{\pi}{3}$
8. $r = 9, \theta = -\frac{\pi}{3}$
9. $r = 10, \theta = \frac{\pi}{6}$
10. $r = 11, \theta = -\frac{\pi}{6}$
11. $r = 12, \theta = \frac{11\pi}{4}$
12. $r = 13, \theta = \frac{8\pi}{3}$

In Exercises 13–28, convert the rectangular coordinates given for each point to polar coordinates r and θ. Use radians, and always choose the angle to be in the interval $(-\pi, \pi]$.

13. $(2, 0)$
14. $(-\sqrt{3}, 0)$
15. $(0, -\pi)$
16. $(0, 2\pi)$
17. $(3, 3)$
18. $(4, -4)$
19. $(-5, 5)$
20. $(-6, -6)$
21. 📱 $(3, 2)$
22. 📱 $(4, 7)$
23. 📱 $(3, -7)$
24. 📱 $(6, -5)$
25. 📱 $(-4, 1)$
26. 📱 $(-2, 5)$
27. 📱 $(-5, -2)$
28. 📱 $(-3, -6)$

29. Find the center and radius of the circle whose equation in polar coordinates is $r = 3\cos\theta$.

30. Find the center and radius of the circle whose equation in polar coordinates is $r = 10\sin\theta$.

PROBLEMS

31. Use the law of cosines to find a formula for the distance (in the usual rectangular coordinate plane) between the point with polar coordinates r_1 and θ_1 and the point with polar coordinates r_2 and θ_2.

32. Describe the set of points whose polar coordinates are equal to their rectangular coordinates.

33. What is the relationship between the point with polar coordinates $r = 5, \theta = 0.2$ and the point with polar coordinates $r = 5, \theta = -0.2$?

34. What is the relationship between the point with polar coordinates $r = 5, \theta = 0.2$ and the point with polar coordinates $r = 5, \theta = 0.2 + \pi$?

35. Explain why the polar coordinate θ correspond-ing to a point with rectangular coordinates (x, y) can be chosen as follows:

    - If $x > 0$, then $\theta = \tan^{-1} \frac{y}{x}$.
    - If $x < 0$, then $\theta = \tan^{-1} \frac{y}{x} + \pi$.
    - If $x = 0$ and $y \geq 0$, then $\theta = \frac{\pi}{2}$.
    - If $x = 0$ and $y < 0$, then $\theta = -\frac{\pi}{2}$.

    Furthermore, explain why the formula above always leads to a choice of θ in the interval $[-\frac{\pi}{2}, \frac{3\pi}{2})$.

36. Give a formula for the polar coordinate θ cor-responding to a point with rectangular coordi-nates (x, y), similar in nature to the formula in the previous problem, that always leads to a choice of θ in the interval $[0, 2\pi)$.

WORKED-OUT SOLUTIONS *to Odd-numbered Exercises*

In Exercises 1–12, convert the polar coordinates given for each point to rectangular coordinates in the xy-plane.

1. $r = \sqrt{19}, \theta = 5\pi$

    SOLUTION We have
    $$x = \sqrt{19}\cos(5\pi) \quad \text{and} \quad y = \sqrt{19}\sin(5\pi).$$

    Subtracting even multiples of π does not change the value of cosine and sine. Because $5\pi - 4\pi = \pi$, we have $\cos(5\pi) = \cos\pi = -1$ and $\sin(5\pi) = \sin\pi = 0$. Thus the point in question has rectangular coordinates $(-\sqrt{19}, 0)$.

3. $r = 4, \theta = \frac{\pi}{2}$

    SOLUTION We have
    $$x = 4\cos\frac{\pi}{2} \quad \text{and} \quad y = 4\sin\frac{\pi}{2}.$$

    Because $\cos\frac{\pi}{2} = 0$ and $\sin\frac{\pi}{2} = 1$, the point in question has rectangular coordinates $(0, 4)$.

5. $r = 6, \theta = -\frac{\pi}{4}$

    SOLUTION We have
    $$x = 6\cos(-\frac{\pi}{4}) \quad \text{and} \quad y = 6\sin(-\frac{\pi}{4}).$$

    Because $\cos(-\frac{\pi}{4}) = \frac{\sqrt{2}}{2}$ and $\sin(-\frac{\pi}{4}) = -\frac{\sqrt{2}}{2}$, the point in question has rectangular coordinates $(3\sqrt{2}, -3\sqrt{2})$.

7. $r = 8, \theta = \frac{\pi}{3}$

    SOLUTION We have

$$x = 8\cos\frac{\pi}{3} \quad \text{and} \quad y = 8\sin\frac{\pi}{3}.$$
    Because $\cos\frac{\pi}{3} = \frac{1}{2}$ and $\sin\frac{\pi}{3} = \frac{\sqrt{3}}{2}$, the point in question has rectangular coordinates $(4, 4\sqrt{3})$.

9. $r = 10, \theta = \frac{\pi}{6}$

    SOLUTION We have
    $$x = 10\cos\frac{\pi}{6} \quad \text{and} \quad y = 10\sin\frac{\pi}{6}.$$
    Because $\cos\frac{\pi}{6} = \frac{\sqrt{3}}{2}$ and $\sin\frac{\pi}{6} = \frac{1}{2}$, the point in question has rectangular coordinates $(5\sqrt{3}, 5)$.

11. $r = 12, \theta = \frac{11\pi}{4}$

    SOLUTION We have
    $$x = 12\cos\frac{11\pi}{4} \quad \text{and} \quad y = 12\sin\frac{11\pi}{4}.$$
    Because $\cos\frac{11\pi}{4} = -\frac{\sqrt{2}}{2}$ and $\sin\frac{11\pi}{4} = \frac{\sqrt{2}}{2}$, the point in question has rectangular coordinates $(-6\sqrt{2}, 6\sqrt{2})$.

In Exercises 13–28, convert the rectangular coor-dinates given for each point to polar coordinates r and θ. Use radians, and always choose the an-gle to be in the interval $(-\pi, \pi]$.

13. $(2, 0)$

    SOLUTION The point $(2, 0)$ is on the positive x-axis, 2 units from the origin. Thus we have $r = 2, \theta = 0$.

15. $(0, -\pi)$

    SOLUTION The point $(0, -\pi)$ is on the negative y-axis, π units from the origin. Thus we have $r = \pi, \theta = -\frac{\pi}{2}$.

17. $(3, 3)$

SOLUTION We have

$$r = \sqrt{3^2 + 3^2} = \sqrt{3^2 \cdot 2} = \sqrt{3^2}\sqrt{2} = 3\sqrt{2}.$$

The point $(3, 3)$ is on the portion of the line $y = x$ that makes a $45°$ angle with the positive x-axis. Thus $\theta = \frac{\pi}{4}$.

19. $(-5, 5)$

SOLUTION We have

$$r = \sqrt{5^2 + (-5)^2} = \sqrt{5^2 \cdot 2} = \sqrt{5^2}\sqrt{2} = 5\sqrt{2}.$$

The point $(-5, 5)$ is on the portion of the line $y = -x$ that makes a $135°$ angle with the positive x-axis. Thus $\theta = \frac{3\pi}{4}$.

21. 📱 $(3, 2)$

SOLUTION We have

$$r = \sqrt{3^2 + 2^2} = \sqrt{13} \approx 3.61.$$

Because both coordinates of $(3, 2)$ are positive, we have

$$\theta = \tan^{-1}\tfrac{2}{3} \approx 0.588 \text{ radians.}$$

23. 📱 $(3, -7)$

SOLUTION We have

$$r = \sqrt{3^2 + (-7)^2} = \sqrt{58} \approx 7.62.$$

Because the first coordinate of $(3, -7)$ is positive, we have

$$\theta = \tan^{-1}\left(\tfrac{-7}{3}\right) \approx -1.166 \text{ radians.}$$

25. 📱 $(-4, 1)$

SOLUTION We have

$$r = \sqrt{(-4)^2 + 1^2} = \sqrt{17} \approx 4.12.$$

Because the first coordinate of $(-4, 1)$ is negative and the second coordinate is positive, we have

$$\theta = \tan^{-1}\left(\tfrac{1}{-4}\right) + \pi = \tan^{-1}\left(-\tfrac{1}{4}\right) + \pi$$

$$\approx 2.897 \text{ radians.}$$

27. 📱 $(-5, -2)$

SOLUTION We have

$$r = \sqrt{(-5)^2 + (-2)^2} = \sqrt{29} \approx 5.39.$$

Because both coordinates of $(-5, -2)$ are negative, we have

$$\theta = \tan^{-1}\left(\tfrac{-2}{-5}\right) - \pi = \tan^{-1}\tfrac{2}{5} - \pi$$

$$\approx -2.761 \text{ radians.}$$

29. Find the center and radius of the circle whose equation in polar coordinates is $r = 3\cos\theta$.

SOLUTION Multiply both sides of the equation $r = 3\cos\theta$ by r, obtaining

$$r^2 = 3r\cos\theta.$$

Now convert the equation above to rectangular coordinates in the xy-plane, getting

$$x^2 + y^2 = 3x.$$

Subtract $3x$ from both sides, getting

$$x^2 - 3x + y^2 = 0.$$

Completing the square, we can rewrite this equation as

$$\left(x - \tfrac{3}{2}\right)^2 + y^2 = \tfrac{9}{4}.$$

Thus we see that the polar equation $r = 3\cos\theta$ describes a circle centered at $\left(\tfrac{3}{2}, 0\right)$ with radius $\tfrac{3}{2}$.

6.7 | *Vectors and the Complex Plane*

An Algebraic and Geometric Introduction to Vectors

To see how vectors naturally arise, consider weather data at a specific location and at a specific time. One key item of weather data is the temperature, which is a number that could be positive or negative (for example, 14 degrees Fahrenheit or −10 degrees Celsius, depending on the units used). Another key item of weather data is the wind velocity, which consists of a magnitude that must be a nonnegative number (for example, 10 miles per hour) and a direction (for example, northwest).

Measurements that have both a magnitude and a direction are common enough to deserve their own terminology:

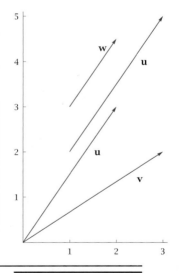

Vector

A **vector** is characterized by its magnitude and its direction. Usually a vector is drawn as an arrow:

- the length of the arrow is the **magnitude** of the vector;

- the direction of the arrowhead indicates the **direction** of the vector.

The figure in the margin above shows vectors **u**, **v**, and **w**.

EXAMPLE 1

(a) Explain why the two vectors labeled **u** are equal to each other.

(b) Explain why **v** ≠ **u**.

(c) Explain why **w** ≠ **u**.

SOLUTION

Symbols denoting vectors appear in boldface in this book to emphasize that these symbols denote vectors, not numbers.

(a) The two vectors with the label **u** have the same length and their arrows are parallel and point in the same direction. Because these two vectors have the same magnitude and the same direction, they are equal vectors and thus it is appropriate to give them the same label **u**.

(b) The vector **v** shown above has the same magnitude as **u** but points in a different direction (the arrows are not parallel); thus **v** ≠ **u**.

(c) The vector **w** shown above has the same direction as **u** (parallel arrows pointing in the same direction) but has a different magnitude; thus **w** ≠ **u**.

A vector is determined by its initial point and its endpoint. For example, the vector **v** shown above has initial point the origin $(0,0)$ and has endpoint $(3,2)$. One version of the vector **u** shown above has initial point the origin $(0,0)$ and has endpoint $(2,3)$; the other version of the vector **u** shown above has initial point $(1,2)$ and has endpoint $(3,5)$.

Sometimes a vector is specified by giving only the endpoint, with the assumption that the initial point is the origin. For example, the vector **v** shown above can be identified as $(3,2)$, with the understanding that the origin is the initial point. In other words, sometimes we think of $(3,2)$ as a point in the coordinate plane, and sometimes we think of $(3,2)$ as the vector from the origin to that point.

The notation $(3,2)$ can be used to denote the point shown above.

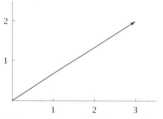

The notation $(3,2)$ can also be used to denote the vector shown above.

Notation for vectors with initial point at the origin

If a and b are real numbers, then (a,b) can denote either a point or a vector, depending on the context. In other words, (a,b) can be used as notation for either of the two following objects:

- the point in the coordinate plane whose first coordinate is a and whose second coordinate is b;

- the vector whose initial point is the origin and whose endpoint has first coordinate a and second coordinate b.

Polar coordinates allow us to be more precise about what we mean by the magnitude and direction of a vector:

Magnitude and direction of a vector

Suppose a vector **u** is positioned with its initial point at the origin. If the endpoint of **u** has polar coordinates r and θ, then

- the **magnitude** of **u**, denoted $|\mathbf{u}|$, is defined to equal r;

- the **direction** of **u** is determined by θ, which is the angle that **u** makes with the positive horizontal axis.

*The endpoint of this vector **u** has polar coordinates r and θ.*

The result below simply repeats the conversion from rectangular to polar coordinates that we saw in the last section:

Computing the magnitude and direction of a vector

If $\mathbf{u} = (a, b)$, then

- $|\mathbf{u}| = \sqrt{a^2 + b^2}$;

- an angle θ that determines the direction of $\mathbf{u}$ satisfies the equation $\tan\theta = \frac{b}{a}$, where θ must be chosen so that $\cos\theta$ has the same sign as a and $\sin\theta$ has the same sign as b.

In the last bulleted item above, as usual we must exclude the case where $a = 0$ to avoid division by 0.

Suppose the vector u shown above has endpoint $(5, 3)$. Find the magnitude of u and an angle that determines the direction of u.

EXAMPLE 2

SOLUTION We have
$$|\mathbf{u}| = \sqrt{5^2 + 3^2} = \sqrt{34} \approx 5.83$$
and
$$\theta = \tan^{-1}\tfrac{3}{5} \approx 0.54.$$

Because the polar coordinate θ is not unique, we could also add any integer multiple of 2π to this choice of θ.

Two vectors can be added, producing another vector. The following definition presents vector addition from the viewpoint of a vector as an arrow and from the viewpoint of identifying a vector with its endpoint (assuming that the initial point is the origin):

Vector addition

- If the endpoint of a vector $\mathbf{u}$ coincides with the initial point of a vector $\mathbf{v}$, then the vector $\mathbf{u} + \mathbf{v}$ has the same initial point as $\mathbf{u}$ and the same endpoint as $\mathbf{v}$.

- If $\mathbf{u} = (a, b)$ and $\mathbf{v} = (c, d)$, then $\mathbf{u} + \mathbf{v} = (a + c, b + d)$.

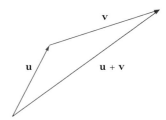

Suppose $\mathbf{u} = (1, 2)$ and $\mathbf{v} = (3, 1)$.

EXAMPLE 3

(a) Draw a figure illustrating the sum of $\mathbf{u}$ and $\mathbf{v}$ as arrows.

(b) Compute the sum $\mathbf{u} + \mathbf{v}$ using coordinates.

SOLUTION

(a) The figure below on the left shows the two vectors **u** and **v**, both with their initial point at the origin. In the figure below in the middle, the vector **v** has been moved parallel to its original position so that its initial point now coincides with the endpoint of **u**. The figure below on the right shows that the vector **u** + **v** is the vector with the same initial point as **u** and the same endpoint as the second version of **v**.

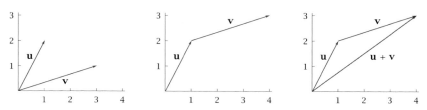

To add two vectors, position one vector so that its initial point coincides with the endpoint of the other vector.

(b) The coordinates of **u** + **v** are obtained by adding the corresponding coordinates of **u** and **v**. Thus **u** + **v** = $(1, 2) + (3, 1) = (4, 3)$. Note that $(4, 3)$ is the endpoint of the red vector above on the right.

Vector addition satisfies the usual commutative and associative properties that are expected for an operation of addition. In other words,

$$\mathbf{u} + \mathbf{v} = \mathbf{v} + \mathbf{u} \quad \text{and} \quad (\mathbf{u} + \mathbf{v}) + \mathbf{w} = \mathbf{u} + (\mathbf{v} + \mathbf{w})$$

for all vectors **u**, **v**, and **w**. The figure in the margin shows why vector addition is commutative.

The zero vector, denoted with boldface **0**, is the vector whose magnitude is 0. The direction of the zero vector can be chosen to be anything convenient and is irrelevant because this vector has magnitude 0. In terms of coordinates, the zero vector equals $(0, 0)$. For every vector **u**, we have

$$\mathbf{u} + \mathbf{0} = \mathbf{0} + \mathbf{u} = \mathbf{u}.$$

Vectors have additive inverses, just as numbers do. The following definition presents the additive inverse from the viewpoint of a vector as an arrow and from the viewpoint of identifying a vector with its coordinates:

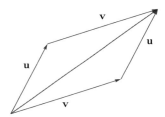

The vector shown here as the red diagonal of the parallelogram equals **u** + **v** *and also equals* **v** + **u**.

Additive inverse

- If **u** is a vector, then −**u** has the same magnitude as **u** and has the opposite direction.

- If **u** has polar coordinates r and θ, then −**u** has polar coordinates r and $\theta + \pi$.

- If **u** = (a, b), then −**u** = $(-a, -b)$.

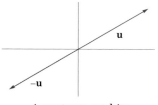

A vector **u** *and its additive inverse* −**u**.

Make sure you understand why the definition above implies that

$$\mathbf{u} + (-\mathbf{u}) = \mathbf{0}$$

for every vector $\mathbf{u}$.

Two vectors can be subtracted, producing another vector. The following definition presents vector subtraction from the viewpoint of a vector as an arrow and from the viewpoint of identifying a vector with its endpoint (assuming that the initial point is the origin):

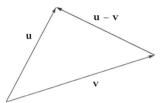

> ### Vector subtraction
>
> - If $\mathbf{u}$ and $\mathbf{v}$ are vectors, then the difference $\mathbf{u} - \mathbf{v}$ is defined by
>
> $$\mathbf{u} - \mathbf{v} = \mathbf{u} + (-\mathbf{v}).$$
>
> - If vectors $\mathbf{u}$ and $\mathbf{v}$ are positioned to have the same initial point, then $\mathbf{u} - \mathbf{v}$ is the vector whose initial point is the endpoint of $\mathbf{v}$ and whose endpoint is the endpoint of $\mathbf{u}$.
>
> - If $\mathbf{u} = (a, b)$ and $\mathbf{v} = (c, d)$, then $\mathbf{u} - \mathbf{v} = (a - c, b - d)$.

To figure out in which direction the arrow for $\mathbf{u} - \mathbf{v}$ points, choose the direction that makes $\mathbf{v} + (\mathbf{u} - \mathbf{v})$ equal to $\mathbf{u}$.

EXAMPLE 4

Suppose $\mathbf{u} = (1, 2)$ and $\mathbf{v} = (3, 1)$.

(a) Draw a figure using arrows illustrating the difference $\mathbf{u} - \mathbf{v}$.

(b) Compute the difference $\mathbf{u} - \mathbf{v}$ using coordinates.

SOLUTION

(a) The figure below on the left shows the two vectors $\mathbf{u}$ and $\mathbf{v}$, both with their initial point at the origin. The figure below in the center shows that the vector $\mathbf{u} - \mathbf{v}$ is the vector whose initial point is the endpoint of $\mathbf{v}$ and whose endpoint is the endpoint of $\mathbf{u}$.

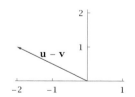

To subtract two vectors, position them to have the same initial point.

(b) The coordinates of $\mathbf{u} - \mathbf{v}$ are obtained by subtracting the corresponding coordinates of $\mathbf{u}$ and $\mathbf{v}$. Thus $\mathbf{u} - \mathbf{v} = (1, 2) - (3, 1) = (-2, 1)$. The figure above on the right shows $\mathbf{u} - \mathbf{v}$ with its initial point at the origin and its endpoint at $(-2, 1)$.

Often the word "scalar" is used to emphasize that a quantity is a number rather than a vector.

The word **scalar** is simply a fancy word for number. The term **scalar multiplication** refers to the operation defined below of multiplying a vector by a scalar, producing a vector.

Scalar multiplication

Suppose t is a real number and **u** is a vector.

- The vector $t\mathbf{u}$ has magnitude $|t|$ times the magnitude of **u**.

  - If $t > 0$, then $t\mathbf{u}$ has the same direction as **u**.
  - If $t < 0$, then $t\mathbf{u}$ has the opposite direction of **u**.

- Suppose **u** has polar coordinates r and θ.

  - If $t > 0$, then $t\mathbf{u}$ has polar coordinates tr and θ.
  - If $t < 0$, then $t\mathbf{u}$ has polar coordinates $-tr$ and $\theta + \pi$.

- If $\mathbf{u} = (a, b)$, then $t\mathbf{u} = (ta, tb)$.

EXAMPLE 5

Suppose $\mathbf{u} = (2, 1)$.

(a) Draw a figure showing **u**, $2\mathbf{u}$, and $-2\mathbf{u}$.

(b) Compute $2\mathbf{u}$ and $-2\mathbf{u}$ using coordinates.

SOLUTION

(a) The figure below on the left shows **u**. The figure below in the middle shows that $2\mathbf{u}$ is the vector having twice the magnitude of **u** and having the same direction as **u**. The figure below on the right shows that $-2\mathbf{u}$ is the vector having twice the magnitude of **u** and having the opposite direction of **u**.

  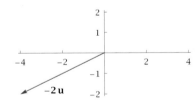

(b) The coordinates of $2\mathbf{u}$ are obtained by multiplying the corresponding coordinates of **u** by 2, and the coordinates of $-2\mathbf{u}$ are obtained by multiplying the corresponding coordinates of **u** by -2. Thus we have $2\mathbf{u} = (4, 2)$ and $-2\mathbf{u} = (-4, -2)$.

Dividing a vector by a nonzero scalar c is the same as multiplying by $\frac{1}{c}$. For example, $\frac{\mathbf{u}}{2}$ should be interpreted to mean $\frac{1}{2}\mathbf{u}$. Note that division by a vector is not defined.

The Dot Product

We have defined the sum and difference of two vectors, and the scalar product of a number and a vector. Each of those operations produces another vector. Now we turn to another operation, called the dot product, that produces a number from two vectors. We begin with a definition in terms of coordinates; soon we will also see a formula from the viewpoint of vectors as arrows.

Dot product

Suppose $\mathbf{u} = (a, b)$ and $\mathbf{v} = (c, d)$. Then the **dot product** of $\mathbf{u}$ and $\mathbf{v}$, denoted $\mathbf{u} \cdot \mathbf{v}$, is defined by

$$\mathbf{u} \cdot \mathbf{v} = ac + bd.$$

Always remember that the dot product of two vectors is a number, not a vector.

Thus to compute the dot product of two vectors, multiply together the first coordinates, multiply together the second coordinates, and then add these two products.

Suppose $\mathbf{u} = (2, 3)$ and $\mathbf{v} = (5, 4)$. Compute $\mathbf{u} \cdot \mathbf{v}$.

EXAMPLE 6

SOLUTION   Using the formula above, we have

$$\mathbf{u} \cdot \mathbf{v} = 2 \cdot 5 + 3 \cdot 4 = 10 + 12 = 22.$$

The dot product has the following pleasant algebraic properties:

Algebraic properties of the dot product

Suppose $\mathbf{u}$, $\mathbf{v}$, and $\mathbf{w}$ are vectors and t is a real number. Then

- $\mathbf{u} \cdot \mathbf{v} = \mathbf{v} \cdot \mathbf{u}$ (commutativity);

- $\mathbf{u} \cdot (\mathbf{v} + \mathbf{w}) = \mathbf{u} \cdot \mathbf{v} + \mathbf{u} \cdot \mathbf{w}$ (distributive property);

- $(t\mathbf{u}) \cdot \mathbf{v} = \mathbf{u} \cdot (t\mathbf{v}) = t(\mathbf{u} \cdot \mathbf{v})$;

- $\mathbf{u} \cdot \mathbf{u} = |\mathbf{u}|^2$.

To verify the last property above, suppose $\mathbf{u} = (a, b)$. Then

$$\mathbf{u} \cdot \mathbf{u} = a^2 + b^2 = (\sqrt{a^2 + b^2})^2 = |\mathbf{u}|^2,$$

as desired. The verifications of the first three properties are left as similarly easy problems for the reader.

The next result gives a remarkably useful formula for computing $\mathbf{u} \cdot \mathbf{v}$ in terms of the magnitude of $\mathbf{u}$, the magnitude of $\mathbf{v}$, and the angle between these two vectors.

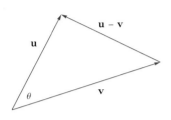

Computing the dot product geometrically

If **u** and **v** are vectors with the same initial point, then

$$\mathbf{u} \cdot \mathbf{v} = |\mathbf{u}|\,|\mathbf{v}|\cos\theta,$$

where θ is the angle between **u** and **v**.

To verify the formula above, first draw the vector $\mathbf{u} - \mathbf{v}$, whose initial point is the endpoint of **v** and whose endpoint is the endpoint of **u**, as shown in the margin here. Next, use the algebraic properties of the dot product to compute a formula for $|\mathbf{u} - \mathbf{v}|^2$ as follows:

$$
\begin{aligned}
|\mathbf{u} - \mathbf{v}|^2 &= (\mathbf{u} - \mathbf{v}) \cdot (\mathbf{u} - \mathbf{v}) \\
&= \mathbf{u} \cdot (\mathbf{u} - \mathbf{v}) - \mathbf{v} \cdot (\mathbf{u} - \mathbf{v}) \\
&= \mathbf{u} \cdot \mathbf{u} - \mathbf{u} \cdot \mathbf{v} - \mathbf{v} \cdot \mathbf{u} + \mathbf{v} \cdot \mathbf{v} \\
&= |\mathbf{u}|^2 - 2\mathbf{u} \cdot \mathbf{v} + |\mathbf{v}|^2.
\end{aligned}
$$

Now apply the law of cosines to the triangle above, getting

$$|\mathbf{u} - \mathbf{v}|^2 = |\mathbf{u}|^2 + |\mathbf{v}|^2 - 2|\mathbf{u}|\,|\mathbf{v}|\cos\theta.$$

Finally, set the two expressions that we have obtained for $|\mathbf{u} - \mathbf{v}|^2$ equal to each other, getting

$$|\mathbf{u}|^2 - 2\mathbf{u} \cdot \mathbf{v} + |\mathbf{v}|^2 = |\mathbf{u}|^2 + |\mathbf{v}|^2 - 2|\mathbf{u}|\,|\mathbf{v}|\cos\theta.$$

Subtract $|\mathbf{u}|^2 + |\mathbf{v}|^2$ from both sides of the equation above, and then divide both sides by -2, getting $\mathbf{u} \cdot \mathbf{v} = |\mathbf{u}|\,|\mathbf{v}|\cos\theta$, completing our derivation of this remarkable formula.

EXAMPLE 7

Find the angle between the vectors $(1, 2)$ and $(3, 1)$.

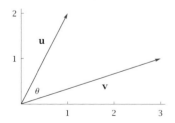

SOLUTION Let $\mathbf{u} = (1, 2)$, let $\mathbf{v} = (3, 1)$, and let θ denote the angle between these two vectors, as shown in the margin here.

We could solve this problem without using the dot product by noting that the angle between the positive horizontal axis and **u** equals $\tan^{-1} 2$ and the angle between the positive horizontal axis and **v** equals $\tan^{-1} \frac{1}{3}$; thus $\theta = \tan^{-1} 2 - \tan^{-1} \frac{1}{3}$. Neither $\tan^{-1} 2$ nor $\tan^{-1} \frac{1}{3}$ can be evaluated exactly, and thus it appears that this expression for θ cannot be simplified.

However, we have another way to compute θ. Specifically, from the formula above we have

Problem 42 gives a nice application of this example.

$$\cos\theta = \frac{\mathbf{u} \cdot \mathbf{v}}{|\mathbf{u}|\,|\mathbf{v}|} = \frac{5}{\sqrt{5}\sqrt{10}} == \frac{5}{\sqrt{5}\sqrt{5}\sqrt{2}} = \frac{1}{\sqrt{2}} = \frac{\sqrt{2}}{2}.$$

The equation above now implies that $\theta = \frac{\pi}{4}$.

The Complex Plane

We turn now to an interpretation of the coordinate plane that will help us better understand the complex number system. Recall that a complex number has the form $a + bi$, where a and b are real numbers and $i^2 = -1$.

To represent complex numbers graphically, label the horizontal axis of a coordinate plane in the usual fashion but label the vertical axis with multiples of i, as shown here. A complex number $a + bi$, where a and b are real numbers, is then represented by the point whose first coordinate is a and whose second coordinate is b. For example, the figure here shows the complex number $2 + 3i$.

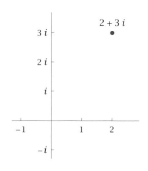

The coordinate plane with the labeling shown here is called the **complex plane**. We can think of the system of complex numbers as being represented by the complex plane, just as we can think of the system of real numbers as being represented by the real line.

When we think of the real numbers as a subset of the complex numbers, then the real numbers correspond to the horizontal axis in the figure above. Thus the horizontal axis of the complex plane is sometimes called the **real axis** and the vertical axis is sometimes called the **imaginary axis**.

Sometimes we identify a complex number $a + bi$ with the vector whose initial point is the origin and whose endpoint is located at the point corresponding to $a + bi$ in the complex plane, as shown here. Because complex numbers are added and subtracted by adding and subtracting their real and imaginary parts separately, complex addition and subtraction have the same geometric interpretation as vector addition and subtraction.

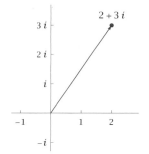

Recall that the absolute value of a real number is the distance from 0 to the number (when thinking of numbers as points on the real line). Similarly, the absolute value of a complex number is the distance from the origin to the complex number (when thinking of complex numbers as points on the complex plane).

When thinking of complex numbers as vectors in the complex plane, the absolute value of a complex number is the magnitude of the corresponding vector. Here is the formal definition:

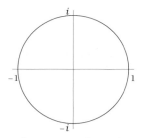

> ### Absolute value of a complex number
>
> If $z = a + bi$, where a and b are real numbers, then the **absolute value** of z, denoted $|z|$, is defined by
>
> $$|z| = \sqrt{a^2 + b^2}.$$

The unit circle in the complex plane is described by the equation $|z| = 1$.

Evaluate $|2 + 3i|$.

EXAMPLE 8

SOLUTION $|2 + 3i| = \sqrt{2^2 + 3^2} = \sqrt{13} \approx 3.60555$

*2 + i and its complex
conjugate 2 − i.*

Recall that the complex conjugate of a complex number $a + bi$, where a and b are real numbers, is defined by $\overline{a + bi} = a - bi$. In terms of the complex plane, the operation of complex conjugation is the same as reflection through the real axis. The figure here shows a complex number and its complex conjugate.

A nice formula connects the complex conjugate and the absolute value of a complex number. To derive this formula, suppose $z = a + bi$, where a and b are real numbers. Then

$$z\bar{z} = (a + bi)(a - bi) = a^2 - b^2 i^2 = a^2 + b^2 = (\sqrt{a^2 + b^2})^2 = |z|^2.$$

We record this result as follows:

Complex conjugates and absolute values

If z is a complex number, then

$$z\bar{z} = |z|^2.$$

Using polar coordinates with complex numbers can bring extra insight into the operations of multiplication, division, and raising a complex number to a power. The basic idea here is to think of a complex number as a point in the complex plane and then use the polar coordinates that were developed in the previous section.

Polar form of a complex number

The **polar form** of a complex number z is an expression of the form

$$z = r(\cos \theta + i \sin \theta),$$

where $r = |z|$ and θ, which is called the **argument** of z, is the angle that z (thought of as a vector) makes with the positive horizontal axis.

When writing a complex number z in polar form, there is only one correct choice for the number $r \geq 0$ in the expression above: we must choose $r = |z|$. However, given any correct choice for the argument θ, another correct choice can be found by adding an integer multiple of 2π.

EXAMPLE 9

Write the following complex numbers in polar form:

(a) 2

(b) $3i$

(c) $1 + i$

(d) $\sqrt{3} - i$

SOLUTION

(a) We have $|2| = 2$. Also, because 2 is on the positive horizontal axis, the argument of 2 is 0. Thus the polar form of 2 is

$$2 = 2(\cos 0 + i \sin 0).$$

We could also write

$$2 = 2(\cos(2\pi) + i \sin(2\pi)) \quad \text{or} \quad 2 = 2(\cos(4\pi) + i \sin(4\pi))$$

or use any integer multiple of 2π as the argument.

(b) We have $|3i| = 3$. Also, because $3i$ is on the positive vertical axis, the argument of $3i$ is $\frac{\pi}{2}$. Thus the polar form of $3i$ is

$$3i = 3(\cos \tfrac{\pi}{2} + i \sin \tfrac{\pi}{2}).$$

As usual, we could add any integer multiple of 2π to the argument $\frac{\pi}{2}$ to obtain other arguments.

(c) We have $|1 + i| = \sqrt{1^2 + 1^2} = \sqrt{2}$. Also, the figure here shows that the argument θ of $1 + i$ is $\frac{\pi}{4}$. Thus the polar form of $1 + i$ is

$$1 + i = \sqrt{2}(\cos \tfrac{\pi}{4} + i \sin \tfrac{\pi}{4}).$$

(d) We have $|\sqrt{3} - i| = \sqrt{\sqrt{3}^2 + 1^2} = \sqrt{4} = 2$. Note that $\tan^{-1}(-\frac{1}{\sqrt{3}}) = -\frac{\pi}{6}$. Thus the figure here shows that the argument θ of $\sqrt{3} - i$ is $-\frac{\pi}{6}$. Thus the polar form of $\sqrt{3} - i$ is

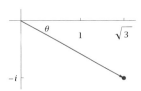

$$\sqrt{3} - i = 2(\cos(-\tfrac{\pi}{6}) + i \sin(-\tfrac{\pi}{6})).$$

Multiplicative inverses of complex numbers have a nice interpretation in polar form. Suppose $z = r(\cos \theta + i \sin \theta)$ is a nonzero complex number (from now on, whenever we write an expression like this, we will assume that $r = |z|$ and that θ is a real number). We know that $|z|^2 = z\bar{z}$. Dividing both sides of this equation by $z|z|^2$ shows that

$$\frac{1}{z} = \frac{\bar{z}}{|z|^2} = \frac{r(\cos \theta - i \sin \theta)}{r^2} = \frac{\cos \theta - i \sin \theta}{r}.$$

We record this result as follows:

> **Multiplicative inverse of a complex number in polar form**
>
> If $z = r(\cos \theta + i \sin \theta)$ is a nonzero complex number, then
>
> $$\frac{1}{z} = \frac{1}{r}(\cos \theta - i \sin \theta) = \frac{1}{r}(\cos(-\theta) + i \sin(-\theta)).$$

This result states that the polar form of $\frac{1}{z}$ is obtained from the polar form $r(\cos \theta + i \sin \theta)$ of z by replacing r by $\frac{1}{r}$ and replacing θ by $-\theta$.

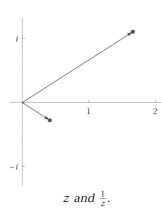

z and $\frac{1}{z}$.

The figure here illustrates the formula above. The longer vector represents a complex number z with $|z| = 2$. The shorter vector represents the complex number $\frac{1}{z}$; it has absolute value $\frac{1}{2}$, and its argument is the negative of the argument of z.

Complex multiplication also has a pretty expression in terms of polar form. Suppose

$$z_1 = r_1(\cos\theta_1 + i\sin\theta_1) \quad \text{and} \quad z_2 = r_2(\cos\theta_2 + i\sin\theta_2).$$

Then

$$z_1 z_2 = r_1 r_2(\cos\theta_1 + i\sin\theta_1)(\cos\theta_2 + i\sin\theta_2)$$

$$= r_1 r_2((\cos\theta_1\cos\theta_2 - \sin\theta_1\sin\theta_2) + i(\sin\theta_1\cos\theta_2 + \cos\theta_1\sin\theta_2))$$

$$= r_1 r_2(\cos(\theta_1 + \theta_2) + i\sin(\theta_1 + \theta_2)),$$

where the addition formulas for cosine and sine from Section 6.4 gave the last simplification.

The quotient $\frac{z_1}{z_2}$ can now be computed by thinking of division by z_2 as multiplication by $\frac{1}{z_2}$. We already know that the polar form of $\frac{1}{z_2}$ is obtained by replacing r_2 by $\frac{1}{r_2}$ and replacing θ_2 by $-\theta_2$. Thus we can summarize our results on complex multiplication and division as follows:

Complex multiplication and division in polar form

If $z_1 = r_1(\cos\theta_1 + i\sin\theta_1)$ and $z_2 = r_2(\cos\theta_2 + i\sin\theta_2)$, then

$$z_1 z_2 = r_1 r_2(\cos(\theta_1 + \theta_2) + i\sin(\theta_1 + \theta_2))$$

Here we assume that $z_2 \neq 0$.

and

$$\frac{z_1}{z_2} = \frac{r_1}{r_2}(\cos(\theta_1 - \theta_2) + i\sin(\theta_1 - \theta_2)).$$

Sometimes words are easier to remember than symbols, so here is a re-statement of the results above:

Complex multiplication and division in polar form

- The absolute value of the product of two complex numbers is the product of their absolute values.

- The argument of the product of two complex numbers is the sum of their arguments.

- The absolute value of the quotient of two complex numbers is the quotient of their absolute values.

- The argument of the quotient of two complex numbers is the differ-ence of their arguments.

De Moivre's Theorem

Suppose $z = r(\cos\theta + i\sin\theta)$. Take $z_1 = z$ and $z_2 = z$ in the formula just derived for complex multiplication in polar form, getting

$$z^2 = r^2(\cos(2\theta) + i\sin(2\theta)).$$

Now apply the formula again, this time with $z_1 = z^2$ and $z_2 = z$, getting

$$z^3 = r^3(\cos(3\theta) + i\sin(3\theta)).$$

If we apply the formula once more, this time with $z_1 = z^3$ and $z_2 = z$, we get

$$z^4 = r^4(\cos(4\theta) + i\sin(4\theta)).$$

This pattern continues, leading to the beautiful result called De Moivre's Theorem:

De Moivre's Theorem

If $z = r(\cos\theta + i\sin\theta)$ and n is a positive integer, then

$$z^n = r^n(\cos(n\theta) + i\sin(n\theta)).$$

Abraham de Moivre first published this result in 1722.

De Moivre's Theorem is a wonderful tool for evaluating large powers of complex numbers.

Evaluate $(\sqrt{3} - i)^{100}$.

EXAMPLE 10

SOLUTION One way to solve this problem would be to multiply $\sqrt{3} - i$ times itself 100 times. But that process would be tedious, it would take a long time, and errors can easily creep into such long calculations. Instead, we will use De Moivre's Theorem.

As the first step in using De Moivre's Theorem, we must write $(\sqrt{3} - i)$ in polar form. However, we already did that in Example 9, getting

$$\sqrt{3} - i = 2(\cos(-\tfrac{\pi}{6}) + i\sin(-\tfrac{\pi}{6})).$$

De Moivre's Theorem tells us that

$$(\sqrt{3} - i)^{100} = 2^{100}(\cos(-\tfrac{100}{6}\pi) + i\sin(-\tfrac{100}{6}\pi)).$$

Now $-\frac{100}{6} = -\frac{50}{3} = -16 - \frac{2}{3}$. Because even multiples of π can be discarded when computing values of cosine and sine, we thus have

$$(\sqrt{3} - i)^{100} = 2^{100}(\cos(-\tfrac{2}{3}\pi) + i\sin(-\tfrac{2}{3}\pi))$$

$$= 2^{100}(-\tfrac{1}{2} - \tfrac{\sqrt{3}}{2}i)$$

$$= -2^{99}(1 + \sqrt{3}i).$$

De Moivre's Theorem also allows us to find roots of complex numbers.

EXAMPLE 11

Find three distinct complex numbers z such that $z^3 = 1$.

SOLUTION   Taking $z = 1$ is one choice of a complex number such that $z^3 = 1$, but the other two choices are not obvious. To find them, suppose $z = r(\cos\theta + i\sin\theta)$. Then

$$z^3 = r^3(\cos(3\theta) + i\sin(3\theta)).$$

We want z^3 to equal 1. Thus we take $r = 1$. Now we must find values of θ such that $\cos(3\theta) = 1$ and $\sin(3\theta) = 0$. One choice is to take $\theta = 0$, which gives us

$$z = 1,$$

which we already knew was one choice for z.

Another choice of θ that satisfies $\cos(3\theta) = 1$ and $\sin(3\theta) = 0$ can be obtained by choosing $3\theta = 2\pi$, which means $\theta = \frac{2\pi}{3}$. This choice of θ gives

$$z = -\tfrac{1}{2} + \tfrac{\sqrt{3}}{2}i.$$

Yet another choice of θ that satisfies $\cos(3\theta) = 1$ and $\sin(3\theta) = 0$ can be obtained by choosing $3\theta = 4\pi$, which means $\theta = \frac{4\pi}{3}$. This choice of θ gives

You should verify that $(-\tfrac{1}{2} \pm \tfrac{\sqrt{3}}{2}i)^3 = 1$.

$$z = -\tfrac{1}{2} - \tfrac{\sqrt{3}}{2}i.$$

Thus three distinct values of z such that $z^3 = 1$ are 1, $-\tfrac{1}{2} + \tfrac{\sqrt{3}}{2}i$, and $-\tfrac{1}{2} - \tfrac{\sqrt{3}}{2}i$.

EXERCISES

1. Suppose $\mathbf{u} = (3, 2)$. Evaluate $|\mathbf{u}|$.

2. Suppose $\mathbf{v} = (-5, 2)$. Evaluate $|\mathbf{v}|$.

3. Find two distinct numbers t such that $|t(1, 4)| = 5$.

4. Find two distinct numbers r such that $|r(3, -7)| = 4$.

5. Suppose $\mathbf{u} = (2, 1)$ and $\mathbf{v} = (3, 1)$.

    (a) Draw a figure illustrating the sum of $\mathbf{u}$ and $\mathbf{v}$ as arrows.

    (b) Compute the sum $\mathbf{u} + \mathbf{v}$ using coordinates.

6. Suppose $\mathbf{u} = (-3, 2)$ and $\mathbf{v} = (-2, -1)$.

    (a) Draw a figure illustrating the sum of $\mathbf{u}$ and $\mathbf{v}$ as arrows.

    (b) Compute the sum $\mathbf{u} + \mathbf{v}$ using coordinates.

7. Suppose $\mathbf{u} = (2, 1)$ and $\mathbf{v} = (3, 1)$.

    (a) Draw a figure using arrows illustrating the difference $\mathbf{u} - \mathbf{v}$.

    (b) Compute the difference $\mathbf{u} - \mathbf{v}$ using coordinates.

8. Suppose $\mathbf{u} = (-3, 2)$ and $\mathbf{v} = (-2, -1)$.

    (a) Draw a figure using arrows illustrating the difference $\mathbf{u} - \mathbf{v}$.

    (b) Compute the difference $\mathbf{u} - \mathbf{v}$ using coordinates.

9. Suppose $\mathbf{u} = (3, 2)$ and $\mathbf{v} = (4, 5)$. Compute $\mathbf{u} \cdot \mathbf{v}$.

10. Suppose $\mathbf{u} = (-4, 5)$ and $\mathbf{v} = (2, -6)$. Compute $\mathbf{u} \cdot \mathbf{v}$.

11. Use the dot product to find the angle between the vectors $(2, 3)$ and $(3, 4)$.

12. ✆ Use the dot product to find the angle between the vectors $(3, -5)$ and $(-4, 3)$.

13. Evaluate $|4 - 3i|$.

14. Evaluate $|7 + 12i|$.

15. Write $2 - 2i$ in polar form.

16. Write $-3 + 3\sqrt{3}i$ in polar form.

17. Evaluate $(2 - 2i)^{333}$.

18. Evaluate $(-3 + 3\sqrt{3}i)^{555}$.

19. Find four distinct complex numbers z such that $z^4 = -2$.

20. Find three distinct complex numbers z such that $z^3 = 4i$.

PROBLEMS

21. Find coordinates for five different vectors $\mathbf{u}$, each of which has magnitude 5.

22. Find coordinates for three different vectors $\mathbf{u}$, each of which has a direction determined by an angle of $\frac{\pi}{6}$.

23. Suppose $\mathbf{u}$ and $\mathbf{v}$ are vectors with the same initial point. Explain why $|\mathbf{u} - \mathbf{v}|$ equals the distance between the endpoint of $\mathbf{u}$ and the endpoint of $\mathbf{v}$.

24. Using coordinates, show that if t is a scalar and $\mathbf{u}$ and $\mathbf{v}$ are vectors, then

$$t(\mathbf{u} + \mathbf{v}) = t\mathbf{u} + t\mathbf{v}.$$

25. Using coordinates, show that if s and t are scalars and $\mathbf{u}$ is a vector, then

$$(s + t)\mathbf{u} = s\mathbf{u} + t\mathbf{u}.$$

26. Using coordinates, show that if s and t are scalars and $\mathbf{u}$ is a vector, then

$$(st)\mathbf{u} = s(t\mathbf{u}).$$

27. Show that if $\mathbf{u}$ and $\mathbf{v}$ are vectors, then

$$2(|\mathbf{u}|^2 + |\mathbf{v}|^2) = |\mathbf{u} + \mathbf{v}|^2 + |\mathbf{u} - \mathbf{v}|^2.$$

[*This equality is often called the Parallelogram Equality, for reasons that are explained by the next problem.*]

28. Draw an appropriate figure and explain why the result in the problem above implies the following result: In any parallelogram, the sum of the squares of the lengths of the four sides equals the sum of the squares of the lengths of the two diagonals.

29. Explain why two vectors with the same initial point are perpendicular if and only if their dot product equals 0.

30. Suppose $\mathbf{u}$ and $\mathbf{v}$ are vectors, neither of which is $\mathbf{0}$. Show that $\mathbf{u} \cdot \mathbf{v} = |\mathbf{u}|\,|\mathbf{v}|$ if and only if $\mathbf{u}$ and $\mathbf{v}$ have the same direction.

31. Suppose $\mathbf{u}$ and $\mathbf{v}$ are vectors. Show that

$$|\mathbf{u} \cdot \mathbf{v}| \le |\mathbf{u}|\,|\mathbf{v}|.$$

[*This result is called the Cauchy-Schwarz Inequality. Although this problem asks for a proof only in the setting of vectors in the plane, a similar inequality is true in many other settings and has important uses throughout mathematics.*]

32. Show that if $\mathbf{u}$ and $\mathbf{v}$ are vectors, then

$$|\mathbf{u} + \mathbf{v}|^2 = |\mathbf{u}|^2 + 2\mathbf{u} \cdot \mathbf{v} + |\mathbf{v}|^2.$$

33. Show that if $\mathbf{u}|$ and $\mathbf{v}$ are vectors, then

$$|\mathbf{u} + \mathbf{v}| \le |\mathbf{u}| + |\mathbf{v}|.$$

[*Hint:* Square both sides and use the two previous problems.]

34. Interpret the inequality in the previous problem (which is often called the Triangle Inequality) as saying something interesting about triangles.

35. Show that if z is a complex number, then the real part of z is in the interval $[-|z|, |z|]$.

36. Show that if z is a complex number, then the imaginary part of z is in the interval $[-|z|, |z|]$.

37. Suppose z is a nonzero complex number. Show that $\bar{z} = \frac{1}{z}$ if and only if $|z| = 1$.

38. Suppose z is a complex number whose real part has absolute value equal to $|z|$. Show that z is a real number.

39. Suppose z is a complex number whose imaginary part has absolute value equal to $|z|$. Show that the real part of z equals 0.

40. Suppose w and z are complex numbers. Show that

$$|wz| = |w|\,|z|.$$

41. Suppose w and z are complex numbers. Show that

$$|w + z| \leq |w| + |z|.$$

42. In Example 7 we found that the angle θ equals $\tan^{-1} 2 - \tan^{-1} \frac{1}{3}$ and also that θ equals $\frac{\pi}{4}$. Thus

$$\tan^{-1} 2 - \tan^{-1} \tfrac{1}{3} = \tfrac{\pi}{4}.$$

   (a) Use one of the inverse trigonometric identities from Section 5.8 to show that the equation above can be rewritten as

   $$\tan^{-1} 2 + \tan^{-1} 3 = \tfrac{3\pi}{4}.$$

(b) Explain how adding $\frac{\pi}{4}$ to both sides of the equation above leads to the beautiful equation

$$\tan^{-1} 1 + \tan^{-1} 2 + \tan^{-1} 3 = \pi.$$

[*Problem 55 in Section 6.4 gives another derivation of the equation above.*]

43. Describe the subset of the complex plane consisting of the complex numbers z such that z^3 is a real number.

44. Describe the subset of the complex plane consisting of the complex numbers z such that z^3 is a positive number.

WORKED-OUT SOLUTIONS *to Odd-numbered Exercises*

1. Suppose $\mathbf{u} = (3, 2)$. Evaluate $|\mathbf{u}|$.

   SOLUTION

   $$|\mathbf{u}| = \sqrt{3^2 + 2^2} = \sqrt{9 + 4} = \sqrt{13}$$

3. Find two distinct numbers t such that $|t(1, 4)| = 5$.

   SOLUTION   Because $t(1, 4) = (t, 4t)$, we have

   $$|t(1, 4)| = |(t, 4t)| = \sqrt{t^2 + 16t^2} = \sqrt{17t^2}.$$

   We want this to equal 5, which means $17t^2 = 25$. Thus $t^2 = \frac{25}{17}$, which implies that $t = \pm\frac{5}{\sqrt{17}}$, which can be rewritten as $t = \pm\frac{5\sqrt{17}}{17}$.

5. Suppose $\mathbf{u} = (2, 1)$ and $\mathbf{v} = (3, 1)$.

   (a) Draw a figure illustrating the sum of $\mathbf{u}$ and $\mathbf{v}$ as arrows.

   (b) Compute the sum $\mathbf{u} + \mathbf{v}$ using coordinates.

   SOLUTION

(a) The figure below on the left shows the two vectors $\mathbf{u}$ and $\mathbf{v}$, both with their initial point at the origin. In the figure below on the right, the vector $\mathbf{v}$ has been moved parallel to its original position so that its initial point now coincides with the endpoint of $\mathbf{u}$. The last figure below shows that the vector $\mathbf{u} + \mathbf{v}$ is the vector with the same initial point as $\mathbf{u}$ and the same endpoint as the second version of $\mathbf{v}$.

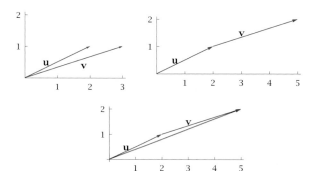

(b) The coordinates of $\mathbf{u} + \mathbf{v}$ are obtained by adding the corresponding coordinates of $\mathbf{u}$ and $\mathbf{v}$. Thus

$$\mathbf{u} + \mathbf{v} = (2, 1) + (3, 1) = (5, 2).$$

7. Suppose $\mathbf{u} = (2, 1)$ and $\mathbf{v} = (3, 1)$.

   (a) Draw a figure using arrows illustrating the difference $\mathbf{u} - \mathbf{v}$.

   (b) Compute the difference $\mathbf{u} - \mathbf{v}$ using coordinates.

   SOLUTION

(a) The figure below shows the two vectors $\mathbf{u}$ and $\mathbf{v}$, both with their initial point at the origin. The vector $\mathbf{u} - \mathbf{v}$ is the vector whose initial point is the endpoint of $\mathbf{v}$ and whose endpoint is the endpoint of $\mathbf{u}$.

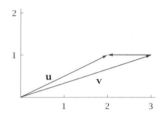

(b) The coordinates of $\mathbf{u} - \mathbf{v}$ are obtained by subtracting the corresponding coordinates of $\mathbf{u}$ and $\mathbf{v}$. Thus

$$\mathbf{u} - \mathbf{v} = (2, 1) - (3, 1) = (-1, 0).$$

9. Suppose $\mathbf{u} = (3, 2)$ and $\mathbf{v} = (4, 5)$. Compute $\mathbf{u} \cdot \mathbf{v}$.

SOLUTION $\mathbf{u} \cdot \mathbf{v} = 3 \cdot 4 + 2 \cdot 5 = 12 + 10 = 22$

11. 📱 Use the dot product to find the angle between the vectors $(2, 3)$ and $(3, 4)$.

SOLUTION   Note that $|(2, 3)| = \sqrt{13}$, $|(3, 4)| = 5$, and $(2, 3) \cdot (3, 4) = 18$. Thus the angle between $(2, 3)$ and $(3, 4)$ is

$$\cos^{-1} \frac{(2, 3) \cdot (3, 4)}{|(2, 3)| \, |(3, 4)|} = \cos^{-1} \frac{18}{5\sqrt{13}} \approx 0.0555.$$

13. Evaluate $|4 - 3i|$.

SOLUTION

$$|4 - 3i| = \sqrt{4^2 + (-3)^2} = \sqrt{16 + 9} = \sqrt{25} = 5$$

15. Write $2 - 2i$ in polar form.

SOLUTION   First we compute $|2 - 2i|$:

$$|2 - 2i| = \sqrt{2^2 + (-2)^2} = \sqrt{8} = \sqrt{4 \cdot 2} = 2\sqrt{2}.$$

The vector whose initial point is the origin and whose endpoint is $2 - 2i$ in the complex plane makes an angle of $-\frac{\pi}{4}$ with the positive horizontal axis. Thus

$$2 - 2i = 2\sqrt{2}\left(\cos\left(-\tfrac{\pi}{4}\right) + i \sin\left(-\tfrac{\pi}{4}\right)\right)$$

gives the polar form of $2 - 2i$.

17. Evaluate $(2 - 2i)^{333}$.

SOLUTION   From Exercise 15 we know that

$$2 - 2i = 2\sqrt{2}\left(\cos\left(-\tfrac{\pi}{4}\right) + i \sin\left(-\tfrac{\pi}{4}\right)\right).$$

Thus

$$(2 - 2i)^{333} = \left(2\sqrt{2}\right)^{333}\left(\cos\left(-\tfrac{333\pi}{4}\right) + i \sin\left(-\tfrac{333\pi}{4}\right)\right).$$

Now

$$\left(2\sqrt{2}\right)^{333} = 2^{333} 2^{333/2} = 2^{333} 2^{166}\sqrt{2} = 2^{499}\sqrt{2}.$$

Also,

$$-\tfrac{333}{4} = -83 - \tfrac{1}{4} = -82 - \tfrac{5}{4}.$$

Thus

$$\left(2\sqrt{2}\right)^{333} = 2^{499}\sqrt{2}\left(\cos\left(-\tfrac{5}{4}\pi\right) + i \sin\left(-\tfrac{5}{4}\pi\right)\right)$$

$$= 2^{499}\sqrt{2}\left(-\tfrac{\sqrt{2}}{2} + i\tfrac{\sqrt{2}}{2}\right)$$

$$= 2^{499}(-1 + i).$$

19. Find four distinct complex numbers z such that $z^4 = -2$.

SOLUTION   Suppose $z = r(\cos\theta + i \sin\theta)$. Then

$$z^4 = r^4(\cos(4\theta) + i \sin(4\theta)).$$

We want z^4 to equal -2. Thus we need $r^4 = 2$, which implies that $r = 2^{1/4}$.

Now we must find values of θ such that $\cos(4\theta) = -1$ and $\sin(4\theta) = 0$. One choice is to take $4\theta = \pi$, which implies that $\theta = \frac{\pi}{4}$, which gives us

$$z = 2^{1/4}\left(\tfrac{\sqrt{2}}{2} + \tfrac{\sqrt{2}}{2}i\right).$$

Another choice of θ that satisfies $\cos(4\theta) = -1$ and $\sin(4\theta) = 0$ can be obtained by choosing $4\theta = 3\pi$, which means $\theta = \frac{3\pi}{4}$, which gives us

$$z = 2^{1/4}\left(-\tfrac{\sqrt{2}}{2} + \tfrac{\sqrt{2}}{2}i\right).$$

Yet another choice of θ that satisfies $\cos(4\theta) = -1$ and $\sin(4\theta) = 0$ can be obtained by choosing $4\theta = 5\pi$, which means $\theta = \frac{5\pi}{4}$, which gives us

$$z = 2^{1/4}\left(-\tfrac{\sqrt{2}}{2} - \tfrac{\sqrt{2}}{2}i\right).$$

Yet another choice of θ that satisfies $\cos(4\theta) = -1$ and $\sin(4\theta) = 0$ can be obtained by choosing $4\theta = 7\pi$, which means $\theta = \frac{7\pi}{4}$, which gives us

$$z = 2^{1/4}\left(\tfrac{\sqrt{2}}{2} - \tfrac{\sqrt{2}}{2}i\right).$$

Thus four distinct values of z such that $z^4 = -2$ are $2^{1/4}\left(\tfrac{\sqrt{2}}{2} + \tfrac{\sqrt{2}}{2}i\right)$, $2^{1/4}\left(-\tfrac{\sqrt{2}}{2} + \tfrac{\sqrt{2}}{2}i\right)$, $2^{1/4}\left(-\tfrac{\sqrt{2}}{2} - \tfrac{\sqrt{2}}{2}i\right)$, and $2^{1/4}\left(\tfrac{\sqrt{2}}{2} - \tfrac{\sqrt{2}}{2}i\right)$.

CHAPTER SUMMARY

To check that you have mastered the most important concepts and skills covered in this chapter, make sure that you can do each item in the following list:

- Compute the area of a triangle given the lengths of two sides and the angle between them.
- Compute the area of a parallelogram given the lengths of two adjacent sides and the angle between them.
- Explain why knowing the sine of an angle of a triangle is sometimes not enough information to determine the angle.
- Compute the area of a regular polygon.
- Find all the angles and the lengths of all the sides of a triangle given only some of this data.
- Use the double-angle and half-angle formulas for cosine, sine, and tangent.

- Use the addition and subtraction formulas for cosine, sine, and tangent.
- Graph transformations of trigonometric functions that change the amplitude, period, and/or phase shift.
- Convert from polar to rectangular coordinates.
- Convert from rectangular to polar coordinates.
- Graph a curve described by polar coordinates.
- Compute the sum, difference, and dot product of two vectors.
- Use De Moivre's Theorem to compute powers and roots of complex numbers.

To review a chapter, go through the list above to find items that you do not know how to do, then reread the material in the chapter about those items. Then try to answer the chapter review questions below without looking back at the chapter.

CHAPTER REVIEW QUESTIONS

1. Find the area of a triangle that has sides of length 7 and 10, with an angle of $29°$ between those sides.

2. Find the area of a regular 9-sided polygon whose vertices are nine equally spaced points on a circle of radius 2.

3. Find the perimeter of a regular 13-sided polygon whose vertices are 13 equally spaced points on a circle of radius 5.

4. Each side of the Pentagon that houses the U.S. Defense Department has length 921 feet. Find the area of the Pentagon.

5. Suppose $\sin u = \frac{3}{7}$. Evaluate $\cos(2u)$.

In Questions 6–12 use the following figure (which is not drawn to scale). When a question requests that you evaluate an angle, give answers in both radians and degrees.

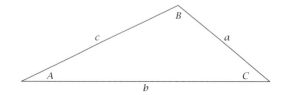

6. Suppose $a = 7$, $B = 35°$, and $C = 25°$. Evaluate:

   (a) A (b) b (c) c

7. Suppose $a = 6$, $A = \frac{3\pi}{11}$ radians, and $B = \frac{5\pi}{11}$ radians. Evaluate:

   (a) C (b) b (c) c

8. Suppose $a = 5$, $b = 7$, and $c = 11$. Evaluate:

   (a) A (b) B (c) C

9. 📱 Suppose $a = 4$, $b = 7$, and $C = 41°$. Evaluate:

    (a) c (b) A (c) B

10. 📱 Suppose $a = 3$, $b = 4$, and $C = 1.5$ radians. Evaluate:

    (a) c (b) A (c) B

11. 📱 Suppose $a = 5$, $b = 4$, and $B = 30°$. Evaluate:

    (a) A (assume that $A < 90°$)

    (b) C

    (c) c

12. 📱 Suppose $a = 5$, $b = 4$, and $B = 30°$. Evaluate:

    (a) A (assume that $A > 90°$)

    (b) C

    (c) c

For Questions 13–18, evaluate the given expression assuming that $\cos v = -\frac{3}{7}$, with $\pi < v < \frac{3}{2}\pi$.

13. $\cos(2v)$ 16. $\cos \frac{v}{2}$

14. $\sin(2v)$ 17. $\sin \frac{v}{2}$

15. $\tan(2v)$ 18. $\tan \frac{v}{2}$

19. Starting with the formula for the cosine of the sum of two angles, derive the formula for the cosine of the difference of two angles.

For Questions 20–25, evaluate the given expression assuming that $\cos u = \frac{2}{5}$ and $\sin v = \frac{2}{3}$, with $-\frac{\pi}{2} < u < 0$ and $0 < v < \frac{\pi}{2}$.

20. $\cos(u + v)$ 23. $\sin(u - v)$

21. $\cos(u - v)$ 24. $\tan(u + v)$

22. $\sin(u + v)$ 25. $\tan(u - v)$

26. Find an exact expression for $\sin 75°$.

27. Suppose θ is an angle such that $\sin \theta$ is a rational number. Explain why $\cos(2\theta)$ is a rational number.

28. Suppose θ is an angle such that $\tan \theta$ is a rational number other than 1 or -1. Explain why $\tan(2\theta)$ is a rational number.

29. Suppose θ is an angle such that $\cos \theta$ and $\sin \theta$ are both rational numbers, with $\cos \theta \neq -1$. Explain why $\tan \frac{\theta}{2}$ is a rational number.

30. Find a number b such that

$$\cos x + \sin x = b \sin(x + \tfrac{\pi}{4})$$

for every number x.

31. Give an example of a function that has amplitude 5 and period 3.

32. Give an example of a function that has period 3π and range $[2, 12]$.

33. Sketch the graph of the function

$$4 \sin(2x + 1) + 5$$

on the interval $[-3\pi, 3\pi]$.

For Questions 34–38, assume that g is the function defined by

$$g(x) = a \sin(bx + c) + d,$$

where a, b, c, and d are constants with $a \neq 0$ and $b \neq 0$.

34. Find two distinct values for a so that g has amplitude 4.

35. Find two distinct values for b so that g has period $\frac{\pi}{2}$.

36. Find values for a and d, with $a > 0$, so that g has range $[-3, 4]$.

37. Find values for a, d, and c, with $a > 0$ and $0 \leq c \leq \pi$, so that g has range $[-3, 4]$ and $g(0) = 2$.

38. Find values for a, d, c, and b, with $a > 0$ and $b > 0$ and $0 \leq c \leq \pi$, so that g has range $[-3, 4]$, $g(0) = 2$, and g has period 5.

39. Sketch the line segment from the origin to the point with polar coordinates $r = 3$ and $\theta = \frac{\pi}{3}$.

40. 📱 Find the rectangular coordinates of the point whose polar coordinates are $r = 4$ and $\theta = 32°$.

41. 📱 Find the polar coordinates of the point whose rectangular coordinates are $(5, 9)$.

Sequences, Series, and Limits

This chapter begins by considering sequences, which are lists of numbers. We particularly focus on the following special sequences:

- arithmetic sequences, meaning that consecutive terms have a constant difference;

- geometric sequences, meaning that consecutive terms have a constant ratio;

- recursive sequences, meaning that each term is defined by previous terms.

Then we consider series, which are sums of numbers. Here you will learn about summation notation, which is used in many parts of mathematics and statistics. We will derive formulas to evaluate arithmetic series and geometric series.

Finally, the chapter and the book conclude with an introduction to limits, one of the central ideas of calculus.

7.1   *Sequences*

Introduction to Sequences

Sequences

A **sequence** is an ordered list of numbers.

For example, $7, \sqrt{3}, \frac{5}{2}$ is a sequence. The first term of this sequence is 7, the second term of this sequence is $\sqrt{3}$, and the third term of this sequence is $\frac{5}{2}$.

Sequences differ from sets in that order matters and repetitions are allowed in a sequence. For example, the sets $\{2, 3, 5\}$ and $\{5, 3, 2\}$ are the same, but the sequences $2, 3, 5$ and $5, 3, 2$ are not the same. As another example, the sets $\{8, 8, 4, 5\}$ and $\{8, 4, 5\}$ are the same, but the sequences $8, 8, 4, 5$ and $8, 4, 5$ are not the same.

A sequence might end, as is the case with all the sequences mentioned in the paragraphs above, or a sequence might continue indefinitely. A sequence that ends is called a **finite sequence**; a sequence that does not end is called an **infinite sequence**.

An example of an infinite sequence is the sequence whose n^{th} term is $3n$. The first term of this sequence is 3, the second term of this sequence is 6, the third term of this sequence is 9, and so on. Because this sequence does not end, the entire sequence cannot be written down. Thus we write this sequence as

$$3, \ 6, \ 9, \ \ldots,$$

where the three dots indicate that the sequence continues without end.

Recall that there is no real number named "infinity". The term "infinite sequence" can be regarded as abbreviation for the phrase "sequence that does not end".

When using the three-dot notation to designate a sequence, information should be given about how each term of the sequence is determined. Sometimes this is done by giving an explicit formula for the nth term of the sequence, as in the next example.

| EXAMPLE 1 | Each of the equations below gives a formula for the nth term of a sequence $a_1, a_2, \ldots$. Write each sequence below using the three-dot notation, giving the first four terms of the sequence. Furthermore, describe each sequence in words. |

(a) $a_n = n$ (c) $a_n = 2n - 1$ (e) $a_n = (-1)^n$

(b) $a_n = 2n$ (d) $a_n = 3$ (f) $a_n = 2^{n-1}$

SOLUTION

(a) The sequence $a_1, a_2, \ldots$ defined by $a_n = n$ is $1, 2, 3, 4, \ldots$; this is the sequence of positive integers.

(b) The sequence $a_1, a_2, \ldots$ defined by $a_n = 2n$ is $2, 4, 6, 8 \ldots$; this is the sequence of even positive integers.

(c) The sequence $a_1, a_2, \ldots$ defined by $a_n = 2n - 1$ is $1, 3, 5, 7 \ldots$; this is the sequence of odd positive integers.

(d) The sequence $a_1, a_2, \ldots$ defined by $a_n = 3$ is $3, 3, 3, 3 \ldots$; this is the sequence of all 3's.

(e) The sequence $a_1, a_2, \ldots$ defined by $a_n = (-1)^n$ is $-1, 1, -1, 1 \ldots$; this is the sequence of alternating -1's and 1's, beginning with -1.

(f) The sequence $a_1, a_2, \ldots$ defined by $a_n = 2^{n-1}$ is $1, 2, 4, 8 \ldots$; this is the sequence of powers of 2, starting with 2 to the zeroth power.

Caution must be used when determining a sequence simply from the pattern of some of the terms, as illustrated by the following example.

| EXAMPLE 2 | What is the fifth term of the sequence $1, 4, 9, 16, \ldots$? |

SOLUTION   This is a trick question. You may reasonably suspect that the nth term of this sequence is n^2, which would imply that the fifth term equals 25.

However, the sequence whose n^{th} term equals

Problem 52 explains how this expression was obtained.

$$\frac{n^4 - 10n^3 + 39n^2 - 50n + 24}{4}$$

has as its first four terms $1, 4, 9, 16$, as you can verify. The fifth term of this sequence is 31, not 25.

Because we do not know whether the formula for the nth term of the sequence $1, 4, 9, 16, \ldots$ is given by n^2 or by the formula above or by some other formula, we cannot determine whether the fifth term of this sequence equals 25 or 31 or some other number.

One way out of the dilemma posed by the example above is to assume that the sequence is defined by the simplest possible means. Unless other information is given, you may need to make this assumption. This then raises another problem, because "simplest" is an imprecise notion and can be a matter of taste. However, in most cases almost everyone will agree on which among the many possibilities is the simplest. In Example 2 above, most people would agree that the expression n^2 is simpler than the expression $\frac{n^4-10n^3+39n^2-50n+24}{4}$.

Arithmetic Sequences

The sequence $1, 3, 5, 7 \ldots$ of odd positive integers has the property that the difference between any two consecutive terms is 2. Thus the difference between two consecutive terms is constant throughout the sequence. Sequences with this property are important enough to deserve their own name:

Arithmetic sequences

An **arithmetic sequence** is a sequence such that the difference between two consecutive terms is constant throughout the sequence.

When we consider the difference between consecutive terms in a sequence $a_1, a_2, \ldots$, we will subtract each term from its successor. In other words, we consider the difference $a_{n+1} - a_n$.

For each of the following sequences, determine whether or not the sequence is an arithmetic sequence. If the sequence is an arithmetic sequence, determine the difference between consecutive terms in the sequence.

(a) The sequence $1, 2, 3, 4, \ldots$ of positive integers.

(b) The sequence $-1, -2, -3, -4, \ldots$ of negative integers.

(c) The sequence $6, 8, 10, 12, \ldots$ of even positive integers starting with 6.

(d) The sequence $-1, 1, -1, 1, \ldots$ of alternating -1's and 1's.

(e) The sequence $1, 2, 4, 8, \ldots$ of powers of 2.

(f) The sequence $10, 15, 20, 25$.

> **EXAMPLE 3**
>
> *An arithmetic sequence can be either an infinite sequence or a finite sequence. All the sequences in this example are infinite sequences except the last one.*

SOLUTION

(a) The sequence $1, 2, 3, 4, \ldots$ of positive integers is an arithmetic sequence. The difference between any two consecutive terms is 1.

(b) The sequence $-1, -2, -3, -4, \ldots$ of negative integers is an arithmetic sequence. The difference between any two consecutive terms is -1.

(c) The sequence $6, 8, 10, 12, \ldots$ of even positive integers starting with 6 is an arithmetic sequence. The difference between any two consecutive terms is 2.

(d) The difference between consecutive terms of the sequence $-1, 1, -1, 1, \ldots$ oscillates between 2 and -2. Because the difference between consecutive terms of the sequence $-1, 1, -1, 1, \ldots$ is not constant, this sequence is not an arithmetic sequence.

(e) In the sequence $1, 2, 4, 8, \ldots$, the first two terms differ by 1, but the second and third terms differ by 2. Because the difference between consecutive terms of the sequence $1, 2, 4, 8, \ldots$ is not constant, this sequence is not an arithmetic sequence.

(f) In the finite sequence $10, 15, 20, 25$, the difference between any two consecutive terms is 5. Thus this sequence is an arithmetic sequence.

When used in the phrase "arithmetic sequence", the word "arithmetic" is pronounced differently from the word used to describe the subject you started learning in elementary school. You should be able to hear the difference when your instructor pronounces "arithmetic sequence".

Consider an arithmetic sequence with first term b and difference d between consecutive terms. Each term of this sequence after the first term is obtained by adding d to the previous term. Thus this sequence is

$$b, \; b + d, \; b + 2d, \; b + 3d, \; \ldots.$$

The nth term of this sequence is obtained by adding d a total of $n - 1$ times to the first term b. Thus we have the following result:

Formula for an arithmetic sequence

The nth term of an arithmetic sequence with first term b and with difference d between consecutive terms is $b + (n-1)d$.

EXAMPLE 4

Suppose at the beginning of the year your iPod contains 53 songs and that you purchase four new songs each week to place on your iPod. Consider the sequence whose n^{th} term is the number of songs on your iPod at the beginning of the nth week of the year.

(a) What are the first four terms of this sequence?

(b) What is the 30th term of this sequence? In other words, how many songs will be on your iPod at the beginning of the 30th week?

SOLUTION

(a) The first four terms of this sequence are $53, 57, 61, 65$.

(b) To find the 30th term of this sequence, use the formula in the box above with $b = 53$, $n = 30$, and $d = 4$. Thus at the beginning of the 30th week the number of songs on the iPod will be $53 + (30 - 1) \cdot 4$, which equals 169.

Geometric Sequences

The sequence $1, 3, 9, 27 \ldots$ of powers of 3 has the property that the ratio of any two consecutive terms is 3. Thus the ratio of two consecutive terms is constant throughout the sequence. Sequences with this property are important enough to deserve their own name:

Geometric sequences

A **geometric sequence** is a sequence such that the ratio of two consecutive terms is constant throughout the sequence.

When we consider the ratio of consecutive terms in a sequence $a_1, a_2, \ldots$, we will divide each term into its successor. In other words, we consider the ratio a_{n+1}/a_n.

For each of the following sequences, determine whether or not the sequence is a geometric sequence. If the sequence is a geometric sequence, determine the ratio of consecutive terms in the sequence.

EXAMPLE 5

(a) The sequence $16, 32, 64, 128, \ldots$ of the powers of 2 starting with 2^4.

(b) The sequence $3, 6, 12, 24, \ldots$ of 3 times the powers of 2 starting with $3 \cdot 2^0$.

(c) The sequence $-1, 1, -1, 1, \ldots$ of alternating -1's and 1's.

(d) The sequence $1, 4, 9, 16, \ldots$ of the squares of the positive integers.

(e) The sequence $2, 4, 6, 8, \ldots$ of even positive integers.

(f) The sequence $2, \frac{2}{3}, \frac{2}{9}, \frac{2}{27}$.

A geometric sequence can be either an infinite sequence or a finite sequence. All the sequences in this example are infinite sequences except the last one.

SOLUTION

(a) The sequence $16, 32, 64, 128, \ldots$ of the powers of 2 starting with 2^4 is a geometric sequence. The ratio of any two consecutive terms is 2.

(b) The sequence $3, 6, 12, 24, \ldots$ of 3 times the powers of 2 starting with $3 \cdot 2^0$ is a geometric sequence. The ratio of any two consecutive terms is 2.

(c) The sequence $-1, 1, -1, 1, \ldots$ of alternating -1's and 1's is a geometric sequence. The ratio of any two consecutive terms is -1.

(d) In the sequence $1, 4, 9, 16, \ldots$, the second and first terms have a ratio of 4, but the third and second terms have a ratio of $\frac{9}{4}$. Because the ratio of consecutive terms of the sequence $1, 4, 9, 16, \ldots$ is not constant, this sequence is not a geometric sequence.

(e) In the sequence $2, 4, 6, 8, \ldots$, the second and first terms have a ratio of 2, but the third and second terms have a ratio of $\frac{3}{2}$. Because the ratio of consecutive terms of the sequence $2, 4, 6, 8, \ldots$ is not constant, this sequence is not a geometric sequence.

(f) In the finite sequence $2, \frac{2}{3}, \frac{2}{9}, \frac{2}{27}$, the ratio of any two consecutive terms is $\frac{1}{3}$. Thus this sequence is a geometric sequence.

Consider a geometric sequence with first term b and ratio r of consecutive terms. Each term of this sequence after the first term is obtained by multiplying the previous term by r. Thus this sequence is

$$b, \ br, \ br^2, \ br^3, \ \ldots.$$

The nth term of this sequence is obtained by multiplying the first term b by r a total of $n - 1$ times. Thus we have the following result:

Formula for a geometric sequence

The nth term of a geometric sequence with first term b and with ratio r of consecutive terms is br^{n-1}.

EXAMPLE 6

Suppose at the beginning of the year $1000 is deposited in a bank account that pays 5% interest per year, compounded once per year at the end of the year. Consider the sequence whose n^{th} term is the amount in the bank account at the beginning of the nth year.

(a) What are the first four terms of this sequence?

(b) What is the 20th term of this sequence? In other words, how much will be in the bank account at the beginning of the 20th year?

SOLUTION

As this example shows, compound interest leads to geometric sequences.

(a) Each term of this sequence is obtained by multiplying the previous term by 1.05. Thus we have a geometric sequence whose first four terms are

$$\$1000, \quad \$1000 \cdot 1.05, \quad \$1000 \cdot (1.05)^2, \quad \$1000 \cdot (1.05)^3.$$

These four terms can be rewritten as $1000, $1050, $1102.50, $1157.63.

(b) To find the 20th term of this sequence, use the formula in the box above with $b = \$1000$, $r = 1.05$, and $n = 20$. Thus at the beginning of the 20th year the amount of money in the bank account will be $1000 \cdot (1.05)^{19}$, which equals $2526.95.

The next example shows how to deal with a geometric sequence when we have information about terms that are not consecutive.

EXAMPLE 7

Find the tenth term of a geometric sequence whose third term is 3 and whose fifth term is 21.

SOLUTION Let r denote the ratio of consecutive terms of this geometric sequence. To get from the third term of this sequence to the fifth term, we must multiply by r twice. Thus

$$3r^2 = 21.$$

Solving the equation above for r, we have $r = \sqrt{7}$.

To get from the fifth term of this sequence to the tenth term, we must multiply by r five times. Thus the tenth term of this sequence is $21r^5$. Now

$$21r^5 = 21\sqrt{7}^5 = 21 \cdot 7^{5/2} = 21 \cdot 7^2 \cdot 7^{1/2} = 21 \cdot 49 \cdot \sqrt{7} = 1029\sqrt{7}.$$

Thus the tenth term of this sequence is $1029\sqrt{7}$.

Recursive Sequences

Sometimes the nth term of a sequence is defined by a formula involving n. For example, we might have the sequence $a_1, a_2, \ldots$ whose n^{th} term is defined by $a_n = 4 + 3n$. This is the arithmetic sequence

$$7, \ 10, \ 13, \ 16, \ 19, \ 22, \ \ldots$$

whose first term is 7, with a difference of 3 between consecutive terms.

Suppose we want to compute the seventh term of the sequence above, which has six terms displayed. To compute the seventh term we could use the formula $a_n = 4 + 3n$ to evaluate $a_7 = 4 + 3 \cdot 7$, or we use the simpler method of adding 3 to the sixth term. Using this second viewpoint, we think of the sequence above as being defined by starting with 7 and then getting each later term by adding 3 to the previous term. In other words, we could think of this sequence as being defined by the equations

$$a_1 = 7 \quad \text{and} \quad a_{n+1} = a_n + 3 \text{ for } n \geq 1.$$

This viewpoint is sufficiently useful to deserve a name:

> ### Recursive sequences
>
> A **recursive sequence** is a sequence in which each term from some point on is defined by using previous terms.

Actually, it is not the sequence that is recursive but its definition. This is a small but common abuse of terminology.

In the definition above, the phrase "from some point on" means that some terms at the beginning of the sequence will be defined explicitly rather than by using previous terms. In a recursive sequence, at least the first term must be defined explicitly because it has no previous terms.

Write the geometric sequence $6, 12, 24, 48 \ldots$ whose n^{th} term is defined by $a_n = 3 \cdot 2^n$ as a recursive sequence.

EXAMPLE 8

SOLUTION Each term of this sequence is obtained by multiplying the previous term by 2. Thus the recursive definition of this sequence is given by the equations

$$a_1 = 6 \quad \text{and} \quad a_{n+1} = 2a_n \text{ for } n \geq 1.$$

If n is a positive integer, then $n!$ (pronounced "n factorial") is defined to be the product of the integers from 1 to n. Thus $1! = 1$, $2! = 2$, $3! = 6$, $4! = 24$, and so on.

Write the sequence $1!, 2!, 3!, 4! \ldots$ whose n^{th} term is defined by $a_n = n!$ as a recursive sequence.

EXAMPLE 9

SOLUTION Note that $(n + 1)!$ is the product of the integers from 1 to $n + 1$. Thus $(n + 1)!$ equals $n!$ times $n + 1$. Hence the recursive definition of this sequence is given by the equations

$$a_1 = 1 \quad \text{and} \quad a_{n+1} = (n + 1)a_n \text{ for } n \geq 1.$$

Perhaps the most famous recursive sequence is the Fibonacci sequence, which was defined by the Italian mathematician Leonardo Fibonacci over eight hundred years ago. Each term of the Fibonacci sequence is the sum of the two previous terms (except the first two terms, which are defined to equal 1). Thus the Fibonacci sequence has the recursive definition

$$a_1 = 1, \quad a_2 = 1, \quad \text{and} \quad a_{n+2} = a_n + a_{n+1} \text{ for } n \geq 1.$$

You may want to do a web search to learn about some of the ways in which the Fibonacci sequence arises in nature.

EXAMPLE 10

Find the first ten terms of the Fibonacci sequence.

SOLUTION   The first two terms of the Fibonacci sequence are $1, 1$.

The third term of the Fibonacci sequence is the sum of the first two terms; thus $a_3 = 2$. The fourth term of the Fibonacci sequence is the sum of the second and third terms; thus $a_4 = 3$. Continuing in this fashion, we get the first ten terms of the Fibonacci sequence:

$$1, \ 1, \ 2, \ 3, \ 5, \ 8, \ 13, \ 21, \ 34, \ 55$$

Leonardo Fibonacci, whose book written in 1202 introduced Europe to the Indian-Arabic decimal number system that we use today.

Recursive sequences provide a method for estimating square roots with remarkable accuracy. To estimate $\sqrt{c}$, the idea is to define a recursive sequence by letting a_1 be any crude estimate for $\sqrt{c}$; then use the recursive formula $a_{n+1} = \frac{1}{2}(\frac{c}{a_n} + a_n)$. The number a_n will be a good estimate for $\sqrt{c}$ even for small values of n; for larger values of n the estimate becomes extraordinarily accurate.

The example below illustrates this procedure to estimate $\sqrt{5}$. Note that we start with $a_1 = 2$, which means that we are using the crude estimate $\sqrt{5} \approx 2$.

EXAMPLE 11

This recursive formula for computing square roots is a special case of Newton's method, which you will learn in your calculus course.

Define a recursive sequence using the equations

$$a_1 = 2 \quad \text{and} \quad a_{n+1} = \frac{1}{2}\Big(\frac{5}{a_n} + a_n\Big) \text{ for } n \geq 1.$$

(a) Compute a_4. For how many digits after the decimal point does a_4 agree with $\sqrt{5}$?

(b) Compute a_7. For how many digits after the decimal point does a_7 agree with $\sqrt{5}$?

SOLUTION

(a) Using the recursive formula above and doing some simple arithmetic, we get $a_2 = \frac{9}{4}$, then $a_3 = \frac{161}{72}$, then $a_4 = \frac{51841}{23184}$.

Using a calculator, we see that

$$a_4 = \frac{51841}{23184} \approx 2.2360679779 \quad \text{and} \quad \sqrt{5} \approx 2.2360679774.$$

Thus a_4, which is computed with only a small amount of calculation, agrees with $\sqrt{5}$ for nine digits after the decimal point.

(b) A typical calculator cannot handle enough digits to compute a_7 exactly. However, a computer algebra system such as *Mathematica* or *Maple* can be used to compute that

$$a_5 = \frac{5374978561}{2403763488}, \quad a_6 = \frac{57780789062419261441}{25840354427429161536},$$

and

$$a_7 = \frac{6677239169351578707225356193679818792961}{2986152136938872067784669198846010266752}.$$

Even though computing a_7 requires only three more calculations after computing a_4, the value for a_7 calculated above agrees with $\sqrt{5}$ for 79 digits after the decimal point. This remarkable level of accuracy is typical of this recursive method for computing square roots.

EXERCISES

For Exercises 1–8, a formula is given for the nth term of a sequence $a_1, a_2, \ldots$.

   (a) *Write the sequence using the three-dot notation, giving the first four terms.*

   (b) *Give the 100th term of the sequence.*

1. $a_n = -n$

2. $a_n = \frac{1}{n}$

3. $a_n = 2 + 5n$

4. $a_n = 4n - 3$

5. $a_n = \sqrt{\frac{n}{n+1}}$

6. $a_n = \sqrt{\frac{2n-1}{3n-2}}$

7. $a_n = 3 + 2^n$

8. $a_n = 1 - \frac{1}{3n}$

For Exercises 9–14, consider an arithmetic sequence with first term b and difference d between consecutive terms.

   (a) *Write the sequence using the three-dot notation, giving the first four terms of the sequence.*

   (b) *Give the 100th term of the sequence.*

9. $b = 2, d = 5$

10. $b = 7, d = 3$

11. $b = 4, d = -6$

12. $b = 8, d = -5$

13. $b = 0, d = \frac{1}{3}$

14. $b = -1, d = \frac{3}{2}$

For Exercises 15–20, consider a geometric sequence with first term b and ratio r of consecutive terms.

   (a) *Write the sequence using the three-dot notation, giving the first four terms.*

   (b) *Give the 100th term of the sequence.*

15. $b = 1, r = 5$

16. $b = 1, r = 4$

17. $b = 3, r = -2$

18. $b = 4, r = -5$

19. $b = 2, r = \frac{1}{3}$

20. $b = 5, r = \frac{2}{3}$

21. Find the fifth term of an arithmetic sequence whose second term is 8 and whose third term is 14.

22. Find the eighth term of an arithmetic sequence whose fourth term is 7 and whose fifth term is 4.

23. Find the first term of an arithmetic sequence whose second term is 19 and whose fourth term is 25.

24. Find the first term of an arithmetic sequence whose second term is 7 and whose fifth term is 11.

25. Find the 100th term of an arithmetic sequence whose tenth term is 5 and whose eleventh term is 8.

26. Find the 200th term of an arithmetic sequence whose fifth term is 23 and whose sixth term is 25.

27. Find the fifth term of a geometric sequence whose second term is 8 and whose third term is 14.

28. Find the eighth term of a geometric sequence whose fourth term is 7 and whose fifth term is 4.

29. Find the first term of a geometric sequence whose second term is 8 and whose fifth term is 27.

30. Find the first term of a geometric sequence whose second term is 64 and whose fifth term is 1.

31. 🖩 Find the ninth term of a geometric sequence whose fourth term is 4 and whose seventh term is 5.

32. 🖩 Find the tenth term of a geometric sequence whose second term is 3 and whose seventh term is 11.

33. 🖩 Find the 100th term of a geometric sequence whose tenth term is 5 and whose eleventh term is 8.

34. 🖩 Find the 400th term of a geometric sequence whose fifth term is 25 and whose sixth term is 27.

For Exercises 35–38, give the first four terms of the specified recursive sequence.

35. $a_1 = 3$ and $a_{n+1} = 2a_n + 1$ for $n \geq 1$.

36. $a_1 = 2$ and $a_{n+1} = 3a_n - 5$ for $n \geq 1$.

37. $a_1 = 2$, $a_2 = 3$, and $a_{n+2} = a_n a_{n+1}$ for $n \geq 1$.

38. $a_1 = 4$, $a_2 = 7$, and $a_{n+2} = a_{n+1} - a_n$ for $n \geq 1$.

For Exercises 39–40, let $a_1, a_2, \ldots$ be the sequence defined by setting a_1 equal to the value shown below and for $n \geq 1$ letting

$$a_{n+1} = \begin{cases} \dfrac{a_n}{2} & \text{if } a_n \text{ is even;} \\ 3a_n + 1 & \text{if } a_n \text{ is odd.} \end{cases}$$

39. Suppose $a_1 = 3$. Find the smallest value of n such that $a_n = 1$.

[No one knows whether a_1 can be chosen to be a positive integer such that the recursive sequence defined here does not contain any term equal to 1. You can become famous by finding such a choice for a_1. If you want to find out more about this problem, do a web search for "Collatz Problem".]

40. Suppose $a_1 = 7$. Find the smallest value of n such that $a_n = 1$.

For Exercises 41–46, consider the sequence whose n^{th} term a_n is given by the indicated formula.

    (a) *Write the sequence using the three-dot notation, giving the first four terms of the sequence.*

    (b) *Write the sequence as a recursive sequence.*

41. $a_n = 5n - 3$

42. $a_n = 1 - 6n$

43. $a_n = 3(-2)^n$

44. $a_n = 5 \cdot 3^{-n}$

45. $a_n = 2^n n!$

46. $a_n = \dfrac{3^n}{n!}$

47. 🖩 Define a recursive sequence by

$$a_1 = 3 \quad \text{and} \quad a_{n+1} = \frac{1}{2}\left(\frac{7}{a_n} + a_n\right) \text{ for } n \geq 1.$$

Find the smallest value of n such that a_n agrees with $\sqrt{7}$ for at least six digits after the decimal point.

48. 🖩 Define a recursive sequence by

$$a_1 = 6 \quad \text{and} \quad a_{n+1} = \frac{1}{2}\left(\frac{17}{a_n} + a_n\right) \text{ for } n \geq 1.$$

Find the smallest value of n such that a_n agrees with $\sqrt{17}$ for at least four digits after the decimal point.

PROBLEMS

Some problems require considerably more thought than the exercises.
Unlike exercises, problems usually have more than one correct answer.

49. Explain why an infinite sequence is sometimes defined to be a function whose domain is the set of positive integers.

50. Find a sequence

$$3, -7, 18, 93, \ldots$$

whose 100th term equals 29.
[*Hint:* A correct solution to this problem can be obtained with no calculation.]

51. Find all infinite sequences that are both arithmetic and geometric sequences.

52. For Example 2, the author wanted to find a polynomial p such that

$$p(1) = 1, \ p(2) = 4, \ p(3) = 9, \ p(4) = 16,$$

and $p(5) = 31$. Carry out the following steps to see how that polynomial was obtained.

(a) Note that the polynomial

$$(x - 2)(x - 3)(x - 4)(x - 5)$$

is 0 for $x = 2, 3, 4, 5$ but is not zero for $x = 1$. By dividing the polynomial above by a suitable number, find a polynomial p_1 such that $p_1(1) = 1$ and

$$p_1(2) = p_1(3) = p_1(4) = p_1(5) = 0.$$

(b) Similarly, find a polynomial p_2 of degree 4 such that $p_2(2) = 1$ and

$$p_2(1) = p_2(3) = p_2(4) = p_2(5) = 0.$$

(c) Similarly, find polynomials p_j, for $j = 3, 4, 5$, such that each p_j satisfies $p_j(j) = 1$ and $p_j(k) = 0$ for values of k in $\{1, 2, 3, 4, 5\}$ other than j.

(d) Explain why the polynomial p defined by

$$p = p_1 + 4p_2 + 9p_3 + 16p_4 + 31p_5$$

satisfies

$$p(1) = 1, \ p(2) = 4, \ p(3) = 9, \ p(4) = 16,$$

and $p(5) = 31$.

53. Explain why the polynomial p defined by

$$p(x) = \frac{x^4 - 10x^3 + 39x^2 - 50x + 24}{4}$$

is the only polynomial of degree 4 such that $p(1) = 1, p(2) = 4, p(3) = 9, p(4) = 16$, and $p(5) = 31$.

WORKED-OUT SOLUTIONS *to Odd-numbered Exercises*

Do not read these worked-out solutions before first struggling to do the exercises yourself. Otherwise you risk the danger of mimicking the techniques shown here without understanding the ideas.

Best way to learn: Carefully read the section of the textbook, then do all the odd-numbered exercises (even if they have not been assigned) and check your answers here. If you get stuck on an exercise, reread the section of the textbook—then try the exercise again. If you are still stuck, then look at the worked-out solution here.

For Exercises 1–8, a formula is given for the nth term of a sequence $a_1, a_2, \ldots$.

(a) *Write the sequence using the three-dot notation, giving the first four terms.*

(b) *Give the 100th term of the sequence.*

1. $a_n = -n$

SOLUTION

(a) The sequence $a_1, a_2, \ldots$ defined by $a_n = -n$ is $-1, -2, -3, -4, \ldots$.

(b) The 100th term of this sequence is -100.

3. $a_n = 2 + 5n$

SOLUTION

(a) The sequence $a_1, a_2, \ldots$ defined by $a_n = 2 + 5n$ is $7, 12, 17, 22, \ldots$.

(b) The 100th term of this sequence is $2 + 5 \cdot 100$, which equals 502.

5. $a_n = \sqrt{\frac{n}{n+1}}$

SOLUTION

(a) The sequence $a_1, a_2, \ldots$ defined by $a_n = \sqrt{\frac{n}{n+1}}$ is $\sqrt{\frac{1}{2}}, \sqrt{\frac{2}{3}}, \sqrt{\frac{3}{4}}, \sqrt{\frac{4}{5}}, \ldots$. Note that $\sqrt{\frac{3}{4}}$ has not been simplified to $\frac{\sqrt{3}}{2}$; similarly, $\sqrt{\frac{4}{5}}$ has not been simplified to $\frac{2}{\sqrt{5}}$. Making those simplifications would make it harder to discern the pattern in the sequence.

(b) The 100th term of this sequence is $\sqrt{\frac{100}{101}}$.

7. $a_n = 3 + 2^n$

SOLUTION

(a) The sequence $a_1, a_2, \ldots$ defined by $a_n = 3 + 2^n$ is $5, 7, 11, 19, \ldots$.

(b) The 100th term of this sequence is $3 + 2^{100}$.

For Exercises 9–14, consider an arithmetic sequence with first term b and difference d between consecutive terms.

(a) *Write the sequence using the three-dot notation, giving the first four terms of the sequence.*

(b) *Give the 100th term of the sequence.*

9. $b = 2, d = 5$

SOLUTION

(a) The arithmetic sequence with first term 2 and difference 5 between consecutive terms is $2, 7, 12, 17, \ldots$.

(b) The 100th term of this sequence is $2 + 99 \cdot 5$, which equals 497.

11. $b = 4, d = -6$

SOLUTION

(a) The arithmetic sequence with first term 4 and difference -6 between consecutive terms is $4, -2, -8, -14, \ldots$.

(b) The 100th term of this sequence is $4 + 99 \cdot (-6)$, which equals -590.

13. $b = 0, d = \frac{1}{3}$

SOLUTION

(a) The arithmetic sequence with first term 0 and difference $\frac{1}{3}$ between consecutive terms is $0, \frac{1}{3}, \frac{2}{3}, 1, \ldots$.

(b) The 100th term of this sequence is $0 + 99 \cdot \frac{1}{3}$, which equals 33.

For Exercises 15–20, consider a geometric sequence with first term b and ratio r of consecutive terms.

(a) *Write the sequence using the three-dot notation, giving the first four terms.*

(b) *Give the 100th term of the sequence.*

15. $b = 1, r = 5$

SOLUTION

(a) The geometric sequence with first term 1 and ratio 5 of consecutive terms is $1, 5, 25, 125, \ldots$.

(b) The 100th term of this sequence is 5^{99}.

17. $b = 3, r = -2$

SOLUTION

(a) The geometric sequence with first term 3 and ratio -2 of consecutive terms is $3, -6, 12, -24, \ldots$.

(b) The 100th term of this sequence is $3 \cdot (-2)^{99}$, which equals $-3 \cdot 2^{99}$.

19. $b = 2, r = \frac{1}{3}$

SOLUTION

(a) The geometric sequence with first term 2 and ratio $\frac{1}{3}$ of consecutive terms is $2, \frac{2}{3}, \frac{2}{9}, \frac{2}{27} \ldots$.

(b) The 100th term of this sequence is $2 \cdot \left(\frac{1}{3}\right)^{99}$, which equals $2/3^{99}$.

21. Find the fifth term of an arithmetic sequence whose second term is 8 and whose third term is 14.

SOLUTION Because the second term of this arithmetic sequence is 8 and the third term is 14, we see that the difference between consecutive terms is 6. Thus the fourth term is $14 + 6$, which equals 20, and the fifth term is $20 + 6$, which equals 26.

23. Find the first term of an arithmetic sequence whose second term is 19 and whose fourth term is 25.

SOLUTION Because the second term of this arithmetic sequence is 19 and the fourth term is 25, and because the fourth term is two terms away from the second term, we see that twice the difference between consecutive terms is 6. Thus the difference between consecutive terms is 3. Thus 19, which is the second term, is 3 more than the first term. This implies that the first term equals 16.

25. Find the 100th term of an arithmetic sequence whose tenth term is 5 and whose eleventh term is 8.

    SOLUTION Because the tenth term of this arithmetic sequence is 5 and the eleventh term is 8, we see that the difference between consecutive terms is 3. To get from the eleventh term to the 100th term, we need to add 3 to the eleventh term $100 - 11$ times, which equals 89 times. Thus the 100th term is $8 + 89 \cdot 3$, which equals 275.

27. Find the fifth term of a geometric sequence whose second term is 8 and whose third term is 14.

    SOLUTION The second term of this geometric sequence is 8, and the third term is 14. Hence the ratio of consecutive terms is $\frac{14}{8}$, which equals $\frac{7}{4}$. Thus the fourth term equals the third term times $\frac{7}{4}$. In other words, the fourth term is $14 \cdot \frac{7}{4}$, which equals $\frac{49}{2}$. Similarly, the fifth term is $\frac{49}{2} \cdot \frac{7}{4}$, which equals $\frac{343}{8}$.

29. Find the first term of a geometric sequence whose second term is 8 and whose fifth term is 27.

    SOLUTION Let r denote the ratio of consecutive terms of this geometric sequence. Because the second term of this sequence is 8 and the fifth term is 27, and because the fifth term is three terms away from the second term, we have $8r^3 = 27$. Solving for r, we get $r = \frac{3}{2}$. Thus the ratio of consecutive terms is $\frac{3}{2}$. Thus 8, which is the second term, is $\frac{3}{2}$ times the first term. This implies that the first term equals $8 \cdot \frac{2}{3}$, which equals $\frac{16}{3}$.

31. ✎ Find the ninth term of a geometric sequence whose fourth term is 4 and whose seventh term is 5.

    SOLUTION Let r denote the ratio of consecutive terms of this geometric sequence. To get from the fourth term of this sequence to the seventh term, we must multiply by r three

times. Thus
$$4r^3 = 5.$$
Solving the equation above for r, we have $r = \left(\frac{5}{4}\right)^{1/3}$.

To get from the seventh term of this sequence to the ninth term, we must multiply by r twice. Thus the ninth term of this sequence is $5r^2$. Now
$$5r^2 = 5\left(\left(\tfrac{5}{4}\right)^{1/3}\right)^2 = 5\left(\tfrac{5}{4}\right)^{2/3} \approx 5.80199.$$
Thus the ninth term of this sequence is approximately 5.80199.

33. ✎ Find the 100th term of a geometric sequence whose tenth term is 5 and whose eleventh term is 8.

    SOLUTION Because the tenth term of this geometric sequence is 5 and the eleventh term is 8, we see that the ratio of consecutive terms is $\frac{8}{5}$. To get from the eleventh term to the 100th term, we need to multiply the eleventh term by $\frac{8}{5}$ a total of $100 - 11$ times, which equals 89 times. Thus the 100th term is $8 \cdot \left(\frac{8}{5}\right)^{89}$, which equals $8 \cdot 1.6^{89}$, which is approximately 1.2×10^{19}.

For Exercises 35–38, give the first four terms of the specified recursive sequence.

35. $a_1 = 3$ and $a_{n+1} = 2a_n + 1$ for $n \geq 1$.

    SOLUTION Each term after the first term is obtained by doubling the previous term and then adding 1. Thus the first four terms of this sequence are $3, 7, 15, 31$.

37. $a_1 = 2$, $a_2 = 3$, and $a_{n+2} = a_n a_{n+1}$ for $n \geq 1$.

    SOLUTION Each term after the first two terms is the product of the two previous terms. Thus the first four terms of this sequence are $2, 3, 6, 18$.

For Exercises 39–40, let $a_1, a_2, \ldots$ be the sequence defined by setting a_1 equal to the value shown below and for $n \geq 1$ letting

$$a_{n+1} = \begin{cases} \dfrac{a_n}{2} & \text{if } a_n \text{ is even;} \\ 3a_n + 1 & \text{if } a_n \text{ is odd.} \end{cases}$$

39. Suppose $a_1 = 3$. Find the smallest value of n such that $a_n = 1$.

    SOLUTION Using the recursive formula above, starting with $a_1 = 3$ we compute terms of the sequence until one of them equals 1. The first eight terms of the sequence are

    $$3, \ 10, \ 5, \ 16, \ 8, \ 4, \ 2, \ 1.$$

    The eighth term of this sequence equals 1, with no earlier term equal to 1. Thus $n = 8$ is the smallest value of n such that $a_n = 1$.

For Exercises 41–46, consider the sequence whose n^{th} term a_n is given by the indicated formula.

   (a) *Write the sequence using the three-dot notation, giving the first four terms of the sequence.*

   (b) *Write the sequence as a recursive sequence.*

41. $a_n = 5n - 3$

    SOLUTION

    (a) The sequence $a_1, a_2, \ldots$ defined by $a_n = 5n - 3$ is $2, 7, 12, 17, \ldots$.

    (b) We have

    $$a_{n+1} = 5(n + 1) - 3 = 5n + 5 - 3 = (5n - 3) + 5$$
    $$= a_n + 5.$$

    Thus this sequence is defined by the equations

    $$a_1 = 2 \quad \text{and} \quad a_{n+1} = a_n + 5 \text{ for } n \geq 1.$$

43. $a_n = 3(-2)^n$

    SOLUTION

    (a) The sequence $a_1, a_2, \ldots$ defined by $a_n = 3(-2)^n$ is $-6, 12, -24, 48, \ldots$.

    (b) We have

    $$a_{n+1} = 3(-2)^{n+1} = 3(-2)^n(-2) = -2a_n.$$

    Thus this sequence is defined by the equations

    $$a_1 = -6 \quad \text{and} \quad a_{n+1} = -2a_n \text{ for } n \geq 1.$$

45. $a_n = 2^n n!$

    SOLUTION

    (a) The sequence $a_1, a_2, \ldots$ defined by $a_n = 2^n n!$ is $2, 8, 48, 384, \ldots$.

    (b) We have

    $$a_{n+1} = 2^{n+1}(n + 1)! = 2 \cdot 2^n n!(n + 1)$$
    $$= 2(n + 1)2^n n! = 2(n + 1)a_n.$$

    Thus this sequence is defined by the equations

    $$a_1 = 2 \quad \text{and} \quad a_{n+1} = 2(n + 1)a_n \text{ for } n \geq 1.$$

47. Define a recursive sequence by

    $$a_1 = 3 \quad \text{and} \quad a_{n+1} = \frac{1}{2}\left(\frac{7}{a_n} + a_n\right) \text{ for } n \geq 1.$$

    Find the smallest value of n such that a_n agrees with $\sqrt{7}$ for at least six digits after the decimal point.

    SOLUTION A calculator shows that $\sqrt{7} \approx 2.6457513$. Using a calculator and the recursive formula above, we compute terms of the sequence until one of them agrees with $\sqrt{7}$ for at least six digits after the decimal point. The first four terms of the sequence are

    $$3, \ 2.6666667, \ 2.6458333, \ 2.6457513.$$

    The fourth term of this sequence agrees with $\sqrt{7}$ for at least six digits after the decimal point; no earlier term has this property. Thus $n = 4$ is the smallest value of n such that a_n agrees with $\sqrt{7}$ for at least six digits after the decimal point.

7.2 *Series*

SECTION OBJECTIVES

By the end of this section you should

- be able to compute the sum of a finite arithmetic sequence;
- be able to compute the sum of a finite geometric sequence;
- understand summation notation.

Sums of Sequences

A **series** is the sum of the terms of a sequence. For example, corresponding to the finite sequence $1, 4, 9, 16$ is the series $1 + 4 + 9 + 16$, which equals 30. In this section we will deal only with the series that arise from finite sequences; in the next section we will investigate the intricacies of infinite series.

We can refer to the terms of a series using the same terminology as for a sequence. For example, the series $1 + 4 + 9 + 16$ has first term 1, second term 4, and last term 16.

The three-dot notation for infinite sequences was introduced in the last section. Now we want to extend that notation so that it can be used to indicate terms in a finite sequence or series that are not explicitly displayed. For example, consider the geometric sequence with 50 terms, where the mth term of this sequence is 2^m. We could denote this sequence by

$$2, \ 4, \ 8, \ \ldots, \ 2^{48}, \ 2^{49}, \ 2^{50}.$$

Here the three dots denote the 44 terms of this sequence that are not explicitly displayed. Similarly, in the corresponding series

$$2 + 4 + 8 + \cdots + 2^{48} + 2^{49} + 2^{50},$$

the three dots denote the 44 terms that are not displayed.

When three dots are used in a sequence, they are placed vertically at the same level as a comma. When three dots are used in a series, they are vertically centered with the plus sign.

Arithmetic Series

An **arithmetic series** is the sum obtained by adding up the terms of an arithmetic sequence. The next example provides our model for evaluating an arithmetic series.

Find the sum of all the odd numbers between 100 and 200.

EXAMPLE 1

SOLUTION   We want to find the sum of the finite arithmetic sequence

$$101, \ 103, \ 105, \ \ldots, \ 195, \ 197, \ 199.$$

We could just add up the numbers above by brute force, but that will become tiresome when we need to deal with sequences that have 50,000 terms instead of 50 terms.

Thus we employ a trick. Let s denote the sum of all the odd numbers between 100 and 200. Our trick is to write out the sum defining s twice, but in reverse order the second time:

$$s = 101 + 103 + 105 + \cdots + 195 + 197 + 199$$
$$s = 199 + 197 + 195 + \cdots + 105 + 103 + 101.$$

Now add the two equations above, getting

$$2s = 300 + 300 + 300 + \cdots + 300 + 300 + 300.$$

The right side of the equation above consists of 50 terms, each equal to 300. Thus the equation above can be rewritten as $2s = 50 \cdot 300$. Solving for s, we have $s = 50 \cdot \frac{300}{2} = 50 \cdot 150 = 7500$.

*As you read this expla-
nation of how to eval-
uate any arithmetic
series, refer frequently
to the concrete exam-
ple above to help vi-
sualize the procedure.*

The trick used in the example above works with any arithmetic series. Specifically, consider an arithmetic series with n terms and difference d between consecutive terms. Write the series twice, in reverse order the second time. With the series in the original order, each term is obtained by adding d to the previous term. With the series written in the reverse order, each term is obtained by subtracting d from the previous term. Thus when the two series are added, the addition of d and the subtraction of d cancel out; in the sum of the two series, all the terms are the same, equal to the sum of the first and last terms.

Thus twice the value of the series is equal to the number of terms times the sum of the first term and the last term. Dividing by 2, we obtain the following simple formula for evaluating an arithmetic series:

Arithmetic series

The sum of a finite arithmetic sequence equals the number of terms times the average of the first and last terms.

EXAMPLE 2

Evaluate the arithmetic series

$$3 + 8 + 13 + 18 + \cdots + 1003 + 1008.$$

SOLUTION The arithmetic sequence $3, 8, 13, 18, \ldots, 1003, 1008$ has first term 3 and a difference of 5 between consecutive terms. We need to determine the number n of terms in this sequence. Using the formula for the terms in an arithmetic sequence, we have

$$3 + (n-1)5 = 1008.$$

Subtracting 3 from both sides of this equation gives the equation $(n-1)5 = 1005$; dividing both sides by 5 then gives $n - 1 = 201$. Thus $n = 202$.

The average of the first and last terms of this series is $\frac{3+1008}{2}$, which equals $\frac{1011}{2}$. The result in the box above now tells us that the arithmetic series

$$3 + 8 + 13 + 18 + \cdots + 1003 + 1008.$$

equals $202 \cdot \frac{1011}{2}$, which equals $101 \cdot 1011$, which equals 102111.

To obtain the symbolic form of the formula in the box above, consider an arithmetic series with n terms, with an initial term b, and with difference d between consecutive terms. The last term of this series is $b + (n-1)d$. Thus the average of the first and last terms is $\frac{b+(b+(n-1)d)}{2}$, which equals $b + \frac{(n-1)d}{2}$. Hence we have the following symbolic version of the formula for evaluating an arithmetic series:

The version in the box above using just words is easier to remember and understand than the symbolic version given below. However, the symbolic version is sometimes useful.

> **Arithmetic series**
>
> $$b + (b+d) + (b+2d) + \cdots + (b+(n-1)d) = n\left(b + \frac{(n-1)d}{2}\right)$$

Geometric Series

A **geometric series** is the sum obtained by adding up the terms of a geometric sequence. The next example provides our model for evaluating a geometric series.

Evaluate the geometric series

$$1 + 3 + 9 + \cdots + 3^{47} + 3^{48} + 3^{49}.$$

EXAMPLE 3

SOLUTION We could evaluate the series above by brute force, but that would become too difficult when we need to deal with geometric series that have 50,000 terms instead of 50 terms.

Thus we again employ a trick. Let s equal the sum above. Multiply s by 3, writing the resulting sum with terms aligned under the same terms of s, as follows:

$$s = 1 + 3 + 9 + \cdots + 3^{47} + 3^{48} + 3^{49}$$
$$3s = \quad\ \ 3 + 9 + \cdots + 3^{47} + 3^{48} + 3^{49} + 3^{50}.$$

Now subtract the first equation from the second equation, getting $2s = 3^{50} - 1$. Thus $s = (3^{50} - 1)/2$.

The trick used in the example above works with any geometric series. Specifically, consider a geometric series with n terms, starting with first term b, and with ratio r of consecutive terms. Let s equal the value of this geometric series. Multiply s by r, writing the resulting sum with terms aligned under the same terms of s, as follows:

$$s = b + br + br^2 + \cdots + br^{n-2} + br^{n-1}$$
$$rs = \quad\ \ br + br^2 + \cdots + br^{n-2} + br^{n-1} + br^n.$$

Now subtract the second equation from the first equation, getting $s - rs = b - br^n$, which can be rewritten as $(1 - r)s = b(1 - r^n)$. Dividing both sides by $1 - r$ gives the following formula:

Geometric series

If $r \neq 1$, then

$$b + br + br^2 + \cdots + br^{n-1} = b \cdot \frac{1 - r^n}{1 - r}.$$

If r is very close to 1, then $\frac{1-r^n}{1-r}$ is very close to n (as you will learn in calculus).

In the formula above, the case $r = 1$ had to be excluded to avoid division by 0. However, the case $r = 1$ is easy. If $r = 1$, then the ratio of consecutive terms is 1, which means all the terms are equal. Thus if $r = 1$, the series is $b + b + b + \cdots + b$; with n terms, this sum equals bn.

To express the formula above in words, first rewrite the right side the equation above as $(b - br^n)/(1 - r)$. The expression br^n would be the next term if we added one more term to this geometric sequence. Thus we have the following description of the formula above:

Geometric series

The sum of a finite geometric sequence equals the first term minus what would be the term following the last term, divided by 1 minus the ratio of consecutive terms.

EXAMPLE 4

Evaluate the geometric series

$$\frac{5}{3} + \frac{5}{9} + \frac{5}{27} + \cdots + \frac{5}{3^{20}}.$$

SOLUTION The first term of this series is $\frac{5}{3}$. The ratio of consecutive terms in this geometric series is $\frac{1}{3}$. If we added one more term to this geometric series, the next term would be $5/3^{21}$. Putting all this together, we see that

$$\frac{5}{3} + \frac{5}{9} + \frac{5}{27} + \cdots + \frac{5}{3^{20}} = \frac{\frac{5}{3} - \frac{5}{3^{21}}}{1 - \frac{1}{3}}$$

$$= \frac{\frac{5}{3} - \frac{5}{3^{21}}}{\frac{2}{3}}$$

$$= \frac{5}{2} - \frac{5}{2 \cdot 3^{20}},$$

where the last expression is obtained by multiplying the numerator and denominator of the previous expression by 3.

Summation Notation

The three-dot notation that we have been using has the advantage of presenting an easily understandable representation of a series. Another notation, called summation notation, is also often used for series. Summation notation has the advantage of explicitly displaying the formula used to compute the terms of the sequence. For some manipulations, summation notation works better than three-dot notation.

The following equation uses summation notation on the left side and three-dot notation on the right side:

$$\sum_{m=1}^{99} m^2 = 1 + 4 + 9 + \cdots + 98^2 + 99^2.$$

The symbol Σ used in summation notation is an upper case Greek sigma.

In spoken language, the left side of the equation above becomes "the sum as m goes from 1 to 99 of m^2". This means that the first term of the series is obtained by starting with $m = 1$ and computing m^2 (which equals 1). The second term of the series is obtained by taking $m = 2$ and computing m^2 (which equals 4), and so on, until $m = 99$, giving the last term of the series (which is 99^2).

There is no specific m in the series above. We could have used k or n or any other letter, as long as we consistently use the same letter throughout the notation. Thus

$$\sum_{m=1}^{99} m^2 \quad \text{and} \quad \sum_{k=1}^{99} k^2 \quad \text{and} \quad \sum_{n=1}^{99} n^2$$

all denote the same series $1 + 4 + 9 + \cdots + 98^2 + 99^2$.

Write the geometric series

$$3 + 9 + 27 + \cdots + 3^{80}$$

using summation notation.

EXAMPLE 5

SOLUTION   The mth term of this series is 3^m. Thus

$$3 + 9 + 27 + \cdots + 3^{80} = \sum_{m=1}^{80} 3^m.$$

You should also become comfortable translating in the other direction, meaning from summation notation to either an explicit sum or the three-dot notation. The following example illustrates this procedure.

EXAMPLE 6	Write the series

$$\sum_{k=0}^{3} (k^2 - 1)2^k$$

as an explicit sum.

Usually the starting and ending values for a summation are written below and above the sigma. Sometimes to save vertical space this information appears alongside the sigma. For example, the sum above might be written as $\sum_{k=0}^{3}(k^2 - 1)2^k$.

SOLUTION In this case the summation starts with $k = 0$. When $k = 0$, the expression $(k^2 - 1)2^k$ equals -1, so the first term of this series is -1. When $k = 1$, the expression $(k^2 - 1)2^k$ equals 0, so the second term of this series is 0. When $k = 2$, the expression $(k^2 - 1)2^k$ equals 12, so the third term of this series is 12. When $k = 3$, the expression $(k^2 - 1)2^k$ equals 64, so the fourth term of this series is 64. Thus

$$\sum_{k=0}^{3} (k^2 - 1)2^k = -1 + 0 + 12 + 64 = 75.$$

Sometimes there is more than one convenient way to write a series using summation notation, as illustrated in the following example.

EXAMPLE 7	Suppose $r \neq 0$. Write the geometric series

$$1 + r + r^2 + \cdots + r^{n-1}$$

using summation notation.

SOLUTION This series has n terms. The mth term of this series is r^{m-1}. Thus

$$1 + r + r^2 + \cdots + r^{n-1} = \sum_{m=1}^{n} r^{m-1}.$$

You should think about why this example required that $r \neq 0$.

We could also think of this series as the sum of powers of r, starting with r^0 (recall that $r^0 = 1$) and ending with r^{n-1}. From this perspective, we could write

$$1 + r + r^2 + \cdots + r^{n-1} = \sum_{m=0}^{n-1} r^m.$$

Note that on the right side of the last equation, m starts at 0 and ends at $n - 1$.

Thus we have written this geometric series in two different ways using summation notation. Both are correct; the choice of which one to use may depend on taste or on the context.

EXERCISES

In Exercises 1–10, evaluate the arithmetic series.

1. $1 + 2 + 3 + \cdots + 98 + 99 + 100$

2. $1001 + 1002 + 1003 + \cdots + 2998 + 2999 + 3000$

3. $302 + 305 + 308 + \cdots + 6002 + 6005 + 6008$

4. $25 + 31 + 37 + \cdots + 601 + 607 + 613$

5. $200 + 195 + 190 + \cdots + 75 + 70 + 65$

6. $300 + 293 + 286 + \cdots + 55 + 48 + 41$

7. $\displaystyle\sum_{m=1}^{80} (4 + 5m)$

8. $\displaystyle\sum_{m=1}^{75} (2 + 3m)$

9. $\displaystyle\sum_{k=5}^{65} (4k - 1)$

10. $\displaystyle\sum_{k=10}^{900} (3k - 2)$

11. Find the sum of all the four-digit positive integers.

12. Find the sum of all the four-digit odd positive integers.

13. Find the sum of all the four-digit positive integers whose last digit equals 3.

14. Find the sum of all the four-digit positive integers that are evenly divisible by 5.

In Exercises 15–24, evaluate the geometric series.

15. $1 + 3 + 9 + \cdots + 3^{200}$

16. $1 + 2 + 4 + \cdots + 2^{100}$

17. $\dfrac{1}{4} + \dfrac{1}{16} + \dfrac{1}{64} + \cdots + \dfrac{1}{4^{50}}$

18. $\dfrac{1}{3} + \dfrac{1}{9} + \dfrac{1}{27} + \cdots + \dfrac{1}{3^{33}}$

19. $1 - \dfrac{1}{2} + \dfrac{1}{4} - \dfrac{1}{8} + \cdots + \dfrac{1}{2^{80}} - \dfrac{1}{2^{81}}$

20. $1 - \dfrac{1}{3} + \dfrac{1}{9} - \dfrac{1}{27} + \cdots + \dfrac{1}{3^{60}} - \dfrac{1}{3^{61}} + \dfrac{1}{3^{62}}$

21. $\displaystyle\sum_{m=1}^{40} \dfrac{3}{2^m}$ 23. $\displaystyle\sum_{m=3}^{77} (-5)^m$

22. $\displaystyle\sum_{m=1}^{90} \dfrac{5}{7^m}$ 24. $\displaystyle\sum_{m=5}^{91} (-2)^m$

In Exercises 25–30, write the series explicitly and evaluate the sum.

25. $\displaystyle\sum_{m=1}^{4} (m^2 + 5)$ 28. $\displaystyle\sum_{k=0}^{4} \ln(2^k + 1)$

26. $\displaystyle\sum_{m=1}^{5} (m^2 - 2m + 7)$ 29. $\displaystyle\sum_{n=2}^{5} \cos \dfrac{\pi}{n}$

27. $\displaystyle\sum_{k=0}^{3} \log(k^2 + 2)$ 30. $\displaystyle\sum_{n=2}^{5} \sin \dfrac{\pi}{n}$

In Exercises 31–34, write the series using summation notation (starting with m = 1). Each series in Exercises 31–34 is either an arithmetic series or a geometric series.

31. $2 + 4 + 6 + \cdots + 100$

32. $1 + 3 + 5 + \cdots + 201$

33. $\dfrac{5}{9} + \dfrac{5}{27} + \dfrac{5}{81} + \cdots + \dfrac{5}{3^{40}}$

34. $\dfrac{7}{16} + \dfrac{7}{32} + \dfrac{7}{64} + \cdots + \dfrac{7}{2^{25}}$

35. Restate the symbolic version of the formula for evaluating an arithmetic series using summation notation.

36. Restate the symbolic version of the formula for evaluating a geometric series using summation notation.

37. Find the total number of grains of rice on the first 18 squares of the chessboard in the fable in Section 3.4.

38. Find the total number of grains of rice on the first 30 squares of the chessboard in the fable in Section 3.4.

PROBLEMS

39. Explain why the polynomial factorization

$$1 - x^n = (1 - x)(1 + x + x^2 + \cdots + x^{n-1})$$

holds for every integer $n \geq 2$.

40. Show that

$$\tfrac{1}{2} + \tfrac{1}{3} + \cdots + \tfrac{1}{n} < \ln n$$

for every integer $n \geq 2$.

[*Hint:* Draw the graph of the curve $y = \frac{1}{x}$ in the xy-plane. Think of $\ln n$ as the area under part of this curve. Draw appropriate rectangles under the curve.]

41. Show that

$$\ln n < 1 + \tfrac{1}{2} + \cdots + \tfrac{1}{n-1}$$

for every integer $n \geq 2$.

[*Hint:* Draw the graph of the curve $y = \frac{1}{x}$ in the xy-plane. Think of $\ln n$ as the area under part of this curve. Draw appropriate rectangles above the curve.]

42. Show that the sum of a finite arithmetic sequence is 0 if and only if the last term equals the negative of the first term.

WORKED-OUT SOLUTIONS *to Odd-numbered Exercises*

In Exercises 1–10, evaluate the arithmetic series.

1. $1 + 2 + 3 + \cdots + 98 + 99 + 100$

    SOLUTION This series contains 100 terms.

    The average of the first and last terms in this series is $\frac{1+100}{2}$, which equals $\frac{101}{2}$.

    Thus $1 + 2 + \cdots + 99 + 100$ equals $100 \cdot \frac{101}{2}$, which equals $50 \cdot 101$, which equals 5050.

3. $302 + 305 + 308 + \cdots + 6002 + 6005 + 6008$

    SOLUTION The difference between consecutive terms in this series is 3. We need to determine the number n of terms in this series. Using the formula for the terms of an arithmetic sequence, we have

    $$302 + (n - 1)3 = 6008.$$

    Subtracting 302 from both sides of this equation gives the equation $(n - 1)3 = 5706$; dividing both sides by 3 then gives $n - 1 = 1902$. Thus $n = 1903$.

    The average of the first and last terms in this series is $\frac{302+6008}{2}$, which equals 3155.

    Thus $302 + 305 + \cdots + 6005 + 6008$ equals $1903 \cdot 3155$, which equals 6003965.

5. $200 + 195 + 190 + \cdots + 75 + 70 + 65$

    SOLUTION The difference between consecutive terms in this series is -5. We need to determine the number n of terms in this series. Using the formula for the terms of an arithmetic sequence, we have

    $$200 + (n - 1)(-5) = 65.$$

    Subtracting 200 from both sides of this equation gives the equation $(n - 1)(-5) = -135$; dividing both sides by -5 then gives $n - 1 = 27$. Thus $n = 28$.

The average of the first and last terms in this series is $\frac{200+65}{2}$, which equals $\frac{265}{2}$.

Thus $200 + 195 + 190 + \cdots + 75 + 70 + 65$ equals $28 \cdot \frac{265}{2}$, which equals 3710.

7. $\displaystyle\sum_{m=1}^{80} (4 + 5m)$

    SOLUTION Because $4 + 5 \cdot 1 = 9$ and $4 + 5 \cdot 80 = 404$, we have

    $$\sum_{m=1}^{80} (4 + 5m) = 9 + 14 + 19 \cdots + 404.$$

    Thus the first term of this arithmetic sequence is 9, the last term is 404, and we have 80 terms. Hence

    $$\sum_{m=1}^{80} (4 + 5m) = 80 \cdot \frac{9 + 404}{2} = 16520.$$

9. $\displaystyle\sum_{k=5}^{65} (4k - 1)$

    SOLUTION Because $4 \cdot 5 - 1 = 19$ and $4 \cdot 65 - 1 = 259$, we have

    $$\sum_{k=5}^{65} (4k - 1) = 19 + 23 + 27 + \cdots + 259.$$

    Thus the first term of this arithmetic sequence is 19, the last term is 259, and we have $65 - 5 + 1$ terms, or 61 terms. Hence

    $$\sum_{k=5}^{65} (4k - 1) = 61 \cdot \frac{19 + 259}{2} = 8479.$$

11. Find the sum of all the four-digit positive integers.

    SOLUTION We need to evaluate the arithmetic series

    $$1000 + 1001 + 1002 + \cdots + 9999.$$

    The number of terms in this arithmetic series is $9999 - 1000 + 1$, which equals 9000.

The average of the first and last terms is $\frac{1000+9999}{2}$, which equals $\frac{10999}{2}$.

Thus the sum of all the four-digit positive integers equals $9000 \cdot \frac{10999}{2}$, which equals 49495500.

13. Find the sum of all the four-digit positive integers whose last digit equals 3.

SOLUTION We need to evaluate the arithmetic series

$$1003 + 1013 + 1023 + \cdots + 9983 + 9993.$$

Consecutive terms in this series differ by 10. We need to determine the number n of terms in this series. Using the formula for the terms of an arithmetic sequence, we have

$$1003 + (n-1)10 = 9993.$$

Subtracting 1003 from both sides of this equation gives the equation $(n-1)10 = 8990$; dividing both sides by 10 then gives $n - 1 = 899$. Thus $n = 900$.

The average of the first and last terms is $\frac{1003+9993}{2}$, which equals 5498.

Thus the sum of all the four-digit positive integers whose last digit equals 3 is $900 \cdot 5498$, which equals 4948200.

In Exercises 15–24, evaluate the geometric series.

15. $1 + 3 + 9 + \cdots + 3^{200}$

SOLUTION The first term of this series is 1. If we added one more term to this series, the next term would be 3^{201}. The ratio of consecutive terms in this geometric series is 3. Thus

$$1 + 3 + 9 + \cdots + 3^{200} = \frac{1 - 3^{201}}{1 - 3} = \frac{3^{201} - 1}{2}.$$

17. $\frac{1}{4} + \frac{1}{16} + \frac{1}{64} + \cdots + \frac{1}{4^{50}}$

SOLUTION The first term of this series is $\frac{1}{4}$. If we added one more term to this series, the next term would be $1/4^{51}$. The ratio of consecutive terms in this geometric series is $\frac{1}{4}$. Thus

$$\frac{1}{4} + \frac{1}{16} + \frac{1}{64} + \cdots + \frac{1}{4^{50}} = \frac{\frac{1}{4} - \frac{1}{4^{51}}}{1 - \frac{1}{4}} = \frac{1 - \frac{1}{4^{50}}}{3},$$

where the last expression was obtained by multiplying the numerator and denominator of the previous expression by 4.

19. $1 - \frac{1}{2} + \frac{1}{4} - \frac{1}{8} + \cdots + \frac{1}{2^{80}} - \frac{1}{2^{81}}$

SOLUTION The first term of this series is 1. If we added one more term to this series, the next term would be $1/2^{82}$. The ratio of consecutive terms in this geometric series is $-\frac{1}{2}$. Thus

$$1 - \frac{1}{2} + \frac{1}{4} - \frac{1}{8} + \cdots + \frac{1}{2^{80}} - \frac{1}{2^{81}}$$
$$= \frac{1 - \frac{1}{2^{82}}}{1 - (-\frac{1}{2})}$$
$$= \frac{1 - \frac{1}{2^{82}}}{\frac{3}{2}} = \frac{2 - \frac{1}{2^{81}}}{3},$$

where the last expression was obtained by multiplying the numerator and denominator of the previous expression by 2.

21. $\sum_{m=1}^{40} \frac{3}{2^m}$

SOLUTION The first term of the series is $\frac{3}{2}$. If we added one more term to this geometric series, the next term would be $\frac{3}{2^{41}}$. The ratio of consecutive terms in this geometric series is $\frac{1}{2}$. Putting all this together, we have

$$\sum_{m=1}^{40} \frac{3}{2^m} = \frac{\frac{3}{2} - \frac{3}{2^{41}}}{1 - \frac{1}{2}} = 3 - \frac{3}{2^{40}}.$$

23. $\sum_{m=3}^{77} (-5)^m$

SOLUTION The first term of the series is $(-5)^3$, which equals -125. If we added one more term to this geometric series, the next term would be $(-5)^{78}$, which equals 5^{78}. The ratio of consecutive terms in this geometric series is -5. Putting all this together, we have

$$\sum_{m=3}^{77} (-5)^m = \frac{-125 - 5^{78}}{1 - (-5)} = -\frac{125 + 5^{78}}{6}.$$

In Exercises 25-30, write the series explicitly and evaluate the sum.

25. $\displaystyle\sum_{m=1}^{4} (m^2 + 5)$

SOLUTION   When $m = 1$, the expression $m^2 + 5$ equals 6. When $m = 2$, the expression $m^2 + 5$ equals 9. When $m = 3$, the expression $m^2 + 5$ equals 14. When $m = 4$, the expression $m^2 + 5$ equals 21. Thus

$$\sum_{m=1}^{4} (m^2 + 5) = 6 + 9 + 14 + 21 = 50.$$

27. $\displaystyle\sum_{k=0}^{3} \log(k^2 + 2)$

SOLUTION   When $k = 0$, the expression $\log(k^2 + 2)$ equals $\log 2$. When $k = 1$, the expression $\log(k^2 + 2)$ equals $\log 3$. When $k = 2$, the expression $\log(k^2 + 2)$ equals $\log 6$. When $k = 3$, the expression $\log(k^2 + 2)$ equals $\log 11$. Thus

$$\sum_{k=0}^{3} \log(k^2 + 2) = \log 2 + \log 3 + \log 6 + \log 11$$

$$= \log(2 \cdot 3 \cdot 6 \cdot 11) = \log 396.$$

29. $\displaystyle\sum_{n=2}^{5} \cos \frac{\pi}{n}$

SOLUTION   When $n = 2$, the expression $\cos \frac{\pi}{n}$ equals $\cos \frac{\pi}{2}$, which equals 0. When $n = 3$, the expression $\cos \frac{\pi}{n}$ equals $\cos \frac{\pi}{3}$, which equals $\frac{1}{2}$. When $n = 4$, the expression $\cos \frac{\pi}{n}$ equals $\cos \frac{\pi}{4}$, which equals $\sqrt{2}/2$. When $n = 5$, the expression $\cos \frac{\pi}{n}$ equals $\cos \frac{\pi}{5}$, which equals $(\sqrt{5} + 1)/4$ (from Exercise 9 in Section 6.3). Thus

$$\sum_{n=2}^{5} \cos \frac{\pi}{n} = 0 + \frac{1}{2} + \frac{\sqrt{2}}{2} + \frac{\sqrt{5} + 1}{4} = \frac{3 + 2\sqrt{2} + \sqrt{5}}{4}.$$

In Exercises 31-34, write the series using summation notation (starting with $m = 1$). Each series in Exercises 31-34 is either an arithmetic series or a geometric series.

31. $2 + 4 + 6 + \cdots + 100$

SOLUTION   The mth term of this sequence is $2m$. The last term corresponds to $m = 50$. Thus

$$2 + 4 + 6 + \cdots + 100 = \sum_{m=1}^{50} 2m.$$

33. $\dfrac{5}{9} + \dfrac{5}{27} + \dfrac{5}{81} + \cdots + \dfrac{5}{3^{40}}$

SOLUTION   The mth term of this sequence is $\frac{5}{3^{m+1}}$. The last term corresponds to $m = 39$ (because when $m = 39$, the expression $\frac{5}{3^{m+1}}$ equals $\frac{5}{3^{40}}$). Thus

$$\frac{5}{9} + \frac{5}{27} + \frac{5}{81} + \cdots + \frac{5}{3^{40}} = \sum_{m=1}^{39} \frac{5}{3^{m+1}}.$$

35. Restate the symbolic version of the formula for evaluating an arithmetic series using summation notation.

SOLUTION   Consider an arithmetic series with n terms, with an initial term b, and with difference d between consecutive terms. The mth term of this series is $b + (m - 1)d$. Thus the formula for evaluating an arithmetic series using summation notation is

$$\sum_{m=1}^{n} (b + (m - 1)d) = n\left(b + \tfrac{(n-1)d}{2}\right).$$

This could also be written in the form

$$\sum_{m=0}^{n-1} (b + md) = n\left(b + \tfrac{(n-1)d}{2}\right).$$

37. Find the total number of grains of rice on the first 18 squares of the chessboard in the fable in Section 3.4.

SOLUTION   The total number of grains of rice on the first 18 squares of the chessboard is

$$1 + 2 + 4 + 8 + \cdots + 2^{17}.$$

This is a geometric series; the ratio of consecutive terms is 2. The term that would follow the last term is 2^{18}. Thus the sum of this series is

$$\frac{1 - 2^{18}}{1 - 2},$$

which equals $2^{18} - 1$.

7.3 | *Limits*

SECTION OBJECTIVES

By the end of this section you should

- understand the concept of the limit of a sequence;
- understand how an infinite series is evaluated from partial sums;
- be able to compute the sum of an infinite geometric series;
- be able to convert repeating decimals to fractions.

Introduction to Limits

Consider the sequence

$$1, \tfrac{1}{2}, \tfrac{1}{3}, \tfrac{1}{4}, \ldots;$$

here the nth term of the sequence is $\frac{1}{n}$. For all large values of n, the nth term of this sequence is close to 0. For example, all the terms after the one-millionth term of this sequence are within one-millionth of 0. We say that this sequence has limit 0. More generally, the following informal definition explains what it means for a sequence to have limit equal to some number L.

> ### Limit of a sequence (less precise version)
>
> A sequence has **limit** L if from some point on, all the terms of the sequence are very close to L.

This definition fails to be precise because the phrase "very close" is too vague. A more precise definition of limit will be given soon, but first we examine some examples to get a feel for what is meant by taking the limit of a sequence.

What is the limit of the sequence whose n^{th} term equals $\sqrt{n^2 + n} - n$?   **EXAMPLE 1**

SOLUTION

The limit of a sequence depends on the behavior of the nth term for large values of n. The table to the right shows the values of the nth term of this sequence for some large values of n, calculated by a computer and rounded off to seven digits after the decimal point.

n	$\sqrt{n^2 + n} - n$
1	0.4142136
10	0.4880885
100	0.4987562
1000	0.4998751
10000	0.4999875
100000	0.4999988
1000000	0.4999999

This table leads us to suspect that this sequence has limit $\frac{1}{2}$. This suspicion is correct, as can be seen by rewriting the nth term of this sequence as follows:

$$\sqrt{n^2 + n} - n = \frac{1}{\sqrt{1 + \frac{1}{n}} + 1}.$$

See Problem 25 for a hint on how to derive this identity.

If n is very large, then $1 + \frac{1}{n}$ is very close to 1, and thus the right side of the equation above is very close to $\frac{1}{2}$. Hence the limit of the sequence in question is indeed equal to $\frac{1}{2}$.

Not every sequence has a limit, as shown by the following example:

EXAMPLE 2 Explain why the sequence whose n^{th} term equals $(-1)^{n-1}$ does not have a limit.

SOLUTION The sequence in question is the sequence of alternating 1's and −1's:

$$1, \; -1, \; 1, \; -1, \; \dots.$$

A number that is very close to −1 must be negative, and a number that is very close to 1 must be positive; thus no number can be very close to both −1 and 1. Hence this sequence does not have a limit.

The next example shows why we need to be careful about the meaning of "very close".

EXAMPLE 3 What is the limit of the sequence all of whose terms equal 10^{-100}?

SOLUTION The sequence in question is the constant sequence

$$10^{-100}, \; 10^{-100}, \; 10^{-100}, \; \dots.$$

The limit of this sequence is 10^{-100}. Note, however, that all the terms of this sequence are within one-billionth of 0. Thus if "very close" were defined to mean "within one-billionth", then the imprecise definition above might lead us to conclude incorrectly that this sequence has limit 0.

The example above shows that in our initial definition of limit, we cannot replace "very close to L" by "within one-billionth of L". For similar reasons, no single positive number, no matter how small, could be used to define "very close". This dilemma is solved by considering all positive numbers, including those that are very small (whatever that means). The following more precise definition of limit captures the notion that a sequence gets as close as we like to its limit if we go far enough out in the sequence:

As mentioned in Chapter 0, the Greek letter ε (epsilon) is often used when we are thinking about small positive numbers.

Limit of a sequence (more precise version)

A sequence has **limit** L if for every $\varepsilon > 0$, from some point on all terms of the sequence are within ε of L.

This definition means that for each possible choice of a positive number ε, there is some term of the sequence such that all following terms are within ε of L. How far out in the sequence we need to go to have all the terms beyond there be within ε of L can depend on ε.

For example, consider the sequence

$$-1, \tfrac{1}{2}, -\tfrac{1}{3}, \tfrac{1}{4}, \ldots;$$

here the nth term of the sequence equals $\frac{(-1)^n}{n}$. This sequence has limit 0. If we consider the choice $\varepsilon = 10^{-6}$, then all terms after the millionth term of this sequence are within ε of the limit 0. If we consider the choice $\varepsilon = 10^{-9}$, then all terms after the billionth term of this sequence are within ε of the limit 0. No matter how small we choose ε, we can go far enough out in the sequence (depending on ε) so that all the terms beyond there are within ε of 0.

Because the limit of a sequence depends only on what happens "from some point on", changing the first five terms or even the first five million terms does not affect the limit of a sequence. For example, consider the sequence

$$10, \ 100, \ 1000, \ 10000, \ 100000, \ \tfrac{1}{6}, \ \tfrac{1}{7}, \ \tfrac{1}{8}, \ \tfrac{1}{9}, \ \tfrac{1}{10}, \ \ldots;$$

here the nth term of the sequence equals 10^n if $n \le 5$ and equals $\frac{1}{n}$ if $n > 5$. Make sure you understand why the limit of this sequence equals 0.

The notation commonly used to denote the limit of a sequence is introduced below:

Limit notation

The notation

$$\lim_{n \to \infty} a_n = L$$

means that the sequence $a_1, a_2, \ldots$ has limit L. We say that the limit of a_n as n goes to infinity equals L.

Once again, remember that ∞ is not a real number; it appears here to help convey the notion that only large values of n matter.

For example, we could write

$$\lim_{n \to \infty} \tfrac{1}{n} = 0;$$

we would say that the limit of $\frac{1}{n}$ as n goes to infinity equals 0. As another example from earlier in this section, we could write

$$\lim_{n \to \infty} (\sqrt{n^2 + n} - n) = \tfrac{1}{2};$$

we would say that the limit of $\sqrt{n^2 + n} - n$ as n goes to infinity equals $\frac{1}{2}$.

Evaluate $\lim_{n \to \infty} \left(1 + \tfrac{1}{n}\right)^n$.

EXAMPLE 4

SOLUTION   This is the sequence whose first five terms are

$$2, \left(\tfrac{3}{2}\right)^2, \left(\tfrac{4}{3}\right)^3, \left(\tfrac{5}{4}\right)^4, \left(\tfrac{6}{5}\right)^5.$$

A computer can tell us that the one-millionth term of this sequence is approximately 2.71828, which you should recognize as being approximately e. Indeed, in Section 4.4 we saw that $\left(1 + \tfrac{1}{n}\right)^n \approx e$ for large values of n. The precise meaning of that approximation is that $\lim\limits_{n \to \infty} \left(1 + \tfrac{1}{n}\right)^n = e$.

Consider the geometric sequence

$$\tfrac{1}{2}, \ \tfrac{1}{4}, \ \tfrac{1}{8}, \ \tfrac{1}{16}, \ \dots.$$

Here the nth term equals $\left(\tfrac{1}{2}\right)^n$, which is very small for large values of n. Thus this sequence has limit 0, which we can write as $\lim\limits_{n \to \infty} \left(\tfrac{1}{2}\right)^n = 0$.

Similarly, multiplying any number with absolute value less than 1 by itself many times produces a number close to 0, as illustrated in the following example.

EXAMPLE 5

In the decimal expansion of 0.99^{100000}, how many zeros follow the decimal point before the first nonzero digit?

Note that even though 0.99 is just slightly less than 1, raising it to a large power produces a very small number.

SOLUTION   Calculators cannot evaluate 0.99^{100000}, so take its common logarithm:

$$\log 0.99^{100000} = 100000 \log 0.99 \approx 100000 \cdot (-0.004365) = -436.5.$$

This means that 0.99^{100000} is between 10^{-437} and 10^{-436}. Thus 436 zeros follow the decimal point in the decimal expansion of 0.99^{100000} before the first nonzero digit.

The example above should help convince you that if r is any number with $|r| < 1$, then $\lim\limits_{n \to \infty} r^n = 0$.

Similarly, if $|r| > 1$, then r^n is very large for large values of n. Thus if $|r| > 1$, then the geometric sequence $r, r^2, r^3, \dots$ does not have a limit.

If $r = -1$, then the geometric sequence $r, r^2, r^3, r^4 \dots$ is the alternating sequence $-1, 1, -1, 1, \dots$; this sequence does not have a limit. If $r = 1$, then the geometric sequence $r, r^2, r^3, r^4 \dots$ is the constant sequence $1, 1, 1, 1, \dots$; this sequence has limit 1.

Putting together the results above, we have the following summary concerning the limit of a geometric sequence:

Limit of a geometric sequence

Suppose r is a real number. Then the geometric sequence

$$r, r^2, r^3, \dots$$

- has limit 0 if $|r| < 1$;
- has limit 1 if $r = 1$;
- does not have a limit if $r \leq -1$ or $r > 1$.

Infinite Series

Addition is initially defined as an operation that takes two numbers a and b and produces their sum $a + b$. We can find the sum of a finite sequence $a_1, a_2, \ldots, a_n$ by adding the first two terms a_1 and a_2, getting $a_1 + a_2$, then adding the third term, getting $a_1 + a_2 + a_3$, then adding the fourth term, getting $a_1 + a_2 + a_3 + a_4$, and so on. After n terms we will have found the sum for this finite sequence; this sum can be denoted

$$a_1 + a_2 + \cdots + a_n \quad \text{or} \quad \sum_{m=1}^{n} a_m.$$

Because of the associative property, we do not need to worry about putting parentheses in these sums.

Now consider an infinite sequence $a_1, a_2, \ldots$. What does it mean to find the sum of this infinite sequence? In other words, we want to attach a meaning to the infinite sum

$$a_1 + a_2 + a_3 + \cdots \quad \text{or} \quad \sum_{m=1}^{\infty} a_m.$$

Such sums are called **infinite series**.

The problem with trying to evaluate an infinite series by adding one term at a time is that the process will never terminate. Nevertheless, let's see what happens when we add one term at a time in a familiar geometric sequence.

What value should be assigned to the infinite sum $\displaystyle\sum_{m=1}^{\infty} \frac{1}{2^m}$?

EXAMPLE 6

SOLUTION We need to evaluate the infinite sum

$$\frac{1}{2} + \frac{1}{4} + \frac{1}{8} + \frac{1}{16} + \cdots.$$

The sum of the first two terms equals $\frac{3}{4}$. The sum of the first three terms equals $\frac{7}{8}$. The sum of the first four terms equals $\frac{15}{16}$. More generally, the sum of the first n terms equals $1 - \frac{1}{2^n}$, as can be seen by using the formula from the last section on the sum of a finite geometric series.

Although the process of adding terms of this series never ends, we see that after adding a large number of terms the sum is close to 1. In other words, the limit of the sum of the first n terms is 1. Thus we declare that the infinite sum equals 1. Expressing all this in summation notation, we have

$$\sum_{m=1}^{\infty} \frac{1}{2^m} = \lim_{n \to \infty} \sum_{m=1}^{n} \frac{1}{2^m} = \lim_{n \to \infty} \left(1 - \frac{1}{2^n}\right) = 1.$$

The example above provides motivation for the formal definition of an infinite sum. To evaluate an infinite series, the idea is to add up the first n terms and then take the limit as n goes to infinity:

Infinite series

The infinite sum $\displaystyle\sum_{m=1}^{\infty} a_m$ is defined by

$$\sum_{m=1}^{\infty} a_m = \lim_{n \to \infty} \sum_{m=1}^{n} a_m$$

if this limit exists.

EXAMPLE 7

Evaluate the geometric series $\displaystyle\sum_{m=1}^{\infty} \frac{1}{10^m}$.

SOLUTION   According to the definition above, we need to evaluate the partial sums $\displaystyle\sum_{m=1}^{n} \frac{1}{10^m}$ and then take the limit as n goes to infinity. Using the formula from the last section for the sum of a finite geometric series, we have

$$\sum_{m=1}^{n} \frac{1}{10^m} = \frac{\frac{1}{10} - \frac{1}{10^{n+1}}}{1 - \frac{1}{10}} = \frac{1 - \frac{1}{10^n}}{9},$$

where the last expression is obtained by multiplying the numerator and denominator of the middle expression by 10. Thus

$$\sum_{m=1}^{\infty} \frac{1}{10^m} = \lim_{n \to \infty} \sum_{m=1}^{n} \frac{1}{10^m} = \lim_{n \to \infty} \frac{1 - \frac{1}{10^n}}{9} = \frac{1}{9}.$$

Some infinite sequences cannot be summed, because the limit of the sequence of partial sums does not exist. When this happens, the infinite sum is left undefined.

EXAMPLE 8

Explain why the infinite series $\displaystyle\sum_{m=1}^{\infty} (-1)^m$ is undefined.

SOLUTION   We are trying to make sense of the infinite sum

$$-1 + 1 - 1 + 1 - 1 + \cdots.$$

Following the usual procedure for infinite sums, first we evaluate the partial sums $\displaystyle\sum_{m=1}^{n} (-1)^m$, getting

$$\sum_{m=1}^{n} (-1)^m = \begin{cases} -1 & \text{if } n \text{ is odd} \\ 0 & \text{if } n \text{ is even.} \end{cases}$$

Thus the sequence of partial sums is the alternating sequence of -1's and 0's. This sequence of partial sums does not have a limit. Thus the infinite sum is undefined.

We turn now to the problem of finding a formula for evaluating an infinite geometric series. Fix a number $r \neq 1$, and consider the geometric series

$$1 + r + r^2 + r^3 + \cdots;$$

here the ratio of consecutive terms is r. The sum of the first n terms is $1 + r + r^2 + \cdots + r^{n-1}$. The term following the last term would be r^n; thus by our formula for evaluating a geometric series we have

$$1 + r + r^2 + \cdots + r^{n-1} = \frac{1 - r^n}{1 - r}.$$

By definition, the infinite sum $1 + r + r^2 + r^3 + \cdots$ equals the limit (if it exists) of the partial sums above as n goes to infinity. We have already seen that the limit of r^n as n goes to infinity is 0 if $|r| < 1$ (and does not exist if $|r| > 1$). Thus we get the following beautiful formula:

Evaluating an infinite geometric series

If $|r| < 1$, then
$$1 + r + r^2 + r^3 + \cdots = \frac{1}{1 - r}.$$

If $|r| \geq 1$, then this infinite sum is not defined.

Any infinite geometric series can be reduced to the form above by factoring out the first term. The following example illustrates the procedure.

Evaluate the geometric series $\dfrac{7}{3} + \dfrac{7}{9} + \dfrac{7}{27} + \cdots$.

EXAMPLE 9

SOLUTION   We factor out the first term $\frac{7}{3}$ and then apply the formula above, getting

$$\frac{7}{3} + \frac{7}{9} + \frac{7}{27} + \cdots = \frac{7}{3}\left(1 + \frac{1}{3} + \frac{1}{9} + \cdots\right) = \frac{7}{3} \cdot \frac{1}{1 - \frac{1}{3}} = \frac{7}{2}.$$

Decimals as Infinite Series

A **digit** is one of the numbers $0, 1, 2, 3, 4, 5, 6, 7, 8, 9$. Each real number t between 0 and 1 can be expressed as a decimal in the form

$$t = 0.d_1 d_2 d_3 \ldots,$$

where $d_1, d_2, d_3, \ldots$ is a sequence of digits. The interpretation of this representation is that

$$t = \frac{d_1}{10} + \frac{d_2}{100} + \frac{d_3}{1000} + \cdots,$$

which we can write in summation notation as

$$t = \sum_{m=1}^{\infty} \frac{d_m}{10^m}.$$

In other words, real numbers are represented by infinite series.

If from some point on each d_m equals 0, then we have what is called a **terminating decimal**; in this case we usually do not write the ending string of 0's.

EXAMPLE 10

Express 0.217 as a fraction.

SOLUTION   In this case, the infinite series above becomes a finite series:

$$0.217 = \frac{2}{10} + \frac{1}{100} + \frac{7}{1000} = \frac{200}{1000} + \frac{10}{1000} + \frac{7}{1000} = \frac{217}{1000}$$

If the decimal representation of a number has a pattern that repeats from some point on, then we have what is called a **repeating decimal**.

EXAMPLE 11

Express

$$0.11111\ldots$$

as a fraction; here the digit 1 keeps repeating forever.

SOLUTION   Using the interpretation of the decimal representation, we have

$$0.11111\ldots = \sum_{m=1}^{\infty} \frac{1}{10^m}.$$

The sum above is an infinite geometric series. As we saw in Example 7, this infinite geometric series equals $\frac{1}{9}$. Thus

$$0.11111\ldots = \frac{1}{9}.$$

Every irrational number has a nonrepeating decimal expansion.

Any repeating decimal can be converted to a fraction by evaluating an appropriate infinite geometric series. However, the technique used in the following example is usually easier.

EXAMPLE 12

Express

$$0.52473473473\ldots$$

as a fraction; here the digits 473 keep repeating forever.

SOLUTION   Let

$$t = 0.52473473473\ldots.$$

The trick is to note that

$$1000t = 524.73473473473\ldots.$$

Subtracting the first equation above from the last equation, we get

$$999t = 524.21.$$

Thus

$$t = \frac{524.21}{999} = \frac{52421}{99900}.$$

Special Infinite Series

Advanced mathematics produces many beautiful special infinite series. We cannot derive the values for these infinite series here, but they are so pretty that you should at least see a few of them.

Evaluate $\displaystyle\sum_{m=1}^{\infty} \frac{1}{m!}$.

EXAMPLE 13

SOLUTION   A computer calculation can give a partial sum that leads to a correct guess. Specifically,

$$\sum_{m=1}^{1000} \frac{1}{m!} \approx 1.718281828459.$$

You may recognize the digits after the decimal point as the digits after the decimal point of e. It is indeed true that this infinite sum equals $e - 1$. Adding 1 to both sides of the equation $\displaystyle\sum_{m=1}^{\infty} \frac{1}{m!} = e - 1$ gives the beautiful infinite series

$$1 + \frac{1}{1!} + \frac{1}{2!} + \frac{1}{3!} + \cdots = e.$$

This equation again shows how e magically appears throughout mathematics.

More generally, as you will learn in your calculus class, the following equation is true for every number x:

$$1 + \frac{x}{1!} + \frac{x^2}{2!} + \frac{x^3}{3!} + \cdots = e^x.$$

The next example shows again that the natural logarithm deserves the word "natural".

Evaluate $\displaystyle\sum_{m=1}^{\infty} \frac{(-1)^{m+1}}{m}$.

EXAMPLE 14

SOLUTION   Once again a computer calculation can give a partial sum that leads to a correct guess. Specifically,

$$\sum_{m=1}^{100000} \frac{(-1)^{m+1}}{m} \approx 0.693142.$$

You may recognize the first five digits after the decimal point as the first five digits in the decimal expansion of $\ln 2$. The infinite sum indeed equals $\ln 2$. In other words, we have the following delightful equation:

$$1 - \frac{1}{2} + \frac{1}{3} - \frac{1}{4} + \frac{1}{5} - \frac{1}{6} + \cdots = \ln 2.$$

The next example presents another famous infinite series.

EXAMPLE 15

Evaluate $\displaystyle\sum_{m=1}^{\infty} \frac{1}{m^2}$.

SOLUTION   A computer calculation can give a partial sum. Specifically,

$$\sum_{m=1}^{1000000} \frac{1}{m^2} \approx 1.64493.$$

The value of this infinite series is hard to recognize even from this good approximation. In fact, the exact evaluation of this infinite sum was an unsolved problem for many years, but the Swiss mathematician Leonard Euler showed in 1735 that this infinite series equals $\frac{\pi^2}{6}$. In other words, we have the beautiful equation

$$1 + \frac{1}{4} + \frac{1}{9} + \frac{1}{16} + \cdots = \frac{\pi^2}{6}.$$

Leonard Euler, the most important mathematician of the 18th century.

Euler also showed that

$$\sum_{m=1}^{\infty} \frac{1}{m^4} = \frac{\pi^4}{90} \quad \text{and} \quad \sum_{m=1}^{\infty} \frac{1}{m^6} = \frac{\pi^6}{945}.$$

The next example is presented to show that there are still unsolved problems in mathematics that are easy to state.

EXAMPLE 16

Evaluate $\displaystyle\sum_{m=1}^{\infty} \frac{1}{m^3}$.

SOLUTION   A computer calculation can give a partial sum. Specifically,

$$\sum_{m=1}^{1000000} \frac{1}{m^3} \approx 1.2020569.$$

No one knows an exact expression for the infinite series $\displaystyle\sum_{m=1}^{\infty} \frac{1}{m^3}$. You will become famous if you find one!

EXERCISES

1. Evaluate $\lim\limits_{n\to\infty} \dfrac{3n+5}{2n-7}$.

2. Evaluate $\lim\limits_{n\to\infty} \dfrac{4n-2}{7n+6}$.

3. Evaluate $\lim\limits_{n\to\infty} \dfrac{2n^2+5n+1}{5n^2-6n+3}$.

4. Evaluate $\lim\limits_{n\to\infty} \dfrac{7n^2-4n+3}{3n^2+5n+9}$.

5. Evaluate $\lim\limits_{n\to\infty} \left(1+\frac{3}{n}\right)^n$.

6. Evaluate $\lim\limits_{n\to\infty} \left(1-\frac{1}{n}\right)^n$.

7. Evaluate $\lim\limits_{n\to\infty} n(e^{1/n}-1)$.

8. Evaluate $\lim\limits_{n\to\infty} n\ln(1+\frac{1}{n})$.

9. Evaluate $\lim\limits_{n\to\infty} n\left(\ln(3+\frac{1}{n})-\ln 3\right)$.

10. Evaluate $\lim\limits_{n\to\infty} n\left(\ln(7+\frac{1}{n})-\ln 7\right)$.

11. ✐ Find the smallest integer n such that $0.8^n < 10^{-100}$.

12. ✐ Find the smallest integer n such that $0.9^n < 10^{-200}$.

13. ✐ In the decimal expansion of 0.87^{1000}, how many zeros follow the decimal point before the first nonzero digit?

14. ✐ In the decimal expansion of 0.99^{9999}, how many zeros follow the decimal point before the first nonzero digit?

15. Evaluate $\sum\limits_{m=1}^{\infty} \dfrac{3}{7^m}$.

16. Evaluate $\sum\limits_{m=1}^{\infty} \dfrac{8}{5^m}$.

17. Evaluate $\sum\limits_{m=2}^{\infty} \dfrac{5}{6^m}$.

18. Evaluate $\sum\limits_{m=3}^{\infty} \dfrac{8}{3^m}$.

19. Express
$$0.23232323\ldots$$
as a fraction; here the digits 23 keep repeating forever.

20. Express
$$0.859859859\ldots$$
as a fraction; here the digits 859 keep repeating forever.

21. Express
$$8.237545454\ldots$$
as a fraction; here the digits 54 keep repeating forever.

22. Express
$$5.1372647264\ldots$$
as a fraction; here the digits 7264 keep repeating forever.

PROBLEMS

23. Give an example of a sequence that has limit 3 and whose first five terms are $2, 4, 6, 8, 10$.

24. Suppose you are given a sequence with limit L and that you change the sequence by adding 50 to the first 1000 terms, leaving the other terms unchanged. Explain why the new sequence also has limit L.

25. Show that
$$\sqrt{n^2+n}-n = \dfrac{1}{\sqrt{1+\frac{1}{n}}+1}.$$

[*Hint:* Multiply by $\sqrt{n^2+n}-n$ by $(\sqrt{n^2+n}+n)/(\sqrt{n^2+n}+n)$. Then factor n out of the numerator and denominator of the resulting expression.]
[*This identity was used in Example 1.*]

26. Which arithmetic sequences have a limit?

27. Suppose x is a positive number.

    (a) Explain why $x^{1/n} = e^{(\ln x)/n}$ for every nonzero number n.

    (b) Explain why
    $$n(x^{1/n} - 1) \approx \ln x$$
    if n is very large.

    (c) Explain why
    $$\ln x = \lim_{n \to \infty} n(x^{1/n} - 1).$$

    [*A few books use the last equation above as the definition of the natural logarithm.*]

28. Find the only arithmetic sequence $a_1, a_2, a_3, \ldots$ such that the infinite sum $\sum_{m=1}^{\infty} a_m$ exists.

29. Show that if $|r| < 1$, then
    $$\sum_{m=1}^{\infty} r^m = \frac{r}{1 - r}.$$

30. Explain why 0.2 and the repeating decimal $0.199999\ldots$ both represent the real number $\frac{1}{5}$.

31. Learn about Zeno's paradox (from a book, a friend, or a web search) and then relate the explanation of this ancient Greek problem to the infinite series
    $$\frac{1}{2} + \frac{1}{4} + \frac{1}{8} + \frac{1}{16} + \cdots = 1.$$

32. Explain how the formula
    $$e^x = 1 + \frac{x}{1!} + \frac{x^2}{2!} + \frac{x^3}{3!} + \cdots$$
    leads to the approximation $e^x \approx 1 + x$ if x is very close to 0 (which we derived by another method in Section 4.4).

WORKED-OUT SOLUTIONS *to Odd-numbered Exercises*

1. Evaluate $\lim_{n \to \infty} \frac{3n + 5}{2n - 7}$.

   SOLUTION Dividing numerator and denominator of this fraction by n, we see that
   $$\frac{3n + 5}{2n - 7} = \frac{3 + \frac{5}{n}}{2 - \frac{7}{n}}.$$

   If n is very large, then the numerator of the fraction on the right is close to 3 and the denominator is close to 2. Thus $\lim_{n \to \infty} \frac{3n+5}{2n-7} = \frac{3}{2}$.

3. Evaluate $\lim_{n \to \infty} \frac{2n^2 + 5n + 1}{5n^2 - 6n + 3}$.

   SOLUTION Dividing numerator and denominator of this fraction by n^2, we see that
   $$\frac{2n^2 + 5n + 1}{5n^2 - 6n + 3} = \frac{2 + \frac{5}{n} + \frac{1}{n^2}}{5 - \frac{6}{n} + \frac{3}{n^2}}.$$

   If n is very large, then the numerator of the fraction on the right is close to 2 and the denominator is close to 5. Thus
   $$\lim_{n \to \infty} \frac{2n^2 + 5n + 1}{5n^2 - 6n + 3} = \frac{2}{5}.$$

5. Evaluate $\lim_{n \to \infty} \left(1 + \frac{3}{n}\right)^n$.

   SOLUTION The properties of the exponential function imply that if n is very large, then $\left(1 + \frac{3}{n}\right)^n \approx e^3$; see Section 4.4. Thus $\lim_{n \to \infty} \left(1 + \frac{3}{n}\right)^n = e^3$.

7. Evaluate $\lim_{n \to \infty} n(e^{1/n} - 1)$.

   SOLUTION Suppose n is very large. Then $\frac{1}{n}$ is very close to 0, which means that $e^{1/n} \approx 1 + \frac{1}{n}$. Thus $e^{1/n} - 1 \approx \frac{1}{n}$, which implies that
   $$n(e^{1/n} - 1) \approx 1.$$

   Thus
   $$\lim_{n \to \infty} n(e^{1/n} - 1) = 1.$$

9. Evaluate $\lim_{n \to \infty} n(\ln(3 + \frac{1}{n}) - \ln 3)$.

   SOLUTION Note that
   $$\ln(3 + \tfrac{1}{n}) - \ln 3 = \ln(1 + \tfrac{1}{3n}).$$

   Suppose n is very large. Then $\frac{1}{3n}$ is very close to 0, which implies $\ln(1 + \frac{1}{3n}) \approx \frac{1}{3n}$. Thus $n(\ln(3 + \frac{1}{n}) - \ln 3) = n \ln(1 + \frac{1}{3n}) \approx \frac{1}{3}$. Thus

$$\lim_{n \to \infty} n \left(\ln(3 + \tfrac{1}{n}) - \ln 3 \right) = \tfrac{1}{3}.$$

11. ✐ Find the smallest integer n such that $0.8^n < 10^{-100}$.

SOLUTION The inequality $0.8^n < 10^{-100}$ is equivalent to the inequality

$$\log 0.8^n < \log 10^{-100},$$

which can be rewritten as $n \log 0.8 < -100$. Because 0.8 is less than 1, we know that $\log 0.8$ is negative. Thus dividing by $\log 0.8$ reverses the direction of the inequality, changing the previous inequality into the inequality

$$n > \frac{-100}{\log 0.8} \approx 1031.9.$$

The smallest integer that is greater than 1031.9 is 1032. Thus 1032 is the smallest integer n such that $0.8^n < 10^{-100}$.

13. ✐ In the decimal expansion of 0.87^{1000}, how many zeros follow the decimal point before the first nonzero digit?

SOLUTION Taking a common logarithm, we have

$$\log 0.87^{1000} = 1000 \log 0.87 \approx -60.5.$$

This means that 0.87^{1000} is between 10^{-61} and 10^{-60}. Thus 60 zeros follow the decimal point in the decimal expansion of 0.87^{1000} before the first nonzero digit.

15. Evaluate $\displaystyle\sum_{m=1}^{\infty} \frac{3}{7^m}$.

SOLUTION

$$\sum_{m=1}^{\infty} \frac{3}{7^m} = \frac{3}{7} + \frac{3}{7^2} + \frac{3}{7^3} + \cdots$$

$$= \frac{3}{7}\left(1 + \frac{1}{7} + \frac{1}{7^2} + \cdots\right)$$

$$= \frac{3}{7} \cdot \frac{1}{1 - \frac{1}{7}}$$

$$= \frac{1}{2}$$

17. Evaluate $\displaystyle\sum_{m=2}^{\infty} \frac{5}{6^m}$.

SOLUTION

$$\sum_{m=2}^{\infty} \frac{5}{6^m} = \frac{5}{6^2} + \frac{5}{6^3} + \frac{5}{6^4} + \cdots$$

$$= \frac{5}{36}\left(1 + \frac{1}{6} + \frac{1}{6^2} + \cdots\right)$$

$$= \frac{5}{36} \cdot \frac{1}{1 - \frac{1}{6}}$$

$$= \frac{1}{6}$$

19. Express

$$0.23232323\ldots$$

as a fraction; here the digits 23 keep repeating forever.

SOLUTION Let

$$t = 0.23232323\ldots .$$

Note that

$$100t = 23.23232323\ldots .$$

Subtracting the first equation above from the last equation, we get

$$99t = 23.$$

Thus

$$t = \frac{23}{99}.$$

21. Express

$$8.237545454\ldots$$

as a fraction; here the digits 54 keep repeating forever.

SOLUTION Let

$$t = 8.237545454\ldots .$$

Note that

$$100t = 823.754545454\ldots .$$

Subtracting the first equation above from the last equation, we get

$$99t = 815.517.$$

Thus

$$t = \frac{815.517}{99} = \frac{815517}{99000} = \frac{90613}{11000}.$$

CHAPTER SUMMARY

To check that you have mastered the most important concepts and skills covered in this chapter, make sure that you can do each item in the following list:

- Compute the terms of an arithmetic sequence given any term and the difference between consecutive terms.

- Compute the terms of an arithmetic sequence given any two terms.

- Compute the terms of a geometric sequence given any term and the ratio of consecutive terms.

- Compute the terms of a geometric sequence given any two terms.

- Compute the terms of a recursive sequence given the equations defining the sequence.

- Compute the sum of a finite arithmetic sequence.

- Compute the sum of a finite geometric sequence.

- Work with summation notation.

- Explain the intuitive notion of limit.

- Compute the sum of an infinite geometric sequence.

- Convert a repeating decimal to a fraction.

To review a chapter, go through the list above to find items that you do not know how to do, then reread the material in the chapter about those items. Then try to answer the chapter review questions below without looking back at the chapter.

CHAPTER REVIEW QUESTIONS

1. Explain why a sequence whose first four terms are $41, 58, 75, 94$ is not an arithmetic sequence.

2. Give two different examples of arithmetic sequences whose fifth term equals 17.

3. Explain why a sequence whose first four terms are $24, 36, 54, 78$ is not a geometric sequence.

4. Give two different examples of geometric sequences whose fourth term equals 29.

5. Find a number t such that the finite sequence $1, 5, t$ is an arithmetic sequence.

6. Find a number t such that the finite sequence $1, 5, t$ is a geometric sequence.

7. Find the fifth term of the recursive sequence defined by the equations

$$a_1 = 2 \quad \text{and} \quad a_{n+1} = \frac{1}{a_n + 1}.$$

8. Write the sequence whose n^{th} term equals $4^{-n} n!$ as a recursive sequence.

9. Find the sum of all the three-digit even positive integers.

10. Evaluate $\displaystyle\sum_{j=1}^{22} (-5)^j$.

11. Evaluate $\displaystyle\lim_{n \to \infty} \frac{4n^2 + 1}{3n^2 - 5n}$.

12. Evaluate $\displaystyle\sum_{m=1}^{\infty} \frac{6}{12^m}$.

13. Evaluate $\displaystyle\sum_{m=3}^{\infty} \frac{5}{4^m}$.

14. Express

$$0.417898989\ldots$$

as a fraction; here the digits 89 keep repeating forever.

Photo Credits

- page v: Jonathan Shapiro
- page 1: Goodshot/SUPERSTOCK
- page 33: Public domain image from Wikipedia
- page 117: Public domain image from Wikipedia
- page 122: Brand X/SUPERSTOCK
- page 209: Ingram Publishing/SUPERSTOCK
- page 210: Public domain image from Wikipedia
- page 224: Superstock, Inc./SUPERSTOCK
- page 241: Public domain image from Wikipedia
- page 250: age fotostock/SUPERSTOCK
- page 259: iStockphoto
- page 263: Alex Slobodkin/iStockphoto
- page 266: Adam Kazmierski/iStockphoto
- page 276: Culver Pictures, Inc./SUPERSTOCK
- page 277: Sheldon Axler
- page 290: iStockphoto
- page 310: Christine Balderas/iStockphoto
- page 312: Manuela Miller/iStockphoto
- page 312: Public domain image from Wikipedia
- page 346: Corbis/SUPERSTOCK
- page 357: age fotostock/SUPERSTOCK
- page 361: Paul Kline/iStockphoto
- page 377: Tetra Images/SUPERSTOCK
- page 378: FoodCollection/SUPERSTOCK
- page 381: FoodCollection/SUPERSTOCK
- page 456: PhotoAlto/SUPERSTOCK
- page 462: NewsCom
- page 506: Photodisc/SUPERSTOCK
- page 552: Christie's Images/SUPERSTOCK
- page 560: Public domain image from Wikipedia
- page 586: Jaime Abecasis/SUPERSTOCK

Appendix A

- **Polynomial Functions. Definitions and terminology.**

> Let n be a nonnegative integer and let $a_n, a_{n-1}, a_{n-2}, \ldots, a_2, a_1, a_0$ be real number with $a_n \neq 0$. The function defined by
> $$P(x) = a_n x^n + a_{n-1} x^{n-1} + \cdots + a_2 x^2 + a_1 x + a_0$$
> is called a **polynomial function of x of degree n** (in general form).
>
> **Degree: n, highest power. Notation:** $\deg P = n$.
>
> **Leading term:** $a_n x^n$, term with highest power.
>
> **Leading coefficient:** a_n, the coefficient of the variable to the highest power.

Examples.
What is the degree, leading term, and leading coefficient of the polynomial

a) $f(x) = 3x^2 - 7x + 5$

b) $f(x) = -7x^{10} - 5x^8 + 3x^5 - 7x + 16$

c) $f(x) = 15$

- **Domain.**
  All Polynomial functions have the domain $(-\infty, \infty)$

- Graphs of the Polynomial Functions are continuous smooth curves without jumps and sharp corners.

- **Examples of graphs of Polynomials.**

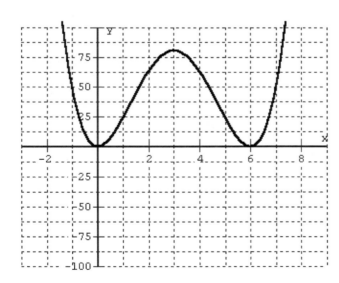

- **"End Behavior" of Polynomial Functions and Leading Coefficient Test.**

The behavior of the graph of a function to the far right $(as\ x \to \infty)$, and to the far left $(as\ x \to -\infty)$ is called the *end behavior* (or the large scale behavior) of a function.

> The "end behavior" (the large scale behavior) of any polynomial function is the same as that of $y = a_n x^n$, the term of highest degree (leading term).

$$P(x) = a_n x^n \left(1 + \frac{a_{n-1}}{a_n} \frac{1}{x} + \frac{a_{n-2}}{a_n} \frac{1}{x^2} + \cdots + \frac{a_0}{a_n} \frac{1}{x^n} \right)$$

Hence, for $|x|$ large, $P(x) \approx a_n x^n$ since

$\dfrac{1}{x^k} \to 0$ *when* $x \to \infty$ *for all* $k > 0$.

- Types of the "end behavior" of Polynomials.
- Hands test for "end behavior".

Odd type. $a_n > 0$ $a_n < 0$

 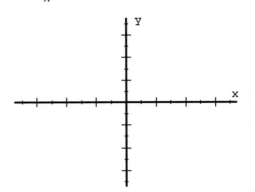

$$f(x) \to -\infty \qquad f(x) \to \infty$$
$$as \ x \to -\infty \qquad as \ x \to \infty$$

$$f(x) \to \infty \qquad f(x) \to -\infty$$
$$as \ x \to -\infty \quad as \ x \to \infty$$

Even type $a_n > 0$ $a_n < 0$

 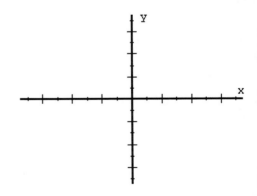

$$f(x) \to \infty \qquad f(x) \to \infty$$
$$as \ x \to -\infty \qquad as \ x \to \infty$$

$$f(x) \to -\infty \qquad f(x) \to -\infty$$
$$as \ x \to -\infty \qquad as \ x \to \infty$$

Exercises.

State the "end behavior" of following polynomial functions.

1. $f(x) = 3x^4 - 50x^3 - 11x^2 + 33x + 125$

$f(x) \rightarrow$	$f(x) \rightarrow$
as $x \rightarrow -\infty$	as $x \rightarrow \infty$

2. $f(x) = -15x^5 + 10x^4 - 25x^3 + 22x^2 + 11x - 111$

$f(x) \rightarrow$	$f(x) \rightarrow$
as $x \rightarrow -\infty$	as $x \rightarrow \infty$

- Range of the Polynomial Functions.

Odd type. $(-\infty, \infty)$	**Even type.** Individual

5

- Turning points of the Polynomial Functions.

> The points where the graph of a polynomial changes direction from increasing to decreasing or vice versa are called the ***turning points of the polynomial***.
> The polynomial function value at a turning point is either a ***local minimum*** of f or a ***local maximum*** of f.
> If f is a polynomial function with degree n, then the graph of f has at most $n-1$ turning points.

- *Y*-intercept of the graphs of Polynomials.

  Question: Does every polynomial function have a *y*-intercept? Give the reason for your answer.

Exercises.

Find the domain, range and *y*-intercept for the polynomial

3. $f(x) = -5x^3 - 11x^2 + 33x - 75$

4. $f(x) = 2x^5 - 11x^3 + 15x^2 - 20x + 150$

5. $f(x) = 3x^3 (x-2)^2 (2x-1)$

- X-intercepts of the graphs of Polynomials.

Exercises.

Find the x-intercepts (zeros) for

6. $f(x) = x^3 - 2x^2 - 5x$

7. $f(x) = 3x^3(x-2)^2(2x-1)$

8. $f(x) = x^4 - 4x^2 + 4$

9. $f(x) = x^4 - 6x^3 + 9x^2$

- **The Factor Theorem.**
  For a polynomial f, if $f(c) = 0$, then $x - c$ is a factor of f.

- **Repeated Zeros of Polynomial Functions and Patterns of x-intercepts.**

  Polynomial Functions have three different patterns of x-intercepts. The graph may touch the x-axis, may cross it like a straight line, and may cross and flatten out at the point of intersection.

The patterns depend on *multiplicity* of corresponding zeros of the polynomial function.

We say that $x = c$ is a zero of a polynomial P with *multiplicity k*, if in the complete factorization of P the factor $(x - c)$ is repeated k times.

Example.

$P(x) = 3x^3 (x - 1)^2 (x + 1)$ has zero $x = 0$ of multiplicity $k = 3$, $x = 1$ of multiplicity $k = 2$, and $x = -1$ of multiplicity $k = 1$.

If $x = c$ is a zero of an even multiplicity, then the graph touches the x-axis; if $x = c$ has the multiplicity 1, then the graph crosses x-axis like a straight line does, and if $x = c$ has an odd multiplicity greater than 1 ($k = 3, 5, ...$), then the graph flattens out when going through x-axis. The graphs shown below have all three patterns of x-intercepts. On the left, the zero $x = 0$ has an even multiplicity, and $x = 2$ has the multiplicity equal to 1. On the right, $x = 0$ has an odd multiplicity greater than 1.

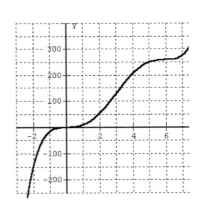

Exercises.

10. Given $f(x) = 5x^4(x+3)^2(x-5)$.

    a) Find all zeros of the polynomial function f and state multiplicity of each zeros.

    b) What is the degree of f?
    c) Find y-intercept of f.
    d) State the "end behavior" of f.
    e) Make a sketch of f.

11. Given $f(x) = -12(x+5)^3(x-3)^2(x+2)$

    a) Find all zeros of the polynomial function f and state multiplicity of each zeros.

    b) What is the degree of f?
    c) Find y-intercept of f.
    d) State the "end behavior" of f.
    e) Make a sketch of f.

12. Make a sketch of a polynomial function that satisfies all Given conditions: even degree; positive leading coefficient; y-int$=-3$; $x=0$ the zero of multiplicity $k=2$; $x=4$ the zero of multiplicity $k=3$.

13. Make a sketch of a polynomial function that satisfies all Given conditions: odd degree; negative leading coefficient; y-int$=4$; $x=-2$ the zero of multiplicity $k=2$; $x=4$ the zero of multiplicity $k=3$.

14. Make a sketch for the "end behavior" and state it Symbolically for $P(x) = -5x^6 - 11x^4 + 20x^3 + 10x - 99$. What is the y-intercept of P ?

15. The graph of a polynomial function $y = f(x)$ is shown below.

Use the graph to answer the following questions.

a) Is the degree of the polynomial function f even or odd?
b) Is the leading coefficient positive or negative?
c) Label with letters (A, B, ...) on the graph all turning points of the polynomial f.
d) Is the multiplicity k of the zero $x = -3$ odd or even?
e) Is the multiplicity k of the zero $x = 0$ equal to 1 or greater than 1?
f) State the "End behavior" of f.

16. The graph of a polynomial Function f is shown below. Use the graph to answer the following questions.

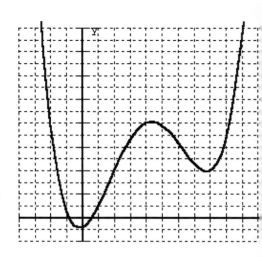

a) Is the degree of the polynomial function f even or odd?
b) Is the leading coefficient positive or negative?

10

c) Label with letters (A, B, ...) on the graph all turning points of the polynomial.

d) Is the multiplicity k of the zero $x = -1$ odd or even?

e) Is the multiplicity k of the zero $x = -1$ equal to1 or greater than 1?

f) State the "End behavior" of f.

- **The Algebra of Polynomials.**

Two polynomials can be added, subtracted, and multiplied. Results are another polynomial. If P *and* Q are polynomials, then

$$(P+Q)(x) = P(x) + Q(x)$$
$$(P-Q)(x) = P(x) - Q(x)$$
$$(PQ)(x) = P(x)Q(x)$$

- **Degree of Sum, Difference, and Product of Polynomials.**

$$\deg(P+Q) \le max\{\deg P, \deg Q\}$$
$$(P-Q)(x) \le max\{\deg P, \deg Q\}$$
$$(PQ)(x) = \deg P + \deg Q$$

- **Long division of the polynomials.**
  Quotient and Remainder.

| Dividend $f(x)$ | $=$ | Divisor $d(x)$ | $\times$ | Quotient $q(x)$ | $+$ | Remainder $r(x)$ |

Note: Divisor $d(x) \neq 0$, and the degree of d is less or equal to the degree of the dividend f. The degree of remainder is always less than the degree of the divisor.

- **Exercises.**

17. Given quotient $q(x) = x^2 - 3x + 3$ and remainder $r(x) = 5x - 12$ after division of

$f(x) = x^4 - 3x^3 + 5x^2 - x - 6$ by $d(x) = r(x) = x^2 + 2$.

Write the presentation of $f(x)$ through $q(x)$ and $r(x)$.

18. Use long division to divide

$f(x) = x^4 - 3x^3 + 4x^2 - 5x + 11$ by $d(x) = x^2 - 2x + 4$.

Write the presentation of the dividend $f(x)$ through quotient $q(x)$ and remainder $r(x)$.

- **The Remainder Theorem.**

If a number c is substituted for x in a polynomial f, then the result $f(c)$ is the remainder that would be found with division of f by the binomial $x - c$.

Synthetic Division.

Synthetic Division is a special algorithm for division a polynomials by a binomial $(x-c)$.

Description of the Synthetic division procedure.

Consider the example: $P_n(x) = 2x^5 - 3x^3 + 4x^2 - x + 10$ and binomial $(x+2)$.

We will fill out special table to perform the division.

1. On the first row of the table need to be written the coefficients of P_n. If some powers of x are absent in the polynomial, corresponding coefficients must be written as 0.

2. On the left of the row of coefficients we put the number, subtracted from x in binomial $(x-c)$. Foe example, in our case (division by $(x+2)$), we have to write on the left -2, because $(x+2) = (x-(-2))$.

-2	2	0	-3	4	-1	10
		-4	8	-10	12	-22
	2	-4	5	-6	11	-12

3. First coefficient of the highest power in the first row (2) must be moved now to the first place in the third row, then multiplied by -2 (the number written in the left) and the result we put in the second position on the second row (under 0 in the first row). Numbers from the first and

second row (0 and -4) we add and their sum (-4) we place in third row.

4. Now the number -4 from the third we multiply by -2 from the left, result (8) should go to the second row, and then the sum of 8 and coefficient above (-3) equal to 5 is comes to the third row.

5. This procedure is repeated until all coefficients will be used.

6. Highlighted coefficients in the third row are the coefficients of quotient (fourth degree polynomial) and $R=-12$ is the remainder.

$$P_n(x) = 2x^5 - 3x^3 + 4x^2 - x + 10 =$$
$$(x+2)(2x^4 - 4x^3 - 6x^2 + 11x) - 12$$

In the case when the remainder $R=0$, P_n can be divided by the binomial $(x-c)$ evenly, $(x-c)$ is a factor of the polynomial P_n, and $x=c$ is a zero of P_n.

▪ **Exercises.**

19. Use Synthetic Division to divide
$f(x) = x^3 - 2x^2 + 3x + 5$ by $d(x) = x + 2$.
Find quotient $q(x)$ and remainder $r(x)$.
Write presentation of the dividend $f(x)$ through quotient and remainder.

What's if remainder $r(x) = 0$?

- **Synthetic Division can be used:**

    a) to find the value $f(c)$ for a polynomial f;

    b) to check if $x = c$ is a zero of a given Polynomial function;

    c) to find the multiplicity of the zero $x = c$;

    d) to find the value of a polynomial function at fixed point.

- **Exercises.**

    20. a) Check that $x = 1$ is a zero of
    the polynomial $f(x) = x^5 - 2x^4 - 2x^3 + 8x^2 - 7x + 2$
    and find multiplicity of this zero.
    b) Use synthetic division to find $f(-2)$.

- **Rational Zeros of Polynomials with Integer Coefficients.**

    The Rational Zero Theorem.

    If $f(x) = a_n x^n + a_{n-1} x^{n-1} + ... + a_1 x + a_0$ has integer

    coefficients and $\dfrac{p}{q}$ is a rational zero, then p is a

    factor of the constant term a_0 and q is a factor of the
    leading coefficient a_n.

Note: If leading coefficient $a_n = 1$, then each integer zero of the polynomial is a factor of constant term a_0.

- **Exercises.**

  21. Make a list of all possible integer zeros of the Polynomial $f(x) = x^5 - 3x^4 + 2x^3 - x^2 + 5x - 10$

Note: Having the list of hypothetical integer zeros of some polynomial, we can use Synthetic Division to check which numbers in the list are zeros and find multiplicity of each zero.

  22. Find all integer zeros of $f(x) = x^4 + 7x^3 + 18x^2 + 20x + 8$ and state multiplicity of each zeros.

- **<u>Finding all Zeros of a Polynomial Function.</u>**

  After all integer (rational) zeros of the polynomial are found, we can use last quotient in Synthetic Division procedure to find rest of the zeros.

  All we need to do is set up equation "last quotient"$= 0$ and solve this equation.

- **Exercises.**

  23. Solve the equation $x^3 + 3x^2 - 7x - 12 = 0$

  24. Given $x = -1$ is a zero of
  $f(x) = x^4 + x^3 - 5x^2 - 9x - 4$, find all other zeros.

- **Number of Zeros of Polynomials.**
  Fundamental Theorem of Algebra.

If f is a polynomial of degree n, where $n \geq 1$, then the equation $f(x) = 0$ has at least one complex root.

- **The Linear Factorization Theorem.**

If $f(x) = a_n x^n + a_{n-1} x^{n-1} + \cdots + a_1 x + a_0$, where $n \geq 1$ and $a_n \neq 0$, then $f(x) = a_n(x - c_1)(x - c_2) \cdots (x - c_n)$, where $c_1, c_2, ..., c_n$ are complex numbers (some of them possibly real and not necessarily distinct).

In words: Each polynomial if the degree n can be expressed as the product of n linear factors, some of them can be repeated.

- **Exercises.**

25. Find a polynomial function of degree 3, having the zeros 2, $3i, -3i$.

26. Find a polynomial function with -1 as a zero of multiplicity 2, 5 as a zero multiplicity 1, and 1 as a zero multiplicity 3.

- **Zeros of Polynomial Functions with Real Coefficients.**

If a complex number $a + bi, b \neq 0$ is a zero of a polynomial function f with real coefficients, then its complex conjugate $a - bi$ is also a zero of f.

Exercises.

27. Find a third-degree polynomial function f with real coefficients that has zeros $x = -2$, $x = 4 - 3i$, and such that $f(0) = 100$. Write your answer in general form.

28. Solve the equation $x^4 - 3x^3 + x^2 + 4 = 0$.
    Note: Equivalent formulation is: find all zeros of the polynomial $f(x) = x^4 - 3x^3 + x^2 + 4$. State multiplicity for each zero.

29. Find all zeros of the polynomial $f(x) = x^4 - 5x^3 + 9x^2 + 4$ and state multiplicity for each zero.

▪ Irrational Zeros of Polynomials with Rational Coefficients.

If an irrational number $a + b\sqrt{c}$, a, b are rational and c is not a perfect square, is a zero of a polynomial f with rational coefficients, then $a - b\sqrt{c}$ is also a zero.

▪ Exercises.

30. Find a polynomial function of lowest degree with integer coefficients that has $2 - \sqrt{3}$ *and* $1 + i$ as some of its zeros.

▪ Polynomial Inequalities.
Because graphs of the Polynomial Functions are continuous smooth curves without jumps, real zeros of the polynomial divide the number line into intervals on which the polynomial is either positive or negative (changes of sign of a polynomial may occur ONLY at x-intercepts).

▪ Strategy of solving polynomial inequalities.

1. Find all real zeros of given polynomial function.
2. Consider the partition of the number line into intervals by founded real zeros.
3. Pick up in every interval a **trial point** and determine sign $(+ \ or \ -)$ of the polynomial at this point.

Due to continuity, the polynomial will keep the same sign $(+ \ or \ -)$ over the **entire interval** (from which the trial point has been chosen).
4. Write the answer in the correspondence with the form of inequality $(f < 0, \ f > 0)$ you are solving using the interval notation.

▪ **Table for computing.**
It is convenient to use the following table to organize the results of computations.

Intervals			
Trial points			
Sign of f at trial points			

Exercises.

31. Solve the following inequalities.
   a) $(x-1)(x+3)(x+2)^2 \geq 0$
   b) $(x-1)(x+3)(x+2)^2 > 0$
   c) $(2x-1)(x-2)(x+2) < 0$

- ## Exponential and Logarithmic Functions.

Recall that in that course the word "function" means a trinity: one set of real numbers (inputs) called "domain", D, a second set of real numbers (outputs) called "range", R, and a rule of correspondence, f, according to which for each number x from the domain is assigned one unique number y in the range. Willing to reverse a function's rule, "undo" actions leads to idea of inverse function, f^{-1}. To get the inverse function we suppose to interchange the roles in input-output relationship. If $y = f(x)$ is a function with the domain D and range R, then $f^{-1}(y) = x$, $D_{f^{-1}} = R_f$, and $R_{f^{-1}} = D_f$.

The graph of f^{-1} can be obtained from the graph of f using reflection with respect to the line $y = x$, horizontal asymptotes (if any) are transformed into vertical and backward.

To be able to reverse a function rule (find the inverse function) we have to assume that each value y the original function takes only once, means having a fixed function's value y, we can restore one unique x value such as $y = f(x)$. Not every function has the inverse function. However, every increasing or decreasing function f has the inverse function f^{-1}.

Important example of a pair of functions which are inverse for each other is the pair of exponential and logarithmic functions.

Exercises.

1. Consider $f(x) = 2^x - 3$
   a) State the domain and range of f.
   b) Write the equation of the horizontal asymptote.
   c) State the domain and range of f^{-1}.
   d) Write the equation of the asymptote (if any) for f^{-1}.
   e) Sketch the graphs of f and f^{-1}. Label the asymptote(s).

2. Consider $h(x) = 5^x + 2$
   a) State the domain and range of h.
   b) Write the equation of the horizontal asymptote.

3. Consider $f(x) = \log_4(x - 1)$.
   a) State the domain and range of f.
   b) Write the equation of the vertical asymptote.
   c) State the domain and range of f^{-1}.
   d) Write the equation of the asymptote (if any) for f^{-1}.
   e) Sketch the graphs of f and f^{-1}. Label the asymptote(s).

4. Consider $g(x) = \log(x + 2)$.
   a) State the domain and range of g.
   b) Write the equation of the vertical asymptote.
   c) State the domain and range of g^{-1}.
   d) Write the equation of the asymptote (if any) for g^{-1}.

22

e) Sketch the graphs of g and g^{-1}. Label the asymptote(s).

5. Identify the basic function for $g(x) = -0.9^{x-4} + 7$ and write a sequence of transformations that leads from the basic function to $y = g(x)$.

Use the sequence to predict the range of g.
Sketch the graph of $y = g(x)$.

6. Identify the basic function for $g(x) = \log_{0.7}(x - 53) + 37$ and write a sequence of transformations that leads from the basic function to $y = g(x)$.

Use the sequence to state the domain of g.
Sketch the graph of $y = g(x)$.

7. Identify the basic function for $g(x) = 5^{x+4} - 8$ and write a sequence of transformations that leads from the basic function to $y = g(x)$.

Use the sequence to predict the range of g.
Sketch the graph of $y = g(x)$.

8. Identify the basic function for $g(x) = \log(-x) - 25$ and write a sequence of transformations that leads from the basic function to $y = g(x)$. Use the sequence to find the domain of g. State the range for both basic and transformed functions.
Sketch the graph of $y = g(x)$.

23

9. Find the domain of the function $f(x) = \ln(|x|)$

10. Find the domain of the function $f(x) = \log(-x)$

11*. Find the domain of the function $f(x) = \log_2(|x+1|)$

12. Find the domain of the function $f(x) = \ln(x^2 + x + 1)$

13. Find the domain of the function $f(x) = \log(\sqrt{x^2 + 1})$

14. Find the range of the function $f(x) = -2^x$.

15. Find the range of the function $f(x) = -e^{x-1} + 3$.

16. Find the range of the function $f(x) = \left(\dfrac{1}{5}\right)^x - 4$.

17. Find the domain and range of $f(x) = \ln(-x)$.

18. What is the range of $f(x) = -\dfrac{1}{3}e^{x+2} + 4$?

19. What is the domain of $g(x) = \ln(1 - 5x)$? Write the equation for vertical asymptote of the graph of g.

20. What is the domain of $h(x) = \log(7x - 21)$?

Write the equation for vertical asymptote of the graph of h.

21. Which graph corresponds to $f(x) = \log_2(x+3)$?

a

b

c

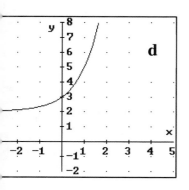

d

e
None of these

22. Which graph corresponds to $f(x) = 3^x + 2$?

a

b

c

25

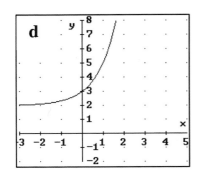
d

Use the properties of the logarithms and given INFO to find the following.

23. Given

$\log_b 3 = 0.6131$	$\log_b 5 = 0.8982$	$\log_b 11 = 1.3383$

Find the following

$\log_b 55 =$	$\log_b 5\sqrt{11} =$	$\log_b 9 =$	$\log_b \dfrac{3}{5} =$	$\log_b \dfrac{11}{9} =$

24. Given

$\log_b 2 = -0.5757$	$\log_b 13 = -2.13$	$\log_b 0.1 = 1.9125$

26

Find the following

$\log_b 0.5$	$\log_b 2\sqrt{13}$	$\log_b 20$	$\log_b \sqrt{10}$	$\log_b\left(\dfrac{13}{2}\right)$

Use properties of logarithms to simplify each expression as much as possible. There suppose to be no logarithms in your answers.

25. $10^{\log 5x^2 + \log 3x} + e^{\ln 16x^7 - \ln x^4}$

26. $c^{\frac{1}{3}\log_c 27x - 2\log_c x^2 y}$

27. $e^{3\ln x^2 + 1}$

28. $10^{2\log 5 - 4}$

29*. $2^{\log_4 5}$

30*. $3^{\log_9 2}$

- **Exponential and Logarithmic Equations.**

  Solve the following equations.
  Remember, when solving Logarithmic Equations solution(s) check is MANDATORY. Find **exact** solutions. Your answers may contain logarithms.

31. $9^{1-2x} = 81$

32. $4^{3x+2} = \dfrac{1}{8}$

33. $2^{x^2+4x} = \dfrac{1}{16}$

34. $\log_7(3x-1) + \log_7(x+2) = \log_7(7x-1)$

35. $\log_2 x + \log_4 x = \dfrac{2}{3}$

36. $\log_2\big(\log_2(x+265)\big) = 3$

37. $\ln\big(\ln(x+3)\big) = 1$

38. $\log\big(\log(x-5)\big) = 0$

39*. $2^{|x|} = 8$

40. $\ln|x-1| = 0$

41. $\log_3|2x+1| = 1$

42*. $\big|\log_2(x-10)\big| = 1$

43. $\log_7(x+6)+\log_7(x+3)=\log_7(3x+10)$

44. $\log_{0.1}(x+6)+\log_{0.1}(x+5)=\log_{0.1}(-4x-26)$

45. $\log(x+5)+\log(x-6)=\log(16x-100)$

46. $\log_{15}(2x-3)+\log_{15}(x-2)=\log_{15}(x^2-11x+11)$

47. $3^{4x-5}=7$

48. $10^{3x+1}=11$

49. $2^{x-1}=2012$

50. $7^{3x-6}+4=10$

▪ **Exponential and Logarithmic Inequalities.**

Use properties of exponential and logarithmic functions to solve algebraically the following inequalities.

51*. $3^x>1$

52*. $\left(\dfrac{1}{5}\right)^x>25$

53*. $2^x \leq 1$

54*. $\left(\dfrac{1}{3}\right)^x < 1$

55*. $\log x \geq 0$

56*. $\ln x < 0$

57*. $\log_{0.5} x < 0$

58*. $\log_{0.3} x \geq 0$

Answers for selected problems.

1. a) $D_f : (-\infty, \infty)$, $R_f : (0, \infty)$;   b) $y = -3$;

c) $D_{f^{-1}} : (0, \infty)$, $R_{f^{-1}} : (-\infty, \infty)$;   d) ; $x = -3$

3. a) $D_f : (1, \infty)$, $R_f : (-\infty, \infty)$;   b) $x = 1$;

c) $D_{f^{-1}} : (-\infty, \infty)$, $R_{f^{-1}} : (1, \infty)$;   d) $y = 1$;

9. $(-\infty, 0) \cup (0, \infty)$;   10. $(-\infty, 0)$;   13. $(-\infty, \infty)$;

15. $(-\infty, 3)$;   17. $(-\infty, \infty)$;

19. $\left(-\infty, \dfrac{1}{5}\right)$, $x=-\dfrac{1}{5}$; 21. e;

23.

$\log_b 55 =$ 2.2365	$\log_b 5\sqrt{11} =$ 1.56735	$\log_b 9 =$ 1.2262	$\log_b \dfrac{3}{5} =$ -0.2851	$\log_b \dfrac{11}{9} =$ 0.1121

25. $23x^3$; 27. $e\,x^6$; 29. $\sqrt{5}+\sqrt{2}$; 31. $\left\{\dfrac{1}{2}\right\}$;

33. $\{1\}$; 35. $\left\{\sqrt[9]{16}\right\}$; 37. $;\left\{e^e-3\right\}$ 39. $\{-3,\ 3\}$;

41. $\{1,\ 2\}$; 43. $\{-2\}$; 46. $\varnothing$; 47. $\left\{\dfrac{5+\log_3 7}{3}\right\}$;

49. $\left\{1+\log_2 2012\right\}$; 51. $(0,\infty)$; 53. $(-\infty, 0]$;

55. $[1,\infty)$; 57. $(0,\infty)$.

- Graphical Solution of Systems of Equations with Two Variables.

Example #1.
$$\begin{cases} y = \sin x \\ y = x^3 \end{cases}$$

.9286263, .8007979
-.9286263, -.8007979

Example #2.
$$\begin{cases} y = \cos x \\ y = e^x - 1 \quad -2\pi \le x \le 2\pi \end{cases}$$

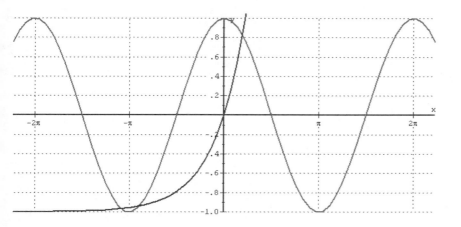

-2.78913, -.9385254;   -3.400593, -.9666465;
.6013468,   .8245745

Example #3.
$$\begin{cases} y = \tan x \\ y = \dfrac{4}{\pi} x \quad -2\pi \le x \le 2\pi \end{cases}$$

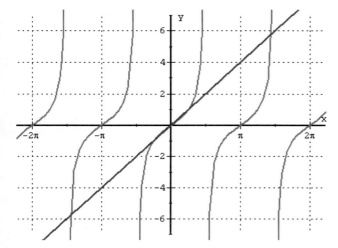

-.7853982,-1;
.7853982, 1

Exercises.

Solve graphically the following systems of equations

1. $\begin{cases} y = 2\sin x \\ x^2 + y^2 = 9\pi^2 \end{cases}$

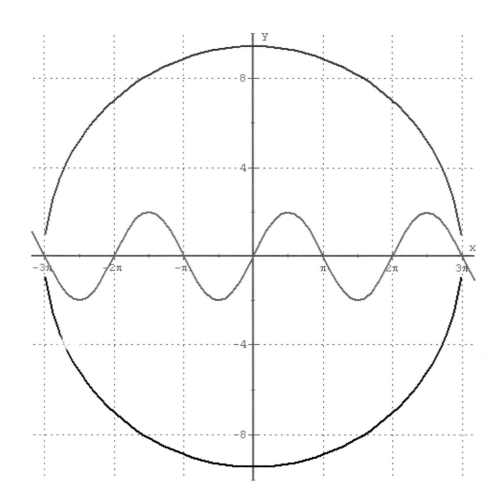

2. $\begin{cases} y = \tan x \\ y = -x \end{cases}$ $\quad -2\pi \le x \le 2\pi$

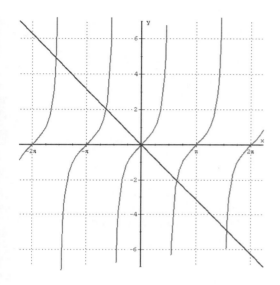

3. $\begin{cases} x^2 + y^2 = 4 \\ y = x^2 - 4 \end{cases}$

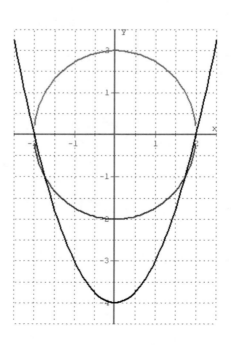

4. $\begin{cases} x^2 + y^2 = 9 \\ y = x^2 - 5 \end{cases}$

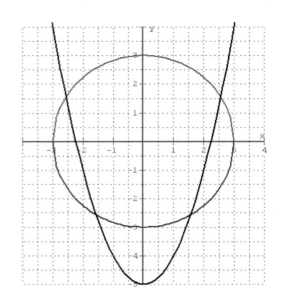

5.

a) $\begin{cases} y = 4 - x^2 \\ y = 2x - 3 \end{cases}$

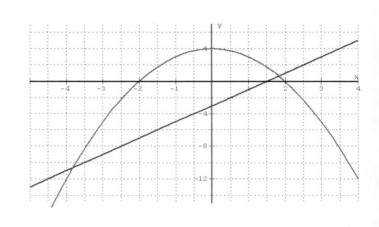

b) $\begin{cases} y = 4 - x^2 \\ y = 2x + 5 \end{cases}$

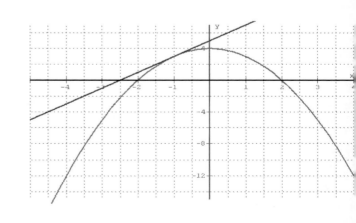

c) $\begin{cases} y = 4 - x^2 \\ y = 2x + 6 \end{cases}$

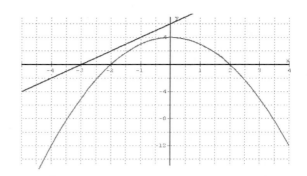

6. $\begin{cases} x^2 + y^2 = 2 \\ y = e^x \end{cases}$

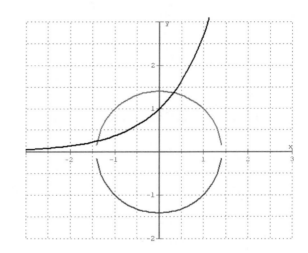

7. $\begin{cases} 2x + y = 3 \\ x - y = -1 \end{cases}$

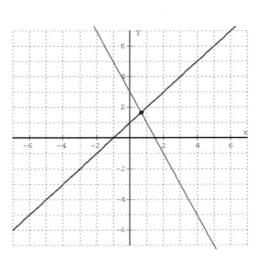

8. $\begin{cases} x^2 + y^2 = 9 \\ y = \cos x \end{cases}$

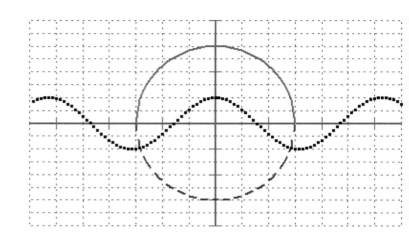

- Solving System of Equations by Substitution.

   1. Use one of the equations in the system of equations to solve for one of variables in terms of another variable.

   2. Substitute the expression obtained in the previous step into another equation, resulting in a new equation with only one variable and solve it.

   3. Do back substitution to find the value of the eliminated variable.

▪ Identities and Conditional Equations.

An equation in one or more variables is said to be an ***identity*** if the left side is equal to the right side for all replacements of the variable(s) for which both sides are defined. For example,
$$x^2 - 5x + 6 = (x-2)(x-3), \ (a-b)(a+b) = a^2 - b^2.$$

An equation in one or more variables is a ***conditional equation*** if the equation holds only for some values of variable(s) and not for all values for which both sides are defined. For example, $x^2 - 6x + 8 = 0$ is a conditional equation. Only values $x = 2$ *and* $x = 4$ when substituted into the equation result in true statement $0 = 0$.

To ***establish (prove) an identity*** means to show that both sides of an equation are equal for all replacements of the variables for which both sides are defined. Such a proof might use basic identities, factoring, combining and reducing fractions, multiplying one side by some special form of "1". The methods of proving particular identities are not unique.

▪ Basic Trigonometric Identities.

Reciprocal identities

$$\csc u = \frac{1}{\sin u} \qquad \sec u = \frac{1}{\cos u} \qquad \cot u = \frac{1}{\tan u}$$

Pythagorean Identities

$$\cos^2 u + \sin^2 u = 1 \qquad 1 + \tan^2 u = \sec^2 u \qquad 1 + \cot^2 u = \csc^2 u$$

Co-Function Identities

$$\sin\left(\frac{\pi}{2} - u\right) = \cos u \qquad \cos\left(\frac{\pi}{2} - u\right) = \sin u \qquad \tan\left(\frac{\pi}{2} - u\right) = \cot$$

$$\csc\left(\frac{\pi}{2} - u\right) = \sec u \qquad \sec\left(\frac{\pi}{2} - u\right) = \csc u \qquad \cot\left(\frac{\pi}{2} - u\right) = \tan u$$

Even-Odd Identities

$$\sin(-u) = -\sin u \qquad \cos(-u) = \cos u \qquad \tan(-u) = -\tan u$$
$$\csc(-u) = -\csc u \qquad \sec(-u) = \sec u \qquad \cot(-u) = -\cot u$$

Exercises.

Prove the following identities.

1. $\cos \theta \csc \theta = \cot \theta$

2. $\dfrac{\tan x}{\sec x} = \sin x$

3. $\tan x \sin x + \cos x = \sec x$

4. $\dfrac{\sin x}{\csc x} + \dfrac{\cos x}{\sec x} = 1$

5. $\sin^2 t \, (1 + \cot^2 t) = 1$

6. $\sec^2 w \cot^2 w - \cos^2 w \csc^2 w = 1$

7. $\dfrac{\sin^2 x}{\cos x} + \cos x = \sec x$

8. $\dfrac{\sec x \csc x}{\tan x + \cot x} = 1$

9. $2 - \sin^2 \theta = 1 + \cos^2 \theta$

10. $\tan \theta + \cot \theta - \sec \theta \csc \theta = 0$

11. $\dfrac{\tan \theta - \cot \theta}{\tan \theta + \cot \theta} = \sin^2 \theta - \cos^2 \theta$

12. $\dfrac{\sin x+\cos x}{\sin x}-\dfrac{\cos x-\sin x}{\cos x}=\sec x\csc x$

13. $\dfrac{\sec x-\cos x}{\sec x+\cos x}=\dfrac{\sin^2 x}{1+\cos^2 x}$

14. $\dfrac{1}{1-\sin\theta}+\dfrac{1}{1+\sin\theta}=2\sec^2\theta$

15. $\csc x-\cot x=\dfrac{\sin x}{1+\cos x}$

16. $\dfrac{(\tan\alpha+\sec\alpha)(\cos\alpha-ctg\alpha)}{(\cos\alpha+ctg\alpha)(\tan\alpha-\sec\alpha)}=1$

17. $\dfrac{\sin\alpha+\cos\alpha}{\sin\alpha-\cos\alpha}=\dfrac{\tan\alpha+1}{\tan\alpha-1}$

18. $\dfrac{1+\cos\alpha+\cos^2\alpha}{1+\sec\alpha+\sec^2\alpha}=\cos^2\alpha$

19. $1-\dfrac{\sin^2\theta}{1+\cot\theta}-\dfrac{\cos^2\theta}{1+\tan\theta}=\sin\theta\cdot\cos\theta$

20. $\dfrac{\cos\theta}{1+\sin\theta}+\tan\theta=1$

21. $\dfrac{\sin 4\theta}{1+\cos 4\theta}\cdot\dfrac{\cos 2\theta}{1+\cos 2\theta}=\cot\left(\dfrac{3\pi}{2}-\theta\right)$

▪ Methods of Solving Trigonometric Equations.

I. Solving Simplest Trigonometric Equations.

$\sin x = c$, *in particular*

$(\sin x = 0, \ \sin x = 1, \ \sin x = -1)$

$\cos x = c$, *in particular*

$(\cos x = 0, \ \cos x = 1, \ \cos x = -1)$

$\tan x = c$, *in particular*

$(\tan x = 0, \ \tan x = 1, \ \tan = -1)$

$\cot x = c$, *in particular*

$(\cot x = 0, \ \cot x = 1, \ \cot x = -1)$

II. Often when solving a trigonometric equation we need to re-write the equation in the terms of ***one function of one angle*** and use algebraic methods (substitution, factoring) to reduce work to solving simplest trigonometric equations.

When we need to re-write an equation in terms of one function of one angle, all basic trigonometric identities, formulas for double or half angles, formulas for addition/subtraction may be helpful.

Number of Solutions of Trigonometric Equations.

Usually trigonometric equations have infinitely many solutions due to the fact that trigonometric functions are periodic. However, some trigonometric equations have no solutions at all, for example, the equation $\sin x = 2$ has no solution because the range of the function $y = \sin x$ is the interval $[-1, 1]$.

Sometimes the solution(s) of the trigonometric equation need to be found in the indicated interval, such that $[0, 2\pi)$, $[0, 4\pi)$, $(-2\pi, 0]$, $\left(-\dfrac{\pi}{2}, \dfrac{\pi}{2}\right)$ and so on.

Exercises.

Solve the following trigonometric equations.

1. $2\sin x - 1 = 0$

2. $2\sin 3x - 1 = 0$

3. $\sin x + \sqrt{2} = -\sin x, \ 0 \le x < 2\pi$

4. $3\tan^2 x - 1 = 0$

5. $\cot x \cos^2 x = 2\cot x$

6. $2\sin^2 x - \sin x - 1 = 0, \ 0 \le x < 4\pi$

7. $2\cos(3x-1)=0$

8. $\sec^2 x - 2\tan x = 4, \quad -\pi < x < \pi$

9. $\sin(2x)\sin x = \cos x$

10. $\cos(2\theta) = 2 - 2\sin^2 \theta$

In this Appendix, you will find five sample hour tests given by one of the MSU Professors in MTH 116 recently. We encourage you to work on these tests and go to MSU Math Learning Center if you need assistance.

MTH 116   Sample Test 1

1. (20 pts) Consider the function $f(x) = x^2 - 2x$. Answer the following questions about $f(x)$.

(a) Sketch the graph of $f(x)$.

(b) Find $\dfrac{f(a+h) - f(a)}{h}$. Give your answer in the simplest form. Show all your work.

(c) Draw the secant line to the graph of $f(x)$ through the points $(-1, f(-1))$ and $(4, f(4))$, and find the slope of this line. Show all your work.

(d) Determine whether or not $f(x)$ is one-to-one. Support your answer.

---

2. (20 pts) Let $f(x) = x^2 - x$ and $g(x) = \dfrac{3}{1 - \sqrt{1-x}}$. Answer the following questions. Show all your work.

(a) Evaluate (if it exists) $\left(\dfrac{f}{g}\right)(-3)$

(b) Evaluate (if it exists) $(f \circ g)(0)$

(c) Find and simplify $(f \circ f)(x)$

(d) Find the domain of g.

---

3. (8 pts) Find $f(x)$ and $g(x)$ (both f and g must be simpler functions than h, such that $h(x) = (f \circ g)(x)$, where $h(x) = \dfrac{1}{\sqrt[5]{3x^2 + 1}}$). Show all your work.

---

4. (20 pts) Let $r(x) = -(x+3)^3 + 1$.

(a) Sketch the graph of $r(x)$.

(b) Sketch the graph of $r^{-1}(x)$.

(c) Find an equation for $r^{-1}(x)$. Show all your work.

---

5. (32 pts) The graphs of f and g are given below. Answer the following questions about f and g.

(a) Find the domains of $f, g, f + g$. Find the ranges of f and g.

(b) Evaluate each of the following, if possible.

$$f(0), (f+g)(-1), \left(\frac{f}{g}\right)(-2), (f \circ g)(2), (g \circ g)(-1), f^{-1}(2), (f \circ f^{-1})(3), (g^{-1} \circ g)(-4).$$

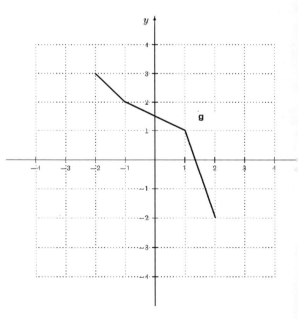

1. (10 pts) Evaluate each of the following, if possible.

(a) $\left(\dfrac{\sqrt{2}}{2}-\dfrac{\sqrt{2}}{2}i\right)^2$

(b) i^{231}

2. (8 pts) Graph the inverse function for $f(x)=-x^2-1$ with the domain $0,\infty$.

3. (6 pts) Find the equation of the line that contains the point (-2, -2) and is perpendicular to the line containing points (2, 0) and (2, 2).

4. (12 pts) Find two numbers whose sum equals 6 and whose product equals 7.

Answer_____

5. (8 pts) Find the range of the following function. $g(x) = -(x+2)^2 - 1$

Answer_____

6. (12 pts) Given that $2i$ is a zero of the polynomial $p(x) = x^3 - 5x^2 + 4x - 20$. Find all other zeros of $p(x)$ and factor $p(x)$ into linear factors.

7. (20 pts) Given the function $q(x) = (2x-1)(x+2)^2(x+3)$.

(a) Make a hand-drawn graph of q. Make sure to label the zeros.

(b) Solve the following inequality. $(2x-1)(x+2)^2(x+3)<0$

---

8. (10 pts) Given the function $m(x)=1-24x+3x^2-0.5x^3$. What is the behavior of $m(x)$ for x near ∞ and $-\infty$?

---

9. (10 pts) Find all solutions of the following equation.

$x^4+2x^2=8$

Answer_____

10. (4 pts) Give an example of two polynomials p and q such that
$\deg(p+q) < \deg p$ and $\deg(p+q) < \deg q$

MTH 116 Sample Test 3

---

1. (10 pts) Evaluate each of the following, if possible.

(a) $\log_2(-20)$

(b) $\log\left(\dfrac{1}{10^{-9}}\right)$

---

2. (15 pts) The following statements are either always true (T) or not always true (F). Circle the one choice that best describes each. **Do not use calculator**.

(a) $\log(x^7 + z^4) = 7\log x + 4\log z$ T   F

(b) $\log 30 - \log 6 + \log\left(\dfrac{1}{5}\right) = 0$ T   F

(c) The range of $f(x) = \ln x$ is all real numbers.   T   F

---

3. (12 pts) Suppose $10,000 is placed in a bank account and it grows to $16,500 in 10 years (no money withdrawn). Given that the interest is compounded continuously, what is the doubling time for this account?

Answer_____

---

4. (22 pts) Solve each of the following equations algebraically. Show all your work.

(a) $\log_2(x-3)+\log_2(x+3)=4$

Answer_____

(b) $3^{2x}-27=6\cdot 3^x$

Answer_____

5. (12 pts) Radioactive element carbon-14 has half-life of 5750 years. Percentage of carbon-14 in the remains of organic matter can be used to determine the age of that organic matter. Archaeologists discovered that the linen wrapping from one of the Dead Sea Scrolls had lost 26% of its carbon-14 at the time it was found. How old was the linen wrapping?

Answer_____

6. (22 pts) Given the function $r(x) = \dfrac{x-3}{(x-1)(x+1)}$.

(a) Make a hand-drawn graph of r . Label all asymptotes and zeros.

(b) Solve the following inequality. $\dfrac{x-3}{(x-1)(x+1)} \leq \dfrac{1}{x+1}$

---

7. (7 pts) Given the function $g(x) = \dfrac{(3x-2)(2x^2+2x+1)}{4x^3+2x^2-x+1}$. What is the behavior of $g(x)$ for x near ∞ or $-\infty$?

1. (28 pts) Fill in the blanks.

$\sin^2 \theta +$ _____ $= 1$

$\cot \theta = \dfrac{}{\sin \theta}$

$\sin \underline{\quad} - \theta = \cos \theta$

$\tan \left(\theta + \pi \right) =$ _____

$\cos \left(\theta + 2\pi \right) =$ _____

The range of $\cos^{-1}$ is _____

The domain of $\tan^{-1}$ is _____

---

2. (4 pts) Convert $\dfrac{23\pi}{6}$ into degrees. Give exact value for your answer.

Answer_____

---

3. (10 pts) Find the coordinates of the endpoint of the radius of the unit circle corresponding to the following angles. Give exact values for your answers.

(a) $-660°$

(b) $\dfrac{25\pi}{6}$

---

4. (12 pts) Given $\tan u = -4$ where $\dfrac{\pi}{2} < u < \pi$. Find the exact value of each of the following. Show all your work.

(a) $\cos u$

Answer_____

(b) $\sin u$

Answer_____

5. (10 pts) Find the points on the unit circle whose y-coordinates are twice their x-coordinates.

coordinates.

Hint: You need to find the intersections of the unit circle and the line $y = 2x$.

Answer_____

6. (10 pts) Find a formula for $\tan(\cos^{-1} t)$. Your answer must be in terms of t with no trigonometric functions in it. Show all your work.

Answer_____

7. (8 pts) Find the four smallest positive numbers θ such that $\sin \theta = -1$.

Answer_____

8. (10 pts) Solve the following system of equations.

$$x^2 + y^2 = 16\pi^2$$
$$y = \sin x$$

Answer_____

---

9. (8 pts) Suppose a slice of a 12-inch pizza has an area of 10 square inches. What is the angle of this slice?

Answer_____

---

1. (12 pts) Find the formula for each of the following.

(a) $\sin\left(\theta + \dfrac{\pi}{2}\right)$

(b) $\tan\left(\theta - \dfrac{\pi}{4}\right)$

---

2. (8 pts) Find the exact value of $\sin\left(\tan^{-1} 2 - \cos^{-1}\dfrac{2}{3}\right)$. Show all your work.

Answer_____

---

3. (15 pts) Consider the function $f(x) = -2\cos\left(2x + \dfrac{\pi}{2}\right)$.

(a) Find the amplitude of f.

(b) Find the period of f.

(c) Find the phase shift of f.

(d) Sketch the graph of f. Show two full periods of the function and be sure to label all x-intercepts.

4. (8 pts) Prove the following identity algebraically (remember to work with one side at a time). Show all your work.

$$\frac{\sin \theta}{1+\cos \theta} = \frac{1-\cos \theta}{\sin \theta}$$

5. (12 pts) Given $\sin u = -\dfrac{3}{5}$ where $\pi < u < \dfrac{3\pi}{2}$. Find the exact value of each of the following. Show all your work.

(a) $\cos\left(\dfrac{u}{2}\right)$

Answer_____

(b) $\sin\ 2u$

Answer_____

---

6. (10 pts) Consider the sequence $5\sqrt{2}, 10, 10\sqrt{2}, \dots$. Answer the following questions about this sequence. Show all your work.

(a) Find the common ratio.

Answer_____

(b) Find the nth (general) term.

Answer_____

---

7. (10 pts) Find the sum: $\sum_{k=0}^{3} -1^{k-1} \dfrac{k-1}{k+1}$. Give exact value for your answer. Show all your work.

Answer_____

8. (15 pts) Find the following limits, if they exist.

$$\lim_{n\to\infty} \left(3+\dfrac{2}{n}\right)^2$$

$$\lim_{n\to\infty} \dfrac{2n^2+3n-10}{7n^2+1}$$

$$\lim_{n\to\infty} -1^{n}$$

9. (10 pts) Evaluate the following infinite series, if it is defined.

$$\sum_{m=1}^{\infty} \dfrac{3}{2^m}$$

Answer_____

Some Useful Formulas:

$$\sin(u \pm v) = \sin u \cos v \pm \cos u \sin v$$

$$\cos(u \pm v) = \cos u \cos v \mp \sin u \sin v$$

$$\tan(u \pm v) = \frac{\tan u \pm \tan v}{1 \mp \tan u \tan v}$$

$$\sin 2x = 2 \sin x \cos x$$

$$\cos 2x = \cos^2 x - \sin^2 x$$

$$\tan 2x = \frac{2 \tan x}{1 - \tan^2 x}$$

$$\sin \frac{x}{2} = \pm \sqrt{\frac{1 - \cos x}{2}}$$

$$\cos \frac{x}{2} = \pm \sqrt{\frac{1 + \cos x}{2}}$$

$$\tan \frac{x}{2} = \pm \sqrt{\frac{1 - \cos x}{1 + \cos x}}$$